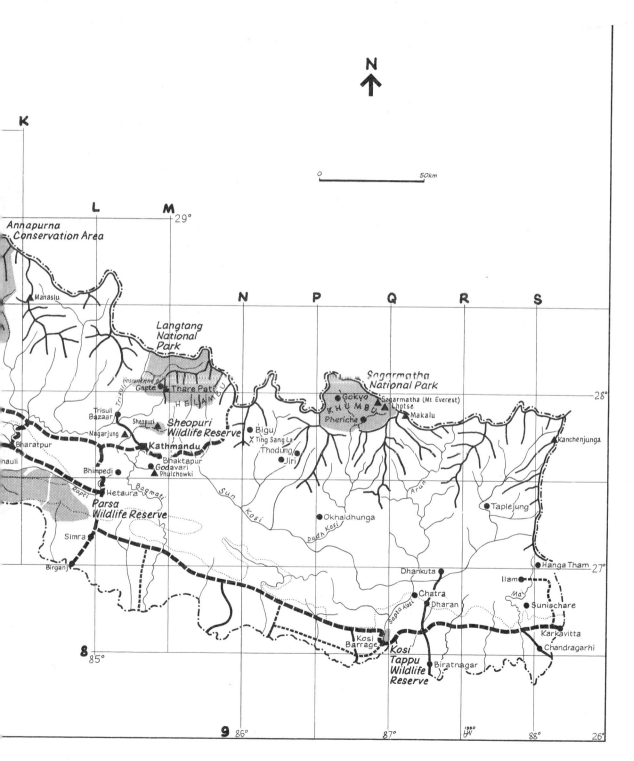

A GUIDE TO THE
BIRDS *of* NEPAL

A GUIDE TO THE
BIRDS of NEPAL

Second Edition
Carol and Tim Inskipp

Colour illustrations by Clive Byers, Richard Grimmett,
Craig Robson, and Steve Rooke

Line drawings by Clive Byers, Steen Christensen,
Dave Farrow, Richard Grimmett, Patrick Hamon,
Dave Mills, Mike Parker, Craig Robson, Steve Rooke,
Ray Turley, and James Wolstencroft

CHRISTOPHER HELM
A & C Black · London

© 1985 Carol and Tim Inskipp

Second edition © 1991

Christopher Helm (Publishers) Ltd,
a subsidiary of A & C Black (Publishers) Ltd, 35 Bedford Row,
London WC1R 4JH

ISBN 0-7136-8109-8

A CIP catalogue record for this book is available from the British Library.

Laser-set by The Nature Conservation Bureau Ltd,
36 Kingfisher Court, Newbury, Berkshire, UK.

Printed and bound in Great Britain by the Bath Press
on 100 per cent re-cycled paper.

CONTENTS

LIST OF ILLUSTRATIONS

Identification Drawings

Vignettes

Dave Farrow
9, 94, 118, 164, 171, 178, 189, 200, 201, 203, 226, 242, 255, 272, 279, 292, 306, 321, 334, 338

Richard Grimmett
11, 18, 26, 29, 103, 113, 120, 125, 126, 129, 130, 133, 139, 142, 143, 144, 145, 146, 147, 157, 158, 160, 161, 163, 167, 176, 183, 186, 187, 210, 211, 221, 223, 224, 237, 239, 240, 245, 246, 251, 259, 266, 278, 281, 284, 288, 290, 298, 299, 304, 307, 309, 312, 313, 331, 344, 361

Patrick Hamon
109, 111, 206

Dave Mills
108, 132, 138, 246, 319, 320, 343, 372

Mike Parker
21, 87, 89, 157, 168, 197, 212, 232, 250, 287, 289, 357

Craig Robson
28, 30, 95, 96, 98, 104, 121, 123, 133, 151, 156, 166, 172, 177, 191, 195, 199, 205, 207, 214, 222, 229, 234, 235, 238, 241, 248, 260, 261, 268, 276, 277, 283, 285, 286, 291, 297, 300, 305, 309, 314, 316, 317, 323, 325, 328, 329, 336, 350, 359, 364, 371

Steve Rooke
15, 23, 25, 28, 86, 87, 88, 92, 96, 109, 110, 125, 154, 159, 215, 227, 234, 244, 248, 271, 279, 294, 314, 323, 324, 340, 350, 352, 355, 367, 369, 373

Ray Turley
85, 104, 156, 162, 360, 362

James Wolstencroft
17, 341, 346, 348, 349, 351, 353

Colour Plates

DEDICATED TO

ARUN

ACKNOWLEDGEMENTS

This book is a result of the contributions of a great many people. We wish we could adequately thank each of them.

We are most grateful to the artists, Clive Byers, Steen Christensen, Dave Farrow, Richard Grimmett, Patrick Hamon, Dave Mills, Mike Parker, Craig Robson, Steve Rooke, Ray Turley, and James Wolstencroft who generously donated their work.

This book would not have been possible without the assistance of many people who provided us with their bird records. Special thanks go to Jack Cox Junior, Hari Sharan Nepali and Arend van Riessen for their important contributions. We also warmly thank the many other observers who gave us their bird records: Alan Adams, Per Alind, Per Alstrom, Per Andell, Ulrik Andersen, Tim Andrews, Tony Baker, Hem Sag Baral, Ian Barber, Larry Barnes, Dave Barrett, Sattish Battachan, Carl-Axel Bauer, Mark Beaman, Staffan Bensch, Arnoud van den Berg, T. Bergstrom, Mark Bezuijen, Rob Bijlsma, Lawrence Binford, Biswamoy Biswas, Jan Bolding, Geoff Bond, Chris Bowden, Paul Bradbear, Dave Brearey, Seb Buckton, Clive Byers, Dick Byrne, John Calladine, Pete Carty, Srikumar Chattopadhyay, Steen Christensen, Andy Clements, Dave Clugston, Mark Cocker, Andy Collins, Pete Colston, Peter Conder, Simon Cook, John Cooper, Gordon Corbett, Bernard Couronne, Simon Cox, Kai Curry-Lindahl, Jon Curson, Adam Davison, Ian Dawson, Ridge De Witt, Adrian del-Nevo, Paul Deluce, Tim Dodman, Philippe Dubois, Paul Dukes, Alan Dunkley, Dinash Durrai, Nick Dymond, Jon Eames, Enno Ebels, Jens Eggers, R.E.T. Ellen, Vernon Eve, Pete Ewins, Richard Fairbank, Dave Farrow, Robert Fleming Jr., Elizabeth Forster, Steve Gantlett, Sharifin Gardiner, Simon Gawn, John Brodie Good, Andy Goodwin, Tony Gaston, Michael Green, Alan Greensmith, Richard Gregory-Smith, Richard Grimmett, Gunter Groh, Yvonne Guinan, K.K.Gurung, Kaj Halberg, Jim Hall, Phil Hall, John Halliday, Patrick Hamon, Per Hansen, Simon Harrap, Edward Harris, Kerry Harrison, Andrew Harrop, Bill Harvey, Phil Heath, Peter and Pauline Heathcote, Mortens Heegard, Joel Heinen, Mogens Henriksen, Darla Hillard, Peter Hines, Thor Hjarsen, Goran Holmstrom, Paul Holt, John Hopkins, Jon Hornbuckle, Michael Hornby, Jesper Hornskov, Stuart Housden, Sir Anthony Hurrell, Keith Hyatt, Rob Innes, Richard Isherwood, Simon Jackson, Ole Jakobsen, Bob Jarman, Paul Jepson, Ron Johns, Bas Jongeling, Torben Jorgensen, Rafi Juliusberger, Stan Justice, Mikael Kall, Pete Kennerley, Ben King, Niels Kjellen, Jerry Klapste, Jean-Christophe Kovacs, Erling Krabbe, Niels Krabbe, Andy Kratter, Lalit Lalchan, Frank Lambert, Roy Lancaster, Jens Larsen, Christer Larsson, Steve LeClerq, John Leece, Tony Lelliott, Paul Lewis, Svend Linderstrom, Vaughan Lister, Steve Madge, Jesper Madsen, Stig Toft Madsen, Soren Malling, Trevor Marshall, Jochen Martens, Rod Martins, Sjoerd Mayer, Barry McCarthy, Chris McCarty, Gillian McKnight, Hans Meilstrup, David Melville, David Millin, David Mills, Tino Mischler, Erik Molgaard, Masayuki Morita, Kathleen Munthe, David Murdoch, Chris Murphy, John Muston, Herbert Nickel, Serge Nicolle, Jan Tottrup Nielsen, Thomas Nilsson, Torgny Nordin, Gunnar Numme, Bill Oddie, William Oliver, Klaus Malling Olsen, Urban Olsson, Mike Parr, David Percival, Mikael Persson, Ib Petersen, Richard Pickering, Ray Pierce, Oleg Polunin, Richard Porter, Peter Post, Mikael Koie Poulsen, Neil Powell, Anders Prieme, Dave Pritchard, Peter Pyle, Pol Rassel, Nigel Redman, Tim Reid, Cliff Rice, Gerry and Lucy Richards, James Roberts, Mike Roberts, Peter Roberts, Philip Robinson, Tim Robinson, Craig Robson, Frank de Roder, Mike Rogers, Steve Rooke, Jonathon Ross, John Rossetti, Valentine Russell, Bjorn Sandgren, D. Sayers, Jelle Scharringa, Richard Schofield, Linda Schrijver, Mike Searle, Suresh Shakya, Mahendra Shrestha, Peter Sieurin, Neil Simpson, Russell Slack, Stewart Smith, Uffe Sorensen, Graham Speight, Simon Stirrup, Anthony Stones, Aidan Sudbury, Werner Suter, Rajendra Suwal, Ian Taylor, Barna Bahadur Thapa, Jean-Marc Thiollay, Dave Thorns, Rob Tolk, Tim Toohig, Mick Turton, Charles Tyler, Rae Vernon, Christer Wahlstrom, Goran Walinder, Johan Wallander, Steve Whitehouse, Wolfgang Winkel, Jorg Wittenberg, Martin Woodcock, Brian Woolly, James Wolstencroft, Mark Wotham and naturalists at the Karnali Tented Camp and Machan Wildlife Camp. Many spent a great deal of time extracting information from their notebooks and answering our queries or requests for more details on particular records. Mortens Heegard from DAFIF, the working group of the Dansk Ornitologisk Forening for international bird protection, kindly collected some useful reports for us. Gyamcho Wangdi provided records made by the naturalists of the Karnali Tented Camp.

We are especially grateful to the British Museum (Natural History) and the Kathmandu Natural History Museum for allowing access to their bird specimens and to the Chicago Field Museum for extracting useful data from their bird collection on our behalf. We also wish to thank the Bombay Natural History Society; Booth Museum of Natural History, Brighton; Cambridge University, Museum of Zoology, Cliffe Castle Art Gallery and Museum; Glasgow Art Gallery and Museum; Hancock Museum, Newcastle-upon-Tyne; Manchester University Museum; Merseyside County Museum; Oxford University Museum;

Rijksmuseum van Natuurlijke Histoire; Royal Albert Memorial Museum Exeter; Sheffield City Museums, and the Zoological Museum of Copenhagen for their assistance. Many useful data were extracted on our behalf by Erling Krabbe from the Zoological Museum of Copenhagen and by Philip Round from the Thai National Reference Collection. Humayun Abdulali, the late Con Benson, Peter Colston, Clem Fisher, Ian Galbraith, J. Hull, Peter Morgan, Derek Read, Melvin Traylor Jr., Michael Walters, and David Williard were also particularly helpful with our museum work.

The section on species identification was written with the help of many people who provided valuable information and criticised the text. Steen Christensen wrote the text and illustrated the *Aquila* eagles. Per Alstrom, Jon Eames, Richard Grimmett and Craig Robson provided assistance with numerous species and the following assisted with particular groups: Clive Byers (buntings), Goran Holmstrom (*Phylloscopus* warblers), Alan Kitson (buzzards), Steve Madge (buzzards and *Phylloscopus* warblers), Richard Porter (birds of prey), Goran Walinder (*Phylloscopus* warblers). Special thanks go to Richard Grimmett, Craig Robson and Jon Eames who examined museum skins for information used in this section. Richard Fairbank, Peter Grant, Bill Oddie, Urban Olsson, Nick Preston, and Philip Round all made useful comments on the identification section.

We are indebted to Steve Broad who generously gave much of his time providing computing assistance. Without his help the production of the book would have been much more difficult.

We are particularly grateful to Dick Newell for his enormous efforts in writing and running a computer programme to plot the altitude and period of occurrence bars on the species maps. Robary Ltd. generously donated free computer time for production of these bars. We also thank Bob Tonks, Louise Cook and other staff at Robary for their invaluable help.

We are grateful to Mark Beaman for making the publication of the first edition of this book possible, for his advice on its content and his constant encouragement. We also thank Tim Sharrock for his encouragement in the early stages.

Thanks go to the Nature Conservation Bureau for setting the text, Dick Filby for letrasetting the distribution maps and Hilary Welch for drawing some of the maps.

Useful criticism and advice on the introductory section was received from Mark Cocker, Tim Dee, Jon Eames, Rod Martins, Craig Robson and Helen Taylor. Doris Noe kindly translated some German papers for us.

We both appreciated the moral support of our parents, Tom and Joyce Robinson and John and Cesca Inskipp, while writing the book.

The artists wish to thank Clive Denby, Alan Kitson, Steve Madge, Nigel Redman, Richard Porter, Charlie Williams and particularly Urban Olsson for lending photographic material. They are also grateful to John Dunscombe, John Goldsmith, Jeff Haynes, and F.W. and M.M. Grimmett, and to the Conservation Monitoring Centre, Exmoor National Park, the Polytechnic of North London, the Norwich Castle Museum, for borrowing skins from the British Museum (Natural History) on their behalf.

We are grateful to the British Museum (Natural History), Royal Geographical Society and Zoological Society of London for use of their libraries, and to the Expedition Advisory Centre for providing information.

We thank Adam Stainton for the use of information on vegetation types from his book *Forests of Nepal* and the Centre National de la Recherche Scientifique who kindly gave permission to reproduce maps from *Le Nepal, ecologie et biogeographie* by Jean-Francois Dobremez.

Striated Bulbul

INTRODUCTION

Nepal has a great wealth of birds. A total of 834 species have been definitely recorded, nearly one tenth of the world's known birds. There are 14 species newly recorded since the first edition of this book was published. However, 15 species collected in the last century, which were previously included, have now been deleted from the Nepalese list.

The main aim of this book was to map and summarise the distribution of birds within the country. The information was collected from published literature, museum specimens, and unpublished reports and other records received from numerous ornithologists, comprising a total of over 800 references referred to throughout by numbers. These references constitute a comprehensive bibliography of Nepalese ornithology. This second edition includes nearly 3000 additional distributional records compared to the first edition of the book published in 1985. All records of rare species and those occurring outside their normal range have been carefully checked. Unpublished records lacking adequate supporting evidence have not been included. Erroneous and dubious published records, including those of 23 species additional to those on the Nepalese list, have been discussed in the species accounts.

Scientific nomenclature follows Voous[1] for the sequence of families and for the Palearctic species, and largely follows Morony, Bock and Farrand[2] or King *et.al.*[3] for Oriental species. The English names are, as far as possible, those likely to be adopted in a list of Oriental (Indomalayan) bird species currently being prepared by the Oriental Bird Club. The names of some species are different to those used in the first edition of the book, but in such cases the alternative names are listed as synonyms. Other names used by various authors[3,4,5], also Ali and Ripley 1971-1983, Fleming *et al.* 1984 and Ripley 1982, are given as synonyms where appropriate.

A detailed and fully illustrated identification section covering some of the more difficult groups of species is also included and has been updated. Since 1985 a substantial amount of new ornithological information has been received, especially from the western half of the country and from the Arun valley eastwards. However, some areas of Nepal are still virtually unknown or under-recorded ornithologically (Map 6). In general all of the country west of the Kali Gandaki valley still falls into one of these categories. Those areas which would be rewarding to visit include Api, Humla, Mugu, Dolpo, Mustang, Baitidi and Dandeldhura Districts, Royal Sukla Phanta Wildlife Reserve, Royal Bardia, Khaptad and Shey Phoksundo National Parks, Dang, the Tamur valley, and the far south-east. However, access to a few of these areas is at present forbidden or restricted to foreigners, and obtaining access, accommodation and food in others presents problems.

Much work on the breeding behaviour of Nepalese birds remains to be done, as the details for no less than 70 species are either little known or completely undescribed.

We are still collecting information and hope that this will be of use in future decisions relating to the conservation of Nepalese birds and their habitats. Data on distribution, status, altitudinal limits, breeding and migration will be welcomed and acknowledged. Please send to Carol and Tim Inskipp, Oriental Bird Club, c/o The Lodge, Sandy, Beds. SG19 2DL, U.K.

Finally during a visit to Nepal there are many species to look out for, which could occur but have not been recorded so far. A total of 68 species have been recorded within 100km of the border, 42 from the east (E), 21 from the south (S), 6 from the north (N) and 6 from the west (W). Some of these are unlikely to be found now in Nepal: the Himalayan Quail has not been recorded for 100 years, and the habitat for many of the eastern species no longer exists. The migrant species (m) are perhaps the most likely ones to appear, although some such as the Siberian Crane, have become much rarer in recent years:-

Indian Cormorant *Phalacrocorax fuscicollis* (S,E)
Dalmatian Pelican *Pelecanus crispus* (S-m)
Little Bittern *Ixobrychus minutus* (W,S)
Greater White-fronted Goose *Anser albifrons* (S-m)
Lesser White-fronted Goose *A. erythropus* (S-m)
Marbled Teal *Marmaronetta angustirostris* (S-m)
White-headed Duck *Oxyura leucocephala* (S-m)
Jerdon's Baza *Aviceda jerdoni* (E)
Manipur Bush Quail *Perdicula manipurensis* (E)
Chestnut-breasted Partridge *Arborophila mandellii* (E)
Red Spurfowl *Galloperdix spadicea* (S)
Himalayan Quail *Ophrysia superciliosa* (W)
Grey Peacock-Pheasant *Polyplectron bicalcaratum* (E)
Siberian Crane *Grus leucogeranus* (S-m)
Spotted Crake *Porzana porzana* (S-m)
Black-tailed Crake *P. bicolor* (E)
Sociable Lapwing *Chettusia gregaria* (S-m)
Tibetan Sandgrouse *Syrrhaptes tibetanus* (N)
Pale-backed Pigeon *Columba eversmanni* (S-m)
Green Imperial Pigeon *Ducula aenea* (S,E)
Blossom-headed Parakeet *Psittacula roseata* (E)
Oriental Bay Owl *Phodilus badius* (E)
Mottled Wood-Owl *Strix ocellata* (S)
Hodgson's Frogmouth *Batrachostomus hodgsoni* (E)
Eurasian Nightjar *Caprimulgus europaeus* (S-m)
Oriental Kingfisher *Ceyx erithacus* (E)
Wreathed Hornbill *Rhyticeros undulatus* (E)

Oriental Bay Owl

Heart-spotted Woodpecker *Hemicircus canente* (E)
Singing Bushlark *Mirafra cantillans* (S)
Indian Bushlark *M. erythroptera* (S)
Long-billed Lark *Melanocorypha maxima* (E,N)
Dusky Crag Martin *Ptyonoprogne concolor* (S)
Blue-winged Leafbird *Chloropsis cochinchinensis* (S)
Rusty-bellied Shortwing *Brachypteryx hyperythra* (E)
Nightingale *Luscinia megarhynchos* (S-m)
Firethroat *L. pectardens* (N)
Daurian Redstart *Phoenicurus auroreus* (E-m)
Blue-fronted Robin *Cinclidium frontale* (E)
Rufous-tailed Rock-Thrush *Monticola saxatilis* (E-m)
White-crowned Forktail *Enicurus leschenaulti* (E)
Rufous Prinia *Prinia rufescens* (E)
Dark-necked Tailorbird *Orthotomus atrogularis* (E)
Mountain Tailorbird *O. cuculatus* (E)
Moustached Warbler *Acrocephalus melanopogon* (W)
White-spectacled Warbler *Seicercus affinis* (E)
Eastern Crowned Warbler *Phylloscopus coronatus* (E-m)

Vivid Blue Flycatcher *Cyornis vivida* (E)
Long-billed Wren-Babbler *Rimator malacoptilus* (E)
Wedge-billed Wren-Babbler *Sphenocichla humei* (E)
Buff-chested Babbler *Stachyris ambigua* (E)
Jerdon's Babbler *Moupinia altirostris* (E)
Rufous-headed Parrotbill *Paradoxornis ruficeps* (E)
Black-browed Parrotbill *P. atrosuperciliaris* (E)
Grey-headed Parrotbill *P. gularis* (E)
Giant Babax *Babax waddelli* (E,N)
Brown-cheeked Laughing-thrush *Garrulax henrici* (N)
Yellow-throated Fulvetta *Alcippe cinerea* (E)
Rufous-throated Fulvetta *A. rufogularis* (E)
Striated Yuhina *Yuhina castaniceps* (E)
Beautiful Nuthatch *Sitta formosa* (E)
Spotted Creeper *Salpornis spilonotus* (S)
Black-billed Magpie *Pica pica* (N)
Collared Treepie *Dendrocitta frontalis* (E)
Small Snowfinch *Montifringilla davidiana* (E-m)
Finn's Weaver *Ploceus megarhynchus* (W,E)
Pink-backed Rosefinch *Carpodacus grandis* (W)
Grey-headed Bullfinch *Pyrrhula erythaca* (E)
Black-and-yellow Grosbeak *Mycerobas icterioides* (W,E).

1   Voous, K.H. (1977) *List of recent Holarctic bird species*. London: British Ornithologists' Union.
2. Morony, J.J., Bock, W.J. and Farrand, J. (1975) *Reference list of the birds of the world*. New York: American Museum of Natural History.
3. King, B.F. and Dickinson, E.C. (1975) *A field guide to the birds of South-East Asia*, London: Collins.
4. Heinzel, H., Fitter, R.S.R., and Parslow, J.L.F. (1972) *The birds of Britain and Europe with North Africa and the Middle East*. London: Collins.
5. American Ornithologists Union (1983) *Check-list of North American birds*. Sixth edition. A.O.U.

12

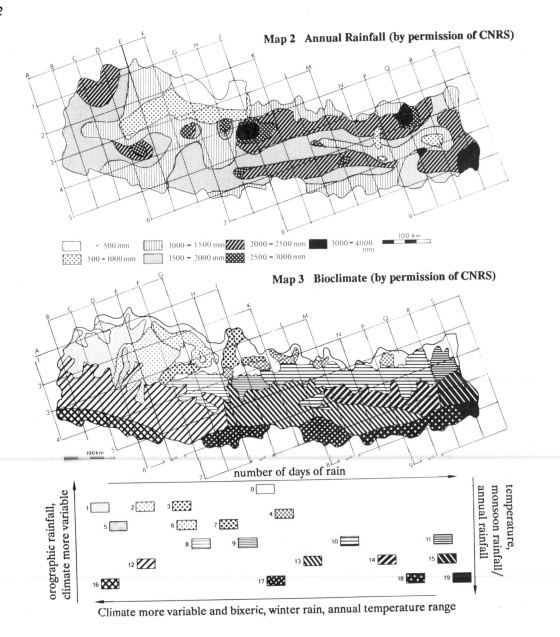

Map 2   Annual Rainfall (by permission of CNRS)

< 500 mm   1000 - 1500 mm   2000 - 2500 mm   3000 - 4000 mm
500 - 1000 mm   1500 - 2000 mm   2500 - 3000 mm   100 km

Map 3   Bioclimate (by permission of CNRS)

100km

number of days of rain

orographic rainfall, climate more variable

temperature, monsoon rainfall/annual rainfall

Climate more variable and bixeric, winter rain, annual temperature range

0   High altitude - too cold for any vegetation.
1-3   Mediterranean - two dry periods each year (bixeric) with winter rain an important factor.
4   Internal valleys - low rainfall with a good proportion in the winter.
5-7   Steppe - characterised by droughts or dryness; in 5 wind is important, in 6 and 7 also rainfall very low.
8-11   Temperate monsoonal - mean temperature of coldest month below 15⁰C.
       8 slightly bixeric; 9 rainfall very high,

       >3000mm/year; 10 rainfall 2000-2500mm; 11 high number of days of rain, >150/year
12-15 Subtropical - mean temperature of coldest month 15-20⁰C. 12 always bixeric; 13 sometimes bixeric, rainfall 1000-1500mm; 14 rainfall <1000mm; 15 high number of days of rain
16-19 Tropical - mean temperature of coldest month 20-25⁰C.
       The rainfall and number of days of rain increases eastwards, and the climate becomes less variable.

TOPOGRAPHY, CLIMATE AND VEGETATION

Nepal is remarkable for its great beauty and visual variety. The country is land-locked between China to the north, and India to the south, east and west. It lies between the latitudes of 26^0 20'N and 30^026'N, and between the longitudes of 80^015'E and 88^010'E. Most of Nepal lies in the Himalayas and forms the central part of the range, one third of its entire length. The country is small, only averaging about 870km from east to west and has a land area little more than England and Wales combined.

The topography changes dramatically within a short lateral distance. There is a narrow strip of lowlands in the south. Further north lie the Himalayan foothills and ranges, which run roughly east-west across the country and include eight of the highest peaks in the world, each over 8000m. Nepal is also notable for its great variety of climate and vegetation.

Climate

The climate ranges from tropical in the lowlands to arctic in the high peaks. It is dominated by the monsoon. About 90% of the rain falls during June to September. In addition there is a less well defined period of winter rain, falling between December and the end of March. The monsoon winds carry moist air from the Bay of Bengal north and west. On reaching the great barrier of the Himalayas the air rises, cools, and the moisture condenses as rain on the southern slopes. The air crossing the Himalayas is now dry resulting in rain shadow on the northern side of the mountains in regions such as Mustang and the Dolpo. The monsoon rains reach east Nepal first, resulting in the rainfall here being generally higher and the monsoon lasting for a longer period than in the west. Rainfall also tends to increase with altitude until about 2500m by which time clouds have lost most of their moisture. Above this altitude rainfall tends to decrease. At elevations above 6100m precipitation falls as snow rather than rain. Aspect of slopes greatly affects the climate. Those facing south receive more rain and sunshine than north-facing slopes. In the tarai and dun, summer temperatures are hot, often greater than 38^0C, and winters cold with temperatures down to about 10^0C. The Kathmandu Valley has a pleasant and mild climate with a summer maximum of about 30^0C and mean winter temperature of about 10^0C. The variety of vegetation can be largely explained by the variation in monsoon rainfall experienced in different regions of the country, both the total amount of rainfall and the length of the period over which it falls. Local conditions such as steepness of slopes, amount of sunshine and aspect are also very important in determining vegetation. Steeper and shadier slopes tend to be damper and have a more interesting flora. Undergrowth burns less easily in shady areas and so the forests are much less affected by fire.

Vegetation

Stainton[1] divided Nepal into nine climatic and vegetational divisions; Dobremez[2] considered that there were four main phytogeographical domains: west, north-west, central and east; eleven altitudinal vegetation zones; and nineteen distinct bioclimatic types. The following account is mainly a summary of their work. The natural vegetation has been much affected by deforestation.

Tarai and bhabar (Tropical zone)

The tarai is the flat narrow lowland strip 25 to 45km wide lying north of the Indian frontier. It is a continuation of the Gangetic plains of India and comprises the most fertile land in Nepal. Most of it is now highly cultivated and little forest remains except in the west. There is a steady rise from the tarai to the foothills. The dry bhabar zone, characterised by its highly porous gravelly soil, extends up to about 300m immediately to the north of the tarai. Sal *Shorea robusta*, predominates over wide areas forming light, open forest. Dense evergreen forest occurs in damp shaded areas and mixed broadleaved forest often grows along rivers.

Dun valleys and outer foothills

Beyond the bhabar zone are the first outer Himalayan foothills known as the Churia or Siwalik hills, rising to 1220m. To the north lies the Mahabharat Lekh rising to 2740m, the most densely populated region in Nepal. Between the two ranges are a series of longitudinal valleys, often heavily forested and separated by narrow ridges called duns, from about 300m to 1370m. In the west sal and subtropical forest occur at the lowest altitudes, Chir Pine *Pinus roxburghii* from 610m to 1830m, and mainly oak forests, *Quercus incana* and *Q. lanata*, with rhododendron higher up. In the east sal and tropical forests are found at lower altitudes, then subtropical forest and temperate mixed broadleaved forest at higher altitudes.

Midlands and the southern slopes of the main Himalayan ranges (Subtropical, temperate and subalpine zones)

A broad complex of hills and valleys including the Kathmandu Valley. It is densely populated in central and eastern areas, where most hillsides have been cleared for grazing or terraced for agriculture. Relatively little forest remains except in the west.

West Midlands
The West Midlands lie west of the Kali Gandaki River. Chir Pine forests occur up to 1980m and the oaks *Q. incana* and *Q. lanata* up to 2440m. The Prickly-leaved Oak *Q. semecarpifolia* often predominates above 2440m, although Himalayan Fir *Abies spectabilis* is widespread between 3050m and the treeline.

East Midlands
The East Midlands lie east of the Arun Kosi River system. Subtropical wet forest is found lower down, and temperate mixed broadleaved forest followed by evergreen forest higher up. Oaks are common, and rhododendron species are much more numerous than in the west, extending from middle elevations to the treeline.

Central Midlands
The Central Midlands lie between the east and west Midlands and comprise complex mixtures of both vegetation types.

South of Annapurna and the Himal Chuli
This area has much higher rainfall than other parts of the central midlands because the monsoon rain from India has relatively low hills to cross before reaching it. Chilaune *Schima wallichii* and Chestnut *Castanopsis* forests and subtropical semi-evergreen forests occur at lower altitude. Lower temperate mixed broadleaved forests are found higher up, on north and west faces; oak *Q. lamellosa* higher up on north and south faces. At higher altitudes upper temperate mixed broadleaved forest or rhododendrons flourish, rather than coniferous forests, because of the high rainfall. Thickets of bamboo *Arundinaria* are widespread. There is a marked contrast between this area and the dry temperate forest west of the Kali Gandaki with a consequent change in the avifauna.

Alpine zone on slopes to the south of the main ranges
This zone lies above the treeline and receives monsoon rains. It is similar to alpine zones in other regions of the world. Shrubs grow up to 4500m and above 4900m there is a high altitude flora where cushion plants flourish. Species of *Primula, Meconopsis, Ranunculus, Anemone, Geum* and *Potentilla* are common.

Inner valleys and dry river valleys
Nepal's rivers cut deeply through the Himalayas producing impressive gorges, often in a north-south direction. The vegetation in their valleys is often differ-
ent from that of immediate surrounding areas, and frequently shows sharp contrasts in habitat within a short distance. Strong winds usually blow upstream, and as a result rainfall in the centres of these valleys and lower valleys is much reduced. In gorges, eastern slopes close to the river receive little sunshine and are damper as a result. The usual altitudinal vegetation succession is often replaced by damp forest close to the river, coniferous forest on the dry lower and middle slopes, and broadleaved forest on the wetter upper slopes. The Bhote Kosi in central Nepal is a typical example of this type of valley. Valleys lying deep within the main Himalayan ranges receive significantly less rainfall than those on southern sides of these ranges, and those in the west are drier than those in the east. In the east this reduction is not great at lower altitudes, but is much lower at and above the treeline. Junipers and other species more typical of the trans-Himalayas grow here. In west Nepal the reduced rainfall is marked even at low elevations and affects the forest composition. Conifers predominate, especially Bhutan Pine *Pinus wallichiana*, except above the treeline where Himalayan Birch *Betula utilis* is common. Such valleys include Khumbu, Langtang and the upper Kali Gandaki. The upper Kali Gandaki is the deepest valley in the world where it cuts through the narrow gap between Dhaulagiri and Annapurna. This causes an exceptionally strong wind and results in an amazing change of climate and vegetation in a short distance. Subtropical monsoon flora grows below Ghasa. In a day's walk up the valley from here one passes through coniferous forests and then into typical Tibetan flora, reflecting the effects of strong wind and associated low rainfall beyond Marpha. Scrub grows on the lower slopes and as the rainfall increases is replaced by a belt of steppe forest of Black Juniper *Juniperus wallichiana* and dry alpine scrub, and above this wetter alpine flora on the upper slopes at about 4100m.

Mediterranean zone (Humla-Jumla area)
This zone lies south of the main Himalayan chain but is much drier than expected because it is sheltered by a chain of mountains to the south where much of the rain falls. Forests are mixed coniferous, *Pinus wallichiana* or Morinda Spruce *Picea smithiana* predominating up to 3050m, *Abies spectabilis* higher up, and *Betula utilis* at the treeline.

Steppe zone
North of Dhaulagiri and Annapurna the country is almost treeless with a climate and flora of Tibetan character. This area lies in the rain shadow of the Himalayas. The predominant vegetation is of shrubs, grasses and alpine flora. Shrubs grow up to 4900m and cushion plants at 5500m.

High altitude zone

The treeline is at about 4100m in the east but considerably lower in the west, generally at about 3050m. The snow-line and associated plant-line are greatly affected by local climatic conditions and vary between about 3655m and 5485m. Plants have been found as high as 5200m.

1. Stainton, J.D.A. 1972. *Forests of Nepal*. John Murray, London.
2. Dobremez, J.-F. 1976. *Le Nepal, ecologie et biogeographie.* Centre National de la Recherche Scientifique, Paris.

Siberian Rubythroat

BIRD DISTRIBUTION

The avifauna of Nepal is exceptionally diverse and includes 611 species which breed or probably breed. There are 124 species whose breeding distributions are restricted to an area encompassing the Himalaya, north-east India, northern south-east Asia and south-west China, for which Nepal may hold internationally significant populations. The country may be especially important for 35 of these species. They either have particularly restricted ranges within the general area considered or have been described as uncommon or rare in the Indian subcontinent (437). There is only one endemic species, the Spiny Babbler, but the world ranges of 92 species extend no further west than Nepal, and 15 species reach the easternmost limit of their ranges in the country.

Nepal's species-richness can be partly attributed to the dramatic changes of altitude within the country, from the tarai at about 75m above sea level to the high peaks of Khumbu culminating in Sagarmatha (Mount Everest) only 145km distant. Species diversity decreases with increase in altitude. The richest areas for Nepalese birdlife lie in the tropical lowlands below 300m where over 500 species have been recorded. In sharp contrast only about 80 species have been found above 4270m in the alpine zone. Also important is Nepal's geographical position, a region of overlap between the Palearctic realm to the north and the Oriental (Indomalayan) realm to the south.

The other major factor contributing to Nepal's species-richness is the extremely varied climate in the country. Nepal can be conveniently divided into eastern and western sections at the Kali Gandaki valley. The river runs north/south through almost the middle of Nepal and the centre of the Himalayan chain. In general forests to the east of the valley are wetter and richer in plant species than western forests. Conifers are much more widespread in the west and rhododendrons in the east. The valley is an important divide for forest birds as well as plant species as first pointed out by Robert Fleming (243). Approximately 440 breeding forest bird species have been found west of the valley and 340 species to the east. The west is however poorly recorded compared to the east. There are 36 breeding species which have been located east of the Kali Gandaki and also occur to the west of Nepal. Assuming there is suitable habitat they could all be found in west Nepal, but even if all of them do occur the east is still considerably richer.

The apparent world ranges of 73 Nepalese breeding species lie east of the valley, including 32 Himalayan species which reach the western limit of their ranges either in the valley or its watershed. These latter species are: Ashy Woodpigeon; Golden-throated Barbet; Darjeeling and Crimson-breasted Woodpeckers; Grey-chinned Minivet; Striated Bulbul; Rufous-breasted Bush-Robin; White-tailed Robin; Large Niltava; Pygmy Blue, Ferruginous, Slaty-backed and White-gorgetted Flycatchers; Slender-billed Scimitar-Babbler; Golden and Grey-throated Babblers; Brown and Fulvous Parrotbills, Grey-sided, Lesser Necklaced, Blue-winged and Scaly Laughing-thrushes; Fire-tailed Myzornis; Black-headed and Black-eared Shrike-Babblers; Rusty-fronted Barwing; Red-tailed Minla; Golden-breasted and Rufous-winged Fulvettas; Rufous-vented Yuhina; Black-browed Tit and Crimson-browed Finch.

There are 17 other species with apparent western limits of their world breeding ranges in central Nepal (between 84^0 and 85^0 30'E) but these may yet be found west to the Kali Gandaki if suitable habitats still exist. They include skulking species such as Blue-naped Pitta and Smoky Warbler, and the Hill Blue Flycatcher which is rare in the subcontinent and may be restricted to a few disjunct populations.

Another very deep river valley, the Arun in east Nepal also marks a change in avifauna but is less important than that of the Kali Gandaki. Rainfall in the Arun valley and eastwards is higher than in most of the rest of the country. There are 17 species whose range in Nepal is confined to this area. A few species, including Blue-eared Barbet, Pale-headed Woodpecker and Rufous-faced Warbler are restricted to the few remaining lowland forests in the south-east. Forests to the south of Annapurna and Himal Chuli in central Nepal area are the wettest in the country. Four species are restricted to these wet forests of both central and eastern Nepal: Golden Babbler, Brown Parrotbill, Rusty-fronted Barwing, and Golden-breasted Fulvetta.

Nepal's lowland evergreen forests become scarcer in the west, but occur in patches at least as far as Butwal. There are 20 lowland breeding species whose western Nepal limits lie in this zone. Of these 13 extend as far as the extensive remaining forests of Chitwan National Park or the recently depleted forests around Hetaura. These include White-vented Needletail with an apparently endemic race isolated from the main population to the south-east; also Mountain Imperial Pigeon, Vernal Hanging Parrot, Asian Fairy Bluebird and Little Spiderhunter which all have disjunct populations in south-west India. Eight species extend a little further west to scattered forests at Tamaspur, Butwal and Pokhara and include Black Baza, Pompadour Green Pigeon and Large Woodshrike which also occur in south-west India.

A further 16 breeding species reach the western limits of their world ranges between the Kali Gandaki and the western border.

Lanceolated Jay

A few species which have not been recorded in Nepal since last century reach the western limits of their ranges in the country. Most of them have no locality details.

The Kali Gandaki valley is a significant but less important eastern barrier to species occurring in the west. The species involved largely inhabit coniferous forests. The world ranges of three breeding species are found east to the river or its watershed: Cheer Pheasant, Mistle Thrush and Rufous-naped Tit. The Nepalese ranges of the Koklass Pheasant, Bar-tailed Treecreeper and Chestnut-eared Bunting cease at the Kali Gandaki watershed but other races of all of them occur much further east in China or Burma. A further four species: Himalayan Woodpecker, Spot-winged Tit, Kashmir Nuthatch and White-cheeked Nuthatch reach the limit of their ranges west of the Kali Gandaki although the latter also occurs further east in China.

There are 12 west Himalayan species whose breeding ranges apparently terminate in Nepal east of the Kali Gandaki watershed. although the Upland Pipit, Red-billed Blue Magpie and Eurasian Golden Oriole have populations further east. All three have been re-corded virtually to the eastern border and probably also occur in the Darjeeling area. The limit of the range of Stolicza's Tit-Warbler lies only a short distance east of the Kali Gandaki.

A total of 15 species characteristic of the Tibetan plateau occurs in Nepal: Himalayan Snowcock, Tibetan Partridge, Hill Pigeon, Little Owl, Brown Accentor, Desert Wheatear, Stolicza's Tit-Warbler, Hume's Ground Jay, Plain-backed, Rufous-necked, White-rumped and Tibetan Snowfinches, Fire-fronted Serin, Twite and Streaked Rosefinch. Most of these species have so far only been recorded either in the upper Kali Gandaki or in the area to the north or north-west of the valley; the Tibetan facies extend into Nepal mainly in this region. However the Himalayan Snowcock, Brown Accentor, Twite and Tibetan Snowfinch have been found in similar habitat in upper Langtang and the Rufous-necked and Tibetan Snowfinches and Streaked Rosefinch in Khumbu. All of these species occur further east in Tibet except Fire-fronted Serin; this species has been found recently east of the Kali Gandaki at Syabru in the Trisuli valley.

The species accounts include available information on subspecies. Many Nepalese species exhibit clinal variation so their taxonomy is largely a matter of opinion. The nomenclature mainly follows Biswas (95-107). There are at least 55 species with more than one breeding subspecies in Nepal. The division between subspecies is mainly east-west and often at either the Kali Gandaki or Arun rivers. At the former 10 species (e.g. Pallas's Leaf Warbler) show a well-marked change, and it is a likely divide for a further eight. At the Arun valley 12 species (e.g. Indian Roller, Striated Laughing-thrush) show a change. Some species are poorly known e.g. Brown-flanked Bush Warbler with specimens only from the far west and east, and Barn Swallow with only one record of *H. r. gutturalis*. Six species have subspecies replacing each other altitudinally (e.g. Hoopoe, House Sparrow).

BIRD CONSERVATION

Rufous-breasted Bush-Robin

Nepal's major habitat-types consist of forests, wet-lands and grasslands. The country has few wetlands other than fast-flowing rivers and streams. By far the most important is the Kosi Barrage area, a large expanse of open water, marshes, grassland and scrub situated in the far south-eastern lowlands. It is of international importance for migrating wildfowl, gulls, terns and waders. A total of 25 wildfowl species has been recorded. Those regularly found include the Black-necked Stork which is endangered in the Indian subcontinent (642), and the Lesser Adjutant Stork, Greater Adjutant Stork, Pallas's Fish Eagle, Swamp Francolin, Bengal Florican and Hodgson's Bushchat, all of which are listed in *Birds to Watch,* the Interna-tional Council for Bird Preservation world checklist of threatened birds. There are small lakes scattered throughout the country. Those in lowlands and the Pokhara lakes support the richest variety of birds, while the lakes in the Himalayas are very species-poor, although they are staging posts for small num-bers of a wide range of wetland migrants which overfly the Himalayas. During a bird survey of the lowlands in western Nepal, Shrestha and Suwal found several interesting wetlands which were previously very poorly known ornithologically, notably an unpro-tected lake Ghodaghodi Tal in Kailili District (750). With the exception of the Kosi Barrage area and Royal Chitwan National Park, wetlands in the eastern half of Nepal have been almost entirely reclaimed for agriculture.

The spread of cultivation has also reduced the country's lowland grasslands in recent years and the small remaining areas are almost all within protected forests. Twelve breeding grassland bird species are nationally threatened, notably the Bengal and Lesser Floricans, two of the world's most endangered bus-tard species. Intensive annual cutting and burning of the grasslands are likely to alter their species compo-sition, encouraging a lower variety of coarser grasses. The numbers of Bengal Floricans have declined in the Royal Chitwan National Park, possibly as a result of

this, and it seems likely that other grassland bird species are also being adversely affected.

However, Nepal is of great value for birds, mainly because of its forests which cover much larger areas than the country's wetlands or grasslands. There is a wide range of forests comprising tropical, subtropical, temperate, subalpine and alpine types, which together hold the high proportion of 77% of Nepal's breeding birds (429). Subalpine and upper temperate forests are the most internationally important for breeding birds, as they support high numbers of species which may have significant world populations in Nepal. These total over half the subalpine species and 42% of those in the upper temperate zone (429).

Forest losses and deterioration are by far the greatest threats to Nepal's birds. Only 16% of all forest birds have adapted to breed in habitats heavily modified or created by people (429). A few species, such Grey Bushchat and White-cheeked Bulbul, which prefer open forests or scrub, must have in-creased as a result of forest depletion, but nearly all of them are common and widespread. Overall the popu-lations of most Nepalese forest birds are likely to have decreased.

As much as 84% of the country's nationally threat-ened birds are dependent on forests (429). Once the country was extensively forested, but by 1979 an aerial survey showed that only 43% of Nepal was forest land, i.e. partially covered in trees and shrubs[1]. Moreover, a large proportion of this forest land was covered in forests in poor condition, with only a scattering of trees and shrubs. Forests are declining chiefly because they can no longer meet the needs of the people. The population is rapidly rising and the vast majority of Nepalis depend on forests for their essential require-ments of fuel, animal fodder and other basic materi-als. A combination of deforestation and overgrazing has caused rapid run-off of rain during the monsoon, leading to massive soil erosion. The resulting wide-spread flooding in the lowlands has led to enormous loss of human life, crops and property.

Conservation of the country's forests is therefore vital, for the future of the people as well as its birds. There has recently been a great expansion in afforesta-tion, but the overall impact has been very small. As far as most birds are concerned, the new plantations are preferable to areas devoid of forest. However plantations, even of native broadleaves, can never replace the richness and variety of natural forests which may have taken hundreds of years to develop. Protection of some severely degraded natural forests has resulted in dramatic recoveries of forests well-stocked with native species[2]. Many people in Nepal now believe that the most important aspect of forestry in the country is the improved management of the large existing areas of low-density forest. This has enormous potential and would be much more valuable to forest birds than planting more trees.

The Department of National Parks and Wildlife Conservation (DNPWC) in Nepal is aiming to protect a representative sample of the country's ecosystems. Nepal already has an extensive protected area system which covers 7.4% of the country, comprising six national parks, five wildlife reserves and one hunting reserve. When the Annapurna Conservation Area (not yet officially gazetted, but now in operation) and the Makalu-Barun National Park are fully established, this figure will increase to over 10%. While the majority of Nepal's habitat-types are well represented in the protected areas network, there are three important omissions. These are tropical evergreen forests, subtropical and lower temperate broadleaved forests in the far east (Mai and Tamur valleys), and subtropical broadleaved forests further west, all of which are in urgent need of protection (429). The most outstanding gap is the lack of representation of subtropical broadleaved forests which once covered much of central and east Nepal. Phulchowki mountain in the Kathmandu Valley is the best remaining example of this habitat-type (429).

A total of 95% of Nepal's breeding bird species, 82% of nationally threatened species and 98% of those for which the country may hold internationally significant breeding populations breed in the protected or proposed protected areas (429). Strengthening the existing protected area system can therefore be considered a higher priority than the designation of new protected areas. Protecting 10% of Nepal is a formidable task for the government of one of the world's poorest countries. In addition to the lack of finances, other logistical problems faced by the DNPWC are enormous. Many of the protected areas are remote, accessible only by air or on foot, and lack roads within them. The rugged terrain of the mountain areas makes their coverage especially difficult. There are essential needs for additional staff, more staff training and the provision of resources, such as equipment for maintaining trails and bridges, binoculars, reference books, and warm clothing. Conservation education for local people who may either live in protected areas or in their surrounding land is urgently needed as there is widespread ignorance about the reasons for the establishment of reserves. It is particularly important to justify the relevance of reserves to them as providers of vital resources and as part of their natural heritage.

Nepal's protected areas are attracting more and more tourists and mountaineers each year. It is therefore becoming increasingly important both to manage visitor use and to educate visitors so as to bring economic benefits to Nepal without damaging cultural values or adversely affecting the environment of the reserves.

Innovative management measures are being taken in some protected areas, such as the Annapurna Conservation Area, which is run by the King Mahendra Trust for Nature Conservation, a non-profit-making, non-governmental organisation dedicated to conserving natural resources in Nepal. Here the traditional subsistence activities of local people are being integrated into a framework of sound resource management and ecological development. The aim is to balance the needs of the local people, trekkers and the natural environment. A similar approach would be highly valuable in Nepal's other protected areas. To achieve this and to establish and effectively protect new areas, financial assistance from outside Nepal will be essential.

1. Carson, B., Niel, R., Amatya and Hildreth, G. (1986) *Land Resources Mapping Project.* Kenting Earth Sciences Ltd. Kathmandu: HMG/Govt. of Canada
2. Jackson, J.K. (1987) *Manual of afforestation in Nepal.* Kathmandu: Nepal UK Forestry Project.

Based on Inskipp, C. (1989) Bird Conservation in Nepal. *World Birdwatch* 11(1).

PROTECTED AREAS

The location of Nepal's protected areas is shown on the map on the book's end papers. The Royal Chitwan, Langtang and Sagarmatha National Parks, and the Annapurna Conservation Area are well studied, but the other protected areas are under-recorded.

Royal Chitwan National Park 932km²
This park, gazetted in 1973, was the first protected area in Nepal and is a World Heritage site. It lies in south-central Nepal in a dun valley and extends into the Churia hills. A larger number of bird species (489 in total) have been recorded than in any other protected area in Nepal.

Langtang National Park 1710km²
Langtang is situated in the central Himalayas and is of international importance for birds, especially for upper temperate and subalpine forest species.

Sagarmatha (Mount Everest) National Park 1148km²
A World Heritage site. The park contains some of the world's most spectacular mountain scenery including the highest peak, Sagarmatha. It lies in the high Himalayas in Khumbu District in north-eastern Nepal and is important for some high altitude species.

Royal Bardia National Park 968km²
Bardia is situated in mid-western Nepal, mainly in the bhabar zone and extends into the Churia hills. The Karnali river valley forms its western boundary. It supports a variety of species typical of the western lowlands.

Shey-Phoksundo National Park 3555km²
This is Nepal's largest protected area and is probably the least known ornithologically. It lies in Dolpo, Jumla and Mugu Districts in north-west Nepal. The park is important for species typical of the trans-Himalayan region.

Khaptad National Park 225km²
Khaptad is an isolated massif 3100m high which lies south of the main Himalayan range. The park is well-forested and is important for some forest species including a few western specialities.

Rara National Park 106km²
This small park is situated in the Himalayas in Mugu District in north-west Nepal. It includes the country's largest lake, Rara, situated at 3050m, and its heavily forested catchment area. The park supports some specialities of western Nepal forests.

Parsa Wildlife Reserve 499km²
Parsa is situated in south central Nepal adjacent to the Royal Chitwan National Park. It holds a rich variety of bird species similar to those found at Chitwan.

Kosi Tappu Wildlife Reserve 175km²
Kosi Tappu lies in the Sapta-Kosi river plain in the south-eastern tarai. The reserve includes a wetland which is of international importance and by far the most valuable in Nepal.

Royal Sukla Phanta Wildlife Reserve 155km²
This small reserve is situated in the far south-western tarai on the Indian border. It has the largest grassland area in Nepal as well as forests and a small lake. Sukla Phanta is important for a a few grassland species.

Sheopuri Watershed and Wildlife Reserve 145km²
Sheopuri lies on the northern side of the Kathmandu Valley in central Nepal. About half of the watershed is still forested and supports a good variety of forest birds.

Dhorpatan Hunting Reserve 1325km²
The hunting reserve lies in the Himalayas in Baglung District in west central Nepal. It holds some specialities of Nepal's western forests.

Annapurna Conservation Area 2660km²
The Conservation Area lies north of Pokhara in central Nepal, the Kali Gandaki River forming its western boundary. The Area is of international importance for birds and over 440 species have been recorded. This large number can be attributed to the wide range of habitat types within the Area and to its location roughly in the centre of the Himalayas. Species typical of both the eastern and western Himalayas occur.

Makalu Barun National Park
This is a proposed protected area which lies to the east of Sagarmatha National Park and extends beyond Nepal's northern border into Tibet. Its extensive forests support a diverse avifauna including many eastern Himalayan species.

MIGRATION

Dusky Thrush

Many of Nepal's resident species are seasonal altitudinal migrants. The level to which they descend in winter frequently depends on weather conditions. An example is the Red-billed Chough which has been found as high as 7950m, and usually remains above 2440m in winter, but has been noted as low as 1450m in cold weather (57,682). Approximately 62 species are summer visitors or partial migrants to the Nepalese Himalayas and include species of cuckoos, swifts, bee-eaters, *Phylloscopus* warblers, flycatchers and drongos. The migration routes of a number of these summer migrants are poorly understood or unknown, including those for the Asian Sooty Flycatcher, Ferruginous Flycatcher and Fork-tailed Swift. Many species winter further south in the subcontinent, including the Large Hawk-Cuckoo, Blue-tailed Bee-eater, Hoopoe, Barn Swallow, Greenish Warbler, Asian Brown Flycatcher, Asian Paradise Flycatcher, and Ashy Drongo. Other species such as the White-throated Needletail, Asian Emerald Cuckoo, Tickell's Warbler, and Crow-billed Drongo move southeast, perhaps as far as Malaysia and Indonesia. The origin of these wintering birds is unknown, and it is possible that Nepalese individuals do not travel so far. The Lesser Cuckoo and Common Swift winter in Africa and the Pied Cuckoo may also do so. About 149 species winter in Nepal, originating from a wide area to the north in the Palearctic. These include ducks, birds of prey, waders, gulls, terns, pipits, wagtails, thrushes, *Acrocephalus, Locustella* and *Phylloscopus* warblers, bush warblers, finches and buntings. A few species such as the Yellow-browed Warbler and Greenish Warbler are both summer and winter visitors. There is increasing evidence to suggest that some birds breeding in the Palearctic migrate across the Himalayas to winter in southern Asia. However, Moreau[1] points out that relatively few species take this route compared to the number which migrate to Africa, despite that continent being considerably further away: 137 species from the West Palearctic (west of 45⁰E) winter in Africa and 10 in India, and 82 from the mid-Palearctic (45 to 90⁰E) in Africa compared with only about 50 in India. He suggested that 'the high elevated and ecologically inimical Tibetan plateau flanked by the gigantic Himalayas' is an effective barrier for migrants. Much of the current evidence for the north-south movement across the Himalayas is based on casual observations made by visiting birdwatchers and mountaineering expeditions. There have been few systematic studies of migration in these ranges.

Most trans-Himalayan migrants observed have been non-passerines: large numbers of cranes and birds of prey, small flocks of ducks, geese, waders, gulls, terns, and also Hoopoes and Eurasian Wrynecks.

Birds have been noted flying over the highest regions of these ranges, enabling them to shorten their journeys considerably. Examples include a flock of Bar-headed Geese seen flying as high as 9375m over Sagarmatha (701), and a Steppe Eagle found dead at 7925m on the mountain's South Col (728). There is an unconfirmed report of Siberian Cranes *Grus leucogeranus* migrating over the Himalayas in Nepal (544). A movement of small grey birds across the South Col has also been noted (415), and a Barn Swallow has been recorded in Khumbu as high as 6400m (580), indicating that even small birds can migrate at such heights. In spring and autumn, a variety of species, mainly ducks but also waders, gulls and terns, are regularly recorded stopping off at Himalayan lakes including Phewa Tal, Begnas Tal, Rara, and frequently as high as 4750m at Gokyo lakes in Khumbu.

However, some trans-Himalayan migrants, whether they are the majority is not known, have been observed flying along the main valleys such as those of the Karnali, Kali Gandaki, Dudh Kosi, and Arun rivers.

The first study of trans-Himalayan migration was carried out as long ago as 1831 by Hodgson in the Kathmandu Valley (341). Other migration observations have subsequently been made in the Valley, notably those of Proud (629,635).

Recent observations show that the Kali Gandaki valley is a significant route taken by trans-Himalayan migrants. There have been three important systematic studies of autumn migration in the upper section of the valley: by Martens in 1969 (526), Beaman in 1973 (76) and by Thiollay in 1978 (761). The valley breaches the main Himalayan range, forming a natural route for migrants leaving the Tibetan Plateau.

However to the north in Tibet the valley is bounded by an extensive tract of plateau, so that potential migrants are faced with one of the most arduous crossings in the region.

All three investigations found large numbers of cranes flying south. A total of 31,351 Demoiselle Cranes were estimated between 1 and 11 October 1969 (526). Between 29 September and 14 October 1973, 3751 cranes, including 2220 Demoiselles were seen (76); and about 63,000 cranes, mainly Demoiselles, between 24 September and 5 October 1978 (761).

Thiollay counted a total of 151 birds of prey representing 15 species, and Beaman noted roughly 18 species totalling 404 birds. The largest species totals were of 254 Black Kites flying south between 14 September and 1 October 1973, 45 Common Buzzards between 31 August and 14 October 1973, and 39 Lesser Kestrels between 24 September and 5 October 1978. Some interesting observations of migrant birds of prey were made in the same area between 13 October and 4 November 1984 by Christensen *et al*. They recorded about 130 birds comprising 12 species, including 56 *Aquila* eagles (mainly Steppe Eagles) (145). There are several records of smaller numbers of raptors migrating south down Himalayan valleys in autumn including 276 Steppe Eagles down the Trisuli valley in two and a half hours on 24 October 1980 (516).

Only seven passerine migrant species were found between 1 and 11 October 1969 in the upper Kali Gandaki valley by Martens including Tickell's Warbler which was by far the most abundant species. He attributed this small variety of species to the advanced season. Beaman recorded only about 19 passerine migrant species in October 1973, with significant numbers of Greater Short-toed Larks, Hume's Short-toed Larks, White Wagtails, Black Redstarts, and Tickell's Warblers. Even after bad weather few migrants were seen, indicating that large numbers of passerines were probably not moving over at night. In another study in Khumbu in September and October 1970 Martens found that migration was sparse. A total of 23 species crossed passes over 5700m above sea level including ten passerine species with concentrations of Greater Shorter-toed and Hume's Short-toed Larks and Black Redstarts (526). Other observations also indicate that only small numbers of passerines regularly cross the Tibetan plateau. Species recorded include wagtails, Booted Warbler, Lesser Whitethroat, and Chiffchaff.

The majority of passerines wintering in the subcontinent presumably skirt the Himalayas. Populations of the Dark-throated Thrush and Paddyfield, Blyth's Reed and Greenish Warblers mainly originate in the west and probably fly round the ranges from this direction. Species such as Siberian Rubythroat,

Red-breasted Flycatcher, Brown Shrike, Black-faced Bunting and Yellow-breasted Bunting, which chiefly come from the east, probably skirt the eastern end of the Himalayas.

Birds of prey, especially *Aquila* eagles, have also been found to use the Himalayas as an east-west pathway in autumn, and also in larger numbers than hitherto recorded in Nepal. The phenomenon was first described by Fleming (225) who made observations in October and November 1975 in the Kathmandu Valley, and also at Dhampus, south of Annapurna, where at least 490 birds of three *Aquila* species were seen from 3 to 5 November 1976. Christensen *et.al.* counted 1047 birds of 15 species, including 992 Steppe Eagles, flying west-south-west or west between 26 and 28 October 1984, also south of Annapurna, mainly between Birethante and Naudanda. There are several reports of similar movements involving much smaller numbers of raptors across the breadth of Nepal. The maximum count received is from the Kathmandu Valley where 135 Steppe Eagles and two Greater Spotted Eagles moved west in half an hour on 19 November 1989 (597). Small numbers of Steppe Eagles have also been noted flying west along the Himalayan foothills in Ilam District in extreme east Nepal in October and November 1978 and at Bardia in the far west in November 1985 (162). A systematic study of this east/west migration was made at Khare, south of Annapurna between 20 October and 7 November 1985 by de Roder (683). Nearly 9,000 raptors of some 30 species were counted with Steppe Eagle being the most numerous, totalling 7,852 birds. In addition de Roder found several passerine species undergoing similar movements notably 13,902 Red-rumped Swallows and 109 Red-throated Pipits at Khare in October and November 1985 (684). There is also evidence that Spot-winged Starlings undertake east-west movements along the Himalayas (45). It is possible that other species undergo similar migrations.

Flocks of Lesser Kestrels and Amur Falcons are regularly recorded on passage, particularly in autumn. It is not clear whether they are moving north/south or east/west, although de Roder found 77 Lesser Kestrels and 138 Amur Falcons moving west at Khare in October and November 1985. The largest count of Amur Falcons received is 328 birds near Godavari in the Kathmandu Valley between 8 and 11 November 1985 (201). A mixed flock of falcons, chiefly comprising Lesser Kestrels and Amur Falcons with much smaller numbers of Common Kestrels and Peregrine Falcons, regularly roosts near Phewa Tal in October and November. Over 60 falcons were still present at the roost as late as 11 December in 1977 (495). The maximum count received is of 340 birds, which were all Lesser Kestrels, on 13 October 1982 (244).

Comparatively few reports of spring migration

Yellow-legged Gull

have been received. These are mainly of raptors and include 25 Steppe Eagles in 15 minutes flying north over the Naudanda ridge, south of Annapurna on 10 March 1981 (476) and 150 Steppe Eagles moving north over Namche Bazaar in Khumbu on 10 March 1982 (77). Small flocks of Black Kites have also been recorded migrating in spring including 22 in the upper Arun valley in May 1981 (483).

A valuable investigation of resident and migratory birds along the Rapti and Narayani Rivers in Chitwan National Park, was carried out by Halliday in November and December 1982 (304). He censused 57 species in detail, of which about 16 were migrants. His results showed the National Park provided secure feeding and resting areas for a high percentage of the local waders when the banks outside the park were disturbed.

The marshes and large expanse of open water at Kosi Barrage provide the most important staging point for migratory wildfowl, gulls, terns and waders in Nepal. The area has been well studied by ornithologists between January and May, when useful counts of bird numbers have been made. Fewer counts have been made in autumn, but these clearly show that the numbers of migrants are comparatively small. Peak numbers of wildfowl pass through between mid-February and mid-March. The maximum of over 50,000 was estimated in February 1981 (559, 622). Wader passage has been noted from the end of February to early May, with most birds passing through in March and April. Large numbers have not been reported, with peaks of about 1000 to 1500 birds. They presumably reflect the relatively low numbers of waders crossing the Himalayas.

1. Moreau, R.E. 1972. *The Palaearctic-African bird migration systems*. London: Academic Press.

HISTORY OF ORNITHOLOGY IN NEPAL

The following account summarises major contributions to Nepalese ornithology. The first published observations of Nepalese birds were made by Col. W.J. Kirkpatrick who noted a few gamebird species in 1793 (818). However the first important work was done by Brian Hodgson, a remarkable man, who held governmental posts in the country for over 20 years between 1820 and 1843. This included over ten years as British Resident. He made two extensive collections comprising 9500 bird skins and 1000 skins of mammals, reptiles and fish. These included about 665 Nepalese bird species, over 120 of which were new to science. Most of the skins were acquired through Nepalese collectors as he was not allowed to travel outside the Kathmandu Valley. After leaving Nepal in 1843 he lived in Darjeeling in India for the next 15 years where he made his second collection. Some birds are listed as coming from Nepal in Gray's published catalogue of this collection (277), and are treated as such in the first edition of this book. However in a recently discovered annotated copy of the catalogue Hodgson had deleted Nepal as a source of these specimens (149). It is likely that they originated from forests in India close to Nepal's eastern border. Seven species from this collection have not been recorded in Nepal subsequently. He also trained a Nepalese artist, Raj Man Singh, who painted over 1800 watercolour illustrations of Nepalese wildlife, mainly birds, which rival the work of other artists of this period.

John Scully, who was resident surgeon in 1876 to 1877, also made a large collection comprising nearly 2000 specimens of about 300 species of birds. He was the first person to describe the status of birds in the Kathmandu Valley. His movements within Nepal were restricted, like those of Hodgson.

During his studies of birds of the Sikkim Himalayas between 1911 and 1914 Herbert Stevens visited the upper Mai valley in far east Nepal. He recorded valuable altitudinal and breeding information, and collected skins, still in excellent condition, and held at the Hancock Museum, Newcastle-upon-Tyne, U.K.

An important collection of 2146 skins comprising 381 species, including a number new to the country, was made by Lt.-Col. Frank Bailey between 1935 and 1938 when he was British Envoy Extraordinary in Nepal. Lt.-Col. James Roberts has kindly pointed out that Bailey cannot have travelled widely throughout the country as stated in the first edition of this book as travel by foreigners within Nepal was still restricted highly at that time. His specimens however came from localities throughout Nepal.

Between 1947 and 1949 Dr. Dillon Ripley made a major collection, originating in areas between the far west and far east of the country. He obtained 1600 specimens representing about 300 species.

Desiree Proud published several papers between 1948 and 1961 summarising valuable and comprehensive observations on birds, mainly relating to the Gandak-Kosi watershed and Kathmandu Valley.

In 1952 Oleg Polunin was able to trek extensively throughout the western Nepalese Himalayas while participating in a British Museum (Natural History) botanical expedition. He recorded a number of species for the first time in Nepal, and contributed much to the knowledge of bird distribution in the west.

Dr. Biswamoy Biswas and Dr Walter Koelz collected 3500 bird skins representing about 350 species, around Kathmandu and between there and Raxaul, in 1947. These included a number of new species for the country. Between 1960 and 1968 he published a detailed account of this collection, and included a summary of all Nepalese bird records up to that date.

Dr. G. Diesselhorst provided important data on the distribution, altitude range and breeding of Nepalese birds during his ornithological expedition of 1962. He collected 1700 specimens comprising about 315 species.

An enormous contribution to Nepalese ornithology has been made by Drs. Robert Fleming Sr. and Jr. They have probably travelled more widely throughout the country than any other ornithologists. Between them they built up a large collection of bird skins, many of which are held in the Chicago Field Museum of Natural History, and have published about 35 papers and articles on Nepalese birds. They have also produced the only field guide to the birds of the country, first published in 1976.

Hari Sharan Nepali, the leading Nepalese ornithologist, has also collected a large number of bird skins, many of which are held at the Kathmandu Natural History Museum. He has trekked extensively within the country and has added several species to the Nepalese list.

Since the early 1970s numerous visitors, ranging from serious ornithologists to birdwatchers on holiday have recorded birds in Nepal. Although many have only covered the more easily accessible areas, the knowledge of Nepalese birds has increased enormously as a result of their observations; 67 species have been added to the Nepalese list since 1970 and new species are found each year.

BIRD-WATCHING AREAS

Regularly recorded specialities are listed for each area.

Red-vented Bulbul

Kathmandu Valley
The Valley and surrounding hills are still rich in birdlife despite being well-cultivated and highly populated. It is well worth spending about five days birdwatching based in Kathmandu.

Phulchowki and Godavari Botanical Gardens
Some of the few subtropical broadleaved forests remaining in Nepal are found on Phulchowki mountain in the south-eastern corner of the Valley above the village of Godavari, about 18km south-east of Kathmandu. These are probably the best forests for birds in the Valley and also support a wide variety of plant and insect life. Unfortunately they are rapidly becoming depleted and degraded, but are still the most convenient place to see a number of species which are scarce or local elsewhere in the country.

At least one full day is needed to cover the upper slopes. Taking a taxi from Kathmandu up the winding partly surfaced road to the top of the mountain (2760m) and walking down to Godavari (1525m) is recommended. However the road is very rough in places and can only be easily used by vehicles in good condition. The area can also be reached by bus, changing at Lagankhel for Godavari. Another day spent exploring the Botanical Gardens, which are situated at the foot of Phulchowki, and the mountain's lower slopes will produce some different species. The gardens tend to be crowded on public holidays and Saturdays and are best avoided then.

Species:- Mountain Hawk-Eagle, Mountain Scops Owl, Golden-throated Barbet, Rufous-bellied Woodpecker, Grey-chinned Minivet, Striated Bulbul, Orange-bellied Leafbird, White-tailed Robin, Long-billed Thrush, Black-faced Warbler, Large Niltava, Slaty-backed Flycatcher (Botanical Gardens), Grey-throated Babbler, Black-throated Parrotbill, Spiny Babbler, Rufous-chinned and Grey-sided Laughing-thrushes, Cutia, Black-eared Shrike-Babbler, Hoary Barwing, Nepal Fulvetta, Brown-throated Treecreeper, Mrs Gould's Sunbird, Yellow-bellied Flowerpecker, Lanceolated Jay, Tibetan Serin (Botanical Gardens), Gold-naped Finch, Brown Bullfinch, Spot-winged Grosbeak.

Gokarna Safari Park
A hill (1385m) covered in protected forest about 8.5km east of Kathmandu, easily reached by taxi. The park is open to the public from early in the morning on payment of a small fee and can be covered in half a day. The forest which is open and has some mature trees is favoured by owls, wintering thrushes and flycatchers.

Species:- Brown Fish Owl, Small Niltava, Blue-throated and Asian Brown Flycatchers, Plain Flowerpecker.

Nagarjung
A mountain (2105m) with protected forest on the edge of the Valley above Balaju. It is open to the public from early in the morning on payment of a nominal fee. The entrance gates are about 5km from Kathmandu centre and can be reached by taxi, or by public transport to Balaju, from where it is a short walk along the road to the entrance. Only secondary forest lies within easy walking distance of the entrance. Much richer habitat remains on the far side of the mountain but this can only be covered in a long day's walk.

Species:- Kalij Pheasant, Eurasian Eagle Owl, Chestnut-crowned Warbler, Nepal Fulvetta, Red-billed Blue Magpie.

Sheopuri Wildlife Reserve
A forested mountain (2730m) on the north-eastern edge of the Valley. Although slopes facing the Valley are now degraded those on the north side and the summit area still have interesting forest. It would be necessary to camp on the mountain to explore the northern slopes. The base of Sheopuri can be reached by taxi or bus to Budhanilkantha, 11km from Kathmandu. A strenuous full day is needed to reach and investigate the forest slopes facing the Valley.

Species:- Rufous-bellied Woodpecker, Golden Bush-Robin, Yellow-bellied Bush Warbler, Black-faced Warbler, Snowy-browed Flycatcher, Spiny Babbler (near Tokha Sanatorium), Hoary Barwing, Nepal

Fulvetta, Red-tailed Minla, Scarlet Finch, Brown Bullfinch.

Pashupatinath and Swayambhunath
There are protected groves around Pashupatinath and Swayambhunath temples which are only a few kilometres from Kathmandu centre. Each supports a good variety of common open woodland species including minivets, warblers and flycatchers.

Fields by the Bagmati and Manora Rivers
The fields by the rivers are rapidly being reclaimed for building but are still a regular wintering area for Grey-headed Lapwing. Larks, pipits and buntings can also be found as well as warblers in the bushes. Both rivers are interesting for migrating birds, particularly in autumn.

Bagmati River (near Chobar Gorge) and Basantgaon
At Basantgaon about 5km south of Kathmandu, there are some flooded pools close to the Bagmati River. The pools and the adjacent stretch of river south to Chobar Gorge attract small numbers of a good variety of migrant waders and wildfowl.

Species:- Ibisbill (in autumn), Grey-headed Lapwing.

Royal Chitwan National Park
The park comprises a lowland valley of sal and riverain forests interspersed with grasslands and backed by the forested Churia hills to the north. Over 480 bird species have been recorded in the park. A number of large mammal species can also be seen such as Tiger, Leopard, Indian Rhinoceros, Sloth Bear and Gaur. The park is readily accessible by air or bus from Kathmandu. Tourist accommodation is available at several lodges and tented camps which provide excellent opportunities for observing wildlife, including taking elephant rides, or canoe trips on the rivers. There is also basic accommodation available in vil-

Black Baza

lages just outside the park, mainly at Sauraha. Walking alone in the park can be dangerous because of the wild mammals. An entry fee must be paid each time the park is entered.

Species:- Oriental Darter, Yellow Bittern, Lesser Adjutant Stork, Lesser Whistling Duck, Black Baza, Lesser and Grey-headed Fishing Eagles, Changeable Hawk-Eagle, Collared Falconet, Ruddy-breasted and Brown Crakes, Bengal Florican, Great Stone-plover, Great Black-headed Gull, Orange-breasted Green and Pompadour Green Pigeons, Moustached Parakeet, Chestnut-winged and Banded Bay Cuckoos, Lesser Coucal, Brown Fish and Brown Hawk Owls, Savanna Nightjar, White-rumped and White-vented Needletails, Red-headed Trogon, Blue-eared Kingfisher, Oriental Pied and Great Hornbills, Himalayan Flameback, Hooded and Indian Pittas, Rosy Minivet, White-tailed Stonechat, Pale-footed and Chestnut-crowned Bush Warblers, Bright-capped Cisticola, Yellow-bellied and Grey-crowned Prinias, Large Grass, Yellow-bellied and Smoky Warblers, Asian Paradise Flycatcher, Black-naped Monarch, Chestnut-capped, Yellow-eyed and Slender-billed Babblers, Rufous-necked Laughing-thrush, Crow-billed Drongo, Black-breasted Weaver, Red Avadavat.

Kosi Barrage and Kosi Tappu Wildlife Reserve
The river near Kosi barrage and the adjoining marshes form by far the largest wetland in Nepal. The barrage crosses the Kosi River in the south-eastern tarai. North and south of it are huge expanses of water with mudflats and sandbanks appearing when the level is low. Great bunds to the east and west contain the river, with borrow pits alongside containing reedbeds and water for most of the year. Kosi Barrage is easily reached by daily buses from Kathmandu along the east - west highway to Karkavitta on the far eastern border. Kosi can also be reached by taking a flight from Kathmandu to Birtamod and a taxi from there to Kosi. Basic accommodation and food are available in Kosi village. It is well worth spending about three days in the area. Many recent additions to the Nepalese list have been recorded at Kosi. Wildfowl passage occurs mainly in February and March and waders pass through between February and mid-May. Monsoon visitors can be seen between late May and September.

Species:- Spot-billed Pelican, Yellow Bittern, Black-necked Stork, Black-headed Ibis, Eurasian Spoonbill, Lesser Whistling Duck, Pallas's Fish and White-tailed Eagles, Red-necked Falcon, Swamp Francolin, Baillon's and Ruddy-breasted Crakes, Watercock, Pheasant-tailed Jacana, Great Stone-plover, Great Black-headed and Brown-headed Gulls, Caspian, River, Black-bellied and Whiskered Terns, Indian Skimmer,

Map 4. Chitwan

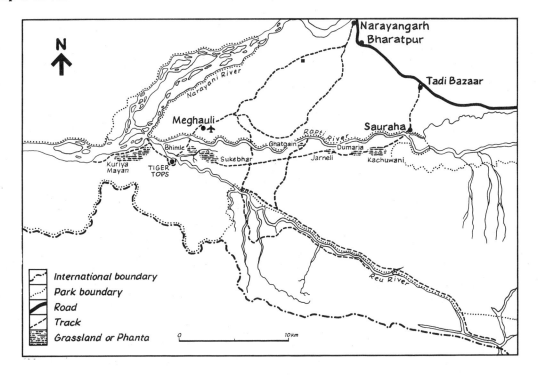

Lesser Coucal, White-tailed Stonechat, Hodgson's Bushchat, Graceful and Yellow-bellied Prinias, Striated Marsh and Smoky Warblers, Black-breasted Weaver, Red Avadavat, Black-faced Bunting.

Hetaura
The Rapti River near Hetaura is a regular wintering area for Ibisbills. Long-billed Plover has also been found. A visit can easily be made to Hetaura en route to Kosi Barrage as Kathmandu to Karkavitta buses all stop there. Spending a night in the town and travelling on the following day is recommended.

Royal Bardia National Park
Much of Bardia National Park consists of lowland sal and riverain forests and the sal-forested Churia hills cover the remainder. The Karnali River forms the western boundary of the park. Bardia is rich in western lowland species. It can be reached by a two day bus journey from Kathmandu via Nepalganj or by flying to Nepalganj and taking a day's bus ride from there. There is a tourist tented camp in the park.

Species:- Changeable Hawk-Eagle, Grey Francolin, Bengal Florican, Great Stone-plover, Orange-breasted Green Pigeon, Brown Fish and Brown Hawk Owls, White-rumped Needletail, Oriental Pied Hornbill, Indian Pitta, White-naped, Great Slaty and Brown-capped Pygmy Woodpeckers, Jungle Prinia, Tickell's Blue Flycatcher, Crow-billed and Greater Racket-tailed Drongos and Red Avadavat.

Trekking
There are few roads in the Nepalese Himalayas so access to much of the country is only possible by trekking on the numerous trails through the mountains. General advice on trekking, and details on all treks described below can be found in various readily available maps and books on the subject.

North-west of Pokhara
Pokhara (915m) is the starting point for several popular treks and can easily be reached by bus or air from Kathmandu or by bus from the Indian border via Tansen. Although the Pokhara valley is heavily cultivated with little remaining forest cover, it is still worth spending a couple of days birdwatching there. The lake Phewa Tal which lies very close to the town, is interesting for migrants, especially waders, gulls and terns in spring and autumn.

Cinnamon Sparrow

Olive-backed Pipit

Pokhara to Thakkhola - Jomosom trek
This trek in the Annapurna Conservation Area is highly recommended as a larger number of species are likely to be seen than on any other trek in Nepal. About 200 species can easily be seen in about three weeks. This is mainly because a great variety of habitat is covered within a short distance. The trek starts amongst subtropical vegetation at Pokhara, climbs north-west through temperate oak-rhododendron forests followed by coniferous forests and finally dry semi-desert country typical of the Tibetan plateau. The region south of Annapurna has unusually high rainfall and supports lush forests which hold some eastern Himalayan species. The trek also provides  opportunities to see species typical of both the western Himalayas and the Tibetan plateau; regions which are difficult to reach in Nepal. Food and accommodation are easily available along the entire route. October is a good month for migrants, particularly birds of prey and cranes. December to March is also an interesting period as a number of unusual wintering species may be seen including some erratic visitors such as Spectacled Finch and Pine Bunting. Snow may lie at times during these months, especially in forests near Ghorepani (2775m) and Ghandrung (2010m), and birds then tend to descend below the snow-line. The route can be shortened by flying from Pokhara to Jomosom, but note that flights are frequently cancelled due to bad weather. The route from Birethante (1065m) to Ghorepani via Ghandrung is recommended in at least one direction as this passes through one of the richest forests on the trek. Other interesting areas for birds include the forested slopes between Chandrakot and Birethante, Birethante to Tirkhedhunge (1575m) (Crested Kingfisher, forktails), Ghorepani forest (pheasants, bush-robins, Long-billed Thrush, Great Parrotbill, Black-eared Shrike-Babbler, Black-browed Tit, rosefinches, Spec-

tacled and Crimson-browed Finches, Collared Grosbeak), forests above Ghasa (2040m) (Koklass and Cheer Pheasants), Tukche to Kagbeni (2805m) and Muktinath (3800m) (Tibetan plateau species and Solitary Snipe), above Muktinath on the Thorong La pass (Tibetan Snowcock). **Other species:-** Lammergeier, Himalayan Griffon Vulture, Mountain Hawk-Eagle, Hill Pigeon, Mountain Scops Owl, Fork-tailed Swift, Orange-rumped Honeyguide, Brown, Robin, and Altai Accentors, White-browed and Rufous-breasted Bush-Robins, White-throated and Guldenstadt's Redstarts, Desert Wheatear, Slaty-backed Forktail, Black-faced Warbler, Stoliczka's Tit-Warbler, Black-throated Parrotbill, Variegated and Rufous-chinned Laughing-thrushes, Fire-capped Tit, Fire-fronted Serin, Spot-winged, White-browed, Streaked and Great Rosefinches, Brown Bullfinch, Pine Bunting.

Modi Khola and Annapurna Sanctuary
This is another trek in the Annapurna Conservation Area and takes about two weeks. It passes through moist oak/rhododendron and bamboo forests in the Modi Khola valley south of Annapurna. These forests are especially rich in birds and it is possible to see some eastern Himalayan species which are scarce and local in Nepal. The trek begins at Pokhara and goes north up the Modi Khola valley to the river's source, a basin on the south-west side of Annapurna called the Annapurna Sanctuary. Accommodation and food are available throughout the trek

Species:- Golden-throated Barbet, Golden, White-browed and Rufous-breasted Bush-Robins, Slender-billed Scimitar-Babbler, Golden Babbler, Fulvous Parrotbill, Scaly Laughing-thrush, Cutia, Black-headed Shrike-Babbler, Golden-breasted Fulvetta, Yellow-bellied Flowerpecker, rosefinches.

Ashy Woodswallow

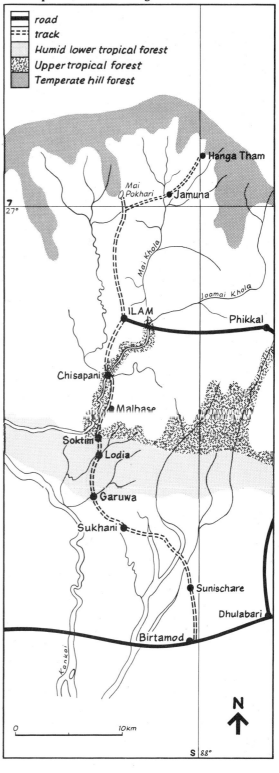

Map 5 Sunischare to Hanga Tham

road
track
Humid lower tropical forest
Upper tropical forest
Temperate hill forest

Sunischare to the upper Mai valley

This trek offers the opportunity to see species of Nepal's south-eastern lowlands and of the eastern Himalayas. It can be conveniently combined with a visit to Kosi and takes about two weeks. The trek can be shortened by two to three days by taking a half day bus journey bus from Birtamod to Ilam. Carrying camping equipment and enough food for a few days is advised. To reach Sunischare take a bus to Birtamod (either the Kathmandu to Karkavitta bus, or one east from Kosi Barrage). The walk from Sunischare to Ilam takes two days but is worth spreading out over four and camping if necessary.

Species between Sunischare and Ilam: Crested Goshawk, Collared Falconet, Barred Cuckoo-Dove, Blue-bearded Bee-eater, Oriental Pied Hornbill, Long-tailed Broadbill, White-throated Bulbul, Asian Fairy Bluebird, Yellow-vented Warbler, Abbott's Babbler, Lesser Necklaced and Greater Necklaced Laughing-thrushes, Ruby-cheeked Sunbird, Little Spiderhunter, Yellow-vented Flowerpecker, Crow-billed Drongo, and Hill Mynah.

It takes about half a day to walk from the small busy town of Ilam to Jamuna (1830m). Buying food in Jamuna is advised as it may not be available further on. Another half day is needed to reach Hanga Tham (2135m), a good base to stay for two to three days while exploring the upper Mai valley. Lodging with local people may be possible here, but be prepared to camp.

Species in the upper Mai valley:- White-browed Piculet, Maroon-backed Accentor, Rufous-breasted Bush-Robin, Hill Prinia, Yellow-bellied Warbler, Large Niltava, Sapphire Flycatcher, Rufous-throated Wren-Babbler, Slender-billed Scimitar-Babbler, Rufous-capped, Golden and Grey-throated Babblers,

Fire-tailed Myzornis nest

Black-throated Parrotbill, Scaly Laughing-thrush, Silver-eared Mesia, Fire-tailed Myzornis, Cutia, Black-eared Shrike-Babbler, Rusty-fronted Barwing, Red-tailed Minla, Golden-breasted Fulvetta, Yellow-cheeked Tit, and Brown Bullfinch.

Langtang trek
Trekking in Langtang National Park is highly recommended in spring, especially late May, when a wide variety of breeding Himalayan birds can be seen. About three weeks are needed for the trek. Accommodation and food are available along various trails. One popular route starts at Sundarijal (1265m) at the edge of the Kathmandu Valley, goes north via Pati Dhunjyung (1770m) and Kutumbang (3170m) to Thare Pati, and then along the Gosainkund trail to Gapte cave (3505m). It is worth spending two to three days here.

Species:- Blood Pheasant, Satyr Tragopan, Gould's Shortwing, White-browed and Rufous-breasted Bush-Robins, Long-billed Thrush, Smoky Warbler, Fire-tailed Myzornis, Black-browed Tit, Spot-winged and White-browed Rosefinches. From Gapte the trail crosses the Laurebina pass (4600m) to Gosainkund lakes (4300m) where Snow Partridge, Grandala and Red-fronted Rosefinch can be seen. Care is needed here as it is easy to lose the way in bad weather. The trail then drops to Chandanbari (3255m) and Syabru (2120m), which is a good area for Satyr Tragopan. The trek then follows the Langtang gorge where Orange-rumped Honeyguide has been seen, to Kyangjin (3750m). The gravel river bed here is a regular breeding site for Ibisbill. Tibetan Snowcock, White-bellied Redstart and Grandala can be found in upper Langtang. The recommended return route goes back down the Langtang and Trisuli valleys to Dhunche, from where a local bus can be taken to Trisuli Bazaar, and then another bus or taxi back to Kathmandu.

Sagarmatha National Park
Although a relatively small number of species are likely to be seen compared with other treks, some high altitude species are more easily found in Sagarmatha National Park than elsewhere in Nepal. The mountain scenery is the most spectacular in the country. The park entrance at Jorsalle can be reached by taking a short flight from Kathmandu to Lukla (2850m) followed by a day's walk. Be prepared to wait a few days for a plane if necessary. All the specialities are found in the park, but a good variety of birds can be seen on the trail towards Kathmandu and it is well worth walking in one direction if time allows. It takes about a week to walk from Namche Bazaar (3445m) to Jiri (2100m) from where a bus can be taken back to Kathmandu. Accommodation and food are available along popular treks in the park. There are several routes available from Namche Bazaar including those to Kala Pattar at the foot of Sagarmatha and to Gokyo lakes. The lakes attract small numbers of migrants especially ducks and waders in spring and autumn.

Species:- Tibetan Snowcock, Snow Partridge, Blood Pheasant, Himalayan Monal, Horned Lark, Robin, Altai and Alpine Accentors, White-throated, Guldenstadt's and White-bellied Redstarts, Grandala, Black-headed Mountain-Finch, White-browed and Great Rosefinches.

IDENTIFICATION
SECTION

GYPS VULTURES

Large to medium-sized vultures which often soar for hours at a great height while looking out for carrion. Gregarious scavengers; they frequently gather in flocks to feed on carcasses. Wings are long and broad, with leading and trailing edges almost parallel. Tails are short and appear square-cut or rounded, depending on abrasion. Head and neck are bare or partially down-covered.

Oriental White-backed Vulture *Gyps bengalensis*
Wing length 535-578mm

A medium-sized vulture. **Adult** can easily be identified in flight from below by white under wing-coverts contrasting with black flight feathers and blackish body. Neck ruff is white. From above the conspicuous white patch on lower back and upper tail-coverts is diagnostic. Rest of upperparts are blackish with grey secondaries producing a pale patch on the upper wing. **Immature** lacks white in plumage and is confusable with immature Eurasian Griffon and immature Long-billed, both of which are often associated with this species. Generally paler than adult, dark brown to dark buffy-brown or rufous-brown with blackish-brown primaries. Separated from Long-billed by darker, heavier appearance with relatively shorter wings and heavier bill; from adult and immature Eurasian Griffon by much smaller size and dark head.

Long-billed Vulture *Gyps indicus*
Wing length 590-630mm

In flight from below **adult** can be distinguished by combination of pale brown body and creamy under wing-coverts contrasting with blackish-brown flight feathers and dark head. Note that the latter may be obscured by the white ruff. The back and upper wing-coverts are brown and contrast with darker flight feathers. Adult and immature Eurasian Griffon are much larger and darker with paler heads and shorter, heavier bills. **Immature** Long-billed is similar to immature White-backed, see that species.

Eurasian Griffon Vulture *Gyps fulvus*
Wing Length 675-747mm

A large vulture. Usually found below 915m, at much lower altitudes than Himalayan Griffon, but the species do overlap. Noticeably smaller than that species. **Adult** has a whitish head, gingery-buff to rufous-brown body, and under wing-coverts contrasting with blackish-brown flight feathers and tail. **Immature** is similar to adult but is generally slightly darker overall and more rufous or cinnamon. Can be distinguished from adult Himalayan Griffon by darker underbody and under wing-coverts. Immature is similar to immature Himalayan but has more obvious pale streaking on the underside of the body and usually some indication of the adult's pale line on the under wing-coverts. See immature Long-billed and White-backed.

Himalayan Griffon Vulture *Gyps himalayensis*
Wing length 755-810mm

A huge vulture; the largest of the *Gyps* vultures. Usually occurs above 900m. **Adult** is easily recognised by its very pale buff to sandy-buff (appearing white at a distance) head, body and under wing-coverts, contrasting with blackish flight feathers and tail. **Immature** has whitish head and neck, blackish-brown primaries and tail, and rest of plumage dark brown, boldly streaked with buffish-white on the upperparts. Similar to Eurasian Griffon, see that species.

Oriental White-backed Vulture 1 ad., Long-billed Vulture 2 ad., Eurasian Griffon Vulture 3 ad., Himalayan Griffon Vulture 4 ad.

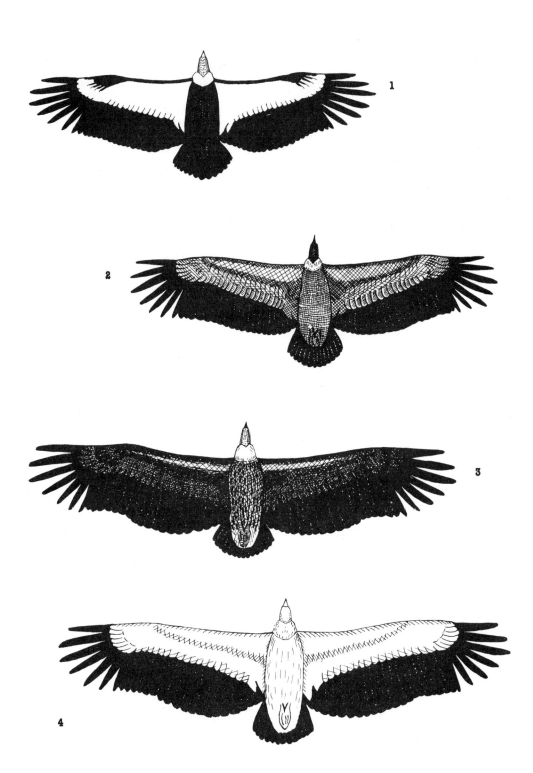

ACCIPITERS

Accipiters are small to medium-sized raptors with long tails and short, rounded wings. All the Nepalese species are forest bird-hunters.

Northern Goshawk *Accipiter gentilis*
Length 48–62cm
The largest Nepalese *Accipiter*. **Adult** Slaty grey above; white below barred with dark brown. **Immature** Brown above, buff below boldly streaked with brown. Some males approach the size of Northern Sparrowhawk or Crested Goshawk and may be confused in silhouette. However can usually be separated by larger size, deeper chest, proportionately shorter and more rounded tail, and longer wings often showing an S-shape curve on trailing edge. Adults (but not immatures) usually have more conspicuous white under tail-coverts and supercilium than Eurasian Sparrowhawk. Often shows a hooded appearance produced by dark ear-coverts. Females are almost size of Common Buzzard and Oriental Honey-Buzzard. Separated by slightly shorter and broader wings, proportionately longer tail and different flight.

Besra *Accipiter virgatus*
Length 30–36cm
A small *Accipiter*, size of Shikra, with plumage resembling that of Crested Goshawk. **Adult** Male is dark slate-grey above, female dark brown with dark grey crown and nape. Adult separated from all other *Accipiter* species except Crested Goshawk by broad blackish mesial stripe and barring on belly. Also by bold orange streaks on breast in male, and orange-brown breast spotted with white in female. Adults and immatures from Crested Goshawk by smaller size and lack of crest, and from Shikra by more heavily barred underwing and more prominent and broader barred tail. Female Shikra has central tail feathers unbarred or only lightly barred. **Immature** Grey-brown above, buff-white boldly streaked with dark brown below. A broad dark line divides throat. Separated from immature Shikra by darker, richer brown upperparts, sometimes with rufous tinge and broader tail bars; and from immature Eurasian Sparrowhawk by completely streaked underparts.

Eurasian Sparrowhawk *Accipiter nisus*
Length 28–38cm
A small to medium-sized *Accipiter*. **Adult** Upperparts grey (male), or brown (female). Underparts narrowly barred with rufous (male), grey-brown (female). Adult male can be confused with Shikra but is usually larger and darker (although *A. n. nisosimilis* is only slightly darker). Lacks faint line down centre of throat

and darker wing tips of adult Shikra. Underparts of Shikra are more extensively and finely barred. **Immature** Dark brown above. Throat and usually upper breast are streaked. From other immature *Accipiter* species by barring rather than streaking on buff breast and belly. All ages separated from Shikra by more heavily barred underwing and broadly banded tail.

Crested Goshawk *Accipiter trivirgatus*
Length 40–46cm
Separated from all other *Accipiter* species by crest, usually visible when perched. Heavier and larger than the other species apart from Northern Goshawk. **Adult** Similar in plumage to much smaller Besra and they differ from other species by combination of white underparts with bold rufous-brown streaks on breast and bars on belly. Has a black mesial streak from chin to breast and lacks a white supercilium. Under tail-coverts sometimes spotted with brown. **Immature** Similar to immature Besra and Shikra. Separated by larger size, crest, and thinner streaks on underparts. When soaring shows long, broad, well-spread tail and very rounded wings which are pinched in at base.

Shikra *Accipiter badius*
Length 30–36cm
A small, pale, stocky *Accipiter*, often with particularly rounded wingtips. Head rather cuckoo-like. **Adults** are dove-grey (male), or grey-brown (female) above. Underparts are orange with extensive fine white barring. The underwing is pale, usually with contrasting dark tips. Central tail feathers unbarred, or only lightly barred. **Immature** Medium or pale brown above with a dark crown, and narrower, less conspicuous barring on tail than immature Besra or Eurasian Sparrowhawk. See Besra and Eurasian Sparrowhawk.

Northern Goshawk: 1 ad., 2 imm.; Crested Goshawk: 3 imm., 4 ad.; Besra: 5 ad. male, 6 ad. female, 7 imm.; Shikra: 8 ad., 9 imm.; Eurasian Sparrowhawk: 10 ad. male, 11 imm., 12 ad. female; Shikra: 13 ad., 14 imm., Besra: 15 ad. male, 16 ad. female, 17 imm.; Eurasian Sparrowhawk: 18 ad. male, 19 ad. female, 20 imm.; Northern Goshawk: 21 ad., 22 imm.; Crested Goshawk 23 ad., 24 imm.

CR.

BUZZARDS

Medium-sized raptors. A particularly confusing group with similar structure and showing considerable plumage variation. The following account is intended as a guide. Not all individuals can be identified with certainty. All three species have light, normal and dark colour phases. They have broad wings, a fairly short, broad tail and short thick neck. Generally soar on raised wings.

Common Buzzard *Buteo buteo*
Two forms occur:-

B. b. 'refectus'
Wing length 39.2-41.6cm
A dark, often strongly rufous form, much larger than the extralimital *B. b. vulpinus*, and more like Long-legged in some features; wings less rounded, and with extensive white subterminally on the underside; tail uniform or only faintly banded. Dark carpal patches on underwing often extensive.

B. b. japonicus
Wing length 36.2-40.8cm
A smaller form, the typical phase paler than *B. b. 'refectus'*, tail whitish and obviously barred, and underwing with much less white and obscure dark carpal patches.

Long-legged Buzzard *Buteo rufinus*
Wing length 40.5-49cm
Slightly larger and longer winged than Common. Head creamy-white, usually paler than Common and Upland. Some birds show a dark belly and vent contrasting with rest of underparts which separates them from all Common and most Upland Buzzards. Adult normal phase has unbarred cinnamon tail but in immatures and dark phase adults the tail is barred and browner. Common and Upland may show a rufous tinge in tail. Upperwing is more contrasting than in Common, showing paler coverts and often a pale greyish patch at base of primaries, the latter not white or as extensive as is normal in Upland. Large dark carpal patches on underwing. See Upland and Common Buzzard.

Upland Buzzard *Buteo hemilasius*
Wing length 42.9-51cm
Largest buzzard occurring in Nepal. Usually has a large white patch at the primary bases on the spread upperwing. If present this is diagnostic because the other two species never show more than a small greyish patch. In a close view Upland usually has tarsus three-quarters feathered and is often feathered to the feet, whereas in Long-legged and Common the tarsus and feet are normally half feathered or less. Tail pattern and colour is variable, but is never completely plain nor cinnamon, thus precluding confusion with adult normal phase Long-legged. The tail is pale brown, basally whitish with a subterminal and other bars often so faint that it appears nearly uniform and very similar to the tails of some immature Long-legged and *B. b. japonicus*. Upland has darker head than a normal phase Long-legged, pale brown with streaky moustachial stripes. Underpart pattern of normal and light phase generally eliminates Common Buzzard, Upland having at least 'thighs' blackish-brown forming a dark V on lower underparts lacking in Common. Many Long-legged show a similar underpart pattern but birds with a dark area right across the belly are more likely to be Long-legged.

Upland Buzzard: 1,2
Long-legged Buzzard: 3,4
Common Buzzard: *B. b. 'refectus'*: **5**
                      B. b. japonicus: **6,7**

CHANGEABLE HAWK-EAGLE
Spizaetus cirrhatus
Wing length 380-462mm

MOUNTAIN HAWK-EAGLE *Spizaetus nipalensis*
Wing length 419-508mm

Both have very broad wings and long rounded tails. Mountain Hawk-Eagle can be separated in all ages when perched by its long crest feathers usually held vertically over its head; absent in Changeable. Pale phase adults can be separated by colour pattern of underparts. Changeable is white to buffy-brown below often irregularly streaked with dark brown; sometimes has heavy streaks on whole of underparts. Barring is usually absent or indistinct and only present on thighs and flanks. Mountain has light cinnamon or whitish breast with darker streaking limited to upper breast; rest of underparts are cinnamon brown with broken white barring. Changeable has a melanistic phase. Entire plumage is dark chocolate-brown or almost black and could lead to confusion with Black Eagle or dark phase Oriental Honey-Buzzard. Intermediates occur. Most easily separated from Black Eagle by underside of primaries and secondaries (especially primaries) much paler than wing lining (outer primaries tipped black), underside of tail pale grey. Immature Changeable and Mountain are probably indistinguishable except when crest can be seen. Feathers of upperparts are edged with white; head and neck are white with dark brown streaking. Underparts are usually white and very faintly barred with cinnamon. Sometimes has streaking but limited to breast only in Mountain. Tail with narrow dark bars, more numerous than in adult.

Mountain Hawk-Eagle: 1,2
Changeable Hawk-Eagle: 3

AQUILA EAGLES

Large raptors with long broad wings and medium-long tail. Most easily identifiable in juvenile plumages but all the species are very variable and field identification of some individuals is likely to be impossible.

Imperial Eagle *Aquila heliaca*
Wing Length 57.5-63cm
Wing Span 190-210mm
Heavy and large, almost size of Golden. Neck and bill protrude more than in other *Aquila* species. Distinguished from Golden by soaring on level more parallel-edged wings, fuller wing-tips, and often narrower-looking, more square-cut tail tip. From Tawny and Spotted Eagles also by greater size in direct comparison. When soaring, wings sometimes held level, but usually slightly above level, tips of primaries often clearly upturned. **Adult** separated from similar-sized Steppe by yellowish-white rear-crown to hind-neck. White braces diagnostic but hard to see in the field. Generally has less pronounced dark barring on flight feathers below and is a blacker bird, with more contrastingly bicoloured upper tail than adult Steppe. **Juvenile** yellower than Steppe, with dark-streaked wing-coverts, mantle and lower neck to breast, latter looking brownish in contrast to pale rear-body; blacker, weakly barred secondaries contrast strongly with pale three inner primaries, more so than in most young Steppe. Underwing lacks pure white greater covert band of juvenile Steppe but has usually larger creamy patch on lower back and rump merging with white upper tail-coverts. More streaky than young Tawny and lacks rufous or creamy white in plumage. Larger, with a longer tail and wings than the unstreaked *fulvescens* Greater Spotted; the latter is also unstreaked and usually lacks pale inner primaries. **Subadult** from Steppe by brownish-yellow rear-crown to hind-neck; greater contrast between blackish-brown breast and yellowish belly below; sometimes by more pronounced pale inner primaries; and, from above, by usually bicoloured tail and less pronounced whitish patch at base of primaries; the latter may be absent. Lower back and rump not uniform dark brown.

Steppe Eagle *Aquila nipalensis*
Wing Length 51-65cm
Wing Span 174-260cm
Size as Imperial. Rather similar in shape to Tawny; larger size of Steppe readily apparent only when the two are together. The white band on greater under wing-coverts of young Steppe best feature to distinguish the two. The first two plumages of Steppe have a broad white trailing edge to wings and tail, and tips of greater upper wing-coverts but these characters are of no value in worn immatures. Darker brown **juvenile** Steppe not rufous or creamy-white as Tawny. Most have dark brown lower back and rump (cf. Tawny). **Sub-adult** sometimes has remains of white band on underwing, lacking in Tawny. Generally, Steppe has darker primaries below, coloured more like secondaries, and all flight-feathers usually have bolder dark barring. Sub-adult Tawny often has paler primaries, sometimes confined to a pale wedge on inner three; dark barring on flight-feathers below may be diffuse and much thinner, denser and basally or absent. Sub-adult Steppe has under wing-coverts pale or dark brown with diffuse yellowish lines or bars, and the carpal patch and underbody are more or less uniform dark brown; sub-adult Tawny has pale rufous or creamy-white under wing coverts, which may have clear-cut dark brown lines or bars; there are no dark carpal patches and the underparts are either contrastingly bi-coloured, or uniform pale rufous/creamy-white. **Adult** Steppe is variably patterned dull medium grey-brown and dark brown on body and wing-coverts. Frequently, the underparts and carpal areas are darker brown than the under wing-coverts, or the latter are as dark as the body. Flight-feathers are usually uniform with, or paler than under wing-coverts; they are seldom darker. Many have boldly dark-barred flight and tail feathers, especially below, and a broader, blackish band along their trailing edges (cf. Imperial). Often have large rusty-yellow patch on rear-crown and nape. Upperwing coverts either dull grey-brown as mantle, or paler grey-brown contrasting with mantle. There is usually a small whitish patch at base of lower back, and the upper tail-coverts are mostly brown. The grey or dark brown upper-tail is variably, often boldly dark-barred, with a broader blackish band at tip, but is sometimes indistinctly patterned. Often has a largish pale patch at base of primaries above. Easily confused with dark form of adult Tawny, but has bolder dark barring on flight feathers below, and a bolder dark band along trailing edge of wings and tail; it often has a clearly defined pale nape-patch, and mainly dark brown rump to upper tail-coverts. Dark adult Tawny either has no pale nape patch (like some Steppe), or it has a pale rear-crown to hind-neck. Lower back and upper tail-coverts are often paler than in Steppe. Steppe has brown iris at all ages, while Tawny has yellowish iris from subadult onwards. The yellow gape is slightly brighter and usually extends to rear edge of eye in Steppe, while it normally only reaches the centre of the eye in Tawny.

Tawny Eagle *Aquila rapax*
Wing Length (48) 50-56cm
Wing span 172-185cm

Same size as Greater Spotted Eagle. Plumage of **adult** more variable than that of Steppe. Two forms occur: dark brown resembling adult Steppe, and pale rufous-buff bleaching to creamy-white, the latter probably retained from juvenile onwards. Dark adults have under wing-coverts and flight feathers of approximately same shade, but pale adults show great contrast between pale body/coverts and dark flight feathers. Primaries often paler than secondaries below, especially in pale adults; some have a pale wedge on inner primaries. Dark barring on flight and tail feathers poorly developed, especially on secondaries; when present placed at their bases as thin dense bars (cf typical Steppe). In some fresh adults there are often thin pale lines on trailing edge of wings and on greater upper wing-coverts, unlike adult Steppe. **Juvenile** usually pale rufous but wears gradually to creamy-white before moulting into next rufous or dark brown plumage (ending as pale and dark adult respectively). Flight-feathers below roughly of same pattern as in pale adult. Some juveniles remain pale throughout their following plumages, while others gradually become darker; latter develop dark or blackish-brown throat and breast in contrast with pale rear-body; in some top of head to hind-neck creamy, in others whole head dark brown; under wing-coverts creamy with some dark brown bars. Most Tawny, irrespective of age and colour, have lower back to upper tail coverts creamy (rump darkest), bleaching to whitish. Some birds in transitional plumage show streaking on underparts like young Imperial. **Subadult** Tawny may sometimes resemble subadult Imperial, but are paler, more creamy on belly and most under wing-coverts, have browner rump, and uniform uppertail; also shorter wings and tail, less protruding neck and bill, and bowed wings. Best distinguished from spotted eagles with similar plumage by larger bill, elongated nostrils and, in photographs, the usually longer fourth primary, if not in moult. Lacks the whitish bars on wings and tail of well-marked juvenile Greater Spotted. When perched, Tawny has heavy baggy 'trousers' covering feathered tarsus, while in both Spotteds trousers are smaller, showing long thin-looking feathered tarsus below. Creamy-whitish Tawny distinguished from *fulvescens* Greater Spotted by bill, nostrils, fourth primary and, if present, a distinct pale wedge on inner primaries. Fresh juvenile *fulvescens* has broad white band on greater upper wing-coverts, always narrower in creamy Tawny. Adult Tawny has yellow iris; in all ages of Spotted it is brownish.

Greater Spotted Eagle *Aquila clanga*
Wing Length 48.5-56cm
Wing Span 155-182cm

Size as Tawny. Easily confused with some Steppe and Lesser Spotted, except for well-marked juveniles. **Adult** is normally dark brown all over with paler flight feathers below (and sometimes lacks whitish markings on tail-coverts and at base of primaries, cf. Imperial and Steppe). Some birds have paler upper wing-coverts than mantle (cf. Lesser Spotted and some Steppe). **Juvenile** blacker, with more contrast between under wing-coverts and paler, dark greyish flight feathers. White bars on trailing edge of wings and tail, and on upper wing-coverts, highly variable in width and size. A largish pale primary patch above, most obvious on inner primaries; gradually reduced with age. Barring on flight and tail feathers below highly variable without age differences. Flight-feathers often completely unbarred, or they are thinly and often densely dark-barred, the dark bars usually not so well-spaced and never as broad as in adult Steppe. Lacks dark band along trailing edge of wings and tail (cf. Steppe and some Imperial). Some have small whitish patch at base of outer primaries below (rare in Steppe, Imperial and Tawny), and some have paler underbody than under wing-coverts, a combination not seen in Steppe, Imperial and Tawny. Scarce *fulvescens* type has very pale body and underwing. Intermediates, or forms with pale brown upper and under wing-coverts, difficult to distinguish from some Steppe, Tawny and Lesser Spotted except by study of pattern of flight feathers, tail, bill, gape, nostrils and leg-feathering.

a above, b below, s soaring, g slow gliding, f fast gliding

Imperial Eagle: 1a ad., 2b ad., 3b juv., 4b subad., 5a juv., 6b ad., 7s,g,f head-on profiles.
Steppe Eagle: 8a ad., 9b subad./ad., 10b juv., 11b subad., 12a juv., 13s,g,f head-on profiles, 14b ad., 15b ad.
Tawny Eagle: 16b dark ad., 17b fresh juv., 18a moulting imm./subad., 19s,g,f head-on-profiles, 20b moulting subad., 21b bleached moulting juv., 22a dark ad., 23a pale ad., 24b pale ad.

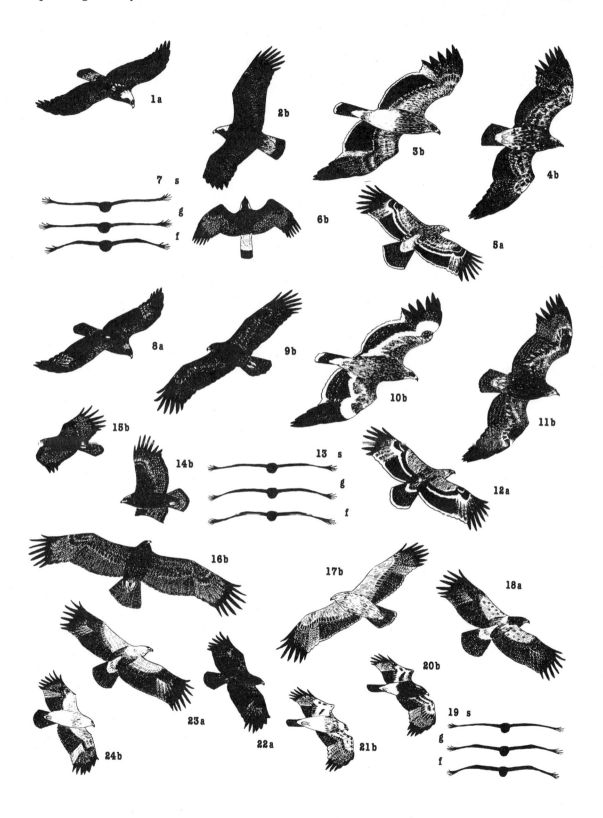

Lesser Spotted Eagle *Aquila pomarina hastata*
Wing Length 47-50.8cm
Wing Span 134-159cm
Slightly smaller than Greater Spotted but size unimportant in the field. **Adult** resembles adult of the nominate race; wing-coverts on both surfaces are grey-brown (bleaching paler), contrasting with dark brown flight feathers and darkish brown mantle; underparts as wing-coverts; a small brownish-yellow primary-patch above, and usually some buffish-white on upper tail-coverts. The contrast between under wing-coverts and darker flight feathers below best character to distinguish it from Greater Spotted (exceptions occur); above, some adult Greater Spotted resemble Lesser Spotted with similar contrast, but usually the former is darker brown, particularly along foremost lesser coverts. **Juvenile** lacks distinct white bands on wing-coverts above and on tips of secondaries, and has less contrast between under wing-coverts and flight feathers than adults. Bill size, length of yellow gape, shape of nostrils, leg-feathering, length of fourth (descendent) primary and barred pattern on flight and tail feathers are similar in Lesser and Greater Spotted, though bill is a little smaller and fourth primary averages shorter in the former. Distinction on flight-silhouette and wing-position not recommended though Greater Spotted on average has broader wings, fuller and more ample wing-tip, and appears slightly more bulky than Lesser Spotted. Confusable with sub-adult Steppe and dark adult Tawny. Clear remains of white band on underwing of some sub-adult Steppe helps separation but some plumages are very alike at a distance. An eagle with pale brown upper and under wing-coverts, and underbody; with darker flight feathers and mantle; and with some whitish on upper tail-coverts and at base of primaries above, is matched by both Lesser Spotted and some Steppe (and by some Tawny and odd Greater Spotted). Compared with Steppe, the Lesser Spotted is relatively shorter-winged, with shorter arm and less ample, less deep-fingered wing-tip. Neck to bill does not protrude as much (bill usually clearly smaller). Smaller size and quicker wing-beats usually apparent only when the two are together. Although the lowered primaries of gliding Lesser Spotted are slightly more arched than that of Steppe, wing position is very alike, as are length and shape of tail. Slightly more compact jizz of Lesser Spotted in flight hard to appreciate.

Golden Eagle *Aquila chrysaetos*
Wing Length 60-72cm
Wing Span 204-220cm
Large eagle. Distinguished from other *Aquila* species by soaring with wings raised to form shallow V. Wings usually narrower at base and tail longer. **Adult** rather uniform dark brown with red-brown rear-crown to

hind-neck. **Juvenile** and immature identified by distinctive plumage, blackish-brown with white tail base, and white patch on inner primaries below, lacking or rather smaller at base of inner primaries above. White markings gradually lost, little remaining after four to five years.

a above, b below, s soaring, g slow gliding, f fast gliding

Greater Spotted Eagle:	**1a ad., 2b ad., 3a bleached ad., 4b juv., 5b variant juv., 6b well marked juv., 7a heavily spotted juv., 8a lightly spotted juv., 9s,g,f head-on profiles, 10b ad.** *fulvescens,* **11b variant ad.**
Lesser Spotted Eagle:	**12b ad., 13a ad., 14b juv., 15a juv., 16b imm., 17s,g,f, head-on-profiles.**
Golden Eagle:	**18b ad., 19b juv., 20s,g,f head-on profiles.**

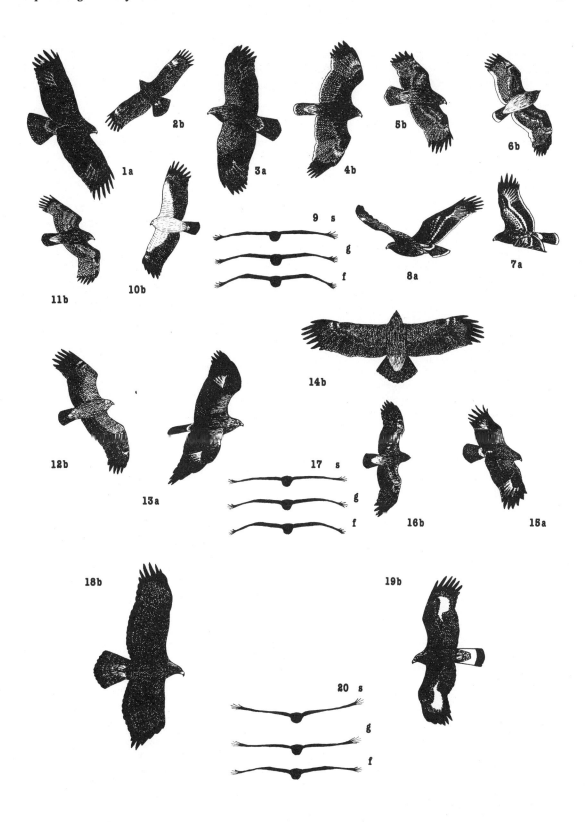

LARGE FALCONS

Powerful raptors with long, narrow, broadly-based wings and medium length tapering tails, square-ended or slightly rounded at the tip. When hunting wing beats are fast and deep. May stoop rapidly on prey in the air. In normal flight wing beats are shallower and slower interrupted by short glides.

Saker Falcon *Falco cherrug*
Length 50-58cm
Wing length 34.1-43.5cm
The largest and heaviest falcon occurring in Nepal, with a long tail and particularly broad-based wings. The wing beats are slow in level flight. Plumage is mainly brown above, lacking blue or grey, and with darker flight feathers. The head is whitish with a dark, streaked, rufous crown and narrow black moustache. **Adult** is mainly whitish below with some black spots on belly and thighs. Wing lining is either dark brown, noticeably darker than flight feathers, or coverts are edged with brown forming diffuse band through centre of underwing. For differences from immature Peregrine see that species. From adult Laggar by its paler brown upperparts with feathers edged orange-buff; crown usually paler; entire tail barred with pale orange or whitish; underparts less heavily marked. Also lacks dark brown patch on thighs, flanks and axillaries of Laggar, the thighs being lightly barred or spotted. **Immature** has boldly streaked underparts.

Laggar Falcon *Falco jugger*
Length 43-46cm
Wing length 30.5-37cm
Usually smaller than Saker and within the same size range as Peregrine Falcon. Flight similar to that of Peregrine but heavier. Has a narrow black moustachial streak, and usually a dark, streaked, rufous crown. **Adult** separated from adult Saker by uniform grey-brown upperparts lacking orange-buff feather edgings. Tail has light barring on outer feathers only. Whitish underparts are more boldly marked and sometimes have heavy streaks on breast, belly and flanks. Flanks, thighs and axillaries are dark brown. Underwing pattern of both species is similar. **Immature** is dark brown above, edged paler, especially on the crown. Chin and throat white, rest of underparts dark brown with pale mottling, sometimes giving the appearance of heavy dark streaking. For differences from Peregrine and Barbary see those species.

Peregrine Falcon *Falco peregrinus*
F. p. calidus
Length 40-48cm
Wing length 30.5-37.8cm
F. p. peregrinator
Length 38-46cm
Wing length 26.5-34.5cm
Adults and immatures can be separated from Saker and Laggar by more contrasting facial pattern: a prominent, broad black moustachial streak and white cheeks. Head is darker than rest of upperparts, while in Saker and Laggar it is usually paler. Underwing of Peregrine shows little contrast while wing lining of other two species is often conspicuously darker than flight feathers. Differs from Laggar in tail barring: central feathers are barred in Peregrine while Laggar has light barring only on outer feathers. Distinguished from Saker by its smaller size, shorter tail, and more pointed wings. Plumage of **adults** differs from other two species: upperparts are slate-grey; underparts are pale rufous-white (*F. p. calidus*), or rusty-red (*F. p. peregrinator*), and heavily barred with black. **Immature** is brown above with a barred tail and heavily streaked below. See Barbary.

Barbary Falcon *Falco pelegrinoides*
Length 38-46cm
Wing length 27.4-34.8cm
Similar in structure and plumage to Peregrine but is often smaller, less bulky and has paler plumage. Both adult and immature can usually be separated from other falcons by a characteristic bright rufous nuchal collar. However Peregrine also shows this feature occasionally. Other features distinguishing Barbary from Saker and Laggar are similar to those separating Peregrine. **Adult** has pale bluish-grey upperparts. Underparts are unbarred or have much less heavy barring than Peregrine, restricted to flanks and lower underparts. Forehead and crown have rufous wash in Barbary, darker and slate-grey in Peregrine. Moustachial streak is narrower and paler than in Peregrine. **Immature** is similar to immature Peregrine but has a narrow moustachial and finer streaks below.

Laggar Falcon:	**1 ad., 2 imm.;**
Saker Falcon:	**3 ad.;**
Peregrine Falcon:	*F. p. peregrinator* **4 ad.,**
	F. p. calidus **5 ad., 6 imm.;**
Barbary Falcon:	**7 ad., 8 imm.**

CALIDRIS SANDPIPERS

Small squat waders with relatively short legs, white wing bars and white sides to the rump.

Dunlin *Calidris alpina*
Length 19cm

Separated from other small waders except Curlew Sandpiper by its longish down curved bill. Summer **adult** has a diagnostic black patch on the belly. Feathers of upperparts are blackish with pale rufous and whitish fringes. Breast is finely streaked with black. In winter brownish-grey above, greyish-white below with greyish streaks on breast. **Juvenile** has black upperpart feathers fringed with chestnut. Breast is streaked and flanks coarsely spotted with brown, belly white. Call is a rasping "treep". See Curlew Sandpiper, Sanderling.

Curlew Sandpiper *Calidris ferruginea*
Length 21cm

Separated at all ages from other small waders by combination of white rump and downcurved bill. Summer **adult** is easily recognised by its rufous breast and upper belly. Adult in winter has similar plumage to Dunlin. **Juvenile** has scaly greyish-brown upperparts with feathers fringed pale buff. Underparts are buff white almost unmarked and usually suffused with peach buff. Call is a gentle 'chirrip'.

Sanderling *Calidris alba*
Length 20cm

Plump and very active, runs rapidly while feeding. Differs from Dunlin and Curlew Sandpiper by having a shorter, straight bill and a more conspicuous white wing bar. In winter distinguished by its almost whitish plumage and contrasting black shoulder patch. In summer it is scalloped with chestnut above and chestnut on breast spotted with black forming a pectoral band. Belly is white.

Stints are tiny sandpipers with straight and comparatively short bills.

Little Stint *Calidris minuta*
Length 12-14cm

Summer **adult** is scaly above, having blackish feathers with bright rufous fringes and whitish tips; a creamy V on the mantle; streaked rufous brown on sides of breast; a rufous patch on face and white belly. Winter **adult** is greyish above, white below. **Juvenile** is similar to summer adult but has more contrasting upperparts, usually showing two clear white Vs. Shows grey outertail feathers in flight. Legs are black. Call is a weak 'tit'.

Temminck's Stint *Calidris temminckii*
Length 13-15cm

From Little and Long-toed by its rather dull uniform plumage lacking pronounced scalloping and streaking; also by the white outer tail feathers. **Juvenile** lacks white Vs on upperparts of other two species. Has a more horizontal stance when feeding and is usually less active. From Little also by dusky patches on sides of breast forming a conspicuous pectoral band, and call. Upperparts are brownish marked with black and dull rufous in summer adult, greyish-brown in juvenile and winter adult. Legs are usually pale yellowish-green or greyish-green, but rarely may be dark. Call is a short purring trill.

Long-toed Stint *Calidris subminuta*
Length 13-14cm

Has a more upright stance than Little and Temminck's, with neck and legs appearing proportionately longer. Richly coloured in all plumages. Can be separated at all ages from Temminck's by its grey brown outer tail feathers and from Little by its pale legs. Summer adult and juvenile have patterned rufous-brown upperparts with dark centres to feathers. Has a dark crown producing a capped appearance absent in Little and Temminck's and the supercilium is creamy and more pronounced than in those species. Ear-coverts are dark. Lacks rufous face of summer Little and pale face of Temminck's. Juvenile may have two white Vs on upperparts as Little. Breast rufous and finely streaked with brown and buff forming a pronounced pectoral band absent in Little. Wing bar is less distinct than in the other two species. Can be separated from both species by its different call, a grating 'priit' or a soft, liquid 'chree'.

Dunlin:	1 wint. ad., 2 summ. ad.;
Curlew Sandpiper:	3 summ. ad., 4 juv.;
Sanderling:	5 wint.;
Temminck's Stint:	6 wint. ad., 7 summ. ad.;
Little Stint:	8 summ. ad., 9 wint. ad., 10 juv.;
Long-toed Stint:	11 summ. ad., 12 juv.

SNIPE AND WOODCOCK

Snipe are medium-sized waders with long bills. They have cryptically patterned, mainly brown plumage and longitudinal stripes on head.

Jack Snipe *Lymnocryptes minimus*
Length 17-19cm
Easily separated from other snipes by small size and relatively short bill (only a little longer than head). Unlike other snipes breast is streaked not scaly, and flanks are unbarred. Flushed only at close range and soon drops into cover. Escape flight is silent and slow without zigzagging. Plumage is similar to Common Snipe but back stripes are broader and contrast more with dark mantle than in other snipe. Lacks cream crown-stripe of Common and has a characteristic forked pale supercilium absent in Common.

Common Snipe *Gallinago gallinago*
Length 26-27cm
Medium-sized snipe with a very long bill. Upperparts are heavily patterned in brown, black and rufous, with cream stripes on crown and back. In flight it shows a broad, prominent white trailing edge to the secondaries, but the feet do not extend beyond the tail. Escape flight is a rapid zigzag and accompanied by a hoarse cry. May be confused with Pintail Snipe. See that species.

Pintail Snipe *Gallinago stenura*
Length 25-26cm
Very similar in size and plumage to Common Snipe. Most easily separated by completely barred under wing-coverts and axillaries which appear dark in flight whereas the underwing of Common usually has a whitish patch. Has a narrow, inconspicuous white trailing edge to the secondaries, and the feet extend beyond the the tail in flight. The upper wing coverts are more heavily mottled with buff than they are in Common, the bars on the flanks are more extensive, and the back stripes usually appear less contrasting. When flushed it flies off with little or no zig-zagging usually dropping into cover more quickly than Common. Shows some similarity to Solitary. See that species.

Swinhoe's Snipe *Gallinago megala*
Length 27-29cm
Similar to Pintail Snipe in plumage but larger and generally longer-billed with a longer tail, beyond which the legs do not project in flight. Plumage is variable and the only consistent difference from Pintail is more white in the outer tail. Flight is slower and heavier with little zigzagging and it frequently rises silently. Slightly larger than Common Snipe and lacks white trailing edge to secondaries.

Solitary Snipe *Gallinago solitaria*
Length 31cm
Differs from Common and Pintail Snipe in larger size and the pattern of the underparts. Generally has a paler face than other snipes. The throat is white, and the breast is brown with white streaks at sides of neck and breast. Rest of underparts are white with fairly heavy blackish bars on sides of breast and flanks sometimes extending right across breast and belly. These individuals are likely to be confused with similar-sized Wood Snipe. Separated from Common and Pintail by combination of pale median wing-coverts and dark lesser coverts, and by different escape flight. Flies off zig-zagging but more heavily and slowly than Common and giving a harsher, louder call.

Wood Snipe *Gallinago nemoricola*
Length 31 cm
A large snipe with broad rounded wings and slow, heavy, wavering flight. From all snipe except some Solitary by underparts pattern. Has a mottled dusky brown breast, and the rest of the underparts are normally completely barred dull buff and brown; rarely the centre of the belly is unbarred. From Solitary by generally darker, more scaly appearance above with very little rufous, and broader, more contrasting buffish back stripes. Crown is darker with a much narrower central stripe. Usually found in forest habitat. More similar to Woodcock than Snipe, see that species.

Eurasian Woodcock *Scolopax rusticola*
Length 33-35cm
A snipe-like wader with similar, cryptically patterned plumage. From all snipe by larger size, transverse bars on hindcrown, and blotched not banded scapulars. Most likely to be confused with Wood Snipe as both have broad, rounded wings, heavy slow flight and are likely to be found in same forest habitat. Its plumage is more brightly coloured with more rufous than Wood Snipe.

Wood Snipe:	**1,2,3;**
Eurasian Woodcock:	**4,5,6;**
Solitary Snipe:	**7,8,9;**
Pintail Snipe:	**10,11,12;**
Common Snipe:	**13,14,15;**
Jack Snipe:	**16,17,18.**

"not to scale"

CR.

GULLS

Gulls are medium-sized to large birds with long wings, webbed feet and strong bills. When adult they are mainly grey above and white below. Immatures have some brown in plumage. In Nepal found by lakes, rivers and, on migration, over the Himalayas.

Yellow-legged Gull
Larus cachinnans mongolicus
Length c. 55cm
Large gull. **Adult** White with pale grey mantle and wings; primary tips are black with one or two large mirrors. Head is white in summer, very faintly streaked in winter. Legs normally pink in this race, confounding the English name. **First winter** Mottled grey-brown above with blackish-brown wing tips. Tail greyish-brown with black subterminal band. Bill blackish with paler base. **Second winter** Dark streaks on head, pale grey on mantle and scapulars. Outer primaries and bar on secondaries blackish, rest of wing greyish-brown. Shows some white on rump, and tail has black band. **Third winter** Like winter adult but has more black on outer wings, lacks white spots on wing tips, and has faint tail band. Usually has some brown on upperwing. For differences from Mew, Lesser Black-back and Great Black-headed Gulls see those species.

Lesser Black-backed Gull *Larus fuscus fuscus* and *L. f. heuglini*
Length 53cm
A large gull similar to Yellow-legged Gull. Mantle of **adult** is darker, varying from slate-grey (*heuglini*) to almost blackish (*fuscus*). Legs yellow. **First winter** can be separated from first winter Yellow-legged by its more contrasting and scaly pattern on upperparts. Birds of the race *fuscus* have a uniform dark band on greater coverts forming a second wing bar which is absent in Yellow-legged. Has both inner and outer primaries blackish. Underwing is dark blackish-brown, pale grey-brown in Yellow-legged. **Second** and **third** winter birds are most easily distinguished by the colour of the upperparts which resemble those of the adult. Bill is all dark.

Great Black-headed Gull *Larus ichthyaetus*
Length 57-61cm
The largest Nepalese gull. Differs structurally from other large gulls. It has a characteristic long sloping forehead, deep chest, and relatively slimmer, longer wings. Can be confused with smaller adult winter Yellow-legged, and some plumages of immature Yellow-legged. **Adult** has black head in summer, and a dark patch behind eye in winter. Yellow bill has reddish tip and black subterminal band. Adult and third winter birds separated from other large gulls by wing pattern. Wing tips and outer wing are white, with broad black band across outer primaries. **First winter** has grey mantle. Differs from second winter Yellow-legged by dark mask through eye, brownish shawl on hindneck, white underparts, and more prominent black band across tail, contrasting with white rump. Much paler grey on mantle than second winter Lesser Black-back. **Second winter** is similar to adult but has black tail band (narrower than first winter), more extensive black on primaries, and hindneck marked blackish.

Yellow-legged Gull:	1 1st wint., 2 2nd wint., 3 ad. summ.;
Lesser Black-backed Gull:	4 1st wint., 5 ad. *heuglini*, 6 ad. *fuscus*;
Great Black-headed Gull:	7 1st wint., 8 2nd wint., 9 ad.

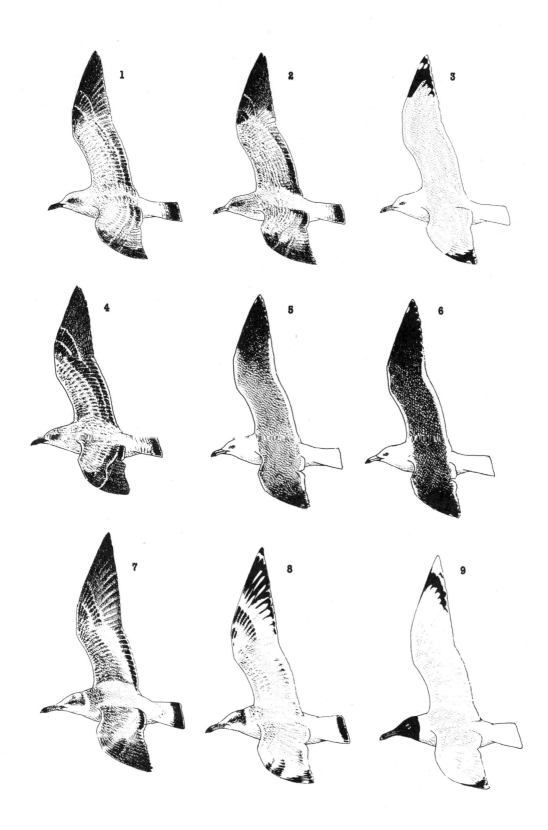

Common Black-headed Gull *Larus ridibundus*
Length 34-37cm
A small gull. **Adult** Head chocolate-brown in summer,
white with blackish mark behind eye in winter. Separated from all gulls except Slender-billed by extensive
white outer primaries visible from above and below in
flight. Bill and legs are red. **First winter** differs from
adult winter in having a brown carpal bar, and a black
tail band; also dark primary tips and a secondary bar,
forming a black band along entire length of rear wing.
Bill flesh with black tip, legs orange-flesh.

Brown-headed Gull *Larus brunnicephalus*
Length 46cm
Medium-sized gull, rather similar to Common Black-
headed when perched, but very distinctive in flight.
Adult has brown head in summer, whitish head with
dark brown patch eye in winter. Both adults and
immatures distinguished from all other medium-sized
and small gulls by large white patch at base of outer
primaries. Has contrasting broad black wing-tips
broken by white spots. Bill is red, and tipped black in
winter. Legs are red. **First winters** have much darker
wings than the winter adult, with some brown on
upper wing-coverts, a small white area on primaries
and dark bar on the secondaries. Bill orange-red,
tipped black, and legs orange-red.

Slender-billed Gull *Larus genei*
Length 42-44cm
A small gull, usually with an all white head (although
may have a pale grey ear-spot in winter). **Adult** has
pink flush on underparts. Legs and bill dark red in
adult, pale orange-flesh in immature. Can be confused with Common Black-headed which has similar
wing pattern. Distinguished by its very long elongated
forehead, long bill and neck, and pale iris. **Immature**
also differs from Common Black-headed by its paler
legs and paler bill, which lacks a darker tip, and less
brown mottling on upperwing.

Mew Gull *Larus canus*
Length 40-42cm
Medium-sized gull, a little smaller than Brown-
headed. Similar plumage to the larger Yellow-legged,
but has a smaller bill, thinner wings, and more delicate
appearance. Adult and second year separated from
Yellow-legged by greenish-yellow bill and greyish
legs. From Common Black-headed and Brown-
headed by white on primaries confined to subterminal
spots and different head pattern. Head is white in
summer, streaked grey in winter. First years have a
different wing pattern to other medium-sized and
small gulls; they have blackish outer primaries, a dark
bar on secondaries, and a brown carpal bar.

Common Black-headed Gull:	1 1st wint., 2 ad. wint., 3 ad summ.;
Brown-headed Gull:	4 1st wint., 5 ad. wint., 6 ad. summ.;
Slender-billed Gull:	7 1st wint., 8 ad. wint., 9 ad. summ.;
Mew Gull:	10 1st wint., 11 ad wint., 12 ad summ.

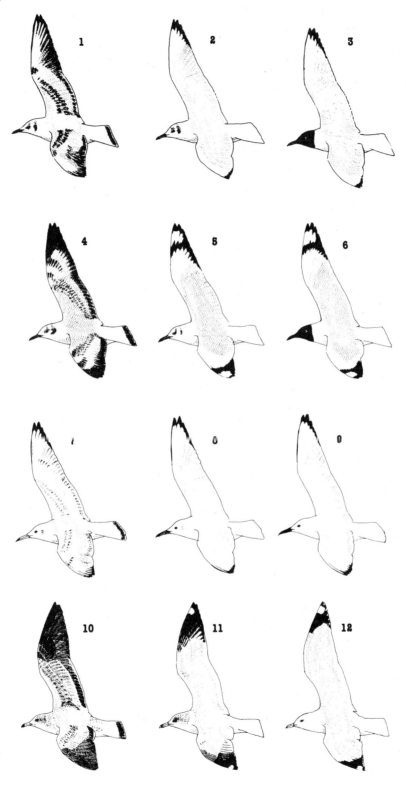

OWLS

Scops Owls

Small eared owls. Nocturnal and most easily separated by their distinctive calls.

Collared Scops Owl *Otus bakkamoena*
Length 22.5cm
From other scops owls by its buff nuchal collar edged with black, sparsely streaked underparts, lack of prominent white scapular spots, and larger size. **Voice** The upland race has a mellow double call, one note often running into the other and descending on the second note. Repeated for periods of 10-15 minutes at a time. The lowland race has a frog-like interrogative (rising) 'wuk?' repeated at irregular intervals, but most often 4-6 seconds apart.

Oriental Scops Owl *Otus sunia*
Length 21cm
Plumage is variable with both greyish-brown and rufous phases occurring. Has bold black streaks below and fine black streaks above. From Collared Scops by heavily streaked underparts. **Voice** A four note call (the third note very short), repeated monotonously and resembling that of a barbet.

Mountain Scops Owl *Otus spilocephalus*
Length 20cm
Similar to Oriental Scops but is smaller, has buff spots on crown and nape and lacks streaking of that species. Upperparts lack streaking, usually rufous-brown, mottled with white and dark brown. Underparts barred white and black and either rufous or brownish. **Voice** A metallic double whistle with an interval of up to one second between each note.

Other small owls

Lack ear tufts, have a squat appearance and are often seen in daylight.

Collared Owlet *Glaucidium brodiei*
Length 17cm
A very small owl. Recognised by its fulvous half-collar and black patch on each side of the nape, which together resemble an owl's face. Head is greyish-brown spotted with white. **Voice** A bell-like whistle 'poop-poopoop-poop' repeated three or four times.

Jungle Owlet *Glaucidium radiatum*
Length 20cm
Similar to Asian Barred Owlet but is slightly smaller and more closely barred above and below. Separated by its bright rufous-brown barred wings contrasting with olive-brown upperparts. Underparts are clearly barred down to lower flanks and lack streaking. **Voice** A loud, slow 'kao kao kao' followed by a 'kao kuk' which is repeated at an increasingly faster rate for several seconds.

Asian Barred Owlet *Glaucidium cuculoides*
Length 22.5cm
Upperparts and breast are uniform olive-brown, barred with buff. Barring on rest of underparts is obscure and sometimes broken, forming streaks on flanks and abdomen. **Voice** A drawn out bubbling whistle, harsh squawking. See Jungle Owlet.

Brown Hawk Owl *Ninox scutulata*
Length 30cm
The only Nepalese owl which lacks a facial disc. Has a hawk-like appearance with broad rounded wings and a long tail. Brown above, white below with brown stripes on throat and upper breast, and spots on belly and flanks. **Voice** A mellow double whistle, the second note higher-pitched than first.

Little Owl *Athene noctua*
Length 22.5cm
The only small owl recorded above 3000m. Also separated by its pale plumage. It is light sandy-brown above, barred and spotted with white, and white streaked with brown below. **Voice** A high pitched note repeated every few seconds.

Spotted Owlet *Athene brama*
Length 20cm
From similar-sized Jungle and Asian Barred Owlets by its white spotting on greyish-brown upperparts and white half-collar on hindneck. **Voice** Varied screeching and cackling notes.

Collared Scops Owl:	1,		
Oriental Scops Owl:	2,	Brown Hawk Owl:	6,
Mountain Scops Owl:	3,	Asian Barred Owlet:	7,
Spotted Owlet:	4,	Jungle Owlet:	8,
Little Owl:	5,	Collared Owlet:	9.

RICHARD GRIMMETT, JAN 85.

Large owls

Brown Wood Owl *Strix leptogrammica*
Length 53cm
The only large owl lacking ear tufts. Has a very dark appearance. Upperparts chocolate brown with white-barred black scapulars. Its whitish eyebrows and broad black ring around eyes form a conspicuous facial pattern. Throat white. Rest of underparts buff-white and closely barred with dark brown. **Voice** A hollow double 'tu-hoooo', the second note prolonged. See Tawny Owl.

Other large owls have ears, and are most easily identified by their underpart pattern and distinctive calls.

Eurasian Eagle Owl *Bubo bubo*
Length 56cm
Upperparts dark brown and mottled. White throat, rest of underparts pale brown with prominent dark brown streaks on breast and flanks, and narrow bars on belly and under tail-coverts. **Voice** A deep resonant 'bu-boo' with emphasis on the second note which is prolonged.

Spot-bellied Eagle Owl *Bubo nipalensis*
Length 63cm
Similar to Northern Eagle Owl but underparts are whitish with black bars on breast, the bars breaking up into V-shaped markings on the belly. From all other large eared owls by lack of streaking below. **Voice** A low deep hoot repeated at intervals of a few seconds

Dusky Eagle Owl *Bubo coromandus*
Length 52.5cm
Underparts are light brownish-grey and finely streaked with dark brown. From other large eared owls by greyish plumage and lack of white on throat. **Voice** A resonant and accelerating 'wo-wo-woooooo', gradually becomer fainter.

Brown Fish Owl *Ketupa zeylonensis*
Length 56cm
Upperparts brownish and heavily streaked with black. Has a conspicuous white throat patch. Underparts are brownish, closely barred (difficult to see in field) with fine black streaks. Lacks the bold markings of Tawny Fish Owl, Forest Eagle Owl, and Northern Eagle Owl and the warm orange of Tawny Fish Owl. **Voice** A deep hollow 'boom boom' repeated at intervals.

Tawny Fish Owl *Ketupa flavipes*
Length 61cm
From other large horned owls by its warmer coloured and boldly streaked plumage. Tawny above with broad black and rufous-buff streaks. Underparts are orange-rufous streaked with dark brown, and lack barring. Usually has a white throat. **Voice** A deep 'whoo-hoo' and a mewing cat-like call.

Medium-sized owls

Tawny Owl *Strix aluco*
Length 45cm
A plump, dark owl with no ear tufts. Its wings are short and lack contrasting dark carpal patches. Plumage is mottled and streaked, varying from warm brown to greyish-brown. Eyes black. Nocturnal. **Voice** A series of hoots running together 'hoo-hoo-hoo-hooooo', and a deep low 'hu-hoo'. Found in mountain forests above 2000m.

Tawny Owl:	**1,**
Brown Wood Owl:	**2,**
Eurasian Eagle Owl:	**3,**
Tawny Fish Owl:	**4,**
Brown Fish Owl:	**5,**
Dusky Eagle Owl:	**6,**
Spot-bellied Eagle Owl:	**7.**

RICHARD GRIMMETT, JAN 85.

Long-eared Owl *Asio otus*
Length 35cm
The only medium-sized owl with long ear tufts. Similar in size to Tawny, and also found in forests. Distinguished by its longer wings and very deep wing beats, ear tufts, and orange-yellow eyes. From Short-eared by its shorter wings, longer ears, indistinct carpal patches on upper wing, and orange-buff patch on primaries. Also separated by different habitat and nocturnal behaviour. **Voice** A low sighing 'ooo' repeated every few seconds and a variety of yelping, wailing and barking calls.

Short-eared Owl *Asio flammeus*
Length 38cm
Found in open country and often diurnal. Hunts by quartering the ground like a harrier. Has long narrow wings which show dark carpal patches on upper and under surfaces and pale buff on primaries. It has short ear tufts wich are not usually visible in flight. **Voice** Silent in winter.

Barn, Grass and Bay Owls

Medium-sized, slim, long-legged owls with heart-shaped faces. Nocturnal.

Barn Owl *Tyto alba*
Length 34cm
A very pale owl lacking ear tufts. Upperparts are a uniform golden-buff finely speckled with black. From all except Grass Owl by its unmarked white underparts and heart-shaped face. Roosts in old buildings usually in urban areas. **Voice** A drawn out screech, hissing and snoring noises.

Grass Owl *Tyto capensis*
Length 35cm
Similar to Barn Owl. Separated by its darker and much more contrasting pattern of upperparts. Dark brown above spotted with white. Has rufous-buff patches at base of primaries. Tail is whitish barred with black and contrasts with dark brown upper tail-coverts. Inhabits tall grassland. **Voice** Like that of Barn Owl.

Oriental Bay Owl *Phodilus badius*
Length 29cm
Has short ear tufts. Chestnut above, spotted with black and buff; flight feathers chestnut lightly barred with black. Facial disc and underparts are vinous-pink, the latter irregularly spotted with black. Head has a striking shape: a wide forehead separates oblong-shaped facial discs. Inhabits forests. **Voice** A soft hoot.

Long-eared Owl:	1,
Short-eared Owl:	2,
Grass Owl:	3,
Barn Owl	4,
Oriental Bay Owl:	5.

WAGTAILS

Wagtails are small, dainty, long-tailed birds, often associated with water in Nepal. Although most species are relatively easy to distinguish, the variation in the Yellow Wagtail, both interracial and intraracial, produces a confusing variety of individuals that could easily be taken for different species by the unwary. This species, and the White Wagtail, are unusual in that a number of races from widely divergent breeding areas, mix together in winter. The Grey Wagtail *M. cinerea* is readily identifiable and is not treated in this section.

White Wagtail *Motacilla alba*
Length 17-18.5cm

Breeding adults and some non-breeding birds distinguished from most other wagtails by their black, grey and white plumage. Individuals of black-backed races are distinguished from White-browed Wagtail by their white foreheads. Many non-breeding birds are basically grey and white but always have at least an indication of a black gorget, a feature lacking in the rather similar first autumn Citrine.

Six races are recorded from Nepal. Breeding plumage males can be separated by the following features:-

Grey-backed races:
1. *M. a. dukhunensis* White ear-coverts, black chin.
2. *M. a. personata* Black ear-coverts.
3. *M. a. baicalensis* White ear coverts and chin.
4. *M. a. ocularis* Black streak through eye

Black-backed races:
5. *M. a. leucopsis* White ear-coverts
6. *M. a. alboides* Black ear-coverts.

White-browed Wagtail *Motacilla maderaspatensis*
Length 21cm

A black and white wagtail with a black back and pronounced white supercilium extending from the lores to the nape. The black forehead distinguishes all plumages from black-backed White Wagtails.

Forest Wagtail *Dendronanthus indicus*
Length 17cm

Differs from all other wagtails by having a broad black band across the upper breast and a broken black band below it. Rest of underparts creamy-white. Olive-brown above with a white supercilium and two broad yellowish-white wing bars.

Yellow Wagtail *Motacilla flava*
Length 16-17cm
Adults have olive-green upperparts and yellow underparts with the head variously coloured depending on
race, sex and age. Most immatures are brownish-olive
above with some yellow on the underparts; wing bars
and tertial edgings are typically buff or off-white and
fairly narrow. Immatures, of some races or aberrant
individuals, are grey above and whitish below with
fairly broad white wing bars and tertial edgings, thus
looking very similar to first autumn Citrines. Normally however there is no pale line separating the ear-
coverts from the nape, and the forehead is uniform
with the crown. The call is typically a loud, disyllabic
'tswee-ip' but in some races is a harsher 'tsreep'.

Four races are recorded from Nepal. Only breeding plumage males are readily identifiable.

M. f. beema Head pale bluish-grey with a complete,
distinct white supercilium and usually a white sub-
moustachial stripe. Ear-coverts grey or brown, often
with white feathers. Chin white.
M. f. leucocephala Whole head to the nape white with
a faint grey shadow on the ear-coverts and back of
crown. Chin white.
M. f. thunbergi Crown and nape slate-grey, occasionally blackish. Lores and ear coverts blackish. Superci-
ium usually lacking, but occasionally a white streak
behind the eye. Chin usually yellow, but sometimes
white. May have white sub-moustachial stripe.
M. f. melanogrisea Whole head black. No supercilium. White chin and sub moustachial stripe.

Three other races have not been recorded but
could be expected to occur:-

M. f. lutea Head yellow-green; forehead and complete
supercilium yellow.
M. f. zaissanensis Crown and nape dark blue-grey.
Narrow white supercilium. Lores and ear-coverts
varying from dark grey to black.
M. f. plexa Crown and nape dark grey. Lores and ear-
coverts blackish. Narrow white supercilium. Chin
white.
M. f. taivana Differs from all other races by having the
crown olive-green, the same colour as the mantle. A
complete broad yellow supercilium. Lores and ear-
coverts blackish. Chin yellow.

Citrine Wagtail *Motacilla citreola*
Length 16-17cm
Breeding males are distinguished from other wagtails
by the complete yellow head and underparts with
either a grey or a black back, and usually a black
collar. Adult non-breeding males and adult females
have crown, nape and upperparts grey, often with an
olive or brown tinge; the forehead, supercilium and

underparts are dull yellow. Young birds in early autumn are greyer than the young of most races of
Yellow Wagtail, lacking olive in the upperparts and
yellow on the underparts. They can be separated from
grey and white Yellow Wagtails by a combination of
characters: the pale grey ear-coverts are dark-bor-
dered, but the lores are contrastingly grey; a complete
pale ear-covert surround divides this area from the
grey of the nape; the forehead is buffy or whitish,
contrasting with crown; the wingbars and tertial edgings are usually broad and white; the call is typically a
harsh 'trrzzeet'. By early November young Citrines
acquire a yellow tinge to the supercilium, forehead
and chin.

Three races are recorded from Nepal. Breeding plumage males can be separated by the following features:-

M. c. citreola Mantle medium grey; flanks grey.
M. c. werae Mantle pale grey; flanks whitish; black
collar sometimes reduced or lacking.
M. c. calcarata Mantle black; flanks olive-grey.

Yellow Wagtail:	1 ad. male *M. f. thunbergi*,
	2 ad. male *M. f. beema*,
	3 ad. male *M. f. taivana*,
	4 ad. male *M. f. leucocephala*,
	5 ad. male *M. f. melanogrisea*,
	6 ad. male *M. f. zaissanensis*,
	7 imm. *M. f. beema*.
Citrine Wagtail:	8 imm., 9 ad. male *M. c. calcarata*.

PIPITS

Small slim terrestrial birds. Mainly brown and streaked. Most species have whitish outer tail feathers. Sexes are alike. They run or walk quickly, have an undulating flight and aerial song flight. Can often be distinguished by their calls.

Olive-backed Pipit *Anthus hodgsoni*
Length 15cm
Dark olive-green above with darker streaking which is indistinct in *A. h. yunnanensis* but can be prominent in *A. h. hodgsoni*. Buff-white below with bold black streaks on breast and flanks. From all except Rosy in autumn by olive-green in upperparts. Has a distinctive face pattern with a prominent black-bordered supercilium which is buffish in front and whitish behind eye; and usually has a white drop-shaped mark at rear end of ear coverts with a small black patch below it. **Voice** A loud 'tseep' or 'pseep', similar to that of Red-throated but shorter and more abrupt. Found in wooded areas. Often perches in trees and vigorously wags its tail.

Tree Pipit *Anthus trivialis*
Length 15cm
Resembles Olive-backed in plumage and call. Separated by paler, brown upperparts lacking olive-green. Supercilium is less prominent, and lacks small black and white patches at rear of ear coverts. Often found in more open areas.

Red-throated Pipit *Anthus cervinus*
Length 15cm
A dark pipit with boldly streaked upperparts. Distinguished by call; a distinctive thin 'psss' starting loud and trailing off. Rather like that of Tree but higher pitched, more drawn out and thinner. However, also has a less distinctive, sharp 'chup'. Male in summer is separated from all pipits by brick-red or cinnamon on throat, often extending to supercilium and breast. Female in summer may have colour only on throat, and this is usually pinkish. In winter the underparts are heavily streaked and throat is usually whitish; the males may have pinkish-red on throat. Can be confused with Tree Pipit in autumn. Separated by call, generally darker appearance, and more heavily streaked flanks. See Buff-bellied Pipit.

Rosy Pipit *Anthus roseatus*
Length 15cm
At all ages from other pipits except Red-throated by heavily streaked upperparts. In summer separated from all except Water by the pink colour of the supercilium and chin to the lower breast. In winter similar to Red-throated, and most easily separated by

call; also by the grey tinged upperparts and olive-green edges to wings and tinge to mantle. Has a thin 'sip' call reminiscent of Water Pipit but less strident. Legs brownish-flesh. Frequents streams and pools in winter and on migration.

Water Pipit *Anthus spinoletta*
Length 15cm
Upperparts brown in autumn and grey in summer, with streaking sparse or absent. Much less heavily streaked above than other pipits except Long-billed and Tawny. Separated from these species by its smaller size, shorter tail, more prominent white supercilium, and different call: a sharp 'pit', 'chip it', or 'pi pi pit' and different habitat: usually in wet fields and marshy areas. In winter similar to Rosy Pipit but much less heavily streaked below and lacks olive-green edges to wings. In summer separated from all except Red-throated and Rosy by the pink tinge to the underparts which may be lightly streaked or unstreaked. At all ages has black legs. See Buff-bellied Pipit.

Buff-bellied Pipit *Anthus rubescens*
Length 15cm
Slightly smaller and shorter-tailed than Water Pipit. Upperparts dark grey-brown in autumn and olive-grey in summer, unstreaked or only faintly so. The underparts are tinged orange-buff in summer with the breast lightly spotted and the flanks heavily streaked. In winter the breast is heavily spotted or streaked black and the flanks are streaked blackish brown. Legs yellowish to reddish-brown. Call is a short 'tsipp' or 'tsiit', lacking the shrill quality of the call of Water Pipit.

Long-billed Pipit *Anthus similis*
Length 20cm
The largest Nepalese pipit. Pale brown, tinged grey-brown, and lightly streaked above; whitish throat; rest of underparts are rich buff or pale orange, sometimes lightly streaked. Separated from other pipits by its particularly heavy build and long tail of rather uniform coloration. The outer feathers are buff, but the colour is not easy to discern in the field. From all except Richard's and Blyth's by its much larger size. Differs from these two species by its lightly streaked upperparts and different call; a deep 'chup' rather like the call of Richard's but lacking the harsh quality of the latter species.

Olive-backed Pipit: *A. h. hodgsoni* 1, *A. h. yunnanensis* 2,
Red-throated Pipit: 3 wint., 4 sum.
Tree Pipit: 5.
Rosy Pipit: 6 wint., 7 sum.
Buff-bellied Pipit: 8 wint., 10 sum;
Water Pipit: 9 wint., 11 sum.

Upland Pipit *Anthus sylvanus*
Length 17cm
A large pipit, distinguished from other species by its short, heavy bill and pointed tail feathers. Light pinkish-brown above, heavily streaked with dark brown. Supercilium white. Buff-white below, finely streaked on lower breast, flanks and belly. Call is a sparrow-like 'chirp'. Its song is atypical for a pipit. Repeats two long drawn out notes with emphasis on the first syllable 'wee-chee.....wee-chee'. Inhabits steep grassy slopes, often perching on boulders. May bob its tail when feeding.

Richard's Pipit
Two distinct races occur differing in size, plumage and call. Both may be confused with Tawny. Head pattern is usually different. Lores, most of the ear coverts and a broad area around eye are pale. Tawny has rather dark ear coverts, a thin pale eyering, and a dark line across lores.

Anthus novaeseelandiae richardi
Length 17cm
A large pipit. Has an erect posture, long legs, long (12-19mm), comparatively weak, and usually straight, hind claw and long tail. Brown above, streaked darker, usually prominently. Median wing-coverts dark-centred but not greatly contrasting with upperparts; edges usually buff but sometimes white. Buff below and usually boldly streaked on breast. The flanks of Richard's are generally washed buff, pale rufous or orange-buff, whereas those of Tawny are pale creamy. Generally more heavily streaked below than Tawny. The tail length is 75-88% of the wing length. Wing/tarsus ratio is 2.9-3.3. Bill length 16-19mm, quite broad and deep. White on inner web of penultimate tail feather usually in the form of a narrow streak up more than half the shaft, sometimes reduced to a short streak near, or at, the tip. Has a harsh 'tchreep' call. See Blyth's and Long-billed.

Paddyfield Pipit *A. n. rufulus*
Length 15cm
Smaller, shorter-legged and with a less erect carriage and paler more lightly streaked plumage than *richardi*. Similar in structure to *richardi* but the tail is relatively shorter (about 70% of the wing length); bill slightly shorter (15.5-17mm) and not as heavy; hind claw slightly shorter (10-18mm). Has a high pitched 'tseep tseep' or 'chip chip' call. Song is a weak trill. Can be confused with Tawny, particularly with juveniles. Separated by smaller size, darker greyish-brown colour, different call, and shorter tail. From adult Tawny also by light streaking across breast and indistinct spots on median coverts. Does not wag tail like Tawny.

Blyth's Pipit *Anthus godlewskii*
Length 16.5cm
Very difficult to separate from Richard's *A. n. richardi* and Tawny Pipits. Intermediate in size but most similar to *richardi* in plumage. Often has orange on the underparts, particularly on the under tail-coverts, but this feature is also shown by some Richard's Pipits, particularly the small, dark race *A. n. sinensis*, which may occur in Nepal. The most distinctive feature is the shape of the dark centres of the new adult or first-winter median wing-coverts. The centres are broader and more square, less triangular, at the tips, and more clear-cut on the sides than on Richard's. Hind claw medium length (10.5-14mm) and comparatively weak. The tail length is 68-81% of the wing length. Wing/tarsus ratio is 3.2-3.8. Bill length 14.5-17mm, not as heavy as in *A. n. richardi*. White on inner web of penultimate tail feather usually in the form of a triangle, broad at the tip and tapering to a point close to the shaft and 15-30mm from the tip. Has two distinct flight calls: one similar to that of Richard's but slightly shriller and higher pitched, but also less harsh; the other is a diagnostic short, hard 'chap', similar to one of the calls of Tawny Pipit.

Tawny Pipit *Anthus campestris*
Length 16cm
A pale long-tailed pipit resembling a wagtail. Hind claw short (7.5-11mm), curved and moderately strong. The tail length is 75-83% of the wing length. Wing/tarsus ratio is 3.3-3.8. Bill length 14-17mm, not as heavy as in *A. n. richardi*. Tail pattern similar to Richard's. Sandy brown and only lightly streaked above. A pronounced buff supercilium. Median wing-coverts dark-centred and contrasting prominently with upperparts; edges buff. Underparts pale sandy, and in adults virtually unstreaked. Juveniles have streaked breasts and distinct spots on upperparts. Call is either a drawn out 'tseep' resembling Yellow Wagtail or a sparrow-like 'chir-rup'. May be confused with Paddyfield and Blyth's Pipits.

Upland Pipit:	1.
Paddyfield Pipit:	2.
Tawny Pipit:	3.
Blyth's Pipit:	4. ad.
Richard's Pipit:	5. ad.
Long-billed Pipit:	6.

CR.

BUSH WARBLERS

Medium-sized very skulking warblers inhabiting marshes, grassland and forest undergrowth. Most are altitudinal migrants. Several species winter in the lowlands and breed at high altitudes. Plumage is dull and brownish. Wings and tail are rounded. Some of the *Cettia* warblers can be identified by their distinctive loud, melodious songs.

Pale-footed Bush Warbler *Cettia pallidipes*
Plate 1 No. 2
Length 11cm
Separated from other bush warblers by its relatively short, square tail and paler, whitish legs. Also by its cleaner, whitish underparts, especially throat, which contrast more sharply with buff-brown flanks and cold olive-brown upperparts. Supercilium is greyish-white. Song is a loud explosive 'zip...zip-tschuk-o-tschuk'. Call is 'chik chik'. Inhabits the lowlands.

Brown-flanked Bush Warbler *Cettia fortipes*
Plate 1 No. 4,5
Length 12cm
Often holds its tail cocked. Two races occur, differing mainly in colour of upperparts and call. Eastern race *C. f. fortipes* is warm olive-brown above, western race *C. f. pallidus* is plain olive-brown. Throat and belly are off-white, cheeks and sides of breast greyish. Shows less contrast between upper and underparts than Pale-footed. Supercilium is buff. Lacks any yellow tinge in underparts and supercilium. Legs are dull brownish. Song is sustained rising whistle 'weeee' followed by an explosive 'chiwiyou'. Eastern race has 'chuk' and loud 'tyit tyu-tyu' calls, western race makes a single harsh 'tchuk'. Recorded between 1800m and 2500m.

Chestnut-crowned Bush Warbler *Cettia major*
Plate 1 No. 3
Length 13cm
From similar Grey-sided by its larger size, more robust build, and longer stouter bill. Also separated by its rufous lores, broad yellowish-white supericilium from eye to nape, curving up slightly at rear, and whiter underparts, particularly on throat, contrasting more with upperparts. Usually has more extensive chestnut on crown, and extending onto nape, although individuals cannot be reliably separated using only this feature. Call is a sharp 'tzip'. Recorded between 75m and 4100m.

Aberrant Bush Warbler *Cettia flavolivacea*
Plate 1 No. 6
Length 12cm
Can be identified by its yellowish or yellowish-olive underparts and supercilium. Also by its uniform olive-green upperparts and olive flanks. Amount of yellow on under parts varies. Care is needed to separate dull birds from Brown-flanked. Song is a short, grating, high-pitched phrase. Call is a sharp 'tsick'. Recorded between 75m and 2745m.

Yellow-bellied Bush Warbler *Cettia acanthizoides*
Plate 1 No. 1
Length 9.5cm
A small bush warbler. Distinguished by its greyish-white throat and breast contrasting with yellowish belly. Also by its olive-brown upperparts and noticeable rufous patch in wing. Pale greyish on forehead, ear-coverts and sides of neck produces a hooded appearance which contrasts with rest of upperparts. Supercilium is off-white. Flanks are warm buff. Immatures are yellower below. Has an extraordinary song; a series of 3 or 4 thin, drawn-out whistles each lasting about 2 seconds, and followed by several fast, repeated 'chee chee' notes. Calls are a short 'brrr' and 'tik tik tik'. Recorded between 2600m and 3660m.

Grey-sided Bush Warbler *Cettia brunnifrons*
Plate 1 No. 7
Length 10cm
A small bush warbler similar to Chestnut-crowned. Has chestnut on both forehead and crown, although less intensely coloured at rear. Upperparts are olive brown. Whitish below with grey sides to throat, breast and upper flanks merging into brown on lower flanks and undertail coverts. Has a prominent whitish-buff supercilium from lores to back of ear-coverts. Call is similar to Chestnut-crowned, a sharp 'tzip'. Song is a loud 'sip ti ti sip' repeated continually. Recorded between 75m and 3660m.

The following 3 species are similar in shape and plumage. All have barred undertail coverts. They winter in marshy habitats and breed at high altitudes.

Spotted Bush Warbler *Bradypterus thoracicus*
Plate 1 No. 11,12
Length 13cm
Shorter tailed than the other *Bradypterus*. Resembles Lanceolated warbler in shape. Upperparts are dark olive-brown. Supercilium is greyish-white. Chin and upper throat are white, sides of throat and breast are grey. Usually has dark greyish-brown spots or blotches on lower throat and upper breast. Has a

distinctive undertail covert pattern. Feathers are brown with prominent white tips, forming bold dark chevrons. Song is a persistent, repeated 'see see'.

Chinese Bush Warbler *Bradypterus tacsanowskius*
Plate 1 No. 9,10
Length 14cm
Plumage is similar to that of Brown Bush Warbler but lacks its rufous tones. Upperparts are dull olive-brown, flanks buffy-brown. Supercilium is whitish to yellowish-white. Lacks grey on underparts. Breast is brownish-buff, rest of underparts buff-white, sometimes sullied with yellow. Undertail coverts lack the bold pattern of Spotted and are paler brown with broader whitish tips to feathers. Call is a 'chirr chirr' similar to Lanceolated Warbler. Has an insect-like song resembling that of Grasshopper Warbler.

Brown Bush Warbler *Bradypterus luteoventris*
Plate 1 No. 8
Length 13.5cm
Generally warmer coloured than other two *Bradypterus*. Upperparts are olive-brown with a rufous tinge. Short supercilium is buffish. Underparts lack any grey and are either warm buff or pale rufous-brown on breast, and rich brown or warm buff on flanks. Less contrast between brown bases and off-white tips to feathers of undertail coverts than in Spotted.

LOCUSTELLA WARBLERS

Very skulking medium-sized warblers with rounded tails. Frequent marsh vegetation. Often creep on the ground. Plumage is dull brownish. Nepalese species differ from Spotted, Chinese and Brown Bush Warblers, which behave similarly and may be found in similar habitat in winter, by noticeable streaking on upperparts.

Pallas's Warbler *Locustella certhiola*
Plate 3 No. 13
Length 13cm
Resembles Grasshopper Warbler but is larger and has a proportionately shorter tail. Darker and more rufous-brown above, particularly on crown. Most easily separated by contrast between dark tail and warm brown upper tail-coverts and rump. The rump is lightly streaked and often appears rufous in adults. Tail feathers have whitish tips, but these are usually only visible at close range. Supercilium is either distinct and buff contrasting with dark crown, or indistinct, the variation probably associated with age. Differs from other two species also by virtually unstreaked brownish-buff under tail-coverts. Call is a 'pit pit' like that of Zitting Cisticola. Song is a series of musical phrases.

Lanceolated Warbler *Locustella lanceolata*
Plate 3 No. 12
Length 11.3cm
Slightly smaller than Grasshopper Warbler with a proportionately shorter tail. Usually has distinct, dark, parallel streaking forming a gorget across breast and down flanks, but some individuals are indistinctly streaked and, conversely some Grasshopper Warblers have extensive streaking. From Grasshopper Warbler by heavier streaking on mantle. Often shows prominent streaking on upper tail-coverts which is rarely present in Grasshopper. Under tail-coverts are usually lightly spotted. Call is a metallic repeated 'pit' and short *Acrocephalus*-like 'teck'. Song resembles that of Grasshopper Warbler.

Grasshopper Warbler *Locustella naevia*
Plate 3 Nos. 10,11
Length 12.5cm
Upperparts are pale olive-brown with bold, dark streaks, tinged grey in breeding plumage. Has an indistinct yellowish-white supercilium. Underparts whitish or yellowish with light streaking on upper breast. Flanks are usually unstreaked. Under tail-coverts are pale brown and heavily spotted. Call is a short 'tchick'. Has a distinctive song, a high pitched insect-like trill continuing for long periods.

ACROCEPHALUS WARBLERS

Medium-sized to large warblers usually having rounded tails. Plumage of Nepalese species is generally rather uniform brown. Most inhabit marshy habitats. Skulking. Song is harsh and often monotonous.

Black-browed Reed Warbler
Acrocephalus bistrigiceps
Plate 3 No. 4
Length 13.5cm.
A small *Acrocephalus* recognised by its distinct head pattern. Has a long buffish-white supercilium, with a broad black band above it, and a dark line below it through eye. Olive-brown above with dark mottling on head and hindcrown. Sides of breast and flanks buff, rest of underparts yellowish-white. Call is 'chrrr' or a clucking note.

Blunt-winged Warbler *Acrocephalus concinens*
Plate 3 No. 5
Length 13cm

Paddyfield Warbler *Acrocephalus agricola*
Plate 3 No. 6
Length 13cm.
Difficult to distinguish in field. Both species are rufous on rump and have fairly rounded heads. Paddyfield is bright rufous above, tawny below in fresh plumage; grey-brown above, whitish below when worn. Blunt-winged Warbler is less rufous than Paddyfield, and is dark olive-brown above, brownish-buff below. Paddyfield has a creamy-white and conspicuous supercilium, extending to well behind eye and bordered by a dark line above it. Blunt-winged has a less distinct and shorter supercilium, resembling that of Blyth's Reed and is not bordered by a dark line. Blunt-winged has a longer, stouter bill, shorter wings and longer tail than Paddyfield. Call is a harsh repeated 'chr chuck'. See Blyth's Reed.

Blyth's Reed Warbler *Acrocephalus dumetorum*
Plate 3 Nos. 8,9
Length 14cm
A small *Acrocephalus*. Adults are greyish-olive above in spring, greyish-brown in autumn. From similar Paddyfield Warbler and Blunt-winged Warbler by generally cold grey not warm rufous tinge to upperparts including rump. This colour difference is however not a reliable feature in autumn. Immature Blyth's Reed often shows a rusty tinge above and worn adult Paddyfield and Blunt-winged can lose their rufous tones and appear cold grey-brown. Underparts are duller. Throat is whitish-buff, rest of underparts buff. Tip of lower mandible is on average paler and less well defined in Blyth's Reed than in

Paddyfield and Blunt-winged. Supercilium is usually indistinct, only ever reaching to just behind eye, and often only discernible in front of eye. Supercilium of Paddyfield is more prominent and usually has a dark line above it which is lacking in Blyth's Reed and Blunt-winged. Paddyfield (but not Blunt-winged) has more sharply marked tertials and alula with dark centres and pale fringes to feathers, but this is not a useful character in autumn as some immature Blyth's Reeds also show this. Bill is longer and stouter than that of Paddyfield. Head is slightly angular. Has a characteristic loud 'chick chick' call. Found in drier habitats than most other *Acrocephalus*, sometimes in trees.

Clamorous Reed Warbler *Acrocephalus stentoreus*
Plate 3 No. 7
Length 19cm
Difficult to distinguish from Great Reed Warbler in field. In a close view can be separated by absence of streaking on underparts. Supercilium is less distinct and shorter behind eye, giving it a gentle facial expression. Lower mandible is dark towards tip producing a dagger-like appearance. Calls are similar to those of Great Reed Warbler. Song is higher pitched, with more broken rhythm, a repeated 'go go cheek'.

Oriental Reed Warbler *Acrocephalus orientalis*
Plate 3 Nos. 2,3
Length 19cm
A large *Acrocephalus* with a rather angular head and heavy bill. Olive-brown above with a prominent buff supercilium and dusky lores. Buff-white below with characteristic faint narrow streaks on lower throat and upper breast. Flanks tawny. Some birds show buff-white tips to outer tail, particularly in fresh plumage, a feature which is absent in Clamorous. Makes a harsh, loud 'chak' and deep churring croak. Song is a series of loud grating phrases, interrupted by shrill notes: 'kawa kawa kawa gurk gurk eek gurk kawa'. See Clamorous Reed Warbler.

Thick-billed Warbler *Acrocephalus aedon*
Plate 3 No. 1
Length 19cm
A large *Acrocephalus* with a rounded head. Can be identified by its lack of supercilium and whitish lores. Also has more rounded wings and a longer graduated tail than other *Acrocephalus*. Has a shorter bill than the other two large *Acrocephalus*. Olive-brown above, buff white below. Generally tinged fulvous. Calls include a loud harsh repeated 'tschok tschok' and a sharp metallic 'clik clik'. Found in scrub, grassland, and bushes in dry habitats.

PRINIAS

Small wren-like warblers, with long graduated tails and rounded wings. A confusing genus. Difficulties in separating species are increased by differences in both plumages and tail lengths of summer and winter adults; the plumages of immatures are also different. Tail length is up to 3cm longer in winter. Undertail feathers of most species have pale tips and dark subterminal spots producing cross barring. Mainly frequent grasses and bushes in the open or on forest edges.

Graceful Prinia *Prinia gracilis*
Plate 2 No. 6
Tail length 5-6.25cm. Body length 6.25cm
A small streaked prinia found in the lowlands. Plumage similar in summer and winter: fulvous-brown streaked with dark brown above, buff-white below. From all prinias except Striated by streaked upperparts. Much smaller than Striated, with a smaller bill and found at a different altitude. The call is a nasal, buzzing 'bzreep', and the song is a fast, wheezy warble: 'ze(r) witze(r) wit'.

Plain Prinia *Prinia inornata*
Plate 2 Nos. 8,9
Tail length 5.8-8.8cm. Body length 7.5cm
Nondescript and brownish. **Adult** Upperparts earthy brown in summer, fulvous-brown in winter with a rufous tinge to wings and tail. Pale buff below. **Immature** Like adult winter but mor rufous above and richer buff below. From similar Jungle Prinia by noticeably smaller size. Has an obvious buffish-white supercilium, a feature which Jungle usually lacks. In summer has white on tail confined to the outermost pair of feathers. The calls include a plaintive 'tee-tee-tee' and a nasal 'beep'. The song is a repeated, rapid wheezy trill reminiscent of a grasshopper: 'tlick tlick tlick'. May also be confused with winter and immature Rufous and Grey-breasted Prinias. See those species.

Ashy Prinia *Prinia socialis*
Plate 2 No. 14
Tail length 5-7.5cm. Body length 7.5cm
Adult Summer: Crown, nape and mantle dark grey, wings and tail rufous. Winter: Grey on head is tinged with rufous. Back and rump are rufous-brown. Has a short white supercilium over lores, which is sometimes retained in summer. Adult may be confused with Grey-crowned and summer Rufous. From all other prinias by colour of underparts: cheeks and throat are buff-white, and the rest of the underparts are tinged pale rufous, especially on flanks and lower belly. In summer dark grey back of adult is diagnostic. **Immature** Similar to Yellow-bellied as both are olive-green on mantle and yellowish on lower underparts. The call is a sharp, nasal 'tee-tee-tee', and the song is a wheezy 'jimmy-jimmy-jimmy' repeated five or six times.

Rufous Prinia *Prinia rufescens*
Plate 2 Nos. 3,4
Tail length 3.75-5cm. Body length 7.5cm
A small prinia. **Adult** In summer from most prinias by combination of grey-brown head, rufous-brown upperparts and buff underparts. Grey-crowned is similar, and most easily distinguished by the appearance of the supercilium: broad, whitish and curves round eye in Rufous; long, narrow buffish-orange in front of eye, and whitish behind eye in Grey-crowned. Crown is paler grey and mantle duller rufous than in Grey-crowned, forming less contrasting upperparts. The song is a repeated series of squeaky notes: 'chewp chewp chewp'. Can also be confused with Ashy Prinia. See that species. Winter adults and immatures have a rufous-brown head almost the same colour as mantle. **Immature** is like winter adult but is tinged yellow below. Easily separated by lack of grey on head. May be confused with Plain but separated by much shorter tail. See also Grey-breasted Prinia.

Grey-crowned Prinia *Prinia cinereocapilla*
Plate 2 No. 5
Tail length 5.5-6.0cm. Body length 5.8cm
Similar to Rufous Prinia in summer plumage. Retains grey on head throughout the year. From all prinias except adult summer Rufous by combination of dark grey on head, rich rufous-brown upperparts and fulvous underparts. The song is a rising trill ending in long drawn out 'swe-ee-e-chor'. May also be confused with winter Ashy Prinia. See those two species. Found in dense jungle and secondary growh, and is more arboreal than other prinias. Song is a squeezed out 'cheeeeesum-zip-zip-zip', and a repeated 'tzit'.

Grey-breasted Prinia *Prinia hodgsonii*
Plate 2 Nos. 1,2
Tail length 5-6.25cm. Body length 6.25cm
A small prinia, ashy-grey above in summer, rufous-brown in winter. In summer **adult** usually has a diagnostic grey breastband contrasting with white underparts. In winter white below, sometimes with grey patches on breast. **Immature** is like adult, but tinged yellow below. Winter adults and immatures are difficult to distinguish from winter Rufous, and also show some similarities to Plain. Most easily separated from both species by smaller, and much finer bill, and different song. The call is a 'chew-chew-chew', and the song is a loud, squeaky 'chiwee-chiwee-chiwi-chip-chip-chip'. Bill of Rufous is stouter and paler, particularly on lower mandible. Plain also has a stouter bill which is black in summer, brown in winter. Grey-

breasted has an all dark bill. Can also be separated from winter Rufous by less rufous upperparts, particularly tail and wing edgings. From Plain also by slightly smaller size. Has different colour of underparts: buff with rich buff flanks in Rufous, and pale buff in Plain.

Yellow-bellied Prinia *Prinia flaviventris*
Plate 2 No. 7
Tail length 8-8.8cm. Body length 5cm
Adult Dark grey head, rest of upperparts olive-green. Throat and breast creamy white contrasting with yellow belly. Sometimes has a short whitish supercilium. **Immature** Yellowish-brown above, pale yellow below. Can be confused with immatures of other species that may be tinged yellow below, especially Ashy. However Yellow-bellied is richer yellow below than other prinias, and in adults the yellow contrasts more with the rest of the underparts. It is found in wetter habitats than other prinias: marshy areas or grassland near water. The call is an incessant 'chink-chink' or 'tzetze-tze' and the song is a sharp chirp followed by a trill of five notes.

Striated Prinia *Prinia criniger*
Plate 2 No. 10
Tail length 7.5-10cm. Body length 8.8cm
A large prinia, with streaked upperparts, found in the hills. Similar to Graceful but much larger, and with underparts pale fulvous, flecked with black on throat and breast. Flanks olive-brown. Has a stout black bill and flesh pink legs. The song is a repeated wheezy squeaking 'tzirt-tzirt'. See Hill Prinia.

Jungle Prinia *Prinia sylvatica*
Plate 2 No. 11
Tail length 6.25-7.5cm. Body length 8.8cm
Large, brownish prinia, usually lacking an obvious supercilium, and with three outer pairs of tail feathers whitish in summer. The song is a repeated loud 'pit pretty', the first note only heard at close range. See Plain Prinia.

Hill Prinia *Prinia atrogularis*
Plate 2 Nos. 12,13
Tail length 11.25cm. Body length 6.25cm
A large prinia, with a very long tail, found in the hills. **Adult** In summer black throat and black and white spotted breast are diagnostic. Head and nape are grey and contrast with upperparts, black chin and throat are bordered by white moustachial stripe. No supercilium. In winter upperparts are dark olive-brown, and the breast is indistinctly striped black. Has a long white supercilium. **Immature** Rich brown above with some black streaks on head, fulvous below. Most likely to be confused with similar-sized Striated which can be found in the same habitat. Separated from this

species by the above-mentioned features and unstreaked upperparts. Song is rather similar to that of Striated Prinia: a raspy repeated 'tze-tze'.

PHYLLOSCOPUS WARBLERS

Small, fast moving, greenish or brownish warblers. Often referred to as leaf warblers. Useful identification features are voice; strength of supercilium; colour of underparts, rump, bill, and legs; and presence of wingbars, coronal bands or white in the tail. Colouration of upper and underparts and presence of wingbars are affected by wear. Here the species are divided into two groups: those with wingbars and those without.

Leaf warblers lacking wingbars

Note that some individuals of these species, especially Chiffchaffs, may show one faint wingbar.

Slender-billed Warbler *Phylloscopus tytleri*
Plate 5 Nos. 1,2
Length 11 cm

Can be recognised by its very long, thin bill, reminiscent of that of a Tailorbird. Juveniles have shorter bills. Upperparts are greyish-olive, and the underparts are whitish with faint yellow streaking in fresh plumage. Call is a single squeaky feeble note or double 'y-it'. Has a distinctive song 'pi-tsi-pi-tsu', repeated at regular intervals. May be confused with worn Greenish apparently lacking a wingbar, and possibly with Tickell's. Most easily separated by its more slender and all darkish bill, and different call. Tickell's also has yellower underparts.

Tickell's Warbler *Phylloscopus affinis*
Plate 5 Nos. 3,4
Length 11 cm

Combination of uniform olive-brown upperparts and yellow underparts (bright yellow on throat and breast and pale yellow on belly and under-tail coverts) are diagnostic. Has a long, prominent yellow supercilium. The race *P. a. arcanus* has yellowish-buff upperparts and supercilium. Usually feeds near the ground. Inhabits alpine scrub in summer, cultivation or scrub in lowlands or foothills in winter. Song is a 'tchip-tsi-tsi-tsi-tsi-tsi-tsi'. Call is a repeated 'tret tret'. See Slender-billed, Chiffchaff, Sulphur-bellied.

Sulphur-bellied Warbler *Phylloscopus griseolus*
Plate 5 No. 8
Length 11cm

Can be identified by combination of its grey-brown upperparts, oily yellow underparts washed brownish-buff on the flanks, and prominent yellow supercilium. Also has a characteristic habit of creeping over stones and up tree trunks. Frequently flicks wings and tail. Call is a soft 'quip'. May be confused with Tickell's but lacks green and olive in plumage and has a duller supercilium and underparts, and a different call.

Smoky Warbler *Phylloscopus fuligiventer*
Plate 5 No. 5
Length 11cm

Easily recognised by its very dark appearance and small size. Dark sooty-brown above, with a greenish tinge in fresh plumage. Very dusky below, grey with yellowish-olive tinge on throat. breast and belly. Sides washed with dark olive. Has an indistinct yellowish-olive supercilium. Call is a 'tzik' or 'tsrr' rather like Red-breasted Flycatcher, or a soft 'stup' like Radde's. In winter often found in waterside vegetation in lowlands.

Chiffchaff *Phylloscopus collybita*
Plate 5 No. 6
Length 11cm

Brown or greyish-brown above. From all other leaf warblers by its short inconspicuous buff supercilium and black legs. From all leaf warblers without wingbars, except Dusky, by its dull buff-white underparts lacking yellow or green. May be confused with Greenish, especially birds showing a faint wingbar. Most easily separated by its call, the very thin, usually dark, bill and less obvious supercilium. Call is a 'peep' or sharp 'chvit'. Song is either a repeated 'chiff-chaff', or a rapid repetition of 'chi-vit' run together by the introduction of a few more musical notes. These differences may indicate that two separate populations are involved, although all specimens have been referred to *P. c. tristis*. Often arboreal, feeding well above the ground. See Dusky.

Dusky Warbler *Phyllscopus fuscatus*
Plate 5 No. 7
Length 11cm

A skulking warbler, found in scrub and low vegetation. Dark brown above, greyish-white below, flanks fulvous. Lacks yellow and green in plumage. Separated from Chiffchaff by its distinctive hard 'tack tack' call, its conspicuous long buff supercilium, rich buff vent, yellowish-brown legs, and secretive behaviour. Often also found in different habitat. See Radde's.

Radde's Warbler *Phylloscopus schwarzi*
Plate 5 Nos. 9,10
Length 12cm

A large, skulking *Phylloscopus*. Upperparts and flanks are brownish-olive. Can be confused with Dusky, particularly with worn plumage. Bigger and heavier, with a thicker bill and longer tail. Undertail coverts are rufous. Supercilium is creamy, and usually longer and more conspicuous, reaching hindcrown. Dark line through the eye is more prominent. Has yellowish tinge to underparts, and black line above supercilium, lacking in Dusky. Legs are reddish or yellowish-flesh. Call is a soft 'stup' similar to that of Smoky.

Leaf warblers with wingbars

All species are very active and constantly on the move. Note The presence or absence of wingbars as a field character for separating species should be treated with caution. In worn plumage birds normally showing two bars may show only one, and birds normally showing one bar may appear to lack this altogether.

Yellow-vented Warbler *Phylloscopus cantator*
Plate 4 No. 6
Length 10cm
A small leaf warbler, recognised by the distinctive colour of underparts. Throat, upper breast and under tail coverts are bright yellow, contrasting with white lower breast and belly. Flanks greyish. Has a striking head pattern: a well-defined yellow supercilium, sides of head yellow; black lateral stripes, and a median yellowish-green stripe on the crown. Has two yellow wing-bars, the upper indistinct. Call is loud continuous 'pio pio'.

Grey-faced Leaf Warbler
Phylloscopus maculipennis
Plate 4 No. 1
Length 10cm
Small. The only leaf warbler with a grey head and throat. Rest of underparts yellowish. Olive-green above with a yellow rump, two yellowish-white wingbars, and white on the inner webs of the outer three pairs of tail feathers. Has a whitish median crown stripe and long distinct whitish supercilium. Call is a short 'tit'. See Orange-barred, Pallas's.

Orange-barred Leaf Warbler *Phylloscopus pulcher*
Plate 4 No. 5
Length 10cm
Similar to Grey-faced in fresh plumage, but throat off-white. Upperparts rather dark brownish-olive, darker on crown, and with a grey tinge. Has a faint yellowish-green crown stripe and yellowish supercilium. Underparts greyish-yellow. Has two orange-buff wingbars but the upper bar may not be visible, and the colour is often difficult to determine. Call is a short repeated 'tsip'. Song is a high-pitched thin twitter, preceded by, or ending with, a drawn out trill. See Pallas's.

Pallas's Leaf Warbler *Phylloscopus proregulus*
Plate 4 No. 2
Length 9cm
A small leaf warbler, similar to Blyth's Crowned but smaller, and has a yellow rump. Grey-green above and whitish below. The prominent median crown stripe, supercilium and two wingbars are all yellowish-white. From Orange-barred and Grey-faced by lack of white

in tail and more conspicuous crown stripe. Call is a sharp 'tsip' or a quiet 'chwee'. Song is a short twittering 'wai-a-wai-a-wai' rapidly repeated.

Blyth's Leaf Warbler *Phylloscopus reguloides*
Plate 4 No. 7
Length 11cm
Has a well marked head pattern: a yellowish-white median crown stripe, particularly prominent in summer; broad, dark olive lateral crown stripes; and a long, yellow supercilium. The mantle is greyish-green, and the lower back is brighter green. Has two yellow wingbars, and the greater coverts are usually darker than the rest of the wing, forming a contrasting band. Underparts yellowish-white. Call is a constantly repeated 'kee-kew-i'. Song is a trill of nine to ten notes 'ch-ti-ch-ti-ch-ti-chi-chi-ti-chee'. See Pallas's, Western Crowned.

Western Crowned Warbler *Phylloscopus occipitalis*
Plate 4 No. 8
Length 13cm
A large leaf warbler, very similar to Blyth's Leaf. Can be separated by combination of the following features: larger size; noticeably longer bill; greyish-white supercilium; coronal bands generally paler grey, forming a less contrasting head pattern; lighter, duller green upperparts; whitish underparts sullied with grey; yellowish-white wingbars; and greater coverts are not contrastingly dark. Call is 'stic' or 'stic-swick'. Song is 'stic-swee-swee-swee-swe-swee-swa', often omitting final 'swa'.

Greenish Warbler *Phylloscopus trochiloides*
Plate 4 Nos. 9,10,11
Length 10-11cm
Extremely variable in size and colouration. Two races occur. Appearance in fresh plumage is quite different. *P. t. trochiloides* is dark olive to olive-green above, whitish below heavily marked with grey, sometimes yellowish-white on breast and belly. Has prominent yellowish-white supercilium, and usually one yellowish-white wingbar. Sometimes shows a faint second bar. *P. t. viridanus* differs in having brighter green upperparts with no olive tinge, whitish underparts, and a yellowish supercilium. Wears to a dull greyish above. Both races lack yellow on rump, dark coronal bands and white in tail. Bill colour is variable but base of lower mandible is always pale pinkish or orange. Calls ar similar, a loud piercing 'che-wee' or 'chis-weet'. The song is based on the call: *P. t. viridanus* a loud, repeated vehement 'chi-chi-chi-chiwee-chiwee', and *P. t. trochiloides* a more regular tit-like 'chis-weet chis-weet'. See Green, Large-billed, Yellow-browed, Chiffchaff.

Green Warbler *Phylloscopus nitidus*
Plate 4 Nos. 12,13
Length 11cm
Similar to Greenish but upperparts are brighter leaf-green, and the supercilium, cheeks and wingbar are noticeably yellow. Underparts have a much stronger suffusion of yellow, sometimes reaching undertail coverts, but birds in worn plumage may have much less yellow. The bill is stouter, and often paler. Call is very similar to Greenish but may be more clearly disyllabic and louder. The song is more complex than that of the Greenish and often includes brief trilling notes.

Large-billed Leaf Warbler
Phylloscopus magnirostris
Plate 4 No. 14
Length 13cm
A large leaf warbler with plumage similar to nominate Greenish, but usually appearing noticeably larger. In fresh plumage it is brighter olive green than Greenish, with a more prominent dark line through the eye, and a longer yellowish-white supercilium extending to rear of ear-coverts. The sides of the breast and flanks are olive-brown. Has one and a half yellowish-white wingbars, but the upper one is usually not visible. Most easily separated by its different voice. Call 'dir-tee', the second syllable half an octave higher than the first. The song is a sweet musical 'see sisi sisi' on three descending notes. Bill is heavier and dark with only a restricted pale orange or brown area at the base of the lower mandible.

Yellow-browed Warbler *Phylloscopus inornatus*
Plate 4 Nos. 3,4
Length 10cm
A small leaf warbler. *P. i. humei* (the commonest race) is greyish-olive above, creamy below, with a long broad supercilium, and one and a half whitish wing-bars. *P. i. inornatus* has brighter greenish-olive upper-parts, and yellower supercilium and wingbars, and yellowish-white underparts. *P. i. humei* is confusable with Greenish because it often appears to have only one wingbar. It is most easily separated by its smaller, virtually all dark bill. The call is a very similar disyllabic 'tiss-yip'. See Greenish. *P. i. inornatus* is separated from Greenish by the presence of two prominent wingbars, white tips to the tertials, and the call, a loud plaintive 'weest'. Both races are generally smaller than Greenish.

BLACK TITS

Small crested tits. All have crown, crest, sides of neck
and throat black. Cheeks and nuchal patch white.
Separated by colour of underparts and presence of
wingbars. Inhabit broadleaved and coniferous forests
between 2100m and 4000m.

Rufous-naped Tit *Parus rufonuchalis*
Length 13cm
A large and dark black tit. Distinguished by extensive
black on underparts covering breast and upper belly.
Lower belly dark grey. Rufous only on undertail
coverts and small patch on flanks. Has rich rufous
tinge at back of white nuchal patch. Upperparts dark
olive-grey. No wing spots.

Rufous-vented Tit
Length 10cm
Western race
Parus rubidiventris rubidiventris
Separated by rufous breast and belly. Flanks pale grey
with a small rufous patch. Has pale rufous tinge at
back of white nuchal patch. Upperparts grey slightly
tinged olive. Under tail-coverts rufous. No wing spots.

Eastern race
Parus rubidiventris beavani
Like *P. r. rubidiventris* but breast and belly medium
grey. Flanks medium grey with a small rufous patch.
Lacks rufous tinge on white nuchal patch.

Spot-winged Tit *Parus melanolophus*
Length 11cm Dark grey upperparts. From other species except Coal by two rows of rusty-white spots
forming wing bars. From Coal by dark grey breast and
belly, small rufous patch on flanks and rufous under
tail-coverts.

Coal Tit *Parus ater*
Length 10cm
The smallest black tit. Grey above. Separated from
other black tits by beige breast and belly and lack of
both rufous patch on flanks and rufous under tail-
coverts. From Rufous-naped and Rufous-vented by
two rows of white spots forming wing bars. Hybrids
between the last two species occur in a zone of
introgression. The hybrids differ strikingly from both
parents in having a cinnamon patch on the lower
breast and belly, thus resembling *P. r. rubidiventris*..

CR

ROSEFINCHES

Males have pinkish plumage and, in most species, a pink rump. Females and immatures are streaked brown and are often difficult to identify. All breed at high altitudes, and all except Common Rosefinch winter above 1000m.

Blanford's Rosefinch *Carpodacus rubescens*
Plate 6 No. 2, Plate 7 No. 2
Length 15cm
Male is similar to Common but has uniform pinkish-red underparts, a thinner and more pointed bill, orange-crimson rump and lacks a dark eyestripe. Female can be separated from Dark-breasted by its paler underparts, and much plainer upperparts with rufescent edges to feathers, especially on rump.

Dark-breasted Rosefinch *Carpodacus nipalensis*
Plate 6 No. 1, Plate 7 No. 1
Length 15.5cm
Has a dark appearance. From other rosefinches by longer and thinner bill. Male separated from all except Dark-rumped by lack of pink or red on rump. Male has a characteristic dusky crimson breast band, contrasting with rosy-pink throat and belly. Fore-crown and forehead are rosy-red; supercilium is broad rosy-pink, contrasting with dark rear crown and dark line through eye. Female is dark olive-brown above with heavy blackish streaks. Has two distinct orange-brown wingbars in fresh plumage. No eye-brow. Separated from all rosefinches except female Blanford's by unstreaked olive-brown underparts. See that species.

Common Rosefinch *Carpodacus erythrinus*
Plate 6 No. 4, Plate 7 No. 4
Length 15cm
Male of subspecies *roseatus* has head, rump and breast rosy-red. Lacks an eye-brow. Rest of upper-parts rosy-red tinged brown, and unstreaked. Rest of underparts pale rose. Subspecies *erythrinus* is paler red. Female of subspecies *roseatus* is olive-brown above with light streaking. Has two pale buff wingbars which wear to whitish. Lacks an eyebrow. Throat and breast are pale buff, lightly streaked with brown, and the belly is whitish. Female *erythrinus* is similar to *roseatus* but is paler, and has grey-brown upperparts. Immatures of both races are similar to female *roseatus*, but have rich buff, boldly streaked upperparts, and are more heavily streaked on the breast. Lower belly and under tail-coverts whitish, lacking streaks. See Beautiful.

Beautiful Rosefinch *Carpodacus pulcherrimus*
Plate 6 No. 6, Plate 7 No. 6
Length 15cm
Identifiable by generally pale colouration, and by heavy dark brown streaks above and below. Supercil-ium is broad and pale pink in male, whitish and indistinct in female. Male is ashy brown above, heavily streaked darker, including crown, lower belly whitish, and rest of underparts pale pink, with streaks on sides of lower breast and flanks. Rump is pale pink and unstreaked. Female is nondescript, pale buffy brown above, heavily streaked dark brown, and greyer on crown. Has broad pale buffish fringes to coverts and tertials. Cheeks and underparts are whitish, heavily marked throughout with narrow dark streaks. Has more extensive streaking than Pink-browed, a pale crown and ear coverts, and is whitish below. From Great and Streaked by smaller size and smaller bill. See Common, Pink-browed.

Pink-browed Rosefinch *Carpodacus rhodochrous*
Plate 6 No. 3, Plate 7 No. 3
Length 14.5cm
Male is distinguished by combination of prominent pink supercilium, and warm brown mantle with darker streaks. Rump and underparts are rosy pink and unstreaked. Crown and line through the eye are crimson-brown and unstreaked. Male and female can have pale tertial tips as in Vinaceous. Female is warm brown with darker streaks above, and with olive tinge to mantle. Underparts are warm buffy-brown, paler on throat, and with dark brown streaks on throat, breast, upper belly and flanks. Rather similar to fe-male Dark-rumped, but has a prominent broad buff supercilium, broad warm buffish fringes to wing coverts and tertials, and is smaller.

Vinaceous Rosefinch *Carpodacus vinaceus*
Plate 6 No. 8, Plate 7 No. 8
Length 13.5cm
A small, dark rosefinch. Male is deep crimson with rosy-red rump, prominent pink supercilium, and dark brown wings and tail. Lacks streaking. Has two pink-ish-white spots on tertials. Female is olive-brown above, warmer brown below, with indistinct dark streaks above and below, and lacks a contrasting supercilium. Rather similar to female Dark-breasted and Blanford's but separated by streaked underparts, more olive colouration, lack of wing bars, and smaller size.

Dark-rumped Rosefinch *Carpodacus edwardsii*
Plate 6 No. 5, Plate 7 No. 5
Length 16cm
A dark rosefinch. Male has pink forehead and supercilium contrasting with dark crown and line through eye. Breast is dark pinkish-brown and remaining underparts paler. Upperparts are deep pinkish-brown streaked darker. Separated from all except Dark-breasted by lack of pink or red in rump. Female is olive-brown above with broad dark streaks and paler, slightly buffy-brown fringes to wing coverts and tertials. Has a narrow buffish supercilium. Buff below, whiter on throat and more olive on breast, and streaked darker on throat and breast. Both sexes resemble Spot-winged - see that species.

Spot-winged Rosefinch *Carpodacus rhodopeplus*
Plate 6 No. 7, Plate 7 No. 7
Length 17cm
Male has a narrow pink rump and prominent pink supercilium. Rest of upperparts are crimson-brown, streaked pink on lower back, with pink edgings to scapulars and tertials. Deep pink below mottled with brown. Female is olive-brown, streaked darker above, with pale buff tips to greater coverts and tertials. Has a very broad, pale buff supercilium, contrasting with dark brown ear coverts. Buffy below, whiter on throat, and heavily streaked on breast and throat. Similar to Dark-rumped. Male and female can be separated by more pronounced supercilium; male also by pink rump, generally brighter and more contrasting plumage, double wing bar, and dark breastband present in Dark-rumped. Female can also be separated by heavier streaks below.

White-browed Rosefinch *Carpodacus thura*
Plate 6 No. 9, Plate 7 No. 9
Length 17.5cm
Male is distinguished by combination of glistening pink and white forehead, pinkish-white supercilium, and double wingbar. Upperparts, including crown, are brown and streaked darker. Flanks olive-brown; lower belly white; rest of underparts and rump are rosy-pink. Throat has white shaft streaks. Female has diagnostic orange-brown rump. Olive-brown, streaked blackish above, with a very broad whitish supercilium contrasting with blackish ear coverts, and a thin white wingbar. Orange-brown on throat and breast, rest of underparts buffy-white. Has blackish streaks below, heavier than in all other rosefinches.

Streaked Rosefinch *Carpodacus rubicilloides*
Plate 6 No. 10, Plate 7 No. 10
Length 19cm
Male is similar to Great, but is darker, and has heavy dark brown streaks on upperparts, and the whole of the head and breast are crimson with narrower white spots. Female has dull ashy-brown upperparts, and

whitish underparts tinged buff on breast and flanks. Streaked above and below much more heavily than Great. Resembles female Red-fronted but lacks greenish tinge to rump, has a more swollen bill, and is much paler, especially on underparts.

Great Rosefinch *Carpodacus rubicilla*
Plate 6 No. 12, Plate 7 No. 12
Length 19cm
A large, high altitude rosefinch. Distinguished by its very pale appearance. Male is almost uniform sandy-grey, tinged pink above, and with a pale pink rump. Forehead, crown, cheeks, throat and upper breast are crimson spotted with white, ear coverts are pink and lack spots. Rest of underparts are pale pink mottled with white. Female is very pale ashy brown above with light streaking, more prominent on crown than on mantle, and whitish-buff below with light streaking more obvious on throat. Similar to female Streaked - see that species.

Red-fronted Rosefinch *Carpodacus puniceus*
Plate 6 No. 11, Plate 7 No. 11
Length 20cm
A large rosefinch, found above 2745m, with a long, heavy bill and short-tailed appearance. Male can be separated from all other rosefinches by bright red forehead and supercilium, bright red throat and upper breast mottled with white, and lower breast pinkish-brown. Rump rosy red. Upperparts are dull grey-brown and broadly streaked darker. Female is nondescript. Dark olive grey brown above, broadly streaked with blackish, and a dull greenish tinge to rump. Throat whitish-buff; rest of underparts dull buff, all heavily streaked with dark brown. Vent olive-brown. See female Streaked.

BUNTINGS

Mainly terrestrial. Frequent grassland or weedy and bushy areas in open country. Seed eaters with short conical bills. Most species have white outer tail feathers. Females and immatures are mainly brown, often streaked and sometimes difficult to identify. Winter males and immatures usually resemble females.

Black-faced Bunting *Emberiza spodocephala*
Plate 8 Nos. 13,14
Length 15cm
A small bunting with a large bill. Male has diagnostic olive-grey head, neck, throat and upper breast contrasting with black round base of bill, lores and eyes. Rest of upperparts brownish-olive with darker streaks. Female lacks black face and grey throat of male. Crown and upperparts olive grey-brown streaked blackish. Heavily streaked black on lower mantle. Submoustachial stripe, supercilium and underparts are very pale yellow or buffy white. Streaked on breast and flanks. Has a dark malar stripe. Females and immatures are most easily distinguished from female Chestnut, Yellowhammer and Reed by olive rump; from female Reed also by lack of dark edges to ear-coverts, smaller size, generally more olive appearance. Reed lacks yellowish tinge in underparts sometimes present in Black-faced. Call is a 'tsik'.

Pine Bunting *Emberiza leucocephalos*
Plate 8 Nos. 1,2
Length 16-17cm
A large greyish-brown bunting with a chestnut rump. Male can be distinguished by head pattern although this is obscured by buffish-brown and black tips in winter. Throat and supercilium are chestnut. In breeding plumage crown and cheeks are white edged with black. Male has chestnut upperparts streaked dark brown. Upper breast and belly white; lower breast and flanks chestnut with white tips to some feathers and black streaks on flanks. Female is much less chestnut than male. Has a brownish-grey streaked head; ear-coverts have obvious pale patch at rear edged with brown. Upperparts as male but paler. Underparts whitish with coarse brown streaks on throat becoming rufous on breast and flanks; belly white. The species is closely related to Yellowhammer but lacks yellow on head, edges to primaries and underparts. It also lacks streaks on belly present in Yellowhammer. Call is very similar to Yellowhammer; a single sharp 'twick'. Winters above 900m. See female Yellowhammer, Reed, White-capped, Black-faced.

Yellowhammer *Emberiza citrinella*
Length 16-17cm
Has chestnut rump and call like Pine. Male can be separated from all other buntings by mainly yellow head. Underparts are yellow streaked with chestnut on breast and flanks. Upperparts are like Pine but have a yellowish-olive tinge lacking in that species. Female and immature are duller, less yellow and have more dark markings on head. Resemble female Pine but have yellow edges to the primaries, some streaks on the belly which is never white; also usually have yellowish wash on head and underparts. See female Reed, Black-faced, Chestnut, Pine.

White-capped Bunting *Emberiza stewarti*
Plate 8 Nos. 3,4
Length 15cm
Has a chestnut rump which is darker and richer than that of Pine. Summer male has distinctive head pattern. Greyish-white crown and ear-coverts with broad black eyestripe from lores to nape. Chin and throat black. Underparts white with broad chestnut breast band. Winter male is generally duller and the chestnut is less extensive below. Wing-coverts and mantle are greyish-brown streaked dark brown and rufous. Female nondescript. Upperparts ashy-brown with dark streaks; two fulvous wing bars; underparts fulvous streaked with brown, often streaked rufous in a band across lower breast and on flanks. Immature is similar to female but usually lacks rufous below; more obviously streaked above and below and has paler creamy wingbars. From Pine and Yellowhammer by indistinct head pattern with a poorly marked malar stripe; more extensive streaking on underparts and noticeably smaller size. Lacks white belly of Pine and yellowish wash on head and underparts of Yellowhammer. Call is a sharp 'tit'. See Black-faced, Reed, Chestnut-eared, Little, Pine, Reed.

Rock Bunting *Emberiza cia*
Plate 8 Nos. 7,8
Length 15-16.5cm
Summer male has pale blue-grey head and throat with black lateral crown stripes and black malar stripe extending back round ear-coverts to join black eyestripe. Rest of underparts and rump chestnut. Winter male paler with less distinct head pattern. Female duller. Immature has brownish head with dark streaks on crown. Throat and upper breast buff-grey; breast and flanks streaked. Call is a thin repeated squeak 'swip'. See Chestnut-eared, White-capped. Recorded above 2135m.

Chestnut-eared Bunting *Emberiza fucata*
Plate 8 Nos. 5,6
Length 16cm
Slim and long-tailed with distinctive plumage. Identified by combination of chestnut ear-coverts, lesser coverts and scapulars and gorget of black streaks or blotches on breast most prominent in male. Upperparts are chestnut with heavy black streaks on mantle. Rump is rufous brown. Crown and nape are olive-grey in male, grey brown in female with dark streaks. Lower breast, flanks fulvous, belly fulvous white. Summer male has a narrow chestnut breastband, indistinct in winter. Female and immature male are generally paler and duller than adult male. Call similar to that of Rustic. See Little, Reed, Pine, Black-faced, White-capped.

Rustic Bunting *Emberiza rustica*
Plate 8 No. 10
Length 14-15cm
A small bunting. Separated from other buntings by a combination of white stripe behind eye and white throat; chestnut blotches across breast and chestnut streaks on flanks; white belly. Upperparts including rump are chestnut streaked darker on mantle with pale edges to feathers (grey in male, brown in female). Summer male has black crown and cheeks. Female, immature and winter male are generally duller and less chestnut and have dark brown streaks replacing black on head. Often raises crown feathers. Call is a repeated high hard 'tsip'. See Reed, Pine, Little.

Little Bunting *Emberiza pusilla*
Plate 8 No. 9
Length 12.5-14cm
The smallest Nepalese bunting. Has a short tail and compact appearance. Identified by combination of chestnut ear-coverts with black lower edge not reaching bill; obvious pale eye-ring and wing-bars; brown lesser coverts and pinkish-brown legs. The adult in summer has a chestnut crown stripe; a band on side of crown, malar stripe and edge of ear-coverts black; supercilium is buffy-rufous in front of eye; upperparts brown streaked darker; lacks a chestnut rump. Whitish below finely streaked black on breast and flanks. Immatures and some adult females are much duller. Call is sharp 'tzik' or quieter 'tip'. See Reed, Rustic, Black-faced.

Chestnut Bunting *Emberiza rutila*
Length 13.5-14.5cm
Small and squat with a short tail. Summer male has distinctive chestnut head, throat, upper breast and upperparts contrasting with yellow belly and under tail-coverts. Streaked grey on flanks. Winter male sometimes has chestnut tinge to head, throat and upper breast. Female identified by combination of

chestnut rump; buff throat; dull yellow underparts indistinctly streaked grey-green on breast and flanks; and lack of noticeable white in tail. Often shows rich dark chestnut edges to tertials. Immature is similar to female but is more distinctly and finely streaked with blackish across breast and flanks; also more distinctly streaked with black on crown and mantle. Immature male usually shows chestnut tinge to crown and breast. Call is a thin high 'teseep'. See female Black-faced, Yellowhammer.

Yellow-breasted Bunting *Emberiza aureola*
Plate 8 Nos. 11,12
Length 13.5-15cm
Male can be identified by narrow chestnut band on upper breast and large white patch on median wing coverts. Yellow underparts, streaked blackish on flanks. In summer has black face, dark chestnut upperparts including rump and nape. Black and chestnut are obscured by buff scales in winter. Female and immature are brown streaked darker above, the latter usually showing sandy braces on mantle, rump may be tinged chestnut. Both are pale buff yellow below, streaked black on flanks. From other buntings by combination of two diffuse whitish wing bars; broad creamy or buff supercilium; pale crown stripe; only a little white in tail. Call is a 'zip' or soft 'trssit'. See female Chestnut, Yellowhammer, Red-headed and Black-headed.

Adult male buntings

Yellowhammer:	1,
Pine Bunting:	2,
White-capped Bunting:	3,
Rustic Bunting:	4,
Reed Bunting:	5,
Yellow-breasted Bunting:	6,
Little Bunting:	7,
Rock Bunting:	8,
Black-headed Bunting:	9,
Black-faced Bunting:	10,
Chestnut-eared Bunting:	11,
Red-headed Bunting:	12,
Chestnut Bunting:	13

Reed Bunting *Emberiza schoeniclus*
Length 14-16cm
Summer male can be recognised by combination of black head and throat, white sub-moustachial stripe and collar. Pale rufous-buff above with heavy black steaks. Whitish below rather coarsely streaked darker on breast and flanks. Rump grey-brown. In winter head pattern is obscured by brown mottling. Female and immature lack black head and throat of adult male. Have well marked black malar and white sub-moustachial streaks and grey-brown rump. Similar to immature Little but larger; bill much larger; ear-coverts usually browner and with the black lower edge reaching bill; indistinct eye-ring and wing-bars; bright chestnut lesser coverts; and dark brown legs. Lacks chestnut rump of Pine and Rustic and also chestnut on underparts of latter. A variety of calls include a loud 'tseek', a plaintive 'tsew', a metallic 'tsing', and a quieter 'tsip'. See Rustic, Little, Pine, Black-faced.

Red-headed Bunting *Emberiza bruniceps*
Length 17cm
Lacks noticeable white in tail. Male can be recognised by chestnut head and throat and yellow nape contrasting with greenish streaked mantle. Underparts are yellow and unstreaked. Female is very similar to female Black-headed. Differs in smaller size; wing bars are usually buff (though may wear to whitish); rump is usually yellowish, often tinged olive; under tail-coverts less yellow. Lacks rufous on mantle or rump usually present in Black-headed. Call is thinner 'twip'.

Black-headed Bunting *Emberiza melanocephala*
Length 16-18cm
A large bunting. Lacks conspicuous white outer tail feathers. From all except Red-headed by usually un-streaked underparts which are yellow in male, yellowish-white in female. Summer plumage male has diagnostic combination of blackish-brown head with yellow collar and grey-chestnut back. Rump is orange-chestnut sometimes tinged yellow. Duller in winter with brown head. Female is dull brown finely streaked darker brown with sandy-beige or chestnut-beige rump and yellow tinge to under tail-coverts. Underparts sometimes finely streaked on breast. Has two whitish wing bars. Usually shows rufous tinge to upperparts. Very similar to female Red-headed. Call is a musical 'tchup'.

Crested Bunting *Melophus lathami*
Length 15-16cm
Long pointed crest is diagnostic. Summer male is black with chestnut wings and tail. Browner in winter. Female is olive brown, edges of wings and outer tail rufous. Dark buff brown below. Call is a repeated 'tip' or 'pink'.

BLUE-EARED KINGFISHER *Alcedo meninting*
Length 16cm

EURASIAN KINGFISHER *Alcedo atthis*
Length 18cm

Small brilliantly coloured kingfishers, generally bright blue above and rufous below with bright red bill, legs and feet. Blue-eared is slightly smaller and generally richer coloured than Eurasian. It has deep purplish-blue upperparts with a darker purplish-blue line down the centre which is conspicuous in flight. It has blue ear-coverts and is a dark rich rufous below. Eurasian is bright bluish-green above with a bright turquoise-blue line down the centre. It has rufous ear-coverts and is rufous below. The species are found in different habitats: Blue-eared frequents streams in shady forests of the lowlands; Eurasian is found by streams, rivers and lakes, and ponds in open areas from the lowlands up to at least 1800m.

BROWN-HEADED BARBET *Megalaima zeylanica*
Length 27cm

LINEATED BARBET *Megalaima lineata*
Length 28cm

Stocky, stout-billed green birds with short tails. Arboreal and frugivorous. Both species have a conspicuous naked yellowish patch around the eye; it is large and invariably extends to the bill in Brown-headed, and often smaller and separated by a line of feathers from the bill in Lineated. Head and upper breast of Brown-headed are dull brown with narrow pale shaft streaks; streaks more obvious on nape; mantle to tail bright green with sparse pale shaft streaks on mantle; pale spots on wing coverts; lower breast and belly paler, unstreaked. Lineated has a whitish chin and un-streaked greyish crown; rest of the head, nape and most of the underparts brown with prominent whitish spots; no spots on wing-coverts. The repetitious calls are very similar but Lineated has a mellower, softer 'kotur' compared with Brown-headed's 'kutroo'.

ASIAN HOUSE-MARTIN *Delichon dasypus*
Length 12.5cm

COMMON HOUSE-MARTIN *Delichon urbica*
Length 13.5cm

Small martins. Upperparts are blue-black with white
rump. Immatures are tinged brown above. Whole of
upper tail-coverts are white in Common. Longest
upper tail-coverts are steel-blue in Asian forming a
noticeably less extensive white area than in the former. Underparts are pure white in Common; white
tinged grey-brown, especially on breast, in Asian. Tail
is distinctly forked in Common, but only slightly in
Asian.

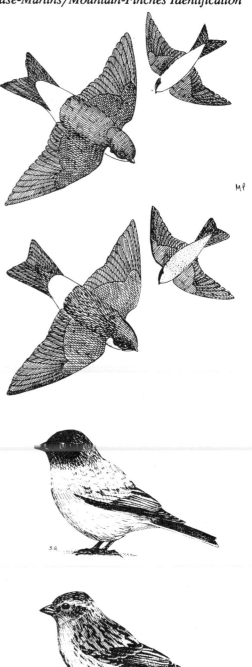

BLACK-HEADED MOUNTAIN-FINCH
Leucosticte brandti
Length 18cm

PLAIN MOUNTAIN-FINCH
Leucosticte nemoricola
Length 15cm

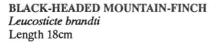

Both species have a slim, sparrow-like appearance
with forked tails. Gregarious. Often occur in large
flocks of 200 or more in winter and smaller parties in
summer. Feed on stony ground. Breed above treeline.
Black-headed is generally found at higher elevations
than Plain; usually above 4200m in summer but in
winter especially in severe weather their altitudinal
ranges overlap. Black-headed is grey-brown scalloped
with sandy above; pale grey below with no streaking;
slightly larger and with overall paler plumage than
Plain. Can be separated by lack of supercilium, dark
brown face, forehead and crown contrasting with
paler underparts. Tail is black with white outer feathers. Has a large whitish patch on wing, pale shoulder
and brownish-pink rump absent in Plain. Plain is
brown streaked darker brown above, pale grey-brown
below with sides of breast streaked. Lacks contrasting
dark head pattern of Black-headed. Has a rufous
tinge to face and an indistinct supercilium. Brown tail
with pale outer feathers. Sometimes shows two obscure buff wing bars. Rump is grey.

WHITE-THROATED NEEDLETAIL
Hirundapus caudacutus
Length 20cm

WHITE-VENTED NEEDLETAIL
Hirundapus cochinchinensis
Length 20cm

Large swifts with long narrow pointed wings and square, short, unforked tails. Flight is very fast. Both species are blackish-brown with pale brown backs, and white under tail-coverts and patch on flanks. The species can be separated by the colour of chin and throat, dirty brownish-white merging with the pale brown underparts in White-vented Needletail, and clear-cut white sharply contrasting with dark brown underparts in White-throated. If the upperparts are seen well, White-throated has some white on the tertials, but this is lacking in White-vented. In Nepal White-vented Needletail occurs mainly in the lowlands whereas White-throated is more frequently seen at higher altitudes. However there is considerable overlap in distribution.

CR

HUME'S SHORT-TOED LARK
Calandrella acutirostris
Length 15cm

GREATER SHORT-TOED LARK
Calandrella brachydactyla dukhunensis
Length 16cm

Both species can be separated from bush-larks by their long tails and lack of rufous in the wing; from Oriental Skylark by smaller size, no crest, paler plumage and shorter stubby bills. Greater Short-toed has tawny upperparts lightly streaked blackish. Underparts are buffish with rufous-buff flanks, unstreaked in adult, streaked on breast in immature. Hume's Short-toed is slightly smaller and paler with less distinct streaking. Has a greyish appearance and lacks fulvous of Greater Short-toed. Brownish-grey above with darker streaks and greyish-buff below. Often shows rufous-pink rump and pinkish-buff tertials, flight feathers and coverts. These latter features would help to distinguish Hume's from a grey race of Greater Short-toed *C. b. longipennis* that may occur in Nepal.

SPECIES ACCOUNTS

KEY TO THE DISTRIBUTION MAPS

The country has been divided up into squares (based on geographical coordinates for ease of reference, each one being half a degree square (i.e. about 56km²). Each square is designated by the coordinates of the left hand bottom corner.

Symbols used

▼   specimen

○   recorded

●   recorded in breeding season

◯   possible breeding

⬤   proved breeding

△   △   breeding season

Possible breeding records
Birds copulating, nest-building, or trapped or collected in breeding condition.

Proved breeding records
Nest with eggs or young, adults feeding young, or carrying food, juveniles of sedentary species.

Range of each species is given for the Indian subcontinent only.

Localities which are mentioned infrequently in the text are given square coordinates. All other localities are shown on Map 1 (see end papers). Langtang refers to Langtang National Park and Kosi to both Kosi Tappu Wildlife Reserve and the Kosi Barrage area.

References are referred to by numbers (see the bibliography), and are included for the first record for each species in Nepal, breeding information and all unusual reports. Only the person who initially recorded the species is included, other names are omitted due to lack of space.

Period of occurrence bars. Shaded areas indicate when species have been recorded. The bar is divided into quarter months.

Altitude bars. Each line or shaded area on the bars indicates an altitude at which the species has been recorded.

First descriptions of a total of 116 species were made from specimens obtained in Nepal. These are given in the text. All records from B. Hodgson refer to specimens. Unfortunately nearly all of these lack locality data.

Status of species is given as abundant, common, fairly common, occasional, uncommon, rare, scarce and vagrant.

Map 6   Number of species recorded per square

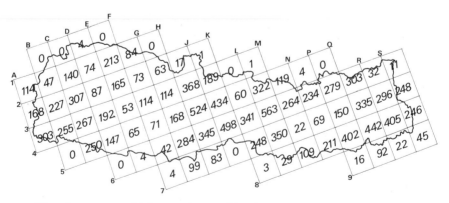

Note that squares with low totals may either be under-recorded or species poor.

LITTLE GREBE   *Tachybaptus ruficollis*
(*Podiceps ruficollis*)

Subspecies *capensis*. First recorded by B. Hodgson (388). A fairly common resident, winter visitor and passage migrant. Occurs mainly between 75m and 1370m. Reported from 3050m at Rara Lake on 1 April 1976 (127). The unusually large number of 60 was seen on passage in April 1976 at Kosi Barrage (293). Frequents lakes and ponds. **Range** Throughout the subcontinent.

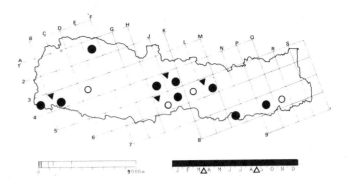

GREAT CRESTED GREBE   *Podiceps cristatus*

Subspecies *cristatus*. First recorded by B. Hodgson (388). A locally frequent winter visitor, possibly breeds. Often seen at Kosi Barrage, Phewa Tal, Begnas Tal and Rara Lake. One was reported on the Kali Gandaki River (H4) at 2660m on 9 March 1987 (594). Favours large areas of deep open water. **Range** Breeds Baluchistan, Ladakh, Gujarat. Winters n. India.

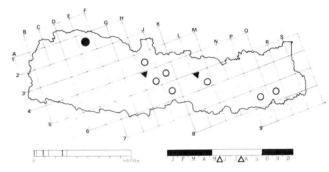

BLACK-NECKED GREBE   *Podiceps nigricollis*
Eared Grebe   (*Podiceps caspicus*)

Subspecies *nigricollis*. First recorded by R.L. Fleming Sr. at Phewa Tal in December 1949 (647). A scarce visitor mainly occurring in winter. Reported from Rara Lake, Phewa Tal and Begnas Tal. The exceptionally high number of about 40 was seen at Begnas Tal on 6 January 1982 (411). One summer record of two first year birds on Rara Lake on 25 June 1979 (626). **Range** Breeds Baluchistan. Winters Baluchistan to Nepal and south to Maharashtra.

GREAT CORMORANT   *Phalacrocorax carbo*
Large Cormorant, Cormorant

Subspecies *sinensis*. First recorded by B. Hodgson (388). A fairly common resident but no definite evidence of breeding. Frequents lakes and large rivers. Often moves up rivers to about 1000m. Three were seen flying over Phortse (P6) at 3960m (244). Congregations of several hundred have been regularly reported from Kosi Barrage and roosting at Chitwan. **Range** Throughout the subcontinent.

GREAT CORMORANT, cont'd ...

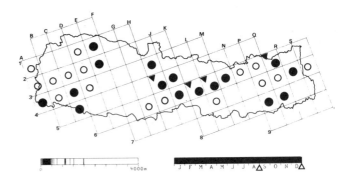

LITTLE CORMORANT   *Phalacrocorax niger*

First recorded by B. Hodgson (388).
Mainly a winter visitor and passage migrant. Common at Kosi but uncommon
elsewhere. Found on lakes, ponds and
forested streams. Usually solitary when
on small ponds and streams but up to 100
have been recorded together at Kosi.
Range Throughout the subcontinent.

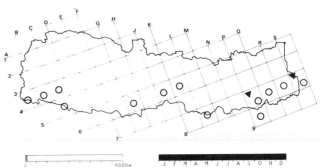

ORIENTAL DARTER   *Anhinga melanogaster*
Darter   *(Anhinga rufa)*

Subspecies *melanogaster*. First recorded
by B. Hodgson (388). Mainly an uncommon resident and non-breeding visitor restricted to below 300m. Common at Chitwan where it is a resident breeder (296)
and occasionally seen at Kosi. One was
seen soaring over the Kathmandu Valley
after a severe dust storm in April (635).
Found on slow-moving rivers, ponds and
lakes. **Range** Throughout the subcontinent.

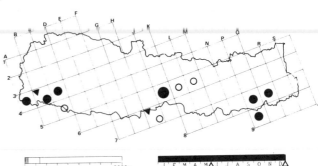

GREAT WHITE PELICAN   *Pelecanus onocrotalus*
Eastern White Pelican, White Pelican

Vagrant. The first record was of a pair
flying over the Kathmandu Valley seen by
J.V. Coapman in 1971 (243). In 1976 described as an uncommon visitor to Kosi
Barrage in the species's non-breeding
season between May and January (293), but only two other
records from there: in March 1988 (418) and a flock of 52
birds on 14 and 15 February 1981 (65,559,622). **Range**
Winters Pakistan and n. India.

SPOT-BILLED PELICAN *Pelecanus philippensis*
Grey Pelican

A local and uncommon non-breeding visitor. First recorded by B. Hodgson who obtained one from the Kathmandu Valley in April (336,388). All other reports are from Kosi. Regularly seen there between early March and May in flocks of up to 12 birds; also recorded in June and July. **Range** Throughout the subcontinent.

GREAT BITTERN *Botaurus stellaris*
Bittern, Eurasian Bittern

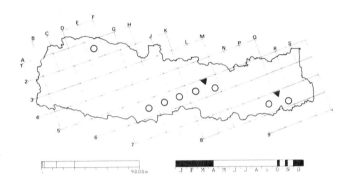

Subspecies *stellaris*. First recorded by B. Hodgson (277). A scarce winter visitor and passage migrant. Mainly found in the tarai. Singles regularly seen at Kosi. Two autumn records from higher altitudes: in the Kathmandu Valley at 1370m (591) and at Rara Lake at 3050m (627). Inhabits dense reedbeds. Skulking and solitary; not often seen in the daytime. **Range** Winters Sind east to Bangladesh; south to Tamil Nadu.

[LITTLE BITTERN *Ixobrychus minutus*

Although mentioned by some authors (51,664) as occurring in Nepal, no records have been traced.]

YELLOW BITTERN *Ixobrychus sinensis*

A local summer visitor, mainly reported from May to October with a few records between mid-February and April. Confusion with Cinnamon Bittern resulted in it being wrongly listed as obtained by B. Hodgson (277). First recorded by R.C. Gregory-Smith on 11 May 1975 at Kosi Barrage. Occasionally seen there during the monsoon with a maximum of 10 birds in June 1975 (293). An uncommon breeding visitor to Chitwan (296). The only other record received is of three at Belatari (G6) on 21 June 1988 (750). Breeds June to September. Frequents reedbeds and marshes of the tarai. Mainly crepuscular and nocturnal. **Range** Throughout the subcontinent south and east from the Indus valley.

CINNAMON BITTERN   *Ixobrychus cinnamomeus*
Chestnut Bittern

First recorded by B. Hodgson although wrongly listed as Yellow Bittern (277,388). Occasional. Mainly a summer visitor to the lowlands. Part of the population is resident at Chitwan and Sukla Phanta. Breeds at Chitwan (296) and has bred in the Kathmandu Valley (639). In the Valley chiefly occurs during the monsoon when it frequents paddy-fields. Elsewhere it is also found in reed beds. **Range** Throughout the subcontinent.

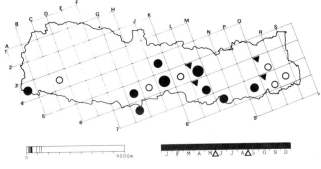

BLACK BITTERN   *Dupetor flavicollis*
(*Ixobrychus flavicollis*)

Subspecies *flavicollis*. Scarce; possibly resident. First recorded at Bilauri (A4) on 5 February 1938 by F.M. Bailey (62). Subsequently it has twice been reported from nearby Sukla Phanta and described as a rare resident there (432,700). The only other reports are of singles at Chitwan on 30 April 1980 (440), and at Kosi Barrage on 19 May 1987 (792) and 29 February 1988 (328). Inhabits forest pools, marshes and reed-edged lakes of the tarai. Breeds June to September. **Range** Sind east to Bangladesh; south to Kerala and Sri Lanka.

MALAY NIGHT HERON   *Gorsachius melanolophus*
Tiger Bittern

Subspecies *melanolophus*. Vagrant. One was flushed near Dharan on 2 and 28 May 1976 by R.C. Gregory-Smith (293). Frequents wet areas in dense forest. Mainly nocturnal and very secretive. **Range** S.w. India, n.e. India and n. Bangladesh.

BLACK-CROWNED NIGHT HERON   *Nycticorax nycticorax*
Night Heron

Subspecies *nycticorax*. First recorded by B. Hodgson (388). Locally common at Kosi, Chitwan and in the Kathmandu Valley. Proved breeding in the latter two areas (296,336,559). Mainly a summer visitor but resident in the Kathmandu Valley and some birds at Chitwan all year. Regularly feeds at Rani Pokhari, a pool by a busy street in Kathmandu. Crepuscular and nocturnal. Occurs on ponds, lakes and reedy pools. **Range** Throughout the subcontinent.

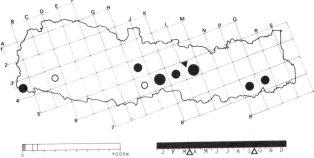

STRIATED HERON *Butorides striatus*
Little Heron, Green-backed Heron, (*Ardeola striatus*)
Little Green Heron

Subspecies *chloriceps*. First recorded by B. Hodgson (388). A fairly common resident and summer visitor. Breeding confirmed at Chitwan (296). Found by lakes and ponds edged with dense foliage and well-wooded streams. Secretive and usually crepuscular or nocturnal. **Range** Throughout the subcontinent.

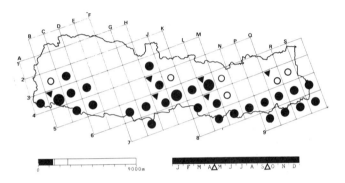

INDIAN POND HERON *Ardeola grayii*

Subspecies *grayii*. First recorded by B. Hodgson (388). A common resident throughout the tarai and up to 1525m in central Nepal. A straggler was seen at the unusually high altitude of 2745m on 22 May 1975 north of Jomosom (302). Reported breeding at Gularia (B4) (432), Chitwan (296) and also in the Kathmandu Valley (629). Inhabits paddy-fields, marshes, streams, ponds and ditches. **Range** Throughout the subcontinent.

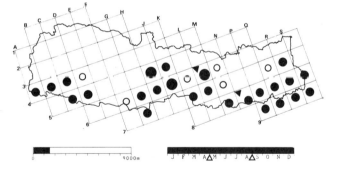

CATTLE EGRET *Bubulcus ibis*

Subspecies *coromandus*. First recorded by B. Hodgson. He found it breeding in the same trees as Black-crowned Night Herons in the Kathmandu Valley (336,388). There is still a colony in Kathmandu. Also proved breeding north-west of Pokhara (499) and outside the national park at Chitwan (296). Common throughout up to 1525m. Mainly resident although most leave the Kathmandu Valley for lower levels in winter. Frequents wet fields, pools and marshes. **Range** Throughout the subcontinent.

LITTLE EGRET *Egretta garzetta*

Subspecies *garzetta*. First recorded by B.
Hodgson (388). A fairly common and
widespread resident up to 1525m. Breed-
ing colonies have been located near
Godavari (629) and at Chitwan (296).
Frequents wet fields, pools and marshes.
Range Throughout the subcontinent.

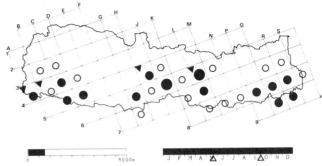

INTERMEDIATE EGRET *Egretta intermedia*
Plumed Egret, Smaller Egret, Yellow-billed Egret

Subspecies *intermedia*. Although no
Hodgson specimens can be traced, the
species was recorded from the Kathmandu Valley in his illustrations (336). A
specimen of Great Egret collected by
Scully in 1876 (708) has been wrongly
attributed to this species (95). Reported
without details by Ripley (659). The first
definite record was a specimen taken by
R.L. Fleming on 24 August 1964 at Chitwan (247). Mainly resident. Occasionally
seen throughout up to 915m. Locally
common at Kosi and also Chitwan where
proved breeding (296). Two reports from
the Kathmandu Valley, both in February
1979 (486,652,418). Frequents wet fields,
pools and marshes. **Range** Throughout
the subcontinent.

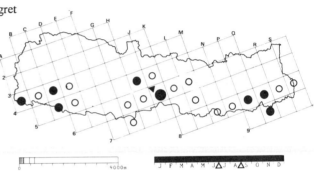

GREAT EGRET *Egretta alba*
Large Egret   (*Casmerodius albus, Ardea alba*)
Great White Egret

Subspecies *modesta*. First recorded by B.
Hodgson (388). A resident, seen occasionally throughout the lowlands up to
300m. A fairly common breeding resident
at Chitwan (296). Common at Kosi. Rare
at higher altitudes. The only recent report
from the Kathmandu Valley is of one seen
in February and March 1981 at Rani
Pokhari. Two were found at the particularly high altitude of 3050m at Rara Lake
on 15 October 1982 (627). Frequents wet
fields, pools and marshes. **Range**
Throughout the subcontinent.

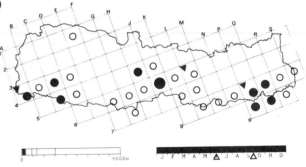

GREY HERON *Ardea cinerea*

Subspecies *cinerea*. First recorded by B.
Hodgson (388). Chiefly a winter visitor,
seen occasionally throughout the tarai
and foothills up to 915m. Common at
Chitwan and Kosi Barrage where some
birds are resident. One was seen at the
unusually high altitude of 3050m at Rara
Lake from 28 February to 2 March 1983
(627). Inhabits large rivers and lakes.
Range Throughout the subcontinent.

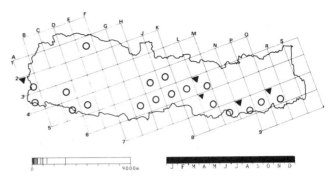

IMPERIAL HERON *Ardea imperialis*
Great White-bellied Heron (*Ardea insignis*)
White-bellied Heron

Recorded only by B. Hodgson who obtained at least two specimens on 5 April
and 10 November from the lower hills,
including one from Hetaura. He described the species as
shy and rare (336, 388). Frequents rivers running through
forest and marshes. **Range** Nepal east to Bangladesh.

PURPLE HERON *Ardea purpurea*

Subspecies *manilensis*. First recorded by
B. Hodgson from the Kathmandu Valley
(336,388). Only one later report from
there (733). Mainly a resident occurring
in the lowlands up to 300m. Common at
Kosi all year. There is also a large influx
there at the start of the monsoon (293).
Fairly common at Chitwan; occasionally
seen at Sukla Phanta and Bardia but only
single records from elsewhere. Inhabits
dense reedbeds, lakes and marshes. Shy
and crepuscular, easily overlooked.
Range Throughout the plains in the subcontinent.

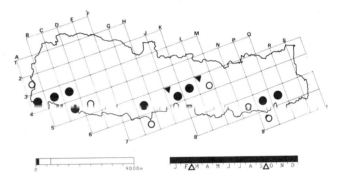

PAINTED STORK *Mycteria leucocephala*
(*Ibis leucocephalus*)

First recorded by B. Hodgson (388).
Mainly a scarce summer visitor; only a few
winter reports. Chiefly occurs at Chitwan
from May to October (296). Occasionally
seen in summer at Kosi Barrage (293).
Single records from elsewhere. The maximum of 57 was found at Gaidhawa Tal on
29 December 1979 (777). One to three
birds found in wetlands in the west in
June 1988: by Dunduwa stream and
Kamdi Ghat, Banke District (D5),
Badhaiya Tal (C5) and near Bhairawa
(G6) (750). Found in large marshes.
Range Throughout the plains of the subcontinent.

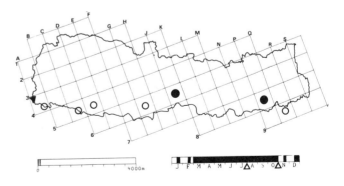

ASIAN OPENBILL STORK *Anastomus oscitans*
Openbill Stork

Obtained by B. Hodgson in his later collection (276) but the specimen may have
originated in India. Reported from the
tarai without details by Ripley (659). First
definitely recorded by R.L. Fleming in
November 1964/65 at Kuriya Mahan,
Chitwan (J6) (247). Resident and passage
migrant. Common at Chitwan, where
proved breeding (296), and in the eastern
tarai. Occasionally reported from elsewhere. Frequents lakes and marshes.
Range Throughout the subcontinent.

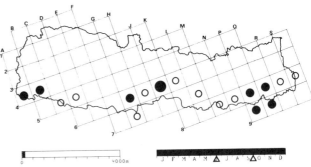

BLACK STORK *Ciconia nigra*

First recorded by B. Hodgson (388).
Occasional. A winter visitor from the tarai up to 1000m and a passage migrant.
Sometimes seen in the hills on migration.
Reported near Dhorpatan (G5) at the
unusually high altitude of 2925m on 22
and 23 May 1981 (499). Found by rivers
and in marshes. **Range** Winters Pakistan
and n. India.

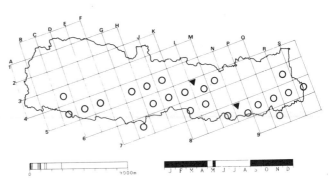

WOOLLY-NECKED STORK *Ciconia episcopus*
White-necked Stork

Subspecies *episcopus*. First recorded by
B. Hodgson (388). A fairly common resident and summer visitor up to 915m.

Occasionally observed up to 1800m especially in summer.
Inhabits flooded fields, marshes and lakes. **Range** Throughout the subcontinent.

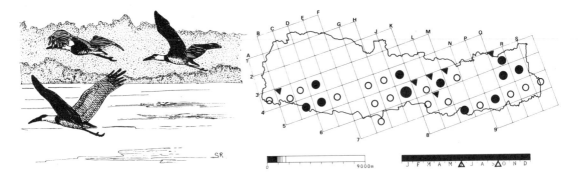

WHITE STORK *Ciconia ciconia*

Subspecies *ciconia*? First recorded by P. Alden near Chitwan in winter (243). Single birds were seen at Jagdishpur Reservoir (G6) on 5 March 1978 (155), east of Pokhara (J5) on 20 February 1986 (55) and at Chitwan on 15 February 1989 (506). The only other record is of 50 seen flying east near Dharan on 6 November 1989 (597). Occurs in wet grassland and ploughed fields. **Range** Winters in Pakistan and n.w. India east to west Bengal.

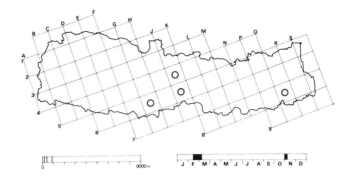

BLACK-NECKED STORK *Ephippiorhynchus asiaticus* (*Xenorhynchus asiaticus*)

Subspecies *asiaticus*. First recorded by B. Hodgson (388). A scarce resident and passage migrant, restricted to the tarai. Regularly reported from Chitwan (J6,K6) and the Kosi marshes. Adults feeding flying young seen at Kosi Barrage in April 1982 (294), and with recently fledged young at Kosi Tappu in February 1988 (481). Over 16 noted at Kosi on 3 April 1986, but only three there the next day (321). Found at Bardia (731). Single records from elsewhere. Frequents large rivers and marshes. **Range** Throughout the subcontinent.

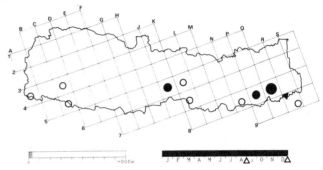

GREATER ADJUTANT STORK *Leptoptilos dubius*
Adjutant Stork

First recorded by B. Hodgson in Kathmandu (336,379). No later reports from the Valley. A scarce visitor. Singles regularly recorded on the Kosi marshes between February and November. Several recent reports of a lone bird at Chitwan (J6,K6) between November and January, and in April. Recorded from the southeastern tarai (P9,Q9) in summer 1976 (293). A pair was noted circling near Chainpur (Q7) on 16 June 1954 at 1500m (109). Inhabits marshes and open fields. **Range** Sind east through n. India and Nepal to Bangladesh.

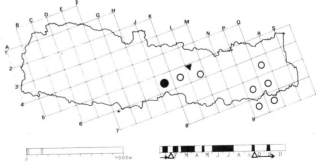

LESSER ADJUTANT STORK *Leptoptilos javanicus*

First recorded by B. Hodgson (379) who found it a scarce visitor to the Kathmandu Valley (336). No further records from there. Occasional. Chiefly a resident in the tarai. Proved breeding at Chitwan (296,734,256) and in the south-east (P8) (481), (Q8) (748), (R8) (518), where it is seen most regularly. Found in flooded fields, marshes and pools. **Range** Kutch south to Tamil Nadu and east to Bangladesh.

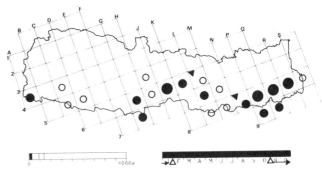

GLOSSY IBIS *Plegadis falcinellus*

Subspecies *falcinellus*? Recorded by B. Hodgson who obtained a specimen from the Kathmandu Valley on 12 September. He described it as a migrant through the Valley remaining in the hills for a few days (336,388). The only other records are of one seen at Kosi Barrage on 14 April 1981 (559) and two at Kosi Tappu on 20 April 1987 (327), and three found at Chitwan on 3 March 1988 (262). Frequents lakes and marshes. **Range** Sind east to Bangladesh; south to the Deccan.

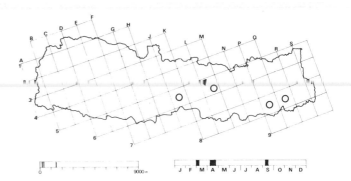

RED-NAPED IBIS *Pseudibis papillosa*
Black Ibis

First recorded by B. Hodgson (388). A resident, found occasionally, chiefly up to 275m. Locally common at Chitwan where proved breeding (296) and in the south-east (293). Fairly common at 760m at Surkhet (D4) in June 1979 (626). Inhabits edges of river banks and open fields. Sometimes found in quite dry areas of cultivation. **Range** Sind east to Bangladesh; south to Karnataka.

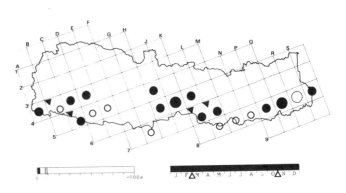

BLACK-HEADED IBIS   *Threskiornis melanocephalus*
Oriental White Ibis   (*T. aethiopica*)

First recorded by B. Hodgson (388). Chiefly a summer visitor, occasionally seen in the south-eastern tarai. Some birds may be resident as there are a number of winter reports. Tends to inhabit wetter areas than the Red-naped Ibis. Found in flooded fields, marshes, rivers and pools. **Range** Throughout the subcontinent.

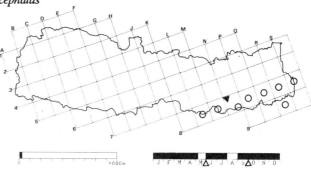

EURASIAN SPOONBILL   *Platalea leucorodia*
Spoonbill, White Spoonbill

Subspecies *leucorodia*. First recorded by B. Hodgson (388). A passage migrant and winter visitor. Occasionally seen on the Kosi marshes where flocks of up to 70 birds are regularly recorded. The exceptionally high number of 288 was found there on 18 December 1979 (206). Single reports from elsewhere. **Range** Throughout the subcontinent.

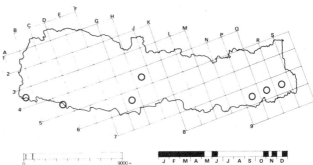

GREATER FLAMINGO   *Phoenicopterus ruber*
Flamingo   (*Phoenicopterus roseus*)

Subspecies *roseus*. Vagrant. Noted by B. Hodgson as a transient visitor to the Kathmandu Valley (341) although no specimen records can be traced. The only other record is of a small group from Kosi Barrage in winter 1973 (243). Frequents lakes and areas of shallow water. **Range** Sind; throughout the rest of the subcontinent.

FULVOUS WHISTLING DUCK   *Dendrocygna bicolor*
Large Whistling Teal, Fulvous Treeduck

A specimen obtained by B. Hodgson was listed for Nepal in the British Museum (Natural History) collection (697), but the bird possibly originated in India. First recorded by F. Lambert *et al.* who saw one with a flock of about 1500 Lesser Whistling Duck at Kosi Barrage on 12 February 1979 (486,651,652). The only other record is also from the Barrage, on 16 March 1987 (327). **Range** Pakistan, n. India south to the Deccan and east to Manipur.

LESSER WHISTLING DUCK   *Dendrocygna javanica*
Lesser Whistling Teal, Lesser Treeduck

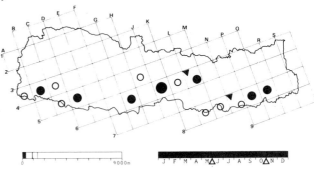

First recorded by B. Hodgson (388) who found it in the Kathmandu Valley (336). Only two later records from there, both of single birds (436,256). Mainly recorded between 75m and 305m. A common winter visitor and passage migrant at Kosi Barrage; some birds remain all year.The largest numbers occur in mid-February.

A maximum of 7000 was estimated on 17 February 1981 (180). A common breeding resident at Chitwan (296). Occasionally seen on passage at Phewa Tal at 915m. Chiefly single records from elsewhere. **Range** Throughout the sub-continent.

TUNDRA SWAN   *Cygnus columbianus*
Bewick's Swan   (*C. bewickii*)

Vagrant. The only record is of one seen on 23 February 1978 on the Narayani River at Chitwan by J. Gooders (283). It occurred during an exceptionally severe winter. **Range** Vagrant to Pakistan and n. India.

WHOOPER SWAN   *Cygnus cygnus*

Subspecies *cygnus*. Vagrant. Only recorded by B. Hodgson who obtained one specimen in January 1829 from the Kathmandu Valley (336,341). **Range** Rare visitor to Pakistan and n.w. India.

BEAN GOOSE   *Anser fabalis*

Subspecies *rossicus*? Vagrant. One was seen with Ruddy Shelduck by the Rapti River, Sauraha (J6) at about 250m. First recorded on 28 November 1985 by K. Halberg (298) and later seen on 3 and 7 December (726) and 12 December 1985 (677). **Range** Vagrant to Assam.

GREYLAG GOOSE *Anser anser*

Subspecies *rubrirostris*. First recorded by B. Hodgson (388). An uncommon passage migrant and winter visitor mainly seen in February and March at Kosi Barrage. Also reported from Rara Lake, Bardia, Kathmandu Valley, and Chitwan. Usually occurs in flocks of less than ten. The particularly high number of about 125 was observed at Kosi Barrage on 8 February 1974 (518). **Range** Winters from Pakistan to Manipur, and south to Orissa.

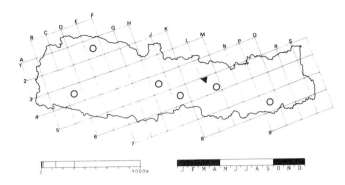

BAR-HEADED GOOSE *Anser indicus*

First recorded by B. Hodgson (388). A fairly common passage migrant. Also winters occasionally at Chitwan and Kosi Barrage. Migrant flocks fly over the main river valleys of the Karnali, Dudh Kosi, Kali Gandaki and Arun, and the Kathmandu Valley chiefly in March, April, October and November. About 1500 flew north over the Karnali at Bardia between 29 March and 14 April 1987 (672) and 963 between 24 March and 5 April 1988 (673). One flock was seen at the exceptionally high altitude of 9375m over Mt. Everest (701). There is a late record of three birds on Begnas Tal from 27 May to 4 June 1979 (668). **Range** Breeds Ladakh. Winters from Pakistan and Kashmir east through n. India to Bangladesh.

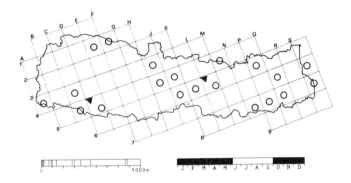

RUDDY SHELDUCK *Tadorna ferruginea*

First recorded by B. Hodgson (388). A common winter visitor throughout the lowlands up to 305m. Breeds in the Himalayas; also a passage migrant. Maximum numbers of up to 4000 have been seen at Kosi Barrage in mid-February. Present at Chitwan from September to May (296). Some birds remain all year in the lowlands at Bardia (192) and Sukla Phanta (700). Ducklings were found in Mustang (J3) in June 1977 (587). A pair with newly hatched young was seen on 27 May 1980 at Gosainkund at 4300m (651,652). Regularly noted on Gokyo Lakes at 4800m (558), and also flying up the Kali Gandaki valley especially in March. **Range** Breeds Ladakh and Nepal. Winters through most of the subcontinent.

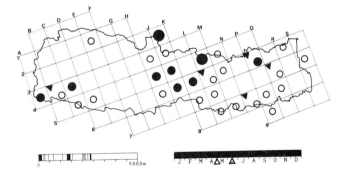

COMMON SHELDUCK *Tadorna tadorna*
Eurasian Shelduck, Northern Shelduck

First recorded by B. Hodgson from the Kathmandu Valley (336,388). A rare winter visitor and spring passage migrant. There a few recent reports from Kosi Barrage in March, April and November.

A maximum of five was seen there on 12 April 1981 (559). Single birds have been recorded at Chitwan (J6) in November and December 1982 (304), December 1986 (306), and January 1989 (707). **Range** Winters in Pakistan and India south to the Deccan and Orissa.

COMB DUCK *Sarkidiornis melanotos*
Nakta

Subspecies *melanotos*. First recorded by R.L. Fleming Sr. near Dhangarhi in December 1952 (647). Local and uncommon. Later reported again from Dhangarhi (247). Other localities in the western tarai are Sukla Phanta where it is resident (700), Bardia (418,750), Baidhaiya Tal (C5) (750), Nepalganj (432) and Gaidhawa Tal (G6) (777). In the east it is a winter visitor in small flocks to Kosi and has also been noted west of Kosi R. (P9) (301). Favours pools in wooded areas. **Range** Sind and Nepal east to Bangladesh, and south to Karnataka.

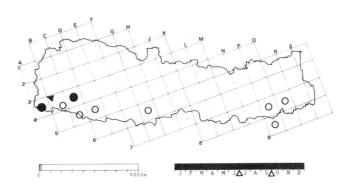

COTTON PYGMY GOOSE *Nettapus coromandelianus*
Cotton Teal

Subspecies *coromandelianus*. First recorded by B. Hodgson (388). Mainly a resident and summer visitor seen occasionally in the lowlands. A fairly common resident at Sukla Phanta (700). Chiefly occurs from April to August at Kosi and possibly breeds there (174,293). Has bred at Begnas Tal (674). Only an uncommon

winter visitor to Chitwan, remaining from November to May (296). Rarely visits the Kathmandu Valley. Mainly single records from elsewhere. Reports from the exceptionally high altitudes of 3050m in May 1977 near Pisang (J4) and 2135m in November 1977 near Dunai (F3) (243,302) listed in the first edition of this book (435) are now considered doubtful. Found on vegetation-covered pools. **Range** Throughout most of the subcontinent.

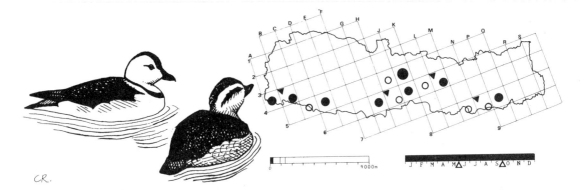

CR.

MANDARIN DUCK *Aix galericulata*

Vagrant. A male was photographed by S. Gardiner on the lower Arun river 1km below Khatike Ghat bridge (Q7) on 21 January 1990 (256,257). **Range** Vagrant to Assam and Manipur.

EURASIAN WIGEON *Anas penelope*

First recorded by B. Hodgson (388). A winter visitor and passage migrant. Common at Kosi Barrage in winter where largest numbers occur in February and March. The maximum recorded is about 2000 seen in mid-March 1982 (770). An uncommon passage migrant to Chitwan in March and April. A few records from Khumbu in May with a peak of 35 at 4750m on Gokyo Lakes in 1977 (679). Occasionally seen elsewhere. **Range** Winters from Pakistan east to Bangladesh and south to Orissa.

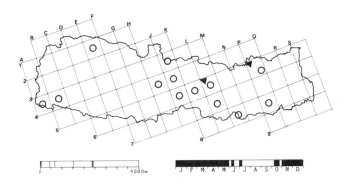

FALCATED DUCK *Anas falcata*
Falcated Teal

First recorded by R.C. Lawrence in 1870 who obtained an immature male from an unknown locality (422). An uncommon, but regular winter visitor between November and April to Kosi Barrage where largest numbers occur in early to mid-February. A maximum of 80 was noted on 7 February 1974 (518). There are a few winter records from Begnas Tal, Sukla Phanta, Phewa Tal, and Chitwan. **Range** Winters in n. India and Nepal.

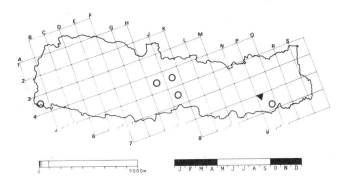

GADWALL *Anas strepera*

Subspecies *strepera*. First recorded by B. Hodgson (388). A common winter visitor and passage migrant to Kosi Barrage. The maximum number reported is 2000 estimated in mid-February 1981 (559) and early March 1989 (172). Regularly recorded at Chitwan and Phewa Tal. Described last century as a spring and autumn migrant to the Kathmandu Valley (708) but few recent records. Passage birds have been seen in the Himalayas: recorded flying north up the upper Kali Gandkaki valley in March (476), on Rara Lake at 3050m in March (137), on Gokyo Lakes at 4750m in April (131) and near Pisang (J4) at 2900m in November (553). **Range** Winters throughout the subcontinent.

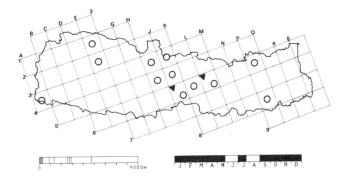

BAIKAL TEAL *Anas formosa*

Vagrant. First recorded by S. Christensen *et al.* who found two resting by the Kali Gandaki river near Larjung (H4) at about 2560m on 16 October 1984 (145). Single adult males were seen at Kosi Barrage on 23 February 1987 (205) and 9 February 1989 (468). **Range** Vagrant to Pakistan and n. India.

COMMON TEAL *Anas crecca*
Green-winged Teal

Subspecies *crecca*. First recorded by B. Hodgson (388). A common winter visitor and passage migrant. Regularly winters up to 915m; possibly also as high as 3050m at Rara Lake. Present at Chitwan from September to April (296). At Kosi Barrage peak numbers of up to 2000 occur in mid-February. Small migrant flocks flew south down the upper Kali Gandaki valley between 26 September and 10 October 1973 (76). Has been recorded in the Himalayas in spring, presumably also on passage: in March from the Kali Gandaki valley (476,559), and in May near Jumla (620) and Gosainkund Lakes at 4300m (440). **Range** Winters throughout the subcontinent.

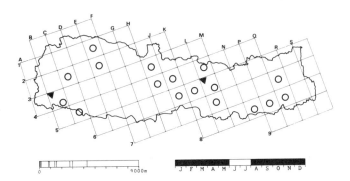

MALLARD *Anas platyrhynchos*

Subspecies *platyrhynchos*. First recorded by B. Hodgson (388). Mainly a winter visitor and passage migrant; also breeds. Fairly common at Rara Lake, Phewa Tal, Begnas Tal, and Kosi Barrage where a maximum of 450 was reported in early February 1987 (647). Uncommon at Chitwan and rare in the Kathmandu Valley. Proved breeding on Titi Lake, upper Kali Gandaki valley (H4) at 2620m in 1970 (527) and 1977 (667). Seen on passage: a few birds flew north up the Kali Gandaki valley in October 1973 (76) and seen at Manang (J4) in November 1984 (142). There is a monsoon record of 11 at Begnas Tal on 5 July 1978 (688). Mainly single reports from elsewhere. **Range** Breeds Kashmir and Nepal. Winters from Pakistan east to Bangladesh and south to Maharashtra.

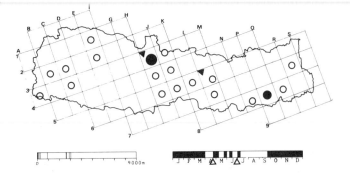

SPOT-BILLED DUCK *Anas poecilorhyncha*
Spotbill

First recorded by B. Hodgson (388).
Occasional. A resident and winter visitor.
Two subspecies occur: *poecilorhyncha* (p)
has been collected in the Kathmandu
Valley (245) and *zonorhyncha* (z) at Kosi
Barrage (671). A maximum of about 200
was seen at Kosi in early March 1986
(197). An irregular winter visitor to Chitwan (296). Several records from Phewa
Tal, but mainly single reports from elsewhere. One seen at Pisang (J4) at 3290m
in November 1984 was presumably a
migrant (142). **Range** Throughout the
subcontinent south to Karnataka.

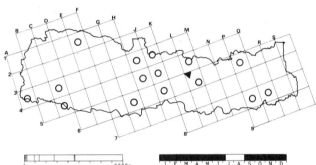

NORTHERN PINTAIL *Anas acuta*
Pintail

Subspecies *acuta*. First recorded by B.
Hodgson (388). Winter visitor and passage migrant. Occurs in far greater numbers than other duck species at Kosi. A
flock of over 5000 has often been seen in
February and March. On 16 February
1981 the exceptionally high number of at
least 50,000 was estimated (559). A fairly
common winter visitor to Phewa Tal.
Occasionally seen elsewhere. A winter
visitor to Chitwan from October to April.
Recorded in October in the Manang valley (J4) (658) and at Jomosom (76). Sev-

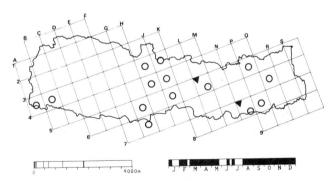

eral May reports from lakes in Khumbu at 4570m and
4650m. There is a monsoon record of one on 5 July 1978 at
Begnas Tal (688). **Range** Winters throughout the subcontinent.

GARGANEY *Anas querquedula*

First recorded by B. Hodgson (388).
Mainly a passage migrant. Common at
Kosi Barrage where a few birds also winter. Greatest numbers occur in mid-February. A peak of 800 was noted on 16
February 1981 (559). Formerly a common
passage migrant in the Kathmandu Valley
(635), but only a few recent reports from
there (589,418,256). Occasionally reported elsewhere between March and
May. Three were found on Gokyo Lakes
at 4570m on 1 May 1984 (764). In autumn
small flocks flew south down the upper
Kali Gandaki valley from late September
to mid-October 1973 (76). Seen at

Manang (J4) in October (658). A few autumn records from
other areas. A pair was seen at Begnas Tal on 5 July 1978
(688). **Range** Winters throughout the subcontinent.

NORTHERN SHOVELER *Anas clypeata*
Shoveler

First recorded by B. Hodgson (388).
Mainly a passage migrant. Occurs in
spring between March and May. Common at Kosi Barrage where a peak of over
1500 was estimated on 5 March 1986
(197). Only occasionally seen elsewhere.
Found as high as 4570m at Gokyo Lakes
in May 1981 (559). Reported in autumn
from Jomosom in October (76) and at
Chitwan and Kathmandu valley in November. There are also a few winter records from Kosi Barrage, Phewa Tal, Begnas Tal and the Kathmandu Valley. A

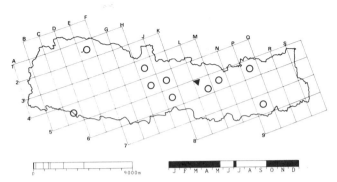

pair was noted on 5 July 1978 at Begnas Tal (688). **Range**
Winters throughout the subcontinent.

PINK-HEADED DUCK *Rhodonessa caryophyllacea*

Only recorded by B. Hodgson who obtained a specimen from the Kathmandu
Valley on 15 September. He described it

as shy and residing in remote large jheels (336,388). **Range**
Probably now extinct, formerly found in n.e. India and
Nepal.

RED-CRESTED POCHARD *Netta rufina*

First recorded by B. Hodgson (388).
Occasional. A winter visitor and passage
migrant. At Kosi most birds are seen in
March and April. A peak of about 80 was
noted there in early March 1906 (197).
Noted throughout the winter at Rara
Lake and mainly in spring at Phewa Tal.
Uncommon at Chitwan and found there
between November and April. Only a few
records from elsewhere. **Range** Winters
mainly in Pakistan and n.w. India.

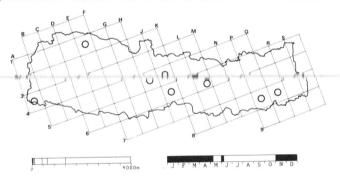

COMMON POCHARD *Aythya ferina*

A Hodgson specimen was listed for Nepal
by Salvadori (697), but it may have come
from India. First definitely recorded by D.
Proud at Bhaktapur, Kathmandu Valley
on 8 January 1948 at about 1320m (629).
A winter visitor and passage migrant.
Fairly common at Kosi. Occasionally seen
at Begnas Tal and also Phewa Tal where
the maximum of 500 was noted on 5
March 1986 (55). Uncommon at Chitwan
and reported there between November
and April (296). There are a few spring
and autumn records from the Himalayas,
presumably of passage birds. Seen in
spring in Khumbu at 3965m and 4570m

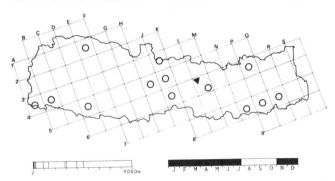

(243,250). Two reports from Rara Lake in October (691)
and one from Pisang (J4) at 2900m in November (553).
Range Winters mainly in Pakistan and n.w. India.

BAER'S POCHARD *Aythya baeri*

First recorded by R.F. Grimmett *et al.* who saw two males and one female at Kosi Barrage on 12 February 1979 (486,651,652). A scarce passage migrant. Regularly reported from Kosi Barrage in small numbers between February and early March. A maximum of 20 was counted there on 20 February 1979 (486,651,652). The only other record is of two at Phewa Tal on 29 October 1984 (145). **Range** Winters mainly in n.e. India and Bangladesh.

FERRUGINOUS DUCK *Aythya nyroca*
White-eyed Pochard

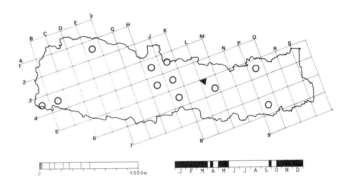

First recorded by B. Hodgson (388). Occasional. Mainly a passage migrant; also a winter visitor. Greatest numbers occur in February and March; a maximum of 150 was reported at Kosi on 13 February 1981 (622). Several records from Phewa Tal and Begnas Tal. There are a number of reports of migrants from the Himalayas: on Rara Lake in February (137), lower Gokyo Lake at 4575m in May (243), in the upper Kali Gandaki valley at 2560m (76,553) and Marsyangdi valley at Bagerchap (J4) at 2160m (553) in October and November, and a few records from the Kathmandu Valley. **Range** Breeds in Kashmir and Ladakh. Winters mainly in Pakistan and n.w. India.

TUFTED DUCK *Aythya fuligula*
Tufted Pochard

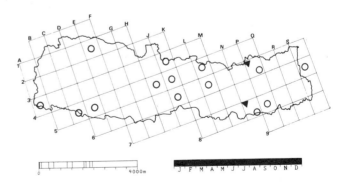

First recorded by B. Hodgson (388). Mainly a winter visitor and passage migrant although some birds occur throughout the year. Reported more frequently than other ducks on high altitude lakes. Resident in small numbers at Kosi Barrage where a maximum of 100 was estimated in mid-February 1979 and 1981 (622,652). Occasionally found elsewhere in winter and spring, especially on Phewa Tal and Begnas Tal. Several May records from lakes in Khumbu between 4650m and 4900m. Fewer records in autumn including four birds on a small lake on Ama Dablam (P6) at 4115m in November (314). Summer reports from Gosainkund lakes at 4300m in June (543) and Rani Pokhari (L6) in July (639). **Range** Winters mainly from Pakistan east to Manipur.

GREATER SCAUP *Aythya marila*
Scaup

Vagrant. Although Gray and Gray (277) listed this species for Nepal, Hodgson apparently considered the bird in question to be a Ferruginous Duck (388). The specimen collected on 21 October in the Kathmandu Valley has not been traced. A drawing of the bird (336) cannot be positively identified but is almost certainly not a Greater Scaup. First definitely recorded by T. Andrews on 8 February 1985 at Phewa Tal (59). The only other record is of a pair on 9 February 1989 at Kosi Barrage (468). **Range** Winter straggler from Pakistan east to Bangladesh.

LONG-TAILED DUCK *Clangula hyemalis*
Oldsquaw

Vagrant. An immature male was recorded by T.P. and C. Inskipp from 13 to 15 March 1980 at Kosi Barrage (440). The only other record was also at the Barrage: a pair noted in February and March 1982 (682,770,804). **Range** Winter straggler to Pakistan and n. India.

COMMON GOLDENEYE *Bucephala clangula*
Goldeneye

Subspecies *clangula*. First recorded at Phewa Tal on 4 January 1971 by T.P. Inskipp *et al.* (111). An uncommon winter visitor and passage migrant. At least six wintered at Begnas Tal from January to February 1977 (243). There are several winter records from Rara Lake, Phewa Tal, Begnas Tal, Chitwan and Kosi Barrage. The only other report is from Khumbu at about 3050m (178). **Range** Winters n. India and Nepal.

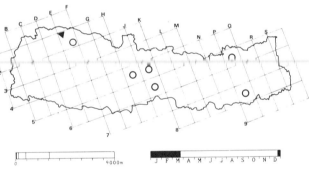

SMEW *Mergus albellus*

Vagrant. First recorded by F.M. Bailey who collected a specimen at Bilauri (A4) at about 160m on 22 January 1937 (62,108). Single birds were seen later on 15 and 16 January 1981 at Kosi Barrage (300) and at Chitwan on 1 February 1983 (296,687). **Range** Winters from Pakistan east to Assam; south to Gujarat and Orissa.

RED-BREASTED MERGANSER *Mergus serrator*

Vagrant. First recorded by V. Eve and G. Hibberd who found a first winter male on 24 and 25 February 1987 at Kosi Barrage (205). The only other record was also from the Barrage: two females or immatures on 9 February 1989 (468). **Range** Vagrant to Pakistan and West Bengal.

GOOSANDER *Mergus merganser*
Common Merganser

Subspecies *comatus*. First recorded by B. Hodgson (388). A fairly common winter visitor throughout up to 3000m. Occurs on lakes and both fast-flowing and slow-moving rivers. **Range** Breeds in Ladakh. Winters in Pakistan and n. India.

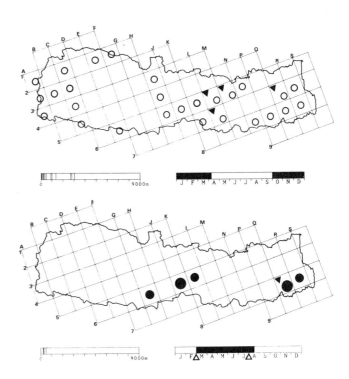

BLACK BAZA *Aviceda leuphotes*
Black-crested Baza

Subspecies *syama*. First recorded by B. Hodgson (350). A scarce and local summer visitor. Breeds at Chitwan where it usually occurs from March to June (296). Three birds seen at the late date of 13 November 1989 (597). A pair displaying near a nest in the Dharan area on 1 May 1986 (321). Several reports from both localities, also north of Sunischare. The only other record is of a pair near Butwal on 23 July 1978 (155). Frequents lightly wooded low foothills and forest edges. **Range** Breeds in the Himalayas from Nepal east to Arunachal Pradesh, and in Kerala. Birds recorded elsewhere in India presumably migrants.

ORIENTAL HONEY-BUZZARD *Pernis ptilorhyncus*
Crested Honey Buzzard, Honey Kite (*P. apivorus*)

Subspecies *ruficollis*. First recorded by B. Hodgson (385). A fairly common resident and passage migrant. Regularly reported throughout the year up to 1700m. Noted up to 3050m in spring and autumn, presumably on migration. In the upper Kali Gandaki valley 13 birds, presumably migrants, flew south between 13 September and 2 October 1973 (76) and in mid-May 1981 three flew north up the Arun valley (Q6) (483). Frequents well-wooded areas, usually of broadleaved trees. **Range** Throughout the subcontinent.

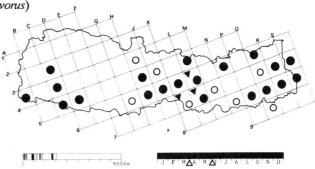

BLACK-SHOULDERED KITE *Elanus caeruleus*
Black-winged Kite

Subspecies *caeruleus*. First recorded by B. Hodgson (376). A fairly common resident, mainly occurring in the tarai. Regularly reported from the Kathmandu Valley at about 1370m, especially in summer, and rarely up to 1550m. Found in areas of cultivation, grassland and open scrub country. **Range** Throughout the subcontinent.

BLACK KITE *Milvus migrans*
Dark Kite, Pariah Kite, Black-eared Kite

First recorded by B. Hodgson (385). A common resident and passage migrant. Two subspecies occur. *M. m. govinda* (g) is found down to 75m in winter and up to 2300m in summer. *M. m. lineatus* (l) winters from 75m to 2135m and summers up to 4900m. Proved breeding in the Kathmandu Valley (243,321). Autumn migrants observed flying south down the upper Kali Gandaki valley: 254 between 14 September and 1 October 1973 (76) and 32 between 24 September and 5 October 1978 (761). A total of 97 migrated west at Khare (H5) between 20 October and 6 November 1985 (683). In the upper Arun valley 22 flew north in May 1981

(483). In Khumbu four were seen in September and October 1970 (526) and a flock of nine flew south between Dingboche and Tengboche (P6) at 4400m on 15 March 1986 (546). Occurs most frequently in towns and villages. **Range** Throughout the subcontinent.

RED KITE *Milvus milvus*

Vagrant. One was observed 2km south of Jomosom at about 2690m on 3 March

1987 by M. Rogers after a week of exceptionally severe weather (685). **Range** Vagrant to n. India.

BRAHMINY KITE *Haliastur indus*

Subspecies *indus*. First recorded by B. Hodgson (365). Mainly an uncommon resident subject to some local seasonal movements governed by water conditions. Occurs most frequently in the eastern lowlands especially on Kosi marshes. Usually found in the lowlands up to about 360m; sometimes at higher altitudes including the Kathmandu Valley and Pokhara, especially in summer. Frequents the vicinity of water. **Range** Throughout most of the subcontinent.

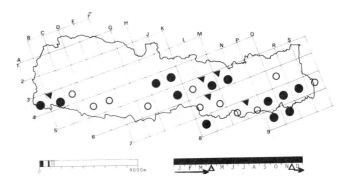

PALLAS'S FISH EAGLE *Haliaeetus leucoryphus*
Ring-tailed Fishing Eagle

First recorded by B. Hodgson (361).
Mainly a winter visitor and passage migrant between September and mid-May;
possibly breeds. Resident at Sukla Phanta
(700). Reported annually at Kosi in recent years where a maximum of four birds
was seen on 4 March 1988 (465). A rare
winter visitor to Chitwan. No records this
century from the Kathmandu Valley.
Noted on passage in the upper Kali Gandaki valley: seven flew south between 4
September and 1 October 1973 (76).
Single birds seen on 17 April 1981 at Hans
Pokhari (S8) (559) and on 4 April 1986
over the upper Mai valley (R8) (321) were

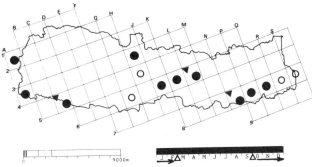

probably also migrants. Frequents large rivers and lakes.
Range Pakistan and Kashmir east through n. India to Bangladesh.

WHITE-TAILED EAGLE *Haliaeetus albicilla*
White-tailed Sea Eagle

First recorded by T.P.Inskipp on 21 December 1970 at Begnas Tal (444). A winter visitor. Recorded annually at Kosi
Barrage from 1979 to 1990 with a maximum of four seen in February 1989 (468).
Rare at Phewa Tal, Begnas Tal, Chitwan
and Kathmandu Valley. Mainly single
records from elsewhere. In 1979 seven
birds were seen at four localities
(486,652). Normally frequents the coast
but in Nepal seen by large rivers and
lakes. **Range** Winters in Pakistan, n.w.
India and Nepal.

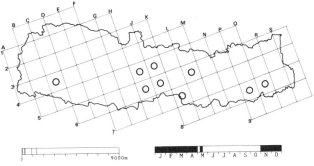

LESSER FISHING EAGLE *Ichthyophaga humilis*
Himalayan Grey-headed Fishing Eagle (*Ichthyophaga nana*)

Subspecies *plumbea*. First recorded by B.
Hodgson (372). A scarce and local resident which has apparently declined during the last 40 years. A rare breeder at
Chitwan (296). Its scarcity and that of
other fish-eating raptors in the park has
been attributed to overfishing (759). Only
a few recent records from elsewhere:
Sukla Phanta, Bardia, Phewa Tal, Begnas
Tal, near Barlabas (G6) and the eastern
tarai (R8). Frequents forested rivers and
lakes chiefly in the tarai, although it has
been recorded at 3500m and 4250m in
Khumbu in May 1954 (109). **Range** Himalayas from Kashmir east to Arunachal
Pradesh; n.e. India and Bangladesh.

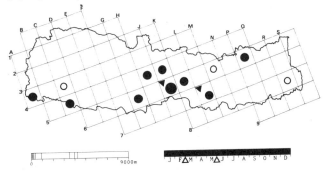

GREY-HEADED FISHING EAGLE   *Ichthyophaga ichthyaetus*

Subspecies *ichthyaetus*. First recorded by B. Hodgson (372). A scarce and local resident in the lowlands. Breeds at Chitwan (296) where it is seen more often than Lesser Fishing Eagle. Mainly single reports from elsewhere: Sukla Phanta (432), Ghodaghodi Tal (B4) (792,750), Phewa Tal (551,154), Begnas Tal (687) and Kosi Barrage (408). Found near slow-moving rivers and streams or lakes in wooded country. **Range** India from Delhi and the Himalayan tarai east to Bangladesh and south to Kerala.

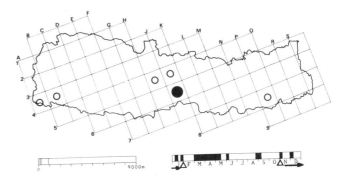

EGYPTIAN VULTURE   *Neophron percnopterus*
Scavenger Vulture

Subspecies *ginginianus*. First recorded by B. Hodgson (388). A fairly common resident up to 915m, also a passage migrant. Some birds migrate altitudinally. Frequently noted up to 2000m in spring and summer and up to 3050m at Khaptad (C3) (657,428). The maximum altitude reported is 3810m at Muktinath in May 1984 (158). Only a winter visitor to Chitwan, occurring from October to May (296). A total of 74 migrated west at Khare (H5) between 20 October and 6 November 1985 (683). Proved breeding in the Kali Gandaki valley (H6) (563). A

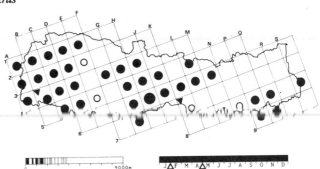

scavenger frequenting the neighbourhood of towns and villages. **Range** Pakistan east to West Bengal and south to s. India.

LAMMERGEIER   *Gypaetus barbatus*
Bearded Vulture

Subspecies *aureus*. First recorded by B. Hodgson (343). A common resident throughout the Himalayas. Usually occurs between 1200m and 4100m but occasionally seen much higher. Observed soaring from 7200m to 7500m in Khumbu by the Sagarmatha expeditions (51). Noted as low as 305m at Mugling (K6) (244). Proved breeding in Khumbu in February and April (109) and above Jharkot (H4) in November (306). Scavenges around villages. Frequently seen gliding majestically across cliff faces and valleys. **Range** Mountains of Pakistan and the Himalayas east to Arunachal Pradesh.

LAMMERGEIER, cont'd ...

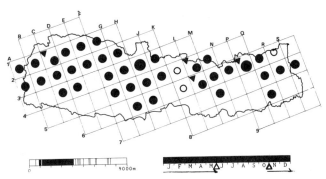

ORIENTAL WHITE-BACKED VULTURE *Gyps bengalensis*

First recorded by B. Hodgson (388). Resident. The commonest vulture up to about 1000m, and in the Kathmandu Valley at 1370m; less frequent up to 1800m. Reported as high as 2440m and 3100m in the far east (S7) in March (735), and up to 3050m at Khaptad (C3) in April and May (428). Birds in the hills including some from the Valley, descend in winter. Found breeding in the Kathmandu Valley (336,629,708) and at Chitwan (296,480,734). Frequents the outskirts of towns and villages. **Range** Throughout the subcontinent.

LONG-BILLED VULTURE *Gyps indicus*

Subspecies *tenuirostris*. First recorded by B. Hodgson (388). A fairly common resident and partial altitudinal migrant up to 1525m. Proved breeding at Bardia (202) and Chitwan (296). Probably overlooked as it is similar in appearance and habits to Oriental White-backed Vulture with which it often associates. **Range** Throughout most of the subcontinent.

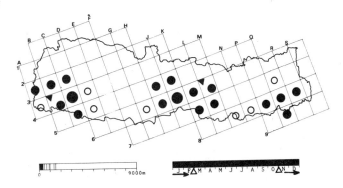

HIMALAYAN GRIFFON VULTURE *Gyps himalayensis*

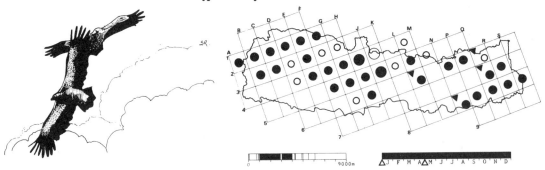

A Hodgson specimen was listed for Nepal by Sharpe (711), but it may have originated in India. First definitely recorded by J. Scully in 1877 who found it in small numbers in the Kathmandu Valley in winter (708). Resident throughout the mountains. Common along the well-used trade routes in the Kali Gandaki and Langtang valleys. Presumably benefits by scavenging on the carcasses of dead pack animals. Fairly common elsewhere. Usually found between 900m and 4000m but may wander as high as 6100m. Occurs in the tarai as a straggler: a specimen was taken at 75m at Raghunathpur (N8) in January 1954 (647). Proved breeding near Marpha (H4) in March (111) and in Marsyangdi valley (J5) in April (484). **Range** Himalayas from N.W.F.P. east to Bhutan and possibly Arunachal Pradesh.

EURASIAN GRIFFON VULTURE *Gyps fulvus*
Indian Griffon Vulture

Subspecies *fulvescens*. First recorded by B. Hodgson (388). Occasional. A resident found mainly between 75m and 915m. Tends to replace the Himalayan Griffon at lower levels although the two species do overlap altitudinally. Common up to 3050m at Khaptad (C3) in April and May (428). Few records from elsewhere above 915m. A specimen was taken at 1980m at Bigu (N6) in November 1960 (246). **Range** Breeds in the mountains of Pakistan, Kashmir and possibly Nepal. Winters south to n.w. India and Nepal.

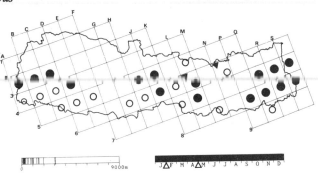

RED-HEADED VULTURE *Sarcogyps calvus*
Indian Black Vulture, King Vulture (*Torgos calvus*)

First recorded by B. Hodgson (388). A fairly common resident throughout; frequent near Pokhara. Normally occurs up to 2000m but has been reported as high as 3050m on the Milke Danda (Q7) in October (302) and at Khaptad (C3) in April and May (428). Some birds descend in winter. Only a winter visitor to Chitwan between September and April (296). Found in open country near habitation. **Range** Throughout the subcontinent.

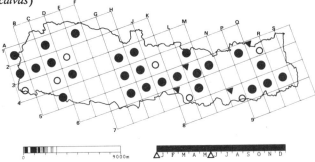

CINEREOUS VULTURE *Aegypius monachus*
Eurasian Black Vulture

First recorded by B. Hodgson (388).
Mainly an uncommon winter visitor most
frequently seen in central Nepal and eastwards. Reported during the breeding
season although no evidence of nesting
has been found. Fairly common at Kosi
(327), and at Pokhara and northwards
along the Kali Gandaki valley. There are
two monsoon records: on 6 August 1973
north-west of Pokhara (H5) (814) and on
25 August 1986 in the Arun valley (590).
Range Breeds in Baluchistan, Assam and
probably w. Himalayas. Winters in n.
India and Nepal.

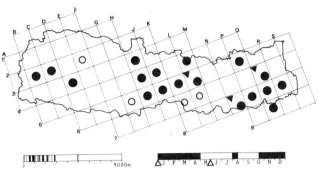

SHORT-TOED SNAKE-EAGLE *Circaetus gallicus*
Short-toed Eagle

First recorded by B. Hodgson (388).
Scarce. Most often seen in the tarai, but
recorded as high as 2130m over Kakani
ridge (L6) in mid-April 1960 (639). Status
uncertain; possibly a passage migrant, but
may also breed. A pair noted displaying
on 16 February 1981 at Biratnagar (S8)
(622). Several records from Kosi marshes
and a few from Chitwan. Single reports
from elsewhere. Found in open country.
Range Throughout the subcontinent.

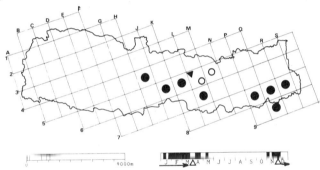

CRESTED SERPENT EAGLE *Spilornis cheela*

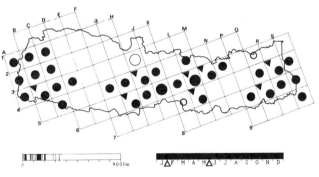

Subspecies *cheela*. First recorded by B.
Hodgson (340). A common resident subject to some altitudinal movements. Usually seen up to about 2100m in summer
although has been recorded up to 3350m
on Machapuchare in October (Q7) (244). Normally winters
below 915m. Some birds remain in the lowlands all year.
Proved breeding at Chitwan (296) and in the Kathmandu
Valley (95). Frequents wooded areas. **Range** Throughout
the subcontinent.

EURASIAN MARSH HARRIER   *Circus aeruginosus*

Subspecies *aeruginosus*. First recorded by
B. Hodgson (388). A fairly common winter visitor and passage migrant. Usually
winters up to 915m. Mainly occurs between October and April but has been
seen as early as 5 September in the Kathmandu Valley (629), and up to the end of
May at Kosi (682). Noted on passage in
the upper Kali Gandaki valley: ten flew
south between 6 September and 3 October 1973 (76). The maximum altitude
recorded is of two single birds at 3050m at
Khaptad (C3) in April 1988 (428), presumably migrants. Prefers marshes, but
also occurs over ricefields and grasslands.
Range Winters throughout the subcontinent.

HEN HARRIER   *Circus cyaneus*

Subspecies *cyaneus*. First recorded by B.
Hodgson (388). A fairly common winter
visitor and passage migrant. The most
common harrier over 1400m. Often seen
up to 3000m in winter and at much higher
altitudes on migration. The maximum
height recorded is of one flying high over
the Thorang La (H4) at 5400m on 4
March 1986 (260). A total of 66 migrated
west at Khare (H5) between 20 October
and 7 November 1985 (683). Frequents
open country, grassland and cultivation.
Range Winters from Pakistan east to Assam and south to Maharashtra.

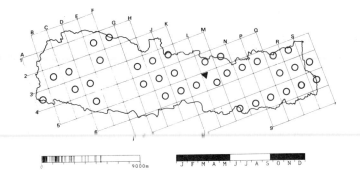

PALLID HARRIER   *Circus macrourus*
Pale Harrier

First recorded by B. Hodgson (388). An
uncommon winter visitor and passage
migrant. Mainly seen up to 2200m but
found at 3350m above Thare Pati (L5) on
19 November 1970 (444). Most birds are
reported between September and April.
An unusually late male was photographed
at Surkhet (D4) on 4 June 1979 (626).
Noted on passage: three flew south down
the upper Kali Gandaki valley in September 1973 (76) and two flew west at Khare
(H5) on 22 October 1985 (683). Several
reports from Pokhara, Begnas Tal, Kathmandu Valley, Chitwan and Kosi Bar-

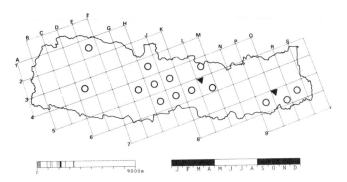

rage. Mainly single records from elsewhere. **Range** Winters
throughout the subcontinent.

MONTAGU'S HARRIER *Circus pygargus*

First recorded by B. Hodgson (388). A scarce winter visitor and passage migrant. There are a few winter reports of lone birds from Chitwan and Kosi Tappu. Single winter records from elsewhere. Noted on migration in the upper Kali Gandaki valley where two flew south on 17 and 19 September 1973 (76) and at Khare (H5) where three flew west between 21 October and 7 November 1985 (683). Migrants also seen in the Kathmandu Valley in April and November (629), and at Chitwan in March, April and November (296,432). Winters in cultivated areas. **Range** Winters throughout the subcontinent.

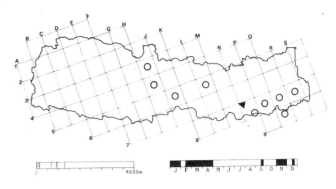

PIED HARRIER *Circus melanoleucus*

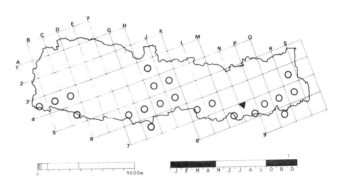

First recorded by B. Hodgson (388). Mainly an uncommon winter visitor, although fairly often reported from Chitwan and Kosi Barrage. A male noted at the unusually high altitude of 3810m at Muktinath on 26 March 1984 (624), was presumably on passage. Frequents fields and open grassy areas. **Range** Winters mainly in the east of the subcontinent.

NORTHERN GOSHAWK *Accipiter gentilis*

Subspecies *schvedowi*. First recorded by B. Hodgson (388). Occasional; presumably resident. Chiefly reported between 1370m and 4880m and most frequently above 2400m. Regularly recorded northwest of Pokhara, Langtang, Kathmandu valley and Khumbu. A rare winter visitor between October and April to Chitwan (296). Usually inhabits oak forest. Sometimes seen above the treeline especially in Khumbu. **Range** Breeds in the w. Himalayas east possibly to Nepal. Winters from Kashmir east to Arunachal Pradesh.

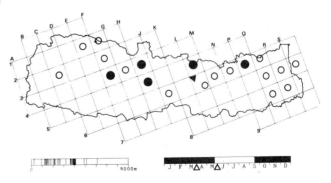

BESRA *Accipiter virgatus*
Besra Sparrowhawk

Subspecies *affinis*. First recorded by B. Hodgson (365). An uncommon resident. Localities include Pokhara, lower Arun valley and Mai valleys. Chiefly summers between 1350m and 2800m. A few reports from higher altitudes, including singles at 3350m at Gapte (L5) in May 1980 (440) and at 3440m at Namche Bazaar (P6) in May 1982 (207). Some birds descend to the foothills in winter, usually to a lower limit of 250m; rarely to the tarai. A pair often breeds at Godavari (243). Usually frequents forested hillsides although also

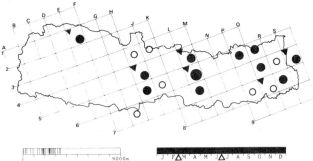

found in more open country in the foothills and lowlands in winter. **Range** Himalayas from Kashmir east to Arunachal Pradesh; n.e. India; Western Ghats.

EURASIAN SPARROWHAWK *Accipiter nisus*
Northern Sparrowhawk

First recorded by B. Hodgson (385). Fairly common. Two subspecies occur, the resident *A. n. melaschistos* (m) and wintering *A. n. nisosimilis* (n). The former mainly summers between 2440m and 3965m. It moves to the foothills and tarai in winter. However the extent of its range there is unclear because of possible confusion with *A. n. nisosimilis* which has been recorded between 250m and 1450m. The species has rarely been reported from the tarai. The maximum height recorded is 5180m on 20 May 1982 at Gokyo (540). Migrants flew south down the upper Kali Gandaki valley: 14 between 6

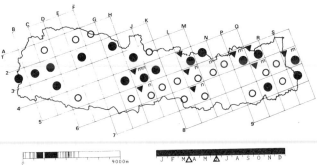

September and 5 October 1973 (76) and 23 between 24 September and 5 October 1978 (761). Inhabits well-wooded areas. **Range** Baluchistan and entire Himalayas.

CRESTED GOSHAWK *Accipiter trivirgatus*

Subspecies *indicus*. First recorded by B. Hodgson (365). Uncommon; presumably resident. Areas include Pokhara, Kathmandu Valley, Chitwan, north of Sunischare and Morang District (Q8). Only one record from the west; at Mahendranagar (A4) (247). Mainly single reports from elsewhere, including two in December 1983 at the particularly high altitudes of 2100m above Ulleri (H5) (177) and 2000m near Ghasa (315). Frequents open broadleaved forests often near streams. **Range** Himalayas from Garwhal east to Sikkim and possibly Bhutan; s.w. and n.e. India; Bangladesh.

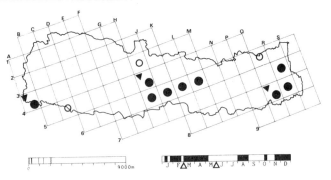

SHIKRA *Accipiter badius*

Subspecies *dussumieri*. First recorded by B. Hodgson (365). A fairly common resident usually found up to 1370m. One was seen at the exceptionally high altitude of 2250m at Khaptad (C3) on 6 May 1988 (428). Proved breeding at Chitwan (296) and in the Kathmandu Valley (792). Occurs in open wooded country in the tarai and hills. **Range** Throughout the subcontinent.

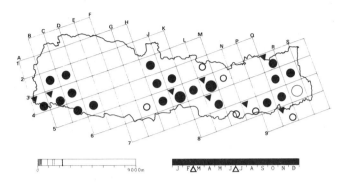

WHITE-EYED BUZZARD *Butastur teesa*

First recorded by B. Hodgson (385). A fairly common, sedentary resident mainly found in the lowlands up to 300m. Several records from 1200m to 1500m in Mechi Zone (R7) (658) and observed up to 1200m in the lower Arun valley (483). Proved breeding at Chitwan (296). Frequents cultivation and open dry deciduous and coniferous forests. **Range** Throughout the subcontinent.

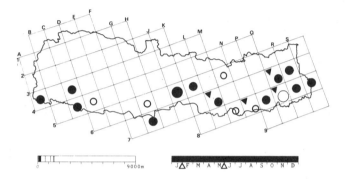

COMMON BUZZARD *Buteo buteo*
Desert Buzzard

First recorded by B. Hodgson (388). A fairly common winter visitor and passage migrant; probably breeds. Two races occur: *B. b. japonicus* (j) (245,482,647) and *B. b. 'refectus'* (r) (647,791), but only specimen records of these are named on the distribution map because the intraspecific variation is very poorly understood. Chiefly recorded above 1000m. A pair was seen nest-building at Gosainkund on 24 April 1984 (624) and summering birds were seen between 3400m and 3800m in the upper Madi Khola valley (J5) from 16 to 19 June and at 3000m above Ghasa on 28 July 1977 (758). Migrants noted flying south in the upper Kali Gandaki valley: 45 between 31 August and 14 October 1973 (76) and 12 between 24 September and 5 October 1978 (761). A total of 32 migrated west at Khare (H5) between 20 October and 7 November 1985 (683). Found in open country. **Range** Breeds in Gilgit and Nepal? Winters in the Himalayan foothills, n.e. India and the peninsula.

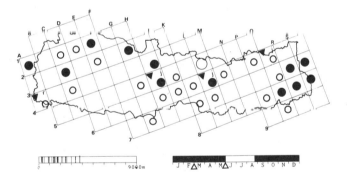

LONG-LEGGED BUZZARD *Buteo rufinus*

Subspecies *rufinus*. First recorded by B. Hodgson (365). Occasional. A winter visitor and passage migrant. Seen regularly north-west of Pokhara (H4,H5) and in the Kathmandu Valley, especially between October and March. Several records from Chitwan and the Arun valley. Recorded in Langtang (L5), presumably on migration, almost daily between 21 October and 2 November with a maximum of five on 29 October 1980 (516). Migrants noted flying south down the upper Kali Gandaki valley: 15 between 5 September and 12 October 1973 (76) and five between 24 September and 5 October 1978 (761). A total of 16 migrated west at Khare (H5) between 20 October and 6 November

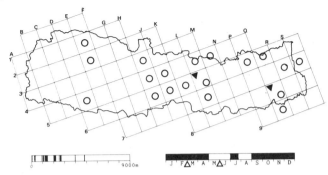

1985 (683). One, presumably a migrant, seen as high as 4800m in the Barun valley on 28 November 1988 (596). Several reports from elsewhere. Inhabits open country. **Range** Breeds in Pakistan, Kashmir and Garwhal. Winters in Pakistan and the Himalayas south to Tamil Nadu.

UPLAND BUZZARD *Buteo hemilasius*

First recorded by B. Hodgson who obtained at least one specimen from the central hills (336,388). Status uncertain. The species is difficult to separate from eastern races of Common Buzzard and Long-legged Buzzard. The only other specimen records are six birds collected by G.B. Gurung from the Kathmandu Valley (243). Localities of sight records include Khaptad (C4), north-west of Pokhara (H4,H5), Langtang, Kathmandu Valley and the Singhalila ridge (S8). One was seen at 250m at Sauraha (J6) in February 1988 (465). A pair of buzzards, probably of this species, was observed attending a nest on 21 June 1977 at 4050m in Manang and one was seen carrying

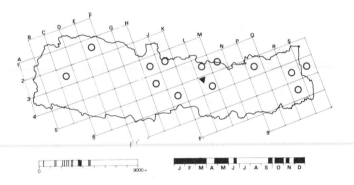

prey to a nest containing at least two young, at 3900m near Braga (J4) on 15 July 1977 (758). Occurs in open country. **Range** Possibly breeds in Nepal; winters in the Himalayas from Kashmir east to Sikkim.

BLACK EAGLE *Ictinaetus malayensis*

Subspecies *perniger*. First recorded by B. Hodgson (361). A fairly common resident from west-central areas eastwards, occasionally seen in the west. Usually found between 1000m and 3100m. The maximum altitude reported is 4000m in the upper Arun valley in May 1981 (483). The only low altitude reports are from Chitwan where it is a rare winter visitor (296), and Kosi Tappu on 16 April 1987 (327). Inhabits broadleaved forested slopes. **Range** Himalayas from Rawalpindi District east to Arunachal Pradesh; n.e. India and Bangladesh; hills of the peninsula.

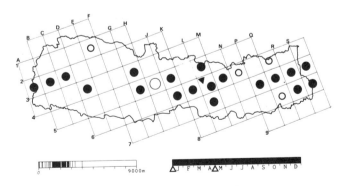

LESSER SPOTTED EAGLE   *Aquila pomarina*

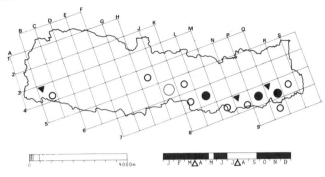

Subspecies *hastata*. A Hodgson specimen was listed from Nepal by Sharpe (711), but may have originated in India. First definitely recorded by R.L. Fleming Sr. who collected a specimen on 26 December 1952 at Dhangarhi at 275m (245). A very uncommon resident. Records of migrating birds are unacceptable as the species is known only as a resident in the subcontinent (51,664). Several reports from Pokhara, Hetaura, Kosi and also Chitwan where observed nest-building (750). Chiefly single records from elsewhere. Usually found in wooded areas in the lowlands. **Range** Mainly n. India, Nepal and Bangladesh.

GREATER SPOTTED EAGLE   *Aquila clanga*
Spotted Eagle

First recorded by B. Hodgson (388). An uncommon winter visitor and passage migrant. No evidence of breeding, *contra* Ali and Ripley (51). Regularly reported north-west of Pokhara (H5), Chitwan, Kathmandu Valley, Kosi Barrage and north of Sunischare. Mainly single reports from elsewhere. Winters in the lowlands. Shows a preference for wooded areas near water. Birds at higher altitudes are probably on passage. Maximum height recorded is 3840m over the Pangsang Pass (L5) on 29 October 1980 (516). **Range** Pakistan, n. India, Nepal and Bangladesh.

STEPPE EAGLE   *Aquila nipalensis*
(*Aquila rapax nipalensis*)

Subspecies *nipalensis*. First recorded by B. Hodgson (340). A common winter visitor and passage migrant. Seen most frequently between 1000m and 2200m. May reach very high altitudes on migration: one was found dead at 7925m on Mt. Everest on 23 May 1960 (728). Large numbers use the Himalayas as an east-west pathway in autumn and have been reported across the breadth of Nepal. Largest counts have been made south of Annapurna (H5) including 992 birds between 26 and 28 October 1984 (145) and 7852 between 20 October and 7 November 1985 (683). Several records of smaller numbers migrating south down Himalayan valleys in autumn including 276 down the Trisuli valley (L5) in two and a half hours on 24 October 1980 (516). Fewer reports of spring migration including 25 flying north in 15 minutes over the Naudanda ridge (H5) on 10 March 1981 (476) and 150 moving north over Namche Bazaar (P6) on 10 March 1982 (77). **Range** Winters Pakistan, n. India, Nepal, and possibly Bangladesh.

STEPPE EAGLE, cont'd ...

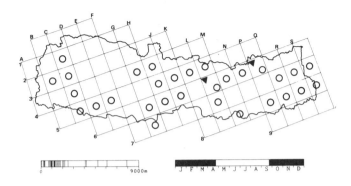

TAWNY EAGLE   *Aquila rapax*

Subspecies *vindhiana*. First recorded by
B. Hodgson (388). Very uncommon,
presumably resident. Localities include
Sukla Phanta, Bardia, Chitwan and Kosi
marshes. Frequents open wooded coun-
try and cultivation in the tarai. **Range**
Pakistan east to Bangladesh; south to
Tamil Nadu.

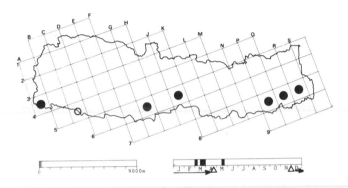

IMPERIAL EAGLE   *Aquila heliaca*

Subspecies *heliaca*. First recorded by B.
Hodgson (388). Uncommon. Chiefly a
passage migrant from March to early May
and late September to November. Reported several times in these months from
the Pokhara and Kali Gandaki valleys,
Chitwan and Kosi Barrage. Nine migrated west at Khare (H5) between 20
October and 4 November 1985 (683).
One recorded at the maximum altitude of
3900m on 10 and 11 May 1981 at Dole
(P6) (559). A few winter records from
Chitwan, Kathmandu Valley and Kosi
Barrage. Mainly single reports from
elsewhere. **Range** Winters from n.w. India and Pakistan east to Bangladesh.

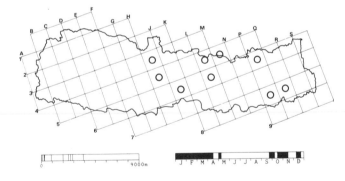

GOLDEN EAGLE *Aquila chrysaetos*

Subspecies *daphanea*. First recorded by B. Hodgson (388). A thinly distributed resident of the high Himalayas mainly occurring above 2745m. Two nests found in upper Langtang (M5) in March (484) and in May (771). The maximum height recorded is 6190m in Khumbu in May 1975 (605). Two seen as low as 75m at Kosi Barrage in February 1990 (256). Inhabits rocky, high mountains, usually well above the treeline. **Range** Baluchistan and the Himalayas east to Arunachal Pradesh.

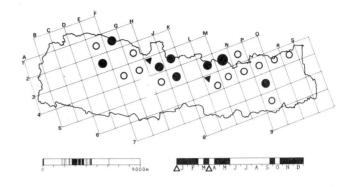

BOOTED EAGLE *Hieraaetus pennatus*
Booted Hawk-Eagle

First recorded by B. Hodgson (388). Mainly an uncommon winter visitor and passage migrant, also a rare resident. Several March records from north-west of Pokhara (H4,H5) could have been migrants. A total of 16 flew south down the upper Kali Gandaki valley between 24 September and 5 October 1978 (761). Six birds soaring over the Trisuli valley (L6) on 24 October 1980 were possibly migrants or a family party (516). A nest was found near Braga, Manang valley (J4) at the unusually high altitude of 3850m on 15 July 1977 (758). Regularly recorded from the Kathmandu Valley and Chitwan. Few reports from elsewhere. Winters in well-wooded country. **Range** Breeds in the Himalayas from N.W.F.P. east to Nepal. Winters throughout the subcontinent.

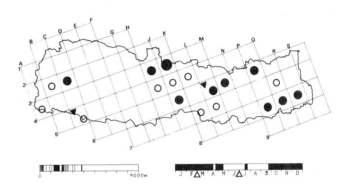

BONELLI'S EAGLE *Hieraaetus fasciatus*
Bonelli's Hawk-Eagle

Subspecies *fasciatus*. First recorded by B. Hodgson (361). A local resident reported occasionally between 1400m and 2600m. Regularly seen north-west of Pokhara on the Jomosom trail north to Kalopani (H4,H5), Nagarjung (L6), and the Trisuli valley (L5). A few records from east of Pokhara (J5); chiefly single reports from elsewhere. Inhabits well-wooded areas. **Range** Throughout the subcontinent, except the extreme north-west.

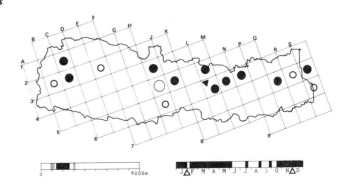

RUFOUS-BELLIED EAGLE *Hieraaetus kienerii*
Rufous-bellied Hawk-Eagle (*Lophotriorchis kienerii*)

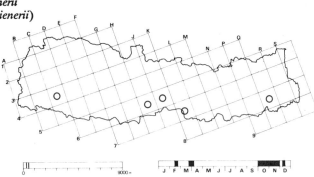

Subspecies *kienerii*. Scarce, presumably resident. First recorded by T.P. Inskipp *et al.* by the Rapti River (K7) on 10 November 1970 (444). Subsequently singles noted at Chitwan in October 1978 (762) and November 1979 (170), Arung Khola (H6) in March 1982 (606), near Dharan in April 1986 (546), Kosi Tappu in October 1987 (328), and two at Bardia in February 1988 (731). Breeding behaviour of the northern population is little known. In Nepal found only in forested areas between 200m and 300m. In the Indian eastern Himalayas seen in moist forests up to about 1500m and could also occur in similar habitat in e. Nepal. **Range** Himalayas from Corbett east to Arunachal Pradesh; n.e. India and Bangladesh; Western Ghats.

CHANGEABLE HAWK-EAGLE *Spizaetus cirrhatus*

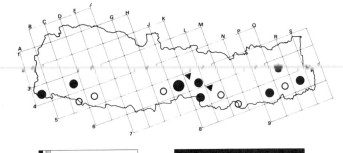

Subspecies *limnaeetus*. First recorded by B. Hodgson (372). A very uncommon resident usually seen up to 360m but occasionally up to 1050m. Regularly reported from Chitwan where it breeds (296). Mainly single records from elsewhere. Inhabits forests. **Range** Himalayas from Garhwal east to Arunachal Pradesh; n.e. India and Bangladesh; Indian peninsula.

MOUNTAIN HAWK-EAGLE *Spizaetus nipalensis*
Hodgson's Hawk-eagle

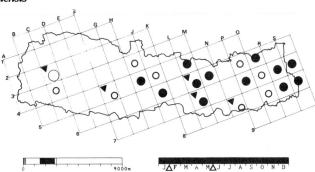

Subspecies *nipalensis*. The species was recorded from Nepal by B. Hodgson (361,797). A locally frequent resident and partial altitudinal migrant. Regularly seen in the hills bordering the Kathmandu Valley, on the Jomosom trail up to Ghorepani, and Trisuli (L5) and Mai valleys (R8). In the breeding season usually found between 1500m and 2835m. Some birds descend as low as the tarai in winter: reported from the far eastern tarai (N8,Q8) (293,647) and as a scarce visitor to Chitwan between October and April (296). Occurs in forests. **Range** Himalayas from Pakistan east to Arunachal Pradesh; s.w. and n.e. India.

OSPREY *Pandion haliaetus*

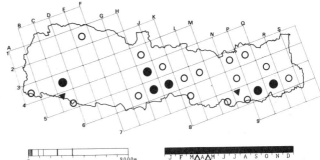

Subspecies *haliaetus*. First recorded by B. Hodgson (385). A fairly common winter visitor and resident up to 915m. Occasionally reported on passage. Migrants flew south down the upper Kali Gandaki valley: singles on 4 and 27 September 1973 (76), in late September/early October 1978 (761), and on 1 April 1984 (421). The maximum altitude recorded is 3965m at Pangboche (P6) in November 1987 (558); presumably also a migrant. Frequents large rivers, lakes and large pools. **Range** Breeds in the Himalayas from Ladakh east to Kumaon and in Assam. Winters throughout the subcontinent.

COLLARED FALCONET *Microhierax caerulescens*
Red-breasted Falconet, Red-thighed Falconet

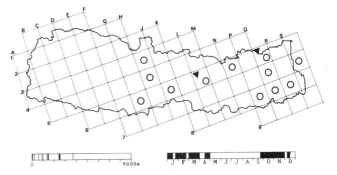

Subspecies *caerulescens*. First recorded by B. Hodgson (385). An uncommon resident in the tarai and foothills up to 915m. Regularly recorded in the Pokhara valley, lower Arun valley, Dharan, north of Su-nischare and Chitwan, where a pair observed mating on 19 February (480). Breeding behaviour is little known. Inhabits forest edges and clearings. **Range** Himalayan foothills from Kumaon east to Arunachal Pradesh; Assam.

LESSER KESTREL *Falco naumanni*

First recorded by B. Hodgson (388). Mainly an uncommon passage migrant in October and November when often seen in flocks. Regularly found roosting near Phewa Tal in autumn with a maximum count of 340 on 31 October 1982 (244), and up to 25 until 26 December 1989 (729). A total of 77 migrated west at Khare (H5) between 20 October and 7 November 1985 (683). Only two spring records: seven flew north over the Kathmandu Valley on 28 April 1981 (483) and one near Santapur (R8) on 22 March 1989 (549). Several winter reports from the Kali Gandaki valley. Seen there at the particularly high altitude of 3700m on 18 February 1982 (770). **Range** Winters in the Himalayas from Gilgit east to Nepal, in n.e. India, and south to Tamil Nadu.

COMMON KESTREL *Falco tinnunculus*
Eurasian Kestrel

First recorded by B. Hodgson (385). Common throughout up to 5200m. Two races occur: *F. t. tinnunculus* (t) is a winter visitor and passage migrant; *F. t. interstinctus* (i) is a resident, winter visitor and passage migrant. Proved breeding in the Kathmandu (755) and upper Kali Gandaki valleys (811,321). Passage birds flew south down the upper Kali Gandaki valley: 11 between 6 September and 6 October 1973 (76) and 39 between 24 September and 5 October 1978 (761). **Range** Breeds in the Himalayas from Ladakh east to Nepal and probably in Manipur; Western Ghats. Winters throughout the subcontinent.

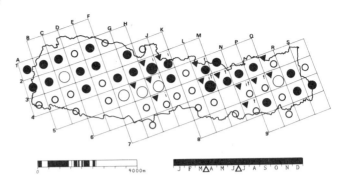

RED-NECKED FALCON *Falco chicquera*
Red-headed Merlin

Subspecies *chicquera*. First recorded by B. Hodgson (385). A scarce resident. Numbers have apparently declined. Described in 1877 as a very common breeding resident in the Kathmandu Valley (708) and not uncommon there in 1947 (95). Only three later records from the Valley. Nowadays only regularly seen at  Kosi Barrage where it is uncommon. Mainly single reports from elsewhere in recent years: Phewa Tal (804), Chitwan (296), Trisuli valley (L6) (516), Buludanda (N6) (207), upper Arun valley (574,588), Biratnagar (180) and eastern tarai (Q8) (293). Inhabits cultivation interspersed with groves. **Range** Throughout the subcontinent.

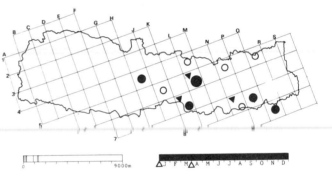

AMUR FALCON *Falco amurensis*
Eastern Red-legged Falcon

First recorded by B. Hodgson (388). Mainly a passage migrant occurring in October and November. Several large flocks reported, sometimes mixed with Lesser Kestrels. The largest count received is 328 birds (all Amurs) from near Godavari (L6) between 8 and 11 November 1985 (201). A total of 138 migrated west at Khare (H5) between 20 October and 4 November 1985 (683). In autumn a flock regularly roosts near Phewa Tal. The maximum number of birds estimated was 220 on 24 and 25 October 1986 (306,590). Only four spring records all of lone birds in April and May in the Trisuli valley (L6) (440), upper Arun valley (483), on Chankeli Lekh (136) and at Sauraha (J6) (730). Two singles in summer in the Dolpo at 4420m in June 1971 (224) and above Jomosom at 3660m in July 1973 (243). A winter record of one at Sauraha in January 1984 (815). **Range** Passage migrant to most of the subcontinent but not Pakistan.

AMUR FALCON. cont'd ...

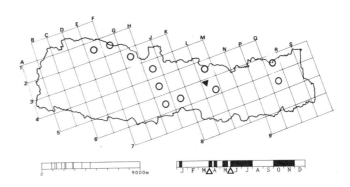

MERLIN *Falco columbarius*

Subspecies *insignis*? First recorded by the Manora River in the Kathmandu Valley on 11 November 1970 by T.P. Inskipp *et al*. (444). Scarce; a winter visitor and possibly also a passage migrant found from the tarai up to 4000m. Other records are from the Namlang valley (F2) (undated) (447); singles at Kagbeni in December 1979 (681), Chandrakot (H5) in March 1981 (610), and Surkya (P6) in April 1981 (159); two at Kosi Barrage in November 1981 (255) and singles at Tashinga (P6) in April 1982 (207), Muktinath in February 1983 (748) and Ghasa in February 1987 (205). Frequents open country. **Range** Winters in Pakistan, n. India and Nepal.

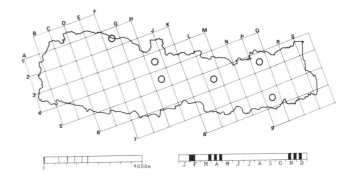

EURASIAN HOBBY *Falco subbuteo*

Subspecies *subbuteo*. First recorded by B. Hodgson (388). Occasional. A resident, passage migrant and winter visitor found up to 3050m. Proved breeding in the Kathmandu (792) and upper Kali Gandaki valleys (76). Present in a communal roost of falcons near Phewa Tal: at least 12 between 10 and 23 November 1977 (495) and over 10 on 24 October 1986 (436). A rare visitor to Chitwan from October to April (296). Inhabits open wooded country and semi-deserts. **Range** Breeds in the Himalayas from N.W.F.P. east to Nepal. Winters throughout most of the subcontinent.

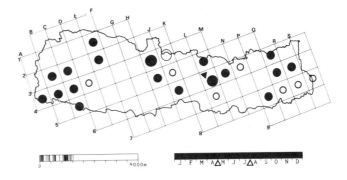

ORIENTAL HOBBY   *Falco severus*

Subspecies *rufipedoides*. First recorded by B. Hodgson (389). Scarce; status uncertain. Formerly bred in the Kathmandu Valley (587,629). A few recent reports of lone birds from the Valley in January (748), April (770) and in summer (417). A rare winter visitor to Chitwan from October to April (296). Single reports from elsewhere. Frequents wooded hills in the breeding season. **Range** Breeds in the Himalayas from Pakistan east to Arunachal Pradesh; n.e. India and Bangladesh. Winters south to Kerala.

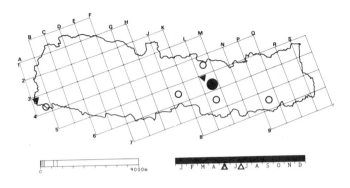

LAGGAR FALCON   *Falco jugger*
(*Falco biarmicus jugger*)

First recorded by B. Hodgson (385). Scarce; possibly resident. A few records from Chitwan and Kathmandu Valley. Scattered, mainly single reports from other areas including Taulihawa (F6) (157), Pokhara (758), lower Arun valley (Q7) (587) and the eastern tarai (N8,P8,Q8). Most frequently seen in areas of cultivation in the tarai. Noted at the unusually high altitude of 1980m over Nagarjung (L6) (301). **Range** Throughout the subcontinent.

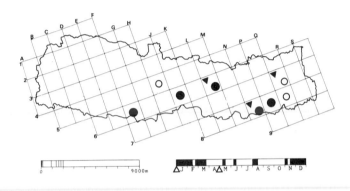

SAKER FALCON   *Falco cherrug*
(*Falco biarmicus cherrug*)

Subspecies *milvipes*. First recorded by B. Hodgson from the Kathmandu Valley (336,385). A scarce winter visitor. Only two later records from the Valley: a bird taken in Kathmandu on 7 December 1957 (482) and one seen on 4 November 1984 (145). Reported in the upper Kali Gandaki valley: at least two seen between Marpha and Muktinath, between 2590m and 3795m, in February and March in 1981, 1983 and 1990, and one at Ghasa at 2040m in February 1986 (403). Singles migrated west at Khare (H5) on 20 and 25 October and 5 November 1985 (683). Found in semi-desert and open dry scrubby areas. **Range** Winters in Pakistan, n.w. India and Nepal.

PEREGRINE FALCON   *Falco peregrinus*
Shaheen Falcon

First recorded by B. Hodgson (385). Two races occur. Shaheen *F. p. peregrinator* (p) is a fairly common resident. A partial altitudinal migrant. Usually occurs between 1500m and 3000m in the breeding season. One recorded as high as 4200m in Khumbu in April 1986 (75). Uncommon in the tarai in winter. Proved breeding on Nagarjung (L6) (4). Frequents mountain areas in the breeding season and nests on steep crags. *F. p. calidus* (c) is a winter visitor. Status uncertain; records received from Kathmandu Valley (708), Kosi Barrage (652) and Kosi Tappu (327). **Range** Throughout the subcontinent.

PEREGRINE FALCON, cont'd ...

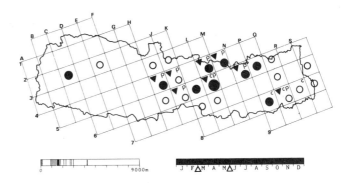

BARBARY FALCON *Falco pelegrinoides*
Red-capped Falcon

Subspecies *babylonicus*. Vagrant. Listed as collected in Nepal by B. Hodgson (388). Several birds were observed at Kagbeni and Tangbe (H4) from 3000 to 3200m in late July 1977 and in September and early October 1978 (758). Singles flew west at Khare (H5) on 26 October and 4 November 1985 (683) and seen at Tengboche (P6) at 3865m in November 1987 (558). **Range** Breeds in s. Pakistan. Winters in Pakistan and n.w. India.

SNOW PARTRIDGE *Lerwa lerwa*

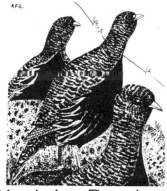

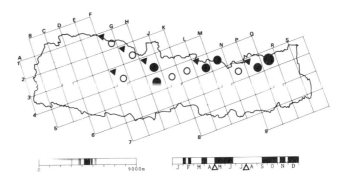

Subspecies *lerwa*. The species was described by B. Hodgson from Nepal (339,797). A fairly common high altitude resident mainly occurring above 4000m in summer. Moves down to about 3050m in winter, although it has been reported at 4880m in December 1954 (109). Breeding confirmed in the Barun valley (Q6) (167). Inhabits alpine meadows and open, rocky hillsides. **Range** Himalayas from N.W.F.P. to Arunachal Pradesh.

TIBETAN SNOWCOCK *Tetraogallus tibetanus*

Subspecies *aquilonifer*. First recorded by R.L. Fleming Sr. above Tukche at 4875m in December 1949 (647). A fairly common resident at high elevations. Usually summers above 4500m. Descends in winter down to 3650m. Fledglings were collected at Gokyo in August (190) and at Nam La (G4) in June (589). Also proved breeding in the Langu valley (F2) (330). Frequents alpine pastures, stony ridges and steep hillsides. **Range** Himalayas from Ladakh east to Arunachal Pradesh.

TIBETAN SNOWCOCK, cont'd ...

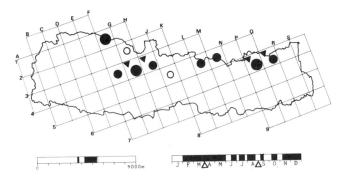

HIMALAYAN SNOWCOCK *Tetraogallus himalayensis*

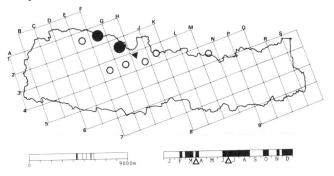

Subspecies *himalayensis*. A Hodgson specimen was described as originating in the snowy regions of Nepal (277) but was later listed as coming from Kumaon (602). First definitely recorded by R.L. Fleming Sr. above Tukche, at 4875m in December 1949. He saw 70 to 80 birds between 4875m and 5180m (647). A resident of uncertain status. Areas include Rara (127), Namlang and Langu valleys (F2) (447,330), Thorang La (H4), and Dolpo (G3). Two found on 15 April 1984 at 4400m near Kyangjin (M5) (624), the eastern limit of the species's range. Proved breeding in the Langu valley (330), and in June in Dolpo (620). Sometimes found in the same areas as Tibetan Snowcock, although usually at slightly higher altitudes (244). **Range** Himalayas from Chitral east to Nepal.

CHUKAR PARTRIDGE *Alectoris chukar*
(*A. graeca*)

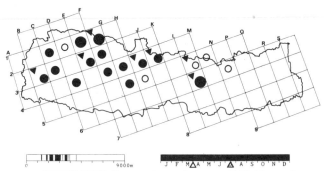

Subspecies *chukar*. First recorded by W.J. Kirkpatrick in 1793 (818). In the last century found breeding in the hills surrounding the Kathmandu Valley (414,708), but only one report from the Valley this century (639). A fairly common resident in the western hills, usually occurring between 2100m and 3960m. Only a few records east of Manang, mainly from Helambu (L5) and upper Langtang (M5). Found as far east as Jiri (N6), the eastern limit of the species's range, in December 1960 (246). Proved breeding in Mugu (E2,F2) (330). Frequents scrub-covered hillsides and grassy slopes. **Range** Baluchistan, Sind, and the Himalayas from Chitral east to Nepal.

BLACK FRANCOLIN *Francolinus francolinus*
Black Partridge

First recorded by B. Hodgson (388). Common in the lowlands and central dun throughout the year. In summer some birds move into the hills and are quite common up to about 2000m. Two subspecies occur: *F. f. asiae* (a) (16,482,647) and *F. f. melanonotus* (m) (95,245). Proved breeding at Fircape (L6) (589). Inhabits cultivation and areas of tall grass and scrub, especially near rivers. **Range** Pakistan and n. India east through the Himalayan foothills to n.e. India and Bangladesh.

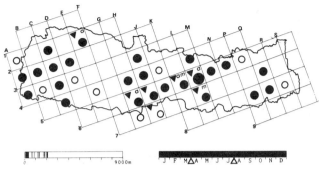

GREY FRANCOLIN *Francolinus pondicerianus*
Grey Partridge

Subspecies *interpositus*. First recorded by B. Hodgson (388). Resident in the lowlands. Status uncertain. Found to be common at Kohalpur (D5) (792). Also reported from Bardia (128,192,432), Kauriala Ghat (C5) (659), Butwal (G6) (647), Sonauli (G7) (230) and as far east as near Mugling (J6) (439). An adult with young was seen near Tilaurakot (G6) in June (157). Found in dry grassy and scrubby areas near cultivation. **Range** Pakistan east to Bangladesh and south through the peninsula.

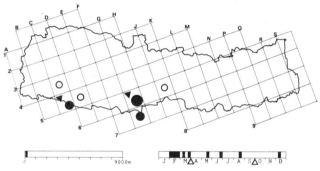

SWAMP FRANCOLIN *Francolinus gularis*
Swamp Partridge

First recorded by B. Hodgson (388). A local resident. Common at Kosi Tappu since 1986; a maximum of 28 birds was counted there in November 1989 (597). Only one earlier report from there, of two birds in February 1984 (408). J. Roberts suggests that changes in the course of the Kosi River during 1986 moved a population of the species into the reserve (674). Up to three birds occasionally seen at Kosi Barrage since 1981. Several reports from the south-west tarai (A4,B4,C4) including recent sightings at Sukla Phanta (238,432) and Bardia (674), and one specimen taken from Tribeni (H7) in 1935 (62). Frequents tall grasses, swamps

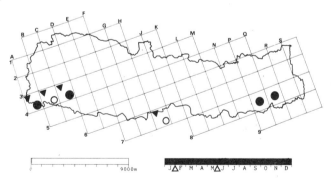

and other wet areas in the lowlands. **Range** Nepal and Uttar Pradesh east across n. India to Bangladesh.

TIBETAN PARTRIDGE *Perdix hodgsoniae*

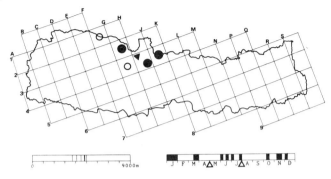

Subspecies *hodgsoniae*. First recorded by O. Polunin on 20 June 1952 at Simengaon, Dolpo (G3) at 4880m (620). A resident of uncertain status. Noted between 3700m and 4100m in winter and up to 5000m in summer. Found in Tibetan plateau country. Several reports from above Muktinath; also from the Namlang valley (F2) (447), Dolpo (G3), Sangda (G4) (301), Khangsar (H4) (512), and north of Jomosom (647). Occurs on rocky slopes with scattered bushes. **Range** Extends marginally from Tibet into Nepal, Sikkim and possibly Arunachal Pradesh.

COMMON QUAIL *Coturnix coturnix*
Grey Quail

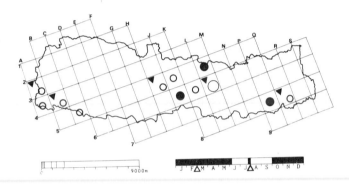

Subspecies *coturnix*. First recorded by B. Hodgson (368). In the Kathmandu Valley it was abundant last century in winter and on passage (708), but only one later report from there (62). Now scarce in winter from the tarai up to 915m, and on passage, but possibly resident and fairly common at Chitwan (296). However only two dated records from there, in April 1982 (432) and January 1987 (702). In May and June 1982 two heard at Syabru (L5) at 2100m (199,294,682). Inhabits standing crops and grasslands. **Range** Resident from Pakistan east through n. India to Bangladesh. Winter visitor throughout the subcontinent.

RAIN QUAIL *Coturnix coromandelica*
Black-breasted Quail

Vagrant. Recorded by B. Hodgson who obtained at least six specimens from the Kathmandu Valley in April, May and August including a female in breeding condition (336,368). Only two other records, both from the Valley: one taken at Bhaktapur on 25 July 1956 (245) and another by New Road, Kathmandu on 11 April 1959 (482). Occurs in cultivation, grass and scrub jungle. **Range** Locally throughout the subcontinent.

BLUE-BREASTED QUAIL *Coturnix chinensis*

Subspecies *chinensis*. Recorded by B. Hodgson who took at least five specimens in April and May including one in breeding condition from the Kathmandu Valley (336,388). Scarce; status uncertain. Possibly resident at Chitwan. Three records from there: singles in November 1979 (813) and April 1980 (440), and two in March 1987 (552). Also recorded from the tarai: at Bilauri (A4), Kosi River (P8) and Haraincha (Q8) in February and March 1936 to 1938 (62). The only recent record is of one from the Kathmandu Valley in June 1963 (247). Inhabits wet grassland, field edges and scrub. **Range** The subcontinent east and south of a line from Bombay to Simla.

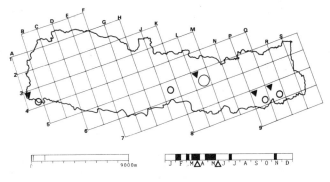

JUNGLE BUSH QUAIL *Perdicula asiatica*

Only collected by B. Hodgson (277) who found it chiefly in the sub-Himalayan valleys, and as a migrant (368). **Range** Throughout most of India.

HILL PARTRIDGE *Arborophila torqueola*
Common Hill Partridge

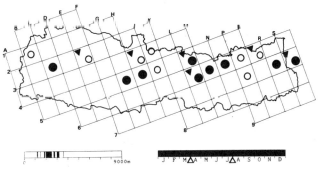

Subspecies *torqueola*. First recorded by B. Hodgson (377). A fairly common resident usually found from 1830m to 3200m. Inhabits ravines and slopes in damp, dense forests of oak and other broadleaved, evergreen trees. Feeds amongst humus on the forest floor. **Range** Himalayas from Chamba east to Arunachal Pradesh and n.e. India.

RUFOUS-THROATED PARTRIDGE *Arborophila rufogularis*
Rufous-throated Hill Partridge

Subspecies *rufogularis*. First recorded by B. Hodgson (388). A scarce resident, formerly reported more frequently. Once occasionally found on Phulchowki's lower slopes, but only three records from there in 1980s: in January and May 1982 (682) and January 1986 (321). The only other recent records are from Pokhara in 1971 (551) and south of Annapurna (H5) in 1977 (762). Chicks seen in May at Godavari, Kathmandu Valley in 1954 (647) and Hetaura in 1947 (95). A record from Ghasa listed in the first edition of this book (435) has been withdrawn. Inhabits dense secondary growth and understorey of broadleaved, evergreen forests. Usually occurs at lower altitudes than Com-

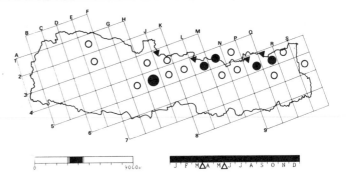

mon Hill Partridge. Favours a zone of 1450m to 1830m. **Range** Himalayas from Kumaon east to Arunachal Pradesh; n.e. India and Bangladesh.

[RED SPURFOWL *Galloperdix spadicea*

Although described as inhabiting the Nepal tarai (63,579,664), no definite evidence of its occurrence has been found. Possibly inhabits the western tarai. Range India.]

[PAINTED SPURFOWL *Galloperdix lunulata*

A specimen is listed as originating in Nepal by Ogilvie-Grant (602). However it seems likely that the skin was mislabelled as the species only occurs south of the Gangetic Plain (664). **Range** India.]

BLOOD PHEASANT *Ithaginis cruentus*

Subspecies *cruentus*. The species was described by T. Hardwicke from a specimen collected in Nepal by E. Gardner. (311,797). Although previously recorded only as far west as Dhaulagiri (G5) (243), there are recent reports west to Rara and Jumla areas (127,464,627). A locally fairly common resident, mainly found between

3200m and 4400m. May withdraw from higher levels in cold weather. Chicks found at 3200m in June 1981 at Pipar (H5) (496,499,505). Inhabits dense bamboo clumps, open forests or scrub of rhododendron and birch or juniper. Usually tame and gregarious; often found in coveys of about ten birds. **Range** Himalayas from Nepal east to Arunachal Pradesh.

SATYR TRAGOPAN *Tragopan satyra*
Crimson Horned Pheasant

First recorded by W.J. Kirkpatrick in 1793 (818). Resident, subject to vertical movements which are not fully understood in Nepal. Mainly reported from 2590m to 3800m in summer and down to 2100m in winter. Reports received suggest it is uncommon, although it is perhaps under-recorded due to its shy and wary nature. Found west to Khaptad (C3) (428,68). Regularly recorded south of Annapurna (H5), at Ghasa, Langtang and Khumbu. Breeding behaviour is little known. A female with young at 2640m on 31 May and a nest and eggs at 3760m in June 1979 were found south of Annapurna (H5) (496,499,505). A female

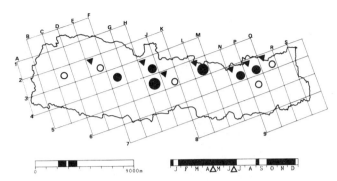

with young was seen on 26 May 1985 above Syabru (L5) (313). Inhabits damp oak and rhododendron forest with dense undergrowth and bamboo patches. Favours steep slopes. **Range** Himalayas from Garhwal east to w. Arunachal Pradesh.

[WESTERN TRAGOPAN *Tragopan melanocephalus*
Western Horned Pheasant

A Hodgson specimen is listed as originating in Nepal by Gray and Gray (277). The subsequent British Museum catalogue (602) included a Hodgson specimen from the 'N.W. Himalayas'. There is also a Hodgson specimen labelled 'Nepal India' in Exeter Museum (133). **Range** W. Himalayas from Swat east to Garwhal and possibly Kumaon.]

KOKLASS PHEASANT *Pucrasia macrolopha*

Subspecies *nipalensis*. First recorded by B. Hodgson (385). A locally fairly common resident, chiefly reported from 2680m to 3200m in summer, and down to 2135m in winter. The maximum altitude recorded is 3500m at Bung Lagna (E3) in May 1985 (160). Few specimens collected (647,708). Birds in the far west may be P. *m. macrolopha*. Found as far east as the Modi Khola (H5) and possibly to the Marsyangdi Khola (H5) (669). Localities include Khaptad (C3), above Ghasa, at Ghorepani and in the upper Dhorpatan valley (G4). Breeding behaviour of this race is poorly known. A female with chicks photographed at Pipar (H5) on 14 May 1985 (800,616). Chicks found on 2 June (244). Frequents forests of conifers, oaks and rhododendron. Favours steep ravines. **Range** Himalayas from Chitral east to Nepal.

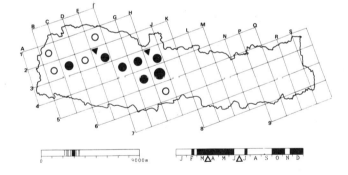

HIMALAYAN MONAL   *Lophophorus impejanus*
Impeyan Pheasant

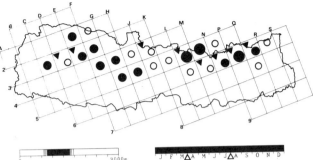

The national bird of Nepal. First recorded by W.J. Kirkpatrick in 1793 (818). A common resident subject to altitudinal movements. Chiefly summers from 3300m to 4570m, and winters down to 2500m. At Khaptad (C3) found at 2500m on 20 April and on several dates in May at 3050m (428). Breeding confirmed at Thare Pati in May (199,294,682), Gapte (321), upper Langtang (M5) (621) and Khumbu (190). Frequents steep grassy slopes above the treeline in summer and rhododendron forests in winter. **Range** Himalayas from N.W.F.P. east to Arunachal Pradesh.

RED JUNGLEFOWL   *Gallus gallus*

Subspecies *murghi*. First recorded by B. Hodgson (388). A locally common resident, usually found up to 915m. Localities include Sukla Phanta, Bardia, Chitwan and Kosi Tappu. Introduced to Gokarna, Kathmandu Valley. Few records from elsewhere. Numbers seem to have declined in recent years. Local farmers claim many have been shot out (155). Breeding reported in 1979 at Begnas Tal where it has been introduced (670), and also at Chitwan (296). Inhabits forest edges and scrub jungle interspersed with patches of grassland or cultivation. **Range** Himalayas from Punjab east to Arunachal Pradesh; n., n.e. and s.w. India and Bangladesh.

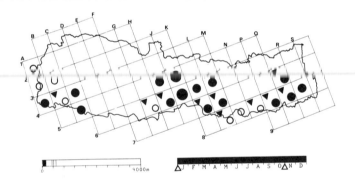

KALIJ PHEASANT   *Lophura leucomelana*

The species was described by J. Latham (493) without precise locality; later given as Nepal by Baker (63). First definitely recorded by W.J. Kirkpatrick in 1793 (818). A fairly common resident from 245m to 3050m. Withdraws from higher levels in cold weather. The maximum altitude recorded is 3700m in Khumbu in May 1986 (75). Three intergrading races occur: *L. l. hamiltonii* (h), the endemic *L. l. leucomelana* (l) and *L. l. melanota* (m). *L. l. hamiltoni* is given in error as occurring at Baglung, west-central Nepal (52). Breeding confirmed at Chitwan (296) and in the Kathmandu Valley (336,632). Frequents forests of all types with dense undergrowth. **Range** Himalayas from N.W.F.P. east to Arunachal Pradesh; n.e. India and Bangladesh.

KALIJ PHEASANT, cont'd ...

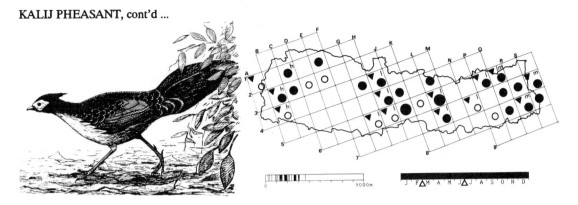

CHEER PHEASANT *Catreus wallichi*
Chir Pheasant

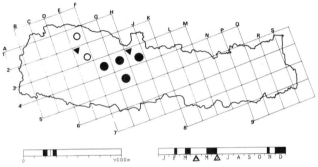

First recorded by B. Hodgson (388). A resident of uncertain status, occurring east to the upper Kali Gandaki valley (669). Reported between 1800m and 3050m, with apparently little altitudinal movement. In the Dhorpatan valley (G5) 50 to 100 birds were estimated in 1981 (500). Regularly seen above Ghasa, but locals claim it is declining there because of hunting pressure (260). Very few records from elsewhere. Inhabits steep, craggy hillsides supporting scrub and stunted trees. In the Dhorpatan valley also found in burnt, felled and cut over areas with secondary growth in pine/juniper/fir/rhododendron forest (500). **Range** Himalayas from Hazara east to Nepal.

BLUE PEAFOWL *Pavo cristatus*
Indian Peafowl, Common Peafowl

Inexplicably not reported by B. Hodgson. First recorded by J. Scully from the central bhabar in 1877 (708). A locally common resident mainly found up to 300m. Localities include Sukla Phanta, Bardia, Chitwan, Kosi Tappu and north of Sunischare. Proved breeding at Chitwan (296), Hetaura (95) and Kosi Tappu (432). Occurs at 1280m in Gokarna, Kathmandu Valley where it has been introduced. Inhabits dense riverine vegetation, tall grassland and open sal forest. **Range** Throughout the subcontinent east of the Indus.

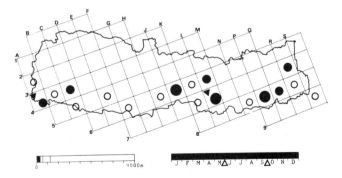

SMALL BUTTONQUAIL   *Turnix sylvatica*
Little Bustard-Quail, Andalusian Hemipode
Striped Buttonquail

Subspecies *dussumier*. First recorded by
B. Hodgson (388). Scarce, presumably
resident. One was taken at Bilauri (A4) at
250m on 15 February 1937 (62). The only

other reports are from tall grasslands at Chitwan where it
has been noted several times since 1982 (296,432,517).
Range Throughout the subcontinent south and east of the
Punjab.

YELLOW-LEGGED BUTTONQUAIL   *Turnix tanki*
Button-Quail

Subspecies *tanki*. First recorded by B.
Hodgson who found it breeding in corn-
fields in the Kathmandu Valley (336,388).
Only one later record from the Valley
(589). Resident. Fairly common at Chitwan (334,432,152), but scarce elsewhere.
Other localities are Bardia (796),
Jayamrui (L5) (636), Hetaura (95,245),
the eastern foothills (Q8) (293,561) and
eastern tarai (Q8) (62). Inhabits grassland, scrub and cultivation. **Range**
Throughout the subcontinent east of
Kohat and Sind.

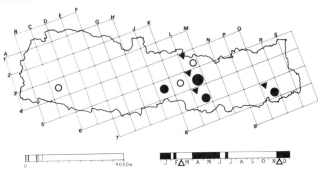

BARRED BUTTONQUAIL   *Turnix suscitator*
Common Bustard-Quail, Northern Bustard-Quail

Subspecies *plumbipes*. First recorded by
B. Hodgson (368). A fairly common resident chiefly occurring up to about 300m.
The maximum height reported is 2050m
on 23 May 1970 at Jamuna (R7) (441).
Occasionally seen at Bardia (C4) (192)
and common at Chitwan (296). Not found
in the Kathmandu Valley this century.
Frequents grassland, also scrub and
weedy patches at the edges of villages and
cultivation. **Range** Throughout much of
the subcontinent.

SLATY-LEGGED CRAKE   *Rallina eurizonoides*
Indian Banded Crake

Subspecies *amauroptera*. Vagrant. First
recorded by B. Hodgson from the tarai
(336,388). Only one other record: three
seen west of Hetaura at 375m on 14 June
1957 (234,245). In India inhabits wooded
and well-watered areas up to 1600m (52).
Range Throughout the subcontinent.

WATER RAIL   *Rallus aquaticus*

Vagrant. First collected by B. Hodgson from the Kathmandu Valley in October (336,721). Two races recorded. *R.
a. indicus* was taken in the tarai at Bilauri (A4) on 27
January 1937, and at Haraincha (Q8) on 16 February 1938
(62). One was found dead at Tribhuvan University, Kathmandu in October 1973 (243). A specimen of *R. a. korejewi*
was obtained at Bilauri on the same date as that of *R. a.
indicus* (62). Inhabits marshes, reedbeds and wet fields.
Range Breeds in Kashmir and possibly Ladakh. Winters in
Pakistan, n. India and Bangladesh.

SLATY-BREASTED RAIL *Rallus striatus*
Blue-breasted Banded Rail

Subspecies *albiventer*. Vagrant; possibly resident. The first record is of one collected on 16 February 1938 in the tarai at Haraincha (Q8) by F.M. Bailey (62,108). The only other reports are of singles at Chitwan on 27 May 1985 (418) and on 6 March 1987 (463). Frequents reedy swamps and wet paddyfields in India (52). **Range** From Gujarat, Madhya Pradesh and Nepal south and east through most of the subcontinent.

BAILLON'S CRAKE *Porzana pusilla*

Subspecies *pusilla*. First recorded by B. Hodgson (388). Mainly a scarce winter visitor and passage migrant; possibly breeds. Several reports from Chitwan between October and April, Kosi Barrage from January to April and the Kathmandu Valley in spring and autumn. Single records from elsewhere. Occurs in reedy lake edges, swamps and wet fields. **Range** Breeds in Kashmir and Uttar Pradesh. Winters throughout the subcontinent.

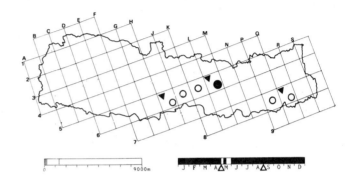

RUDDY-BREASTED CRAKE *Porzana fusca*
Ruddy Crake

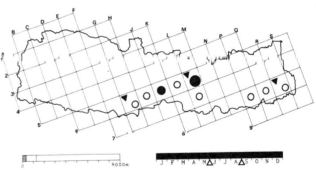

Subspecies *fusca*. First recorded by B. Hodgson (388). A locally distributed resident in the lowlands up to 370m. Fairly common at Chitwan (296). Regularly reported from Kosi Barrage. Other localities include Sukla Phanta, Hetaura, and north of Sunischare. An uncommon visitor to the Kathmandu Valley, breeding in ricefields (591). Frequents reedy lake edges, grassland, marshes and wet fields. **Range** N. Pakistan from Kohat east through Himalayan foothills and n. India to Assam and Bangladesh.

[BLACK-TAILED CRAKE *Porzana bicolor*
Elwes's Crake (*Amauromis bicolor*)

Status uncertain. Specimens collected by B. Hodgson (721) were overlooked due to confusion with Brown Crake, but may have originated in India (443). H. Stevens had three live birds brought to him on 22 May 1912 and was told they were caught on the Nepal/Darjeeling border (S7) between 3660m and 3960m, but he was doubtful of the claim (741,443). Found in dense grass and jungle near streams and ponds in foothills up to 2800m (52,664). **Range** Himalayas from Nepal? east to Arunachal Pradesh; n.e. India.]

BROWN CRAKE *Amauromis akool*

Subspecies *akool*. First recorded by B.
Hodgson in his later collection (276,721),
but the specimen may have originated in
India. First definitely recorded by B.
Biswas from Hetaura on 7 June 1947 (96).
A common breeding resident at Chitwan
(296). A few reports from Kosi and mainly
single records from elsewhere. One was
collected at the unusually high altitude of
3290m at Ongre (J4) on 10 September
1984 (589). Inhabits reedbeds and vegetation along watercourses. **Range** India
from Kashmir east to Bangladesh; south
in the peninsula to Karnataka in the west
and Raipur in the east.

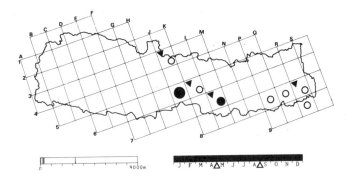

WHITE-BREASTED WATERHEN *Amauromis phoenicurus*

Subspecies *phoenicurus*. First recorded
by B. Hodgson (388). A fairly common
resident from the tarai up to 915m.
Proved breeding at Bagarkot (A3) (657)
and Chitwan (296). A few records from
the Kathmandu Valley. Occurs in marsh
and scrub vegetation at the edges of
ponds, lakes and ditches. **Range**
Throughout the subcontinent.

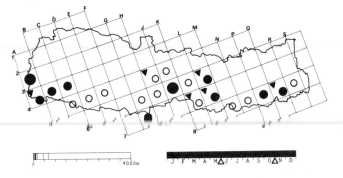

COMMON MOORHEN *Gallinula chloropus*
Indian Gallinule

Subspecies *chloropus*. First recorded by
B. Hodgson (388). A locally common resident and winter visitor, chiefly found in
the tarai. Localities include Sukla Phanta,
Kosi marshes, and also Chitwan where it
occurs from October to May (296). Noted
as high as 4575m (243), presumably on
passage. Other records, probably of migrants, at Jomosom (76), Ongre (J4)
(589) and Taudha lake (L6) (639,589) in
September and October. Inhabits
marshes and reed-edged pools with emer-
gent vegetation. **Range** Throughout the
subcontinent.

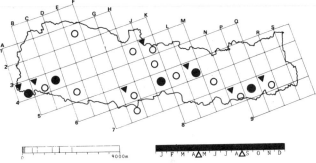

PURPLE SWAMPHEN *Porphyrio porphyrio*
Purple Moorhen, Purple Gallinule

Subspecies *poliocephalus*. First recorded by B. Hodgson (388). Chiefly a winter visitor and passage migrant up to about 915m; also breeds. Locally fairly common at Chitwan, Kosi Barrage, also Sukla Phanta and Ghodaghodi Tal (B4). Proved breeding at the latter site and at Belatari (G6) (750). Only one record this century from the Kathmandu Valley, presumably a migrant: on 2 May 1980 at Chobar (440). Single reports from elsewhere. Frequents dense reedbeds at pool edges and marshes. **Range** Resident through the subcontinent.

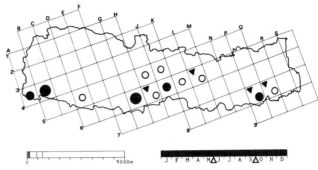

WATERCOCK *Gallicrex cinerea*

Subspecies *cinerea*. Scarce monsoon visitor, although possibly under-recorded. First seen by R. Gregory-Smith and F. Batson on 15 June 1975 on Kosi marshes (293). There are a few later reports from Kosi. One was noted at Begnas Tal on 4 and 5 July 1978. The only other records are from the Kathmandu Valley: three by the Bagmati River on 3 August 1978, four in paddyfields at Gokarna on 4 August 1978 (600) and two there on 27 June 1987 (792). Males at the latter areas were 'singing' in paddyfields. Found in reedy swamps and ditches and flooded fields. **Range** Throughout the subcontinent east of the Indus.

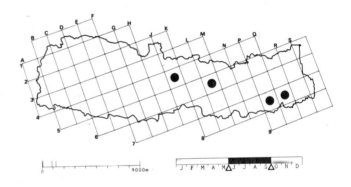

EURASIAN COOT *Fulica atra*
Common Coot

Subspecies *atra*. First recorded by B. Hodgson (388). Mainly an uncommon winter visitor and passage migrant. Regularly reported from Rara Lake, Phewa Tal, Chitwan, Kathmandu Valley and Kosi Barrage. Migrants have also been noted in March at Jomosom (476) and Syang (H4) (480), in June at Manang (J4) (464), in November at Tukche (647), and at the exceptionally high altitude of 5000m at Gokyo lakes in May 1977 (679). Occurs in reed-edged open expanses of water. **Range** Resident and winter visitor throughout the subcontinent.

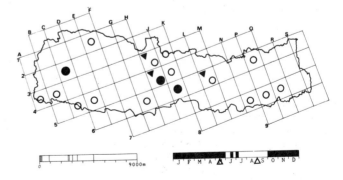

COMMON CRANE *Grus grus*

Subspecies *lilfordi*. Recorded by B. Hodgson (276) in his later collection, but the specimen may have originated in India. First definitely recorded in 1877 by J. Scully who found it common in winter in the tarai and Hetaura dun, and to pass over the Kathmandu Valley on migration (708). Now chiefly a scarce winter visitor and passage migrant. Only one later record from the Valley (243). Small flocks at Chitwan in most winters (244). Large numbers are also reported to fly over there in October/November and March/April (296). A total of 37 flew south down the upper Kali Gandaki valley on 8 October and three on 12 October 1973 (76).

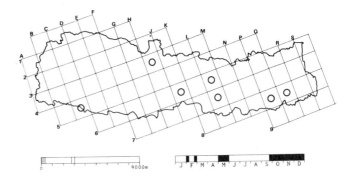

Only three other records: from Kauriala Ghat (C5) (659) and Kosi marshes (319,597). **Range** Winters Pakistan and n. India.

BLACK-NECKED CRANE *Grus nigricollis*

Vagrant. A presumed adult was photographed at Begnas Tal on 4 and 5 July 1978 by J.B.O. Rossetti (688,689). **Range** Breeds Ladakh. Winters in e. Bhutan and Arunachal Pradesh.

SARUS CRANE *Grus antigone*

Subspecies *antigone*. Obtained by B. Hodgson in his later collection (276), but the specimen may have originated in India. First definitely recorded in 1877 by J. Scully who found it common in the central tarai (708). A sedentary resident in the tarai. Only a few recent reports from Chitwan (296). A 1988 survey carried out throughout the western and west-central lowlands west of the Narayani River found the species to be uncommon (751). Local people considered that is was declining, mainly because of wetland losses and hunting (751). Proved breeding in Rupandehi District (G7) and in Kapilvastu District (G6) (751). Forages in grassland and cultivation and roosts in wetlands (751). **Range** Pakistan, n. India, Nepal and Bangladesh.

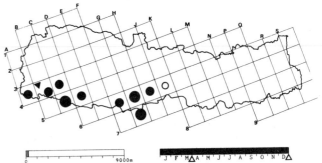

DEMOISELLE CRANE *Anthropoides virgo*

First recorded by B. Hodgson (388). A fairly common passage migrant in April/May and October/November. Passes over Nepal in large flocks. Greatest numbers reported flying south down the upper Kali Gandaki valley in autumn: 31,351 were estimated between 1 and 11 October 1969 (526), about 6,000 cranes including at least 2,220 Demoiselles between 29 September and 10 October 1973 (76), and 63,000 cranes considered to be mainly Demoiselles between 24 September and 5 October 1978 (761). Described last century as common in the central tarai and Hetaura dun in winter (708). Now uncommon on passage at Chitwan, some birds remaining to winter (296). A few records from the Kathmandu Valley and only single reports from elsewhere. Two noted at 2805m at Kagbeni in January 1990 (176). **Range** Winters from Pakistan through n. India to Bangladesh and Assam; south to Karnataka.

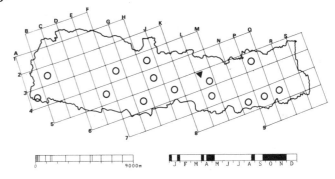

[GREAT INDIAN BUSTARD *Ardeotis nigriceps* (*Choriotis nigriceps*)

B. Hodgson reported a pair from the 'North West' (388). However the record may have been from an area south of the present Nepalese border. **Range** Mainly in Rajasthan, Gujarat and the Deccan south to Karnataka.]

BENGAL FLORICAN *Houbaropsis bengalensis* (*Eupodotis bengalensis*)

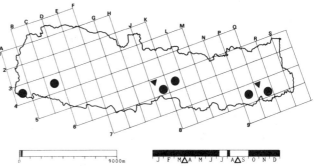

BENGAL FLORICAN, cont'd ...

Subspecies *bengalensis*. First recorded by B. Hodgson (388). Local and uncommon; probably resident. Inhabits the tarai. Regularly observed at Sukla Phanta, Bardia and Chitwan (J6,K6). Several records from Kosi Barrage in the early 1980s, but none received since 1986. Described as a resident, seen occasionally at Kosi Tappu in 1976 (174) but very few later

sightings. The only other records are of specimens taken in Morang District (Q8) in 1936 and 1938 (62). A Nepalese population of only 56 to 82 was estimated in 1982 (431,433). Mainly occurs in grasslands with tall grass clumps interspersed with scattered bushes but sometimes in cultivation. Its grassland habitat in the east has now been almost entirely converted to cultivation. **Range** Mainly Assam and Nepal; also Uttar Pradesh, Bihar, West Bengal, Arunachal Pradesh, Bhutan? and Bangladesh?

LESSER FLORICAN *Sypheotides indica*
Likh

First recorded by B. Hodgson from the Kathmandu Valley (336,388). Chiefly a scarce summer visitor although probably under-recorded. On 26 July 1960 three were seen and a specimen taken in the Kathmandu Valley (245). Singles were found in the Rapti dun (J6) in March and April 1962 (190); at Bardia in February 1980, May 1982 (433) and June 1988 (750), Chitwan (K6) in May 1982 (433), March 1986 (154) and May 1987 (298), and Sukla Phanta (undated) (327). Frequents grasslands with scattered bushes and cultivation. **Range** Mainly Pakistan and India from the Makran coast, Punjab and Rajasthan south to Karnataka and Tamil Nadu.

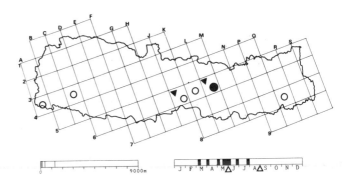

PHEASANT-TAILED JACANA *Hydrophasianus chirurgus*

First recorded by B. Hodgson (388). Mainly a summer visitor although has been reported throughout the year. Fairly common on the Kosi marshes and proved breeding there (256). A resident seen occasionally at Sukla Phanta (700). Rare at Phewa Tal, Begnas Tal and at Chitwan between March and October (296). A few records from the Kathmandu Valley, including a family party seen in summer 1959 (245). The maximum of 85 was seen at Jagdishpur Tal (G6) on 15 June 1988 (750). One was found at the high altitude of 3050m at Rara Lake in October 1982 (190). Frequents lakes and pools with floating vegetation. **Range** Throughout the subcontinent.

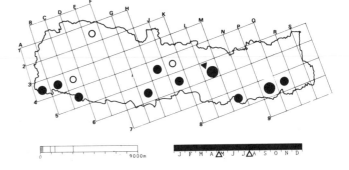

BRONZE-WINGED JACANA *Metopidius indicus*

First recorded by B. Hodgson (388). A fairly common resident throughout the tarai; several records from 915m at Begnas Tal and Phewa Tal. Proved breeding at Belatari (G6) (750) and Kosi Tappu (597). Found on marshes, pools and lakes with floating vegetation. **Range** Nepal to s. India and Bangladesh.

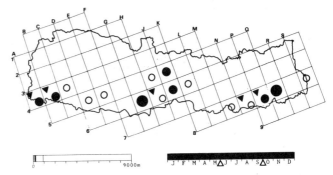

GREATER PAINTEDSNIPE *Rostratula benghalensis*
Painted Snipe

Subspecies *benghalensis*. First recorded by B. Hodgson (388). An uncommon resident mainly found in the lowlands. Areas include Sukla Phanta (432), Dhangarhi (246), Begnas Tal (656), Taulihawa (G6) (157), Kosi Barrage, Chitwan, Hetaura, Tamaspur, and the Kathmandu Valley. The maximum of 40 was noted at Chitwan (undated) (244). An adult and half-grown young one were seen in the Kathmandu Valley on 19 February 1988 (734). Feeds in muddy areas in marshes and along stream banks. **Range** Throughout the subcontinent.

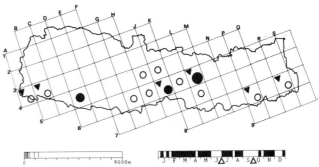

EURASIAN OYSTERCATCHER *Haematopus ostralegus*
Common Oystercatcher

Subspecies *osculans*? Vagrant. Only recorded by B. Hodgson (388) who found it was 'a passage migrant in the hills'. He obtained at least one specimen from the Kathmandu Valley, on 8 October. **Range** Winters on the coasts of Pakistan and India. Has bred in the Sunderbans.

IBISBILL *Ibidorhyncha struthersii*

First recorded by B. Hodgson (344). Frequently seen at Kyangjin, upper Langtang, 3800m (M5), between April and September; a maximum of 18 pairs was reported in April 1984 (624). Proved breeding there (812) and by the Imja Khola (P6) (75). Regularly observed in winter on the Rapti River at Hetaura, between late November and mid-March; the largest number counted there was 12 on 17 February 1981 (656). Several records from the lower Arun (Q7) in winter; mainly single winter reports from elsewhere. Occurs on shingle flats in large river beds. **Range** Himalayas from Gilgit east to Arunachal Pradesh.

IBISBILL, cont'd ...

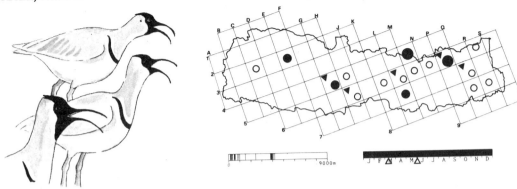

BLACK-WINGED STILT *Himantopus himantopus*

Subspecies *himantopus*. First recorded by B. Hodgson (388). An uncommon spring and autumn passage migrant. Flocks of up to ten regularly seen at Kosi Barrage between February and May. A few records from Chitwan between January and April, and from the Kathmandu Valley in August and September. Mainly single sightings from elsewhere. The only high altitude record is from Muktinath at 3355m on 22 August 1977 (243). Found in marshes and lakes. **Range** Throughout the subcontinent.

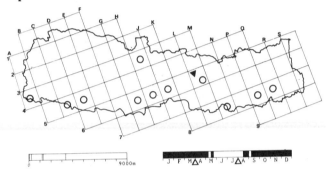

PIED AVOCET *Recurvirostra avosetta*
Avocet

First recorded by B. Hodgson in the Kathmandu Valley in October and November (336,388). A rare passage migrant. A few reports from Kosi Barrage in March and April. The only other records are from Chitwan: in December 1984 (150), November 1989 (597) and November 1982 when a maximum of seven was seen (304). Inhabits marshes, lagoons and mudflats. **Range** Breeds in n. Baluchistan and Kutch. Winters in Pakistan east to n.e. India and south to Tamil Nadu.

EURASIAN THICK-KNEE *Burhinus oedicnemus*
Stone-curlew, Northern Stone-curlew

Subspecies *indicus*. First recorded by B. Hodgson (388). A resident, seen occasionally throughout the tarai and lower hills up to 915m. Breeding confirmed at Kosi Barrage (652) and at Chitwan (296). Several August records from the Kathmandu Valley, presumably of birds undergoing local movements. Frequents sandy or stony river beds and open dry fields. **Range** Throughout the subcontinent.

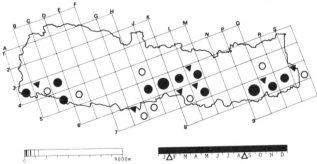

GREAT STONE-PLOVER *Esacus recurvirostris*
Great Thick-Knee

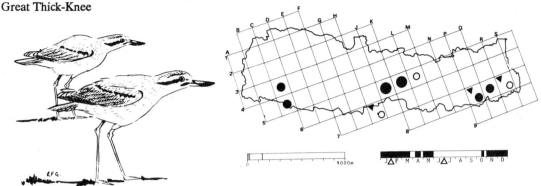

The species was described by C. Cuvier without locality (173); later given as Nepal by Baker (63). First definitely recorded by B. Hodgson who found it in the Kathmandu Valley (349). Only one later report from there: on 5 November 1985 (546). A local resident and winter visitor to the tarai. Occasionally seen at Chitwan (J6,K6) where proved breeding (296,480). Fairly common at Kosi Barrage and Bardia. A few other reports from the eastern tarai (Q8,R8), where the population is augmented by migrants from November to February (293). Occurs on wide rocky or shingle riverbeds. **Range** Throughout the subcontinent.

INDIAN COURSER *Cursorius coromandelicus*

First recorded by B. Hodgson from the tarai (336,388). Scarce, presumably resident. Regularly reported in the early 1980s from the old river bed south of Kosi Barrage; a maximum of six including a chick was seen there on 29 May 1982 (432), but no records received since 1986. The only other record is of a specimen taken in December 1952 at Dhangarhi at 275m (647). Frequents stony ground and dry open areas of scattered scrub. **Range** Locally throughout the subcontinent.

ORIENTAL PRATINCOLE *Glareola maldivarum*
Collared Pratincole (*G. pratincola maldivarum*)

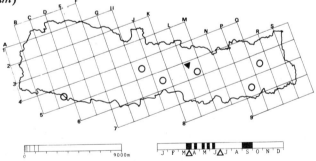

First reported by B. Hodgson in the Kathmandu Valley on 10 June (336,388). A scarce passage migrant. Although described in 1976 as a common local migrant in the Kosi Barrage area (293), only four other records received from there, mainly singles in April and May. The maximum of 25 was seen at Badhaiya Tal (C5) on 13 June 1988 (750). Other reports are from the Kathmandu Valley in September 1973 and October 1983 (243,589), Phewa Tal in April 1977 (563), Tumlingtar (Q7) (483) in May 1981, and Chitwan (undated) (293). **Range** Breeds in Pakistan, n. India and Bangladesh. Winters throughout the peninsula.

LITTLE PRATINCOLE *Glareola lactea*
Small Pratincole

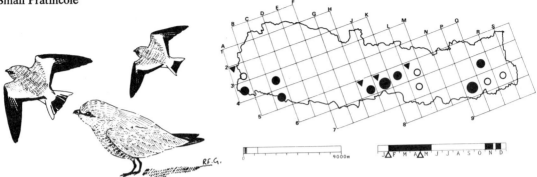

First recorded by B. Hodgson from the Kathmandu Valley on 24 June but no later reports from there (336,388). A resident and local migrant up to 750m. Common over the Karnali River at Bardia, the Arung Khola at Tamaspur, Rapti and Narayani Rivers at Chitwan and at Kosi

Barrage. A few reports from elsewhere. Local movements noted at Chitwan, where concentrations were found between November and January, including a flock of 2000 near Meghauli on 5 January 1983 (304). Proved breeding at Chitwan (296) and Kosi Barrage (483). Occurs on rivers with sandbars or stony beds. **Range** Throughout the subcontinent east of the Indus River.

LITTLE RINGED PLOVER *Charadrius dubius*

First recorded by B. Hodgson (388). Subspecies *jerdoni* is a common resident up to 1500m. Numbers are augmented in winter, presumably by the migratory subspecies *curonicus*, although there is only one definite specimen record of the latter race: from Kosi in November (244). Proved breeding at Phewa Tal (166), Kosi Tappu (481) and in February at Chitwan (J6,K6) (296,481). Found on shingle and mudbanks of rivers, pools and lakes. **Range** Throughout the subcontinent.

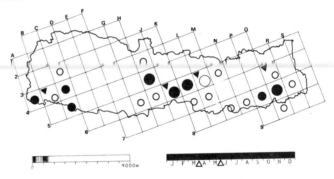

LONG-BILLED PLOVER *Charadrius placidus*
Long-billed Ringed Plover

This species was described from a Hodgson specimen by J.E. Gray (276,797) but it may have originated in India. First definitely recorded by J. Scully in November 1877 in Nawakot District (L6) (708). A rare winter visitor and passage migrant. Seen several times in the Kathmandu

Valley in April, May and in winter, and on the Rapti River at Hetaura between November and February. There are a few reports from the Yamdi Khola (H5) (206,254,150), and single records from elsewhere. Frequents shingle beds of large rivers. **Range** Winters Bangladesh, Nepal, n. and n.e. India.

LONG-BILLED PLOVER, cont'd ...

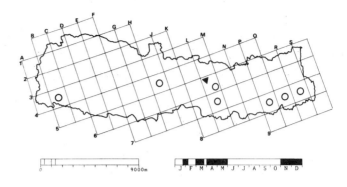

KENTISH PLOVER *Charadrius alexandrinus*
Snowy Plover

Subspecies *alexandrinus*. A Hodgson specimen was listed for Nepal by Sharpe (722) but it may have originated in India. First definitely recorded by R.L. Fleming Sr. at Raghunathpur (N8) at 275m in December 1953 (647). A locally common winter visitor and passage migrant; possibly breeds. Regularly seen in the Kathmandu Valley, at Kosi Barrage, and between October and late April at Chitwan (296). The maximum of over 250 was seen at Kosi on 27 February 1986 (514). Frequents shingle and sandy riverbeds. **Range** Breeds in Pakistan and n. and s. India. Winters throughout the subcontinent.

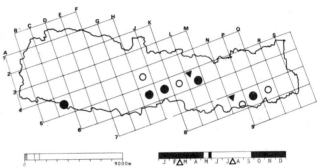

LESSER SAND PLOVER *Charadrius mongolus*
Mongolian Plover

Subspecies *atrifrons*. First recorded by B. Hodgson from the Kathmandu Valley in May (336,388). No later reports until 1981, although possibly overlooked. A rare winter visitor and spring migrant, probably only stopping for short periods. Several sightings from Kosi Barrage between mid-March and late May, and from Chitwan between November and May. The maximum of 43 was photographed by Phewa Tal on 21 May 1985 (800). The only other records are from the Bagmati River, Kathmandu Valley in February 1981 (180) and Rara Lake in May 1985 (160). **Range** Breeds in the Himalayas in Ladakh, Lahul and Sikkim. Winters on the coasts of the subcontinent.

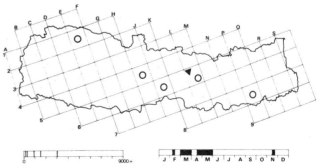

GREATER SAND PLOVER   *Charadrius leschenaultii*
Large Sand Plover

Subspecies *leschenaultii*. Vagrant. First recorded by B. Hodgson on 10 June in the Kathmandu Valley (336,388). The only other record is of one seen at Kosi Barrage on 11 February 1987 (463). **Range** Winters on the coasts of the subcontinent.

PACIFIC GOLDEN PLOVER   *Pluvialis fulva*
Eastern Golden Plover   (*P. dominica*)
Lesser Golden Plover

First recorded by B. Hodgson (388). A winter visitor and passage migrant. Common at Kosi Barrage where flocks of over 50 are frequently recorded; a maximum of 1000 was estimated on 11 April 1982 (207,561). Scarce elsewhere. Several spring and autumn records from the Kathmandu Valley and Chitwan; single records from elsewhere. One was noted in the upper Kali Gandaki valley at about 2590m on 24 September 1973 (76). Found on ploughed fields and muddy riverbanks. **Range** Winters locally throughout the subcontinent.

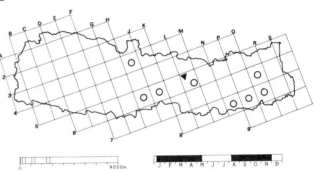

GREY PLOVER   *Pluvialis squatarola*
Black-bellied Plover

Vagrant. First recorded by B. Hodgson from the Kathmandu Valley on 2 January and 2 October (336,388). The only other records are of singles seen on the Rapti River, Chitwan in November 1979 (170) and from December 1988 to February 1989 (67), also from Kosi Barrage where a flock of at least 20 in breeding plumage was observed on 30 April 1982 (244), one on 2 May 1986 (321), and 15 on 15 April 1987 (327). **Range** Winters on the coasts of the subcontinent.

RIVER LAPWING   *Hoplopterus duvaucelii*
Spur-winged Lapwing   (*Vanellus spinosus duvaucelii*)
River Plover

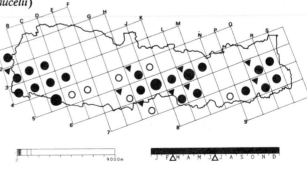

RIVER LAPWING, cont'd ...

First recorded by B. Hodgson (388). A common resident in the tarai and foothills up to 915m. Occasionally seen in the Kathmandu Valley, especially in summer, and proved breeding there in the last century (708). Breeding also confirmed at Chitwan (296,432) and Bardia (C5) (432). Inhabits stony beds and sand bars of rivers. **Range** India from Haryana east through the Himalayan foothills to Bangladesh; south to the Godaveri River.

YELLOW-WATTLED LAPWING   *Hoplopterus malabaricus*
Yellow-wattled Plover   (*Vanellus malabaricus*)

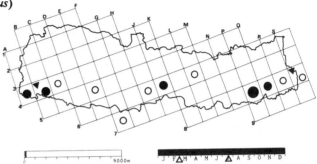

First recorded by B. Hodgson (388). Mainly a rare winter visitor although reported in all months. A resident occasionally seen at Sukla Phanta (432,700). A scarce winter visitor to Chitwan, noted in open areas at the park edges (296). A breeding record from Kosi Barrage (281), listed in the first edition of this book (435), is now considered unacceptable. An infrequent monsoon visitor to the Kathmandu Valley in 1949 (629), but there are no other records. Rare at Kosi Barrage and only single reports from elsewhere. Found in dry fields, open country and river beds in the lowlands. **Range** Sind; India from Haryana and W. Bengal southwards; w. Bangladesh.

GREY-HEADED LAPWING   *Hoplopterus cinereus*
Grey-headed Plover   (*Vanellus cinereus*)

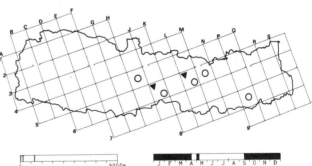

First recorded by F.M. Bailey on 6 April 1937 from Gaucher, Kathmandu Valley (62,108). In 1961 discovered to be a regular and quite common visitor from the end of September to the end of March in the Valley (638); mainly seen by the Manora River. Regularly reported there since with a maximum of 56 in November 1985 (201). The Valley is the westernmost regular wintering area for the species. Irregularly recorded from Kosi Barrage, twice found at Phewa Tal (325,152), and single reports from elsewhere. Winters on river banks and in wet fields. **Range** Winters in n.e. India and Bangladesh.

RED-WATTLED LAPWING *Hoplopterus indicus*
Red-wattled Plover *(Vanellus indicus)*

Subspecies *indicus*. First recorded by B. Hodgson (388). A common resident from the tarai up to 1050m. Breeding confirmed in Banke District (D5) (750), at Chitwan (153,296), north-west of Pokhara (420) and at Hetaura (96). Very common during the monsoon in the Kathmandu Valley and occurs in small numbers all year (629). Frequents fields and open areas near water. **Range** Throughout the subcontinent.

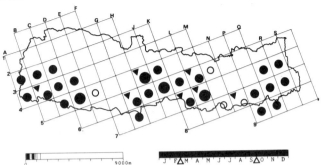

WHITE-TAILED LAPWING *Chettusia leucura*
White-tailed Plover *(Vanellus leucurus)*

First recorded in December 1952 at Bilauri (A4) at 250m by R.L. Fleming Sr. (647). Another was obtained there a month later, and one was seen at Dhangarhi in December 1952 (647). The only reports received are from Nepalganj on 1 January 1977 (464), and by the Babai River near Ghurai (E6) from 7 to 10 January 1981 (576). Inhabits marshes, reedy pools and river edges. **Range** Winters in Pakistan, n. India and Bangladesh.

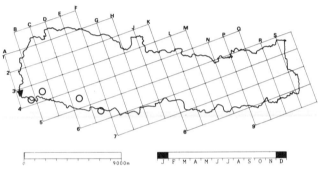

NORTHERN LAPWING *Vanellus vanellus*
Eurasian Lapwing, Peewit

First recorded by B. Hodgson (388). An uncommon winter visitor, mainly seen at Phewa Tal, the Kathmandu Valley, and Kosi Barrage, with a few sightings from Begnas Tal and Chitwan. Singles noted twice in the upper Kali Gandaki valley at about 2700m (243, 658). A maximum of about 300 was seen in early February 1987 at Kosi Barrage (518). Occurs in wet marshes, fields and cultivation. **Range** Winters in Pakistan and n.w. India east to Nepal; erratically to n.e. India and Bangladesh.

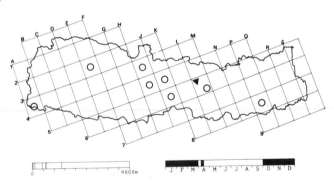

SANDERLING *Calidris alba*

The only record is of one seen on 11 February 1979 at Kosi Barrage by F. Lambert *et al.* (486,651,652); it accompanied a flock of 50 Little Stints and nine Dunlin. The flock could not be relocated the next day. This is apparently the first inland record of Sanderling for the Indian subcontinent. **Range** Winters on the coasts of the subcontinent.

LITTLE STINT   *Calidris minuta*

First recorded by B. Hodgson (388). An uncommon winter visitor and passage migrant mainly recorded from Chitwan, the Kathmandu Valley and Kosi Barrage. Single reports from elsewhere. Two seen by Rara Lake at 3050m in October 1982 (627). An exceptional flock of about 50 was seen on 11 February 1979 at Kosi Barrage (486,651,652). Frequents muddy edges of lakes, streams and rivers. **Range** Winters mainly on the coasts of the sub-continent.

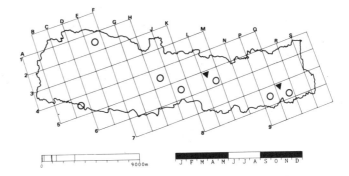

TEMMINCK'S STINT   *Calidris temminckii*

First recorded by B. Hodgson (388). A common winter visitor and passage migrant from the tarai up to 915m and at about 1370m in the Kathmandu Valley. Noted on passage in the Himalayas: a total of 39 counted at Tukche between 6 and 14 October 1973 (76) and 13 seen by Gokyo Lake at 4710m on 2 May 1984 (764). A maximum of 65 was estimated on 20 March 1986 at Sauraha (J6) (403). Frequents marshes, paddyfields, mud and sandy edges of rivers and lakes. **Range** Winters throughout the subcontinent.

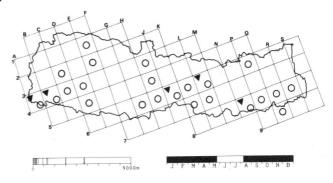

LONG-TOED STINT   *Calidris subminuta*

First recorded by R.L. Fleming Sr. on 11 May 1960: two or three accompanied a flock of Temminck's Stints on mudflats of the Bagmati River, Kathmandu Valley (245). The only other other record is of four on 4 May 1982 at Rani Tal, Sukla Phanta (432). **Range** Winters in n.e. India and Bangladesh.

CURLEW SANDPIPER   *Calidris ferruginea* (*Calidris testacea*)

First recorded by N. Krabbe *et al.* who saw one in full breeding plumage at Kosi Barrage on 22 April 1981 (483). A scarce spring and autumn passage migrant. The only other records are of two seen by the Bagmati River, Kathmandu on 25 October 1982 (305) and up to four along the Rapti River, Chitwan, between 8 November and 28 December 1982 (304,299). Occurs on mud and sandy river banks. **Range** Winters on the coasts of the subcontinent. Small numbers inland.

DUNLIN *Calidris alpina*

Subspecies *alpina*. First recorded by B. Hodgson from the Kathmandu Valley (336,388). A scarce winter visitor and passage migrant. There are several winter sightings from Kosi Barrage, with a maximum of over 30 on 27 February 1986 (514). Small flocks noted at Chitwan in late March 1981 (476) and December 1982 (304). The only other records are of one collected from the Bagmati River, Kathmandu Valley on 1 January 1967 (586,587) and two seen at Begnas Tal on 29 March 1984 (764). Occurs on mud and sand banks of rivers. **Range** Winters mainly on the coasts of Pakistan and n.w. India south to Bombay, also the Gangetic river system.

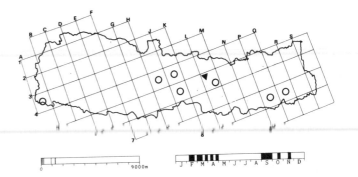

RUFF *Philomachus pugnax*

First recorded by B. Hodgson (388). A very uncommon passage migrant. There are several reports from the Kathmandu Valley in September and October, and from Kosi Barrage between February and April where a maximum of 47 was noted on 12 February 1979 (486,652). Twice found at Chitwan and single records from elsewhere. Found in marshes, and fields and mudbanks of rivers and lakes. **Range** Winters throughout the subcontinent.

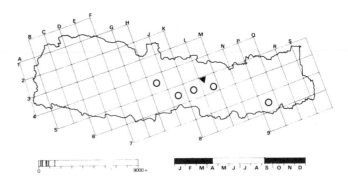

JACK SNIPE *Lymnocryptes minimus* (*Gallinago minima*)

First recorded by B. Hodgson from the Kathmandu Valley (336,388). A scarce winter visitor and passage migrant. In the last century found between early September and end of April, with largest numbers occurring on passage in October, November and March (708). Described in 1949 as a scarce passage migrant; a few probably staying all winter (629). In 1950 the numbers of Jack, Common and Pintail Snipe in the Valley were reported to be severely reduced compared to 20 years before (659), and only three recent records of this species have been traced, all of lone birds, two in winter (155,217), and one in October (589). The only other records are of one or two at Phewa Tal in February 1981 (622), Kosi Barrage in March 1982 (794), and Chitwan (J6,K6) in April 1985 (59) and February 1988 (481). Inhabits swampy areas and wet fields. **Range** Winters throughout the subcontinent.

COMMON SNIPE *Gallinago gallinago*
Fantail Snipe

Subspecies *gallinago*. First recorded by B. Hodgson, who noted that some birds remained in the Kathmandu Valley all year (338). Now a winter visitor and passage migrant; possibly breeds. Locally fairly common at Phewa Tal, Chitwan, Kathmandu Valley and Kosi Barrage; occasionally reported from elsewhere. Mainly found up to 1500m. Noted in the Himalayas, presumably on passage: at 4700m at Gokyo in April 1972 (131,243), at 2650m in the upper Kali Gandaki valley in March 1985 (313) and at 3050m at Khaptad (C3) in September 1989 (68). Frequents marshes, wet fields and muddy

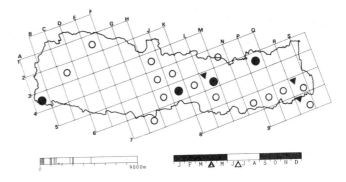

edges of rivers and ponds. **Range** Breeds in the Himalayas from Kashmir to Garhwal. Winters throughout the subcontinent.

PINTAIL SNIPE *Gallinago stenura*

First recorded by B. Hodgson (338). A winter visitor and passage migrant occasionally seen up to 1370m. Sometimes found with Common Snipe, although often in drier habitats than that species. The largest number reported is ten at Kosi Barrage on 16 March 1982 (682). Found in harvested paddyfields with scattered pools, marshy pool edges and dry grass and scrub areas.

SWINHOE'S SNIPE *Gallinago megala*

Vagrant. The only record is of one seen with Pintail Snipe and Common Snipe by S.C. Madge *et al.* on 6 March 1987 in

damp rice fields between Biratnagar and Itahari (Q8) (515). **Range** Scattered winter records throughout India; also Sri Lanka and Maldives.

SOLITARY SNIPE *Gallinago solitaria*

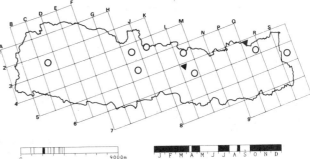

SOLITARY SNIPE, cont'd ...

Subspecies *solitaria*. The species was described by B. Hodgson from Nepal (338,797). An uncommon and local winter visitor and passage migrant; probably also resident. Mainly occurs over 2135m but found at 915m at Phewa Tal on 18 December 1970 (444). Last century described as not uncommon in the Kathmandu Valley from October to April (338,708), although there are very few recent records. Regularly reported in winter near Muktinath at 3795m. A maxi-

mum of 11 was seen there on 1 February 1984 (815). Described as not uncommon in the upper Arun valley (Q6) in December 1979 (574,587) and found there in August 1986 (590). Uncommon at Khaptad in April and May 1988 (428) and still present in the summer of that year (754). Other records are from the upper Kali Gandaki valley, Manang (J4), Langtang and the Singhalila ridge (S7). Breeding behaviour is poorly known. Frequents marshy edges and beds of mountain streams. **Range** Summers in the Himalayas from Ladakh east to Arunachal Pradesh. Winters in the Himalayas. Resident in n.e. India.

WOOD SNIPE *Gallinago nemoricola*

The species was described by B. Hodgson from Nepal (364,797). Scarce; possibly a resident that migrates altitudinally. In the Kathmandu Valley Hodgson found it not uncommon in winter, staying until 11 May. Two specimens contained eggs (336,338). It was apparently rare by 1877 (708), and last recorded from there in 1950, when one or two were shot each year (659). Collected from the Singhalila ridge (S7) at 3050m in January 1912 (735) and from Sundar Gundar (Q8) on 3 February 1938 (62). Proved breeding in the Barun valley (Q6) in 1973 (147,148). The only other records are of one seen at Khangma (Q6) at 3800m in May 1981 (483), two displaying at Pipar (H5) be-

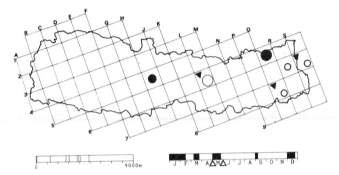

tween 11 and 16 May 1985 (800) and one seen at Jolbari (R7) on 19 January 1989 (307). Inhabits swampy areas in woods. **Range** Breeds in the Himalayas from Kulu east to Arunachal Pradesh and n.e. India. Winters at lower elevations and in the hills of s. India.

EURASIAN WOODCOCK *Scolopax rusticola*
Woodcock

First recorded by B. Hodgson (338). A fairly common resident locally, and an altitudinal migrant. Usually summers between 1980m and 3900m. Descends to about 1350m in winter but a few reports down to 100m at Chitwan (180,481,810) and found as high as 1900m at Pothana in December (58). Seen roding at Khaptad (C3) (428), in the Dhorpatan valley (F4,Q5) (499), Marsyangdi valley (J4) (512), Langtang (440,639), and Khumbu (109). Breeding confirmed in the Gandak-Kosi watershed (L5) (639). Occurs in swampy dense undergrowth in rhododendron and fir forests. **Range** Breeds in the

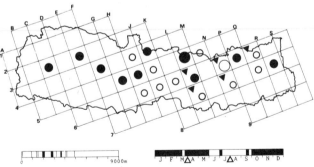

Himalayas from N.W.F.P. east to Arunachal Pradesh. Winters at lower elevations in the Himalayas, and the hills of n.e. and s. India.

BLACK-TAILED GODWIT *Limosa limosa*

Subspecies *limosa*. First recorded by B. Hodgson (388). A scarce and local passage migrant. Found last century in the Kathmandu Valley in April and from mid-August to October, and described as not common (336,708). Only three later records from the Valley: singles in August, in 1978 (243), 1981 (587,244) and 1989 (256). Irregularly reported since 1979 in April and early May at Kosi Barrage. The maximum of 55 was noted in April 1981 (483) and 1983 (56). Occurs in shallow water and mudbanks of rivers and lakes. **Range** Winters mainly in Pakistan, n. and n.e. India.

WHIMBREL *Numenius phaeopus*

Subspecies *phaeopus*. First recorded by B. Hodgson from the Kathmandu Valley in August and September (336,388). A scarce passsage migrant; mainly reported in spring. One was seen at Kosi Barrage between February and April 1981, and 12 on 14 March 1982 (794). The only other records are from Phewa Tal in April 1981 (811), Bagmati Pools, Kathmandu Valley in September 1989 (256) and at Chitwan where it is described as a rare passage migrant from April to September (296), with a maximum of 22 on 10 May 1984

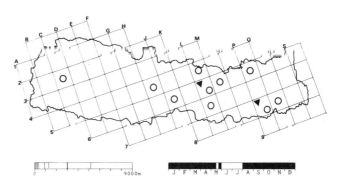

(421). Found on mudflats and grassy areas. **Range** Winters on the coasts of the subcontinent.

EURASIAN CURLEW *Numenius arquata*
Curlew

Subspecies *orientalis*. First recorded by B. Hodgson (388). A common winter visitor and passage migrant to Kosi Barrage, mainly reported there from September to April, with singles also noted on 13 July and 10 August 1975 (293). The maximum of 700 was noted on 16 March 1982 (682,770). A scarce passage migrant elsewhere: small groups at Chitwan in September and April (296), a few reports from the Kathmandu Valley, but only single sightings from elsewhere. Two were seen at 3050m at Khaptad (C3) on 8 September 1989 (68). Occurs on mudflats and grassy fields. **Range** Winters throughout the subcontinent, mainly on the coast.

SPOTTED REDSHANK *Tringa erythropus*

First recorded by B. Hodgson (388). A local winter visitor and passage migrant. Occasionally reported from Chitwan and Kosi Barrage between February and May. Seen three times at Phewa Tal (486,811,764). Single sightings from other areas. Only one record from the Kathmandu Valley since Hodgson's time (486). A maximum of eight was seen on 30 April 1982 at Sukla Phanta (432). Frequents muddy banks and shallow water of rivers and lakes. **Range** Winters in Pakistan, India and Nepal.

SPOTTED REDSHANK, cont'd ...

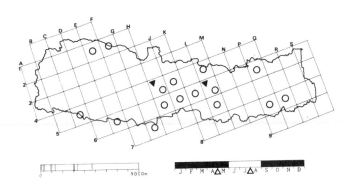

COMMON REDSHANK *Tringa totanus*

Subspecies *eurhinus*. First recorded by B. Hodgson (388). A local winter visitor and passage migrant. Occasionally reported from Kosi Barrage. Uncommon in the Kathmandu Valley, at Phewa Tal and at Chitwan where it is recorded from September to April (296). Evidence of movement there in December 1982 when flocks of up to 20 birds were noted (304). Noted on passage in the Himalayas: twice found by Gokyo Lakes at 4700m in May (243,764), seen by Rara Lake in May (160) and in the Langu valley (F2) (330). Single reports from elsewhere. Found in marshes, rivers and lakes. **Range** Breeds in Kashmir and Ladakh. Winters throughout the subcontinent.

MARSH SANDPIPER *Tringa stagnatilis*

A Hodgson specimen was listed for Nepal by Sharpe (722), but it may have originated in India. First definitely recorded by G. Diesselhorst in the Rapti Dun (K6) on 9 April 1962 (190). An uncommon passage migrant and winter visitor to Chitwan (J6,K6) and Kosi Barrage. Only single reports from elsewhere. The maximum of 11 was seen on 15 March 1982 at Kosi Barrage (794). Frequents marshes and mud banks of rivers and lakes. **Range** Winters throughout the subcontinent.

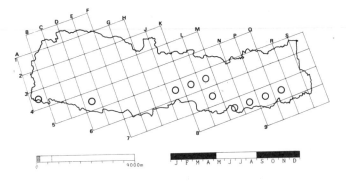

COMMON GREENSHANK *Tringa nebularia*
Greenshank

First recorded by B. Hodgson (388). Common. Mainly a winter visitor and passage migrant between mid-August and May. Chiefly winters up to 370m, with a maximum of over 150 at Kosi Barrage on 8 February 1974 (518). A few birds remain there during the summer (293). The most abundant migrant wader at Chitwan; roosting flocks of up to 102 birds counted in December 1982 (304). In the Kathmandu Valley most often seen from mid-August to mid-September (635). Singles noted on passage in Khumbu at 4800m on 30 August 1962

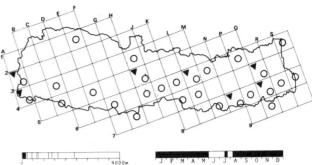

(190), at Tukche in early October 1973 (76) and by Rara Lake (127). Inhabits marshes, river banks and lakes. **Range** Winters throughout the subcontinent.

GREEN SANDPIPER *Tringa ochropus*

First recorded by B. Hodgson (388). A common passage migrant and fairly common in winter up to about 370m. Noted at Chitwan from September to early April (296,304). In the Kathmandu Valley most seen on passage in September, but small numbers regularly winter (629). Observed on passage: several reports between February and May from the upper Kali Gandaki valley; also noted in April at Chitwan (432) and Kosi Barrage (403). Flocks seen in September and October in the upper Kali Gandaki valley (76) and other autumn records from Rara Lake (627), Manang (J4) (295,512), and at

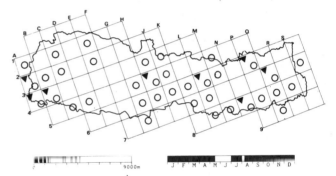

4250m at Pheriche (P6) (190). Frequents marshes, streams, lakes and rivers. **Range** Breeds in Chitral. Winters throughout the subcontinent.

WOOD SANDPIPER *Tringa glareola*

First recorded by B. Hodgson (388). An uncommon winter visitor but observed more frequently on passage, mainly in April, May and September. Regularly seen at Phewa Tal, Chitwan, Kosi Barrage and in the Kathmandu Valley. Noted on passage at Jomosom, where 14 were counted between 10 September and 9 October 1973 (76), and one was seen at Muktinath at 3780m on 4 April 1984 (421). Migrants have also been noted by Rara Lake in February 1977 (464), October 1982 (627) and May 1985 (160). Mainly single records from other areas. The maximum reported is 40 at Kosi

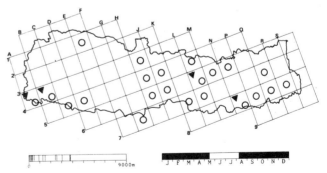

Barrage on 14 April 1981 (559). Found on marshes and banks of rivers and lakes. **Range** Winters throughout the subcontinent.

TEREK SANDPIPER *Xenus cinereus*
(*Tringa terek*)

Vagrant. First recorded by R.F. Grimmett and J. Eames at Kosi Barrage on 18
April 1982 (199,294). The only other records are from Gokyo Lake at about
4710m: two were seen on 2 May 1984 and
one photographed the next day (764).
Range Winters on the coasts of the subcontinent.

COMMON SANDPIPER *Actitis hypoleucos*
(*Tringa hypoleucos*)

First recorded by B. Hodgson (388). A
common winter visitor from the tarai up
to 1370m, mainly occurring between early
August and the end of April. Numbers are
increased by passage birds in spring and
autumn. Occasionally reported from the
Himalayas, presumably on passage.
Noted several times in the upper Kali
Gandaki valley in February; 50 to 52 were
counted there between 7 September and
9 October 1973 (76). Other high altitude
records are from Rara Lake (83,464,785),
Pheriche at 4250m (190), and as high as
5400m at Gorak Shep Lake (P6) (679).
Frequents marshes and banks of streams,
rivers and lakes. **Range** Breeds from
Kashmir east to Garhwal. Winters
throughout the subcontinent.

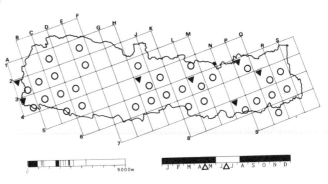
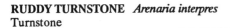

RUDDY TURNSTONE *Arenaria interpres*
Turnstone

Subspecies *interpres*. Vagrant. The only
record is of one photographed on the
gravel flats at Tukche on 14 September
1973 by M. Beaman (76). **Range** Winters
on the coasts of the subcontinent.

RED-NECKED PHALAROPE *Phalaropus lobatus*

Vagrant. One was recorded on Rara Lake shore on 16 October 1982 by D. Brearey and D. Pritchard (627). **Range** Winters off the Pakistan and Gujarat coasts.

GREAT BLACK-HEADED GULL *Larus ichthyaetus*

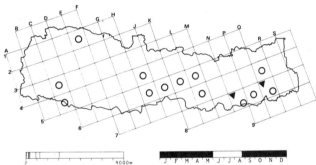

First recorded by F.M. Bailey from the Kosi River on 9 February 1938 (62). A locally fairly common winter visitor and passage migrant. Several reports of up to 20 birds. Most often seen at Tamaspur, Chitwan and Kosi, and occasionally at Bardia. Also recorded in winter from Rara Lake (137) and the Kathmandu Valley (154,506). Several spring and autumn sightings from elsewhere, presumably of passage birds. Found in March and April at Rara Lake (137), Phewa Tal (811,812), Kathmandu Valley (243), Hetaura (476) and the lower Arun valley (546). Seen in the lower Arun valley in August (590), and at Rara Lake in October and November (83,627,691). Frequents large rivers of the lowlands. **Range** Winters on the coasts and rivers of the subcontinent.

COMMON BLACK-HEADED GULL *Larus ridibundus*
Black-headed Gull

First recorded by B. Hodgson (388,698). A winter visitor and passage migrant. Fairly common at Kosi Barrage from November to May. The maximum of about 150 was seen in February in 1974 (518) and 1984 (650). Occasionally found at Phewa Tal. Uncommon at Chitwan; recorded there from September to April (296). Reported from the Himalayas at Rara Lake (127), in the upper Dudh Kosi valley (P6) at over 5490m in May 1977 (243) and on Gokyo lakes at 4700m in November 1988 (453). Mainly single rec-

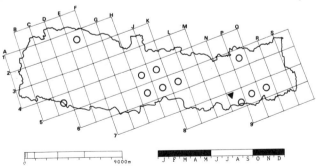

ords from elsewhere. Occurs on lakes and large rivers. **Range** Winters mainly on the coasts of the subcontinent.

BROWN-HEADED GULL   *Larus brunnicephalus*

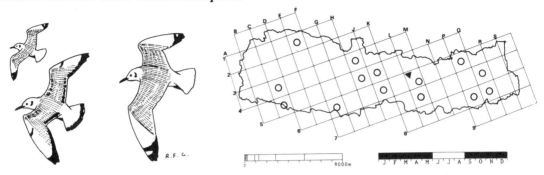

A Hodgson specimen was listed for Nepal by Saunders (698) but may have originated in India. First definitely recorded by R.L. Fleming on the Bagmati River at Patan (L6) at 1280m on 24 October 1963. A winter visitor and passage migrant. Fairly common at Kosi Barrage and uncommon at Chitwan. Also found in winter at Bardia (128,192), Rara Lake (785), and Kapilvastu (F6) (658). Numbers increase

at Kosi in spring; a peak of 35 was reported in April 1979 (486,559,652). Several spring and autumn reports from elsewhere, presumably of migrants. Noted in March at Phewa Tal (598,154), Begnas Tal (111) and the lower Arun valley (546), and in April at Kagbeni (812) and Hetaura (332). Seen in October at Rara Lake (244) and in the Kathmandu Valley (247). A party of 19 with one Black-headed Gull flew over the upper Dudh Kosi valley (P6) at 5490m in May 1977 (243). Inhabits rivers and lakes. **Range** Breeds in Ladakh. Winters throughout the subcontinent.

SLENDER-BILLED GULL   *Larus genei*

First recorded by P.A. Dukes *et al.* on 7 February 1974 at Kosi Barrage. The following day an immature was seen (718). A scarce and irregular winter visitor and passage migrant only seen at the barrage between January and mid-March and in November. The only other records are of one to two birds in February in 1975 (293), 1979 (486,652), and 1981 (65,559), in January 1985 (142), in March 1987 (744,769) and November 1989 (597). **Range** Breeds in Baluchistan. Winters in Sind and n.w. India.

MEW GULL   *Larus canus*
Common Gull

Subspecies *heinei*? Vagrant. A first year bird was recorded at Kosi Barrage on 18 February 1979 by R. Filby *et al.* It was still present on 21 February (486,651,652). Subsequently single adults have been recorded both from Phewa Tal, on 21 January 1981 (180), and on 28 February 1983 (593). **Range** These are the first published records for the subcontinent.

LESSER BLACK-BACKED AND YELLOW-LEGGED GULLS   *Larus fuscus* and *L. cachinnans*

The status of these two species is unclear at present because of nomenclatural confusion; *heuglini* is considered to be a race of Herring Gull *L. argentatus* by some authors (e.g. 47,243), but is here treated as a race of Lesser Black-backed Gull. Most records received have not been identified subspecifically and are treated here as Yellow-legged/Lesser Black-backed Gulls. Winter visitor and

passage migrant. Uncommon at Kosi Barrage: a maximum of six noted on 14 February 1981 (622). Several other reports, mainly in spring and autumn, presumably of passage migrants. Noted at Phewa Tal in March and April (811,519,166) and September (141), Manang in October (658), and the Kathmandu Valley during the monsoon (243,418) and in October (256). One flew over Pheriche (P6) at 4725m on 8 November 1978 (314). Also recorded at Rara Lake (243) and Chitwan (296,746,408).

LESSER BLACK-BACKED AND YELLOW-LEGGED GULLS, cont'd ...

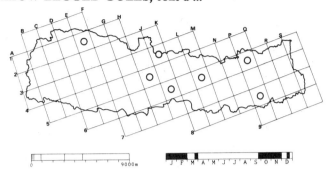

LESSER BLACK-BACKED GULL   *Larus fuscus*

A first year specimen, probably *L. f. heug-lini* was collected from the Bagmati River, Kathmandu in November 1961 by R.L. Fleming Sr. (234,247). Only three other definite reports received, all from Kosi Barrage: an adult of the race *L. f. fuscus* was noted on 14 April 1981 (559), another adult of the race *L. f. heuglini* on 14 February 1984 (650), and a juvenile on 5 November 1989 (597). **Range** Winters on the coasts of Pakistan and w. India.

YELLOW-LEGGED GULL   *Larus cachinnans*

First definitely recorded by R.F. Grimmett who saw one, probably of the race *mongolicus,* at Kosi Barrage on 11 February 1979 (486,652). Singles, probably of the same race, were also seen there on 15 February 1984 (650), 18 November 1988 (596) and from 8 to 9 February 1989 (468). The only other record is of one at Phewa Tal on 9 March 1986 (403). **Range** Winters on the coasts of Pakistan and India; also on the Ganges River.

GULL-BILLED TERN   *Gelochelidon nilotica*

Subspecies *affinis*? First recorded at Kosi Barrage by S.C. Madge *et al.* on 25 January 1974 (518). Winter visitor and passage migrant. Fairly common at Kosi Barrage where up to ten birds are often reported in winter. Peak numbers have been noted in spring; a maximum of about 60 was seen in late April 1981 (483). Only a few spring and autumn records from elsewhere, presumably of passage birds. Observed at Chitwan in April (56), Phewa Tal in May (563,811), Manang (J4) in August (587), the Kathmandu Valley in September (587), and Rara Lake (127). Frequents large rivers and lakes. **Range** Breeds locally in Pakistan, West Bengal and Bangladesh. Winters throughout the subcontinent.

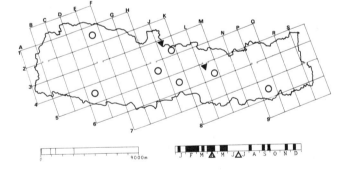

CASPIAN TERN *Sterna caspia*

Subspecies *caspia*. First recorded at Kosi Barrage on 7 and 8 February 1974 by S.C. Madge *et al.* (518). A winter visitor and passage migrant. Fairly common at Kosi where twenty birds have been reported in February and March. Numbers increase in spring; maxima of about 20 were noted in mid-March 1982 (770) and in 1989 (172). The only other reports are from Bardia where one was seen on 8 November 1985 (162) and from Chitwan where it is a rare winter visitor and passage migrant (296). **Range** Breeds locally in Baluchistan and Sri Lanka. Winters throughout the subcontinent.

RIVER TERN *Sterna aurantia*

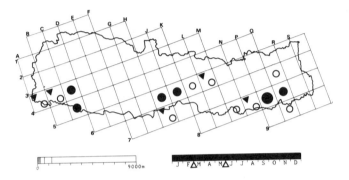

First recorded by B. Hodgson (388). A locally common resident and partial migrant mainly recorded up to 610m. Regularly reported from the Karnali River at Bardia, rivers at Chitwan, and at Kosi. An influx of up to 50 was noted at Kosi during the monsoon (293), but the maximum of 450 was estimated there in late November 1984 (58). An adult was observed feeding young at Kosi in May (432). Frequents marshes, streams and rivers. **Range** Throughout the subcontinent.

COMMON TERN *Sterna hirundo*

First recorded by D. Proud on the Manora River, Kathmandu Valley: a juvenile taken on 8 August 1953 was of the race *tibetana* (628,635). Several other autumn records from the Valley, chiefly from the Bagmati and Manora Rivers between August and October. Uncommon at Kosi and found there in February, April, May, September and November with a maximum of 30 in two flocks seen in late April 1981 (483). An adult observed at the Barrage on 16 April 1982 was apparently of the race *longipennis* (294). Also noted at Chitwan (296), at Phewa Tal in April (82), May (811,800), and in July and August (688). Seen as high as 4000m at Tengboche (P6) in May 1975 (580). **Range** Breeds Ladakh. Winters locally throughout the subcontinent.

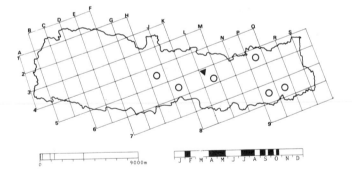

BLACK-BELLIED TERN *Sterna acuticauda*

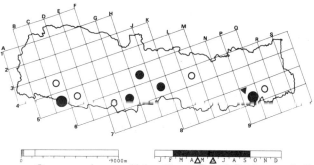

A Hodgson specimen was listed for Nepal by Saunders (698), but it may have originated in India. First definitely recorded by F.M. Bailey from Tribeni (H7) at 75m on 12 January 1936 (62). A common resident and partial summer visitor. Found on marshes and rivers of the tarai and foothills up to about 730m. Numbers generally increase at Kosi Barrage during spring, but the peak of about 60 was noted on 15 February 1984 (650). **Range** Throughout the subcontinent east of the Indus River.

LITTLE TERN *Sterna albifrons*

Subspecies *albifrons*. Noted without details from the Karnali and Kosi Rivers by S.D. Ripley during 1947 to 1949 (659). The first detailed record was of one seen by General Sushil Rana and R.L. Fleming in September 1973 on the Bagmati River, Kathmandu (243). A fairly common summer visitor to Chitwan and Kosi Barrage. The maximum of 100 has been noted at Kosi in May 1987 (792). Adults with young were found in May on the Karnali River at Bardia (432) and at Kosi Barrage (792). Single reports from elsewhere.

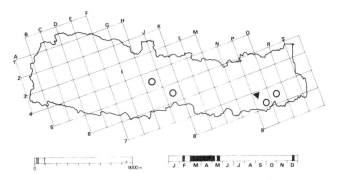

Occurs on rivers and lakes. **Range** Breeds Pakistan, n. India and locally throughout the subcontinent.

WHISKERED TERN *Chlidonias hybridus*

Subspecies *indicus*. First recorded by H.S. Nepali who collected a specimen in Shishawabit-Sapti District (P8) at 190m on 13 February 1971 (589). An irregular and uncommon winter visitor and spring passage migrant to Kosi Barrage. By far the largest number reported is over 400 on 30 April 1982 (561). The only other records are of migrants in March at the Chatra Canal (Q8) (243) and Kosi Tappu (193); in March, April and May at Chitwan (703,205,730) and in May at Phewa Tal (483). **Range** Breeds in Kashmir, n. and n.e. India and Bangladesh. Winters throughout the subcontinent.

WHITE-WINGED TERN   *Chlidonias leucopterus*
White-winged Black Tern

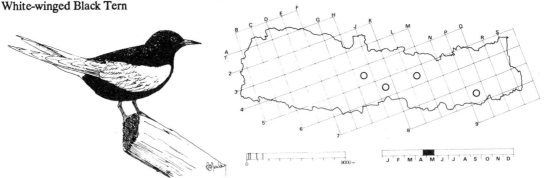

The first confirmed record is one seen at Phewa Tal by N. Krabbe *et al.* on 4 May 1981. They also reported a sighting by another observer at Begnas Tal the previous day (483). A rare spring passage migrant. Small numbers were noted at Kosi Barrage from 30 April to 2 May 1982 (199,294,561), and four there on 19 May 1987 (792,484). The only other sightings are of singles near Sauraha (J6) on 8 May 1982 (703) and in the Kathmandu Valley on 26 April 1985 (418). **Range** Winters in Assam, Bangladesh, and irregularly throughout the rest of the subcontinent.

INDIAN SKIMMER   *Rynchops albicollis*

Obtained by B. Hodgson in his later collection (276), but the specimen may have originated in India. First definitely recorded by R.L. Fleming and H. Gilston at Kosi Barrage on 11 April 1975 (243). Subsequently reported from Kosi Barrage where it is an irregular and uncommon visitor recorded from February to July. A maximum of seven was noted in February and March 1981 (180,442). A pair repeatedly chased other birds from a sandbank in the river in late May 1979, apparently defending territory (509). The only other known locality is the Karnali River close to the Indian border (C5), where two were seen on 30 March 1980 (418). **Range** Large rivers of n. and e. India and Pakistan.

[PAINTED SANDGROUSE
Pterocles indicus

Range Pakistan and India east to Bengal and south to Tamil Nadu.]

[BLACK-BELLIED SANDGROUSE   *Pterocles orientalis*
Imperial Sandgrouse

Subspecies *orientalis*. **Range** Breeds in Pakistan. Winters to n.w. India.]

[CHESTNUT-BELLIED SANDGROUSE
Pterocles exustus
Indian Sandgrouse

Subspecies *erlangeri*. **Range** Baluchistan and India.]

All three sandgrouse species have only been recorded by B. Hodgson (388). The specimens were obtained from the plains and it is possible they originated from an area which nowadays lies in India south of the Nepal border.

ROCK PIGEON *Columba livia*
Rock Dove, Blue Rock Pigeon

Subspecies *intermedia*. First recorded by B. Hodgson (388). An abundant resident subject to altitudinal movements. Summers from the tarai up to 4270m and winters up to at least 2810m. Breeding confirmed in the Kathmandu Valley (659). May nest throughout the year but mainly May to July in the higher Himalayas (53). Inhabits towns and villages, rocky cliffs and gorges. In urban localities the birds are semi-feral interbreeding with domestic varieties. **Range** Throughout the subcontinent.

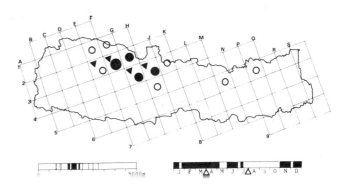

HILL PIGEON *Columba rupestris*
Turkestan Hill Pigeon

Subspecies *turkestanica*. First recorded on 19 December 1963 at Jharkot (H4) at 3350m by R.L. Fleming Jr. (212). A resident usually occurring above 3000m in summer. May move south and to lower elevations in winter after severe weather. Common in the Tibetan plateau region. Found breeding at Shey Gompa (F3) (243). Noted as far south as Macchermo (P6) at 4465m in November 1987 (558), Lamidrung (H5) at 1650m in March 1909 (166), and Kodari (M6) at 2000m (undated) (243). Frequents rocky cliffs, gorges, villages and old buildings. **Range** Himalayas from Gilgit east to Sikkim.

SNOW PIGEON *Columba leuconota*

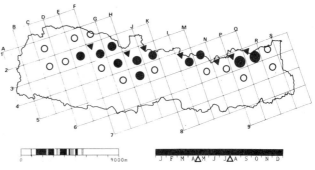

SNOW PIGEON, cont'd ...

Subspecies *leuconota*. The species was first described by Vigors, from a specimen from the Himalayas (788); later given as Nepal by Baker (63). First definitely recorded by B. Hodgson (388). A common

resident of the Himalayas subject to altitudinal movements. Inhabits alpine areas in summer, generally over 3600m. Regularly descends as low as 1500m in winter. Found breeding in the upper Arun (167), and at Khumjung (P6) (190). Occurs on rocky cliffs and gorges. **Range** Himalayas from N.W.F.P. east to Arunachal Pradesh.

COMMON WOODPIGEON *Columba palumbus*
Woodpigeon

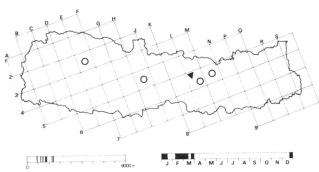

Subspecies *casiotis*. A specimen was listed for Nepal by Salvadori (696), but it may have originated in India. First definitely recorded by R.L. Fleming Sr. on 9 February 1957 at Tin Pani Bhangjang forest, Kathmandu Valley at 2275m (234,245). No further reports until the 1980s. Now an erratic winter visitor occurring in large flocks in some years, but absent in others. Several records from north-west of Pokhara (H5) and the Kathmandu Valley and single reports from Jumla (244) and near Charikot (M6) (748). The maximum of more than 4000 was recorded near Dhampus (H5) at 1800m on 5 March 1983 (66). **Range** Breeds in the Himalayas from N.W.F.P. to Kashmir; east to Nepal in winter.

SPECKLED WOODPIGEON *Columba hodgsonii*

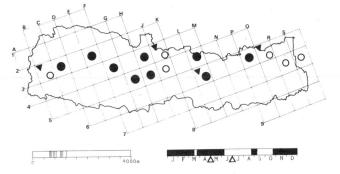

This species was described by Vigors from the Himalayas (789); later given as Nepal by Baker (63). First definitely recorded by B. Hodgson (346). A resident subject to irregular movements appearing wherever its favoured trees have ripe fruit. Over 1000 were estimated near Dhampus

(H5) on 21 January 1985 (150). Occasionally seen in the Kathmandu Valley, Khaptad (C3), north-west of Pokhara and in Langtang. Mainly single reports received from elsewhere. Found in dense broadleaved forests but may also feed on weed seeds and grain. **Range** Himalayas from Gilgit east to Arunachal Pradesh and n.e. India.

ASHY WOODPIGEON *Columba pulchricollis*

This species was described by E. Blyth probably from specimens taken by Hodgson in Nepal (116 ,797). First definitely recorded by B. Hodgson (388). Resident; chiefly occurring above 1100m. Like the Speckled Woodpigeon wanders in search of available fruiting trees. Regularly seen in the Kathmandu Valley and found breeding there in Chapagaon forest (243). Occasionally reported from the upper Mai valley (R7,S7) and from the upper Kali Gandaki valley north to Lete (H4); the western limit of the species's range. Breeding behaviour is little known. Few records from other areas. Frequents dense broadleaved evergreen forests. **Range** Himalayas from Nepal east to Arunachal Pradesh; n.e. India.

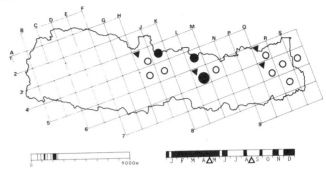

EURASIAN COLLARED DOVE *Streptopelia decaocto*
Indian Ring Dove, Collared Dove

Subspecies *decaocto*. First recorded by B. Hodgson (388). A fairly common resident throughout the tarai and duns mainly found up to 400m; subject to altitudinal movements depending on food supply. Recorded as high as 2440m at Jumla in mid winter (243). Proved breeding at Chitwan (296). Reported feeding on ripening rice in the Kathmandu Valley (635). Found in dry open cultivation with groves. **Range** Throughout the subcontinent.

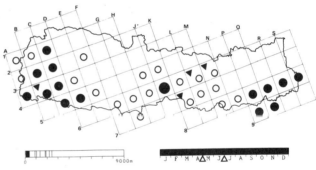

RED TURTLE DOVE *Streptopelia tranquebarica*
Red Collared Dove

First recorded by B. Hodgson (388). A fairly common resident throughout the lowlands up to 300m. Two races occur: *S. t. tranquebarica* (t) and *S. t. humilis* (h). Found breeding at Sukla Phanta (432) and Chitwan (296,432). Mainly a summer visitor at higher altitudes. The maximum height reported is at 1370m in the Kathmandu Valley where it is an uncommon summer visitor from April to September. Occurs in cultivation and open scrub country with scattered broadleaved trees. **Range** Throughout the subcontinent.

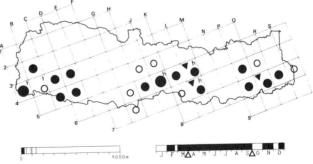

ORIENTAL TURTLE DOVE *Streptopelia orientalis*
Rufous Turtle Dove

First recorded by B. Hodgson (388).
Common. Chiefly a resident and winter
visitor subject to seasonal movements.
Reported from about 365m up to 4570m
in summer. Proved breeding at Jharkot
(H4) (811), the Kathmandu Valley (96),
Hetaura (96) and the upper Mai Valley
(742). In winter mainly occurs below
1370m, occasionally up to 2000m. Some
birds may move south into India. Two
resident races occur *S. o. meena* (m)
(512,647) and *S. o. agricola* (a)
(109,247,659) and intermediates (am)
(96,659,708). Only one record of the
northern race *S. o. orientalis* (o): a pair

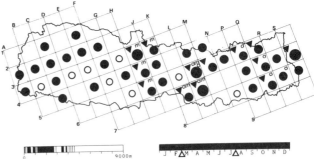

taken on 29 October 1957 at Kapel (L6) (245). Inhabits
open broadleaved forests particularly near cultivation.
Range Throughout the subcontinent except the arid north-
west.

LAUGHING DOVE *Streptopelia senegalensis*
Palm Dove, Little Brown Dove

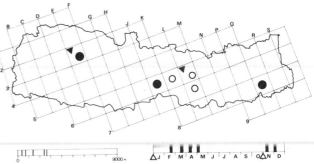

Subspecies *cambayensis*. First recorded
on 2 December 1967 at Balaju (L6) at
1340m by H.S. Nepali (589). Scarce,
status and movements are uncertain.
Reported to winter around Jumla at
2440m (243). A few sightings from Chi-

twan in February, May and November (198,703,813). The
only other records are from Bardia (809), Trisuli River
(243) and Kosi Tappu (327). Breeds chiefly between January and October. Frequents dry cultivation, villages and
open scrub country. **Range** Throughout the subcontinent,
except for n.e. India.

SPOTTED DOVE *Streptopelia chinensis*

Subspecies *suratensis*. First recorded by
B. Hodgson (388). An abundant resident
from the tarai up to 1500m. In summer
occasionally reported up to 2000m and
rarely to 4000m. Proved breeding at
Khaptad (C3) (428), Chitwan (296) and in
the Kathmandu Valley (336,414,756).
Frequents cultivation, gardens and habitation. Generally found in wetter and
more wooded areas than Collared and
Laughing Doves. **Range** Throughout the
subcontinent.

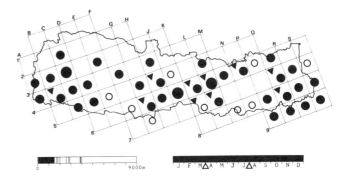

BARRED CUCKOO-DOVE *Macropygia unchall*
Long-tailed Cuckoo-Dove, Bar-tailed Cuckoo-Dove

Subspecies *tusalia*. First recorded by B. Hodgson (388). Mainly a scarce resident. The only place where it is regularly reported is between Sukhani and Garuwa (R8) where flocks of up to seven have been seen (518,559). A few records from Kathmandu Valley forests, particularly on Phulchowki, and near Pokhara. Only single records from elsewhere. Inhabits dense, broadleaved, evergreen forests. **Range** Himalayas from Kashmir to Arunachal Pradesh; n.e. India and Bangladesh.

EMERALD DOVE *Chalcophaps indica*
Green-winged Pigeon, Common Emerald Dove

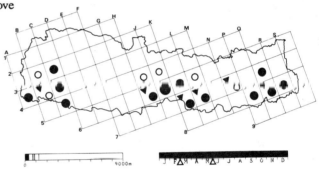

Subspecies *indica*. First recorded by B. Hodgson (388). A sedentary and locally common resident, mainly found up to about 365m. Rarely reported from higher altitudes. Areas include Sukla Phanta, Bardia, Hetaura, north of Sunischare and also Chitwan, where proved breeding (296). Only one record from the Kathmandu Valley: a pair at Gokarna in December 1978 (486). Frequents moist broadleaved forests. **Range** Himalayas from Kashmir east to Arunachal Pradesh; south to Bangladesh and s. India.

ORANGE-BREASTED GREEN PIGEON *Treron bicincta*

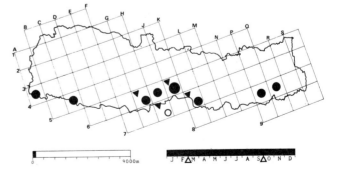

Subspecies *bicincta*. Obtained by B. Hodgson in his later collection (276), but the specimen may have originated in India. First definitely recorded by R.L. Fleming Sr. from Butwal at 275m in January 1950 (647). Locally distributed in the lowlands. A common breeding resident at Chitwan (296). Fairly common at Kosi Tappu (327). Mainly single records from elsewhere. Occurs in sal and riverine forests. **Range** Himalayas from Uttar Pradesh to Arunachal Pradesh; n.e. India, Bangladesh and hills of e. and s.w. India.

POMPADOUR GREEN PIGEON   *Treron pompadora*
Grey-fronted Green Pigeon

The apparently endemic subspecies *conoveri* was first described by R.L. Fleming Sr. from a specimen taken from Butwal at 275m on 25 January 1950 (645,647). A fairly common and locally distributed resident at Chitwan (296,432). Uncommon at Tamaspur, Kosi Tappu and north of Sunischare. Single reports from elsewhere. Sight records from east Nepal at Chatra (518) and Kosi Tappu (174) may refer to *conoveri* or to the eastern subspecies *phayrei*. Frequents sal and riverine forests. **Range** Himalayas from

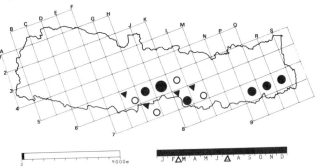

Nepal east to Arunachal Pradesh; n.e. India, Bangladesh and the hills of s.w. India.

THICK-BILLED GREEN PIGEON   *Treron curvirostra*

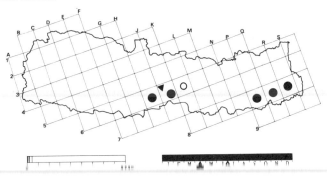

Subspecies *nipalensis*. First recorded by B. Hodgson (355). A scarce and local resident in lowland forests. Several reports from Chitwan (J6,K6). Described as 'occasional' in the eastern tarai (P8,Q8,R8) in 1976 (293) but only six other records received: between Garuwa and Sukhani (R8) (207,559, 561,321,183) and Dharan (561). Found 2 to 3km west of Tamaspur (H6) on 26 April 1978 (159), the westernmost locality for the species. Occurs in sal and riverine forests. **Range** Himalayas from Nepal east to Arunachal Pradesh; n.e. India and Bangladesh.

YELLOW-FOOTED GREEN PIGEON   *Treron phoenicoptera*
Bengal Green Pigeon, Green Pigeon

Subspecies *phoenicoptera*. First recorded by B. Hodgson (388). A resident throughout the lowlands and foothills. Fairly common at Bardia (192) and Chitwan (296), occasionally seen elsewhere up to 250m and uncommon up to 1400m. Noted as high as 1480m in Mechi Zone (658) in January 1989 (658). Occurs in broadleaved forests and groves. **Range** Throughout the subcontinent.

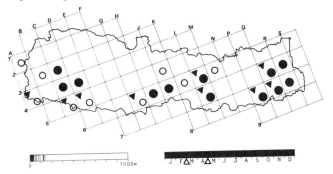

PIN-TAILED GREEN PIGEON *Treron apicauda*

Subspecies *apicauda*. First recorded by B. Hodgson (388). A scarce resident in the lowlands. Several sightings from forests north of Sunischare. Only single records from elsewhere. Noted at Kaneri (B4) (246), Bardia (162), near Pokhara (762), Chitwan (296,762), Tamaspur (486,652), Betrawati (L6) (516) and Hetaura (96). Found in sal and riverine forests. **Range** Himalayas from Kumaon east to Arunachal Pradesh; n.e. India and Bangladesh.

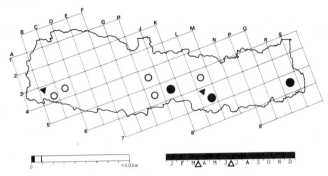

WEDGE-TAILED GREEN PIGEON *Treron sphenura*

Subspecies *sphenura*. First recorded by B. Hodgson (388). A locally fairly common resident subject to seasonal movements, most often seen between 1525m and 2000m. Two seen at 2800m at Chumo (N6) in April 1986 (75). Regularly found in the Kathmandu Valley and Langtang. Occasionally reported north-west of Pokhara and in the Arun and Mai valleys. Mainly single records from elsewhere. Only one record from Chitwan: in the Churia hills (J6) in May 1989 (67). Inhabits mixed broadleaved forests. **Range** Himalayas from Kashmir east to Arunachal Pradesh; n.e. India and Bangladesh.

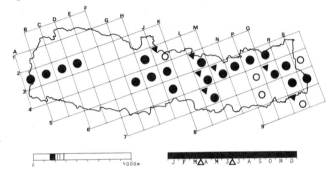

MOUNTAIN IMPERIAL PIGEON *Ducula badia*
Imperial Pigeon, Maroon-backed Imperial Pigeon

Subspecies *insignis*. First recorded by B. Hodgson who obtained a specimen in breeding condition on 24 June from the lower hills (336,355). Scarce, probably resident. Described as possibly occurring in the west (53) but no records have been traced. Three specimens were collected from Walung Forest, Iswa-Arun valley (Q6) between 1150m and 1250m in February 1959 (482). The only other reports are from Chitwan (J6,K6) in October/November 1978 (296,759,762), March 1982 (770) and February 1988 (481), and in the Rapti dun (L7) (undated) (223). Inhabits dense broadleaved forests. **Range** Himalayas from Nepal east to Arunachal Pradesh; n.e. India, Bangladesh and hills of s.w. India.

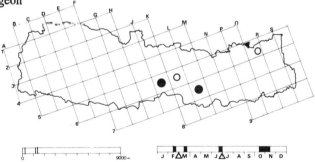

[GREEN IMPERIAL PIGEON *Ducula aenea*

A specimen was listed as doubtfully from
Nepal by Salvadori (696), and others have
also included Nepal in the range of the
species (46,63). No definite records have
been traced. **Range** From e. Uttar
Pradesh east to n.e. India and south to s.
India.]

VERNAL HANGING PARROT *Loriculus vernalis*
Indian Lorikeet

Subspecies *vernalis*. Scarce, probably resident. First recorded by B. Hodgson from the tarai on 20 June (336,358).
Only three other reports: noted as rare at Chitwan (296);
found in the eastern tarai at Jhapa (R9) (undated) (247);
and at Chisapani (N8) at 275m on 23 June 1965 (247). Nests
January to April. Frequents humid forests. **Range** Himalayas from Nepal east to Arunachal Pradesh; n.e. India and
Bangladesh; s. and e. India.

ALEXANDRINE PARAKEET *Psittacula eupatria*
Large Parakeet

Subspecies *nipalensis*. First recorded by
B. Hodgson (358). A common resident in
the tarai and lower hills up to about 365m;
rare at higher altitudes. Proved breeding
at Chitwan (296). Inhabits sal and riverine
forests. **Range** Throughout the subcontinent.

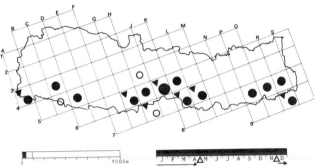

ROSE-RINGED PARAKEET *Psittacula krameri*
Ring-necked Parakeet

Subspecies *borealis*. First recorded by B.
Hodgson (300). An abundant resident up
to 365m. Only occasionally seen at higher
altitudes with the exception of the Kathmandu Valley. It has been frequently
reported from there since 1979, but the
population may have originated from
escaped cage birds. Discovered breeding
in Kathmandu in April 1982 (517); also
proved breeding at Sukla Phanta (432)
and Chitwan (296). Frequents
broadleaved forests, secondary growth,
gardens, cultivation and villages. **Range**
Throughout the subcontinent.

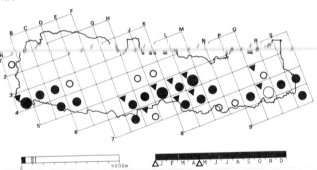

SLATY-HEADED PARAKEET *Psittacula himalayana*

First recorded by B. Hodgson (358). Resident. The only parrot commonly found
above 1350m. Usually summers up to
2000m and winters down to 1000m. Seen
at the unusually high altitude of 3260m on
Machapuchare (244). Infrequently found
at lower altitudes in winter. Common north-west of
Pokhara (H5) and fairly common on hills surrounding the
Kathmandu Valley. Only occasionally seen elsewhere. Frequents broadleaved forests and favours flowering silk cotton trees. **Range** Himalayas from Pakistan east to Arunachal Pradesh.

SLATY-HEADED PARAKEET, cont'd ...

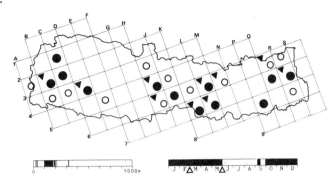

PLUM-HEADED PARAKEET *Psittacula cyanocephala*
Blossom-headed Parakeet

Subspecies *bengalensis*. First recorded by B. Hodgson (388). A fairly common resident throughout the tarai and lower hills up to 500m; occasionally reported up to 1525m. Proved breeding at Chitwan (296). Described in 1949 as moderately common in the Kathmandu Valley and surrounding hills (629), but there are very few later records. Occurs in well-wooded areas. **Range** Pakistan, India east to Bhutan duars and Nepal.

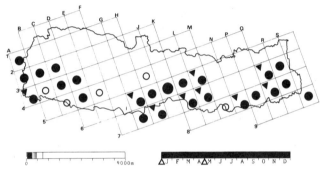

MOUSTACHED PARAKEET *Psittacula alexandri*
Rose-breasted Parakeet

Subspecies *fasciata*. First recorded by B. Hodgson (336,358). A locally fairly common resident, rarely found above 365m. Areas include north of Sunischare and also Chitwan where proved breeding (296). Described as a common local migrant from January to June in Morang District (Q8) (293). Recorded from the Kathmandu Valley last century (336,708), but no later records. Frequents open broadleaved forests and groves. **Range** Himalayas from Kumaon east to Arunachal Pradesh; n.e. India and Bangladesh.

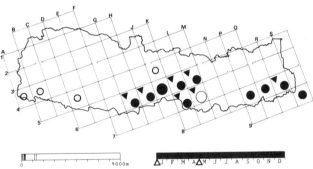

PIED CUCKOO *Clamator jacobinus*
Pied Crested Cuckoo, Jacobin Cuckoo

Subspecies *serratus*. First recorded by B. Hodgson (388). A summer visitor mainly occurring up to 365m, but one noted as high as 3660m in Khumbu (243). Most reports are during the monsoon. Uncommon at Chitwan and scarce elsewhere.

Localities include Sukla Phanta (700), Dipayal (B3) (68), Hetaura (96,245, 601), the Kathmandu Valley, Kosi Tappu (174,432,597) and elsewhere in the east (P8,Q8) (293). One was collected in the Kathmandu Valley on 11 January 1962 (190), the only winter record for the Indian subcontinent. Inhabits broadleaved forests. **Range** Throughout the subcontinent.

PIED CUCKOO, cont'd ...

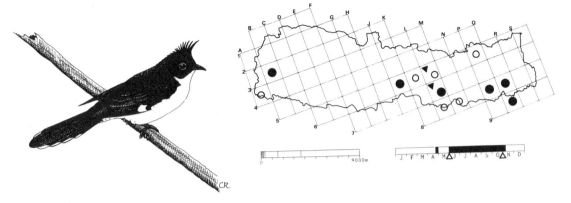

CHESTNUT-WINGED CUCKOO *Clamator coromandus*
Red-winged Crested Cuckoo

First recorded by B. Hodgson (388). A very local summer visitor, mainly occurring from 250m to 365m. Fairly common at Chitwan where proved breeding (296). A few have been seen passing through the Kathmandu Valley from April to June (243), in August (68) and October (589). Fairly common in the Hetaura duns in May and June 1947 (96), but no later records. The only other reports are from near Pokhara in 1977 (762) and near Dharan in April 1986 (763,546). Frequents both dense and light broadleaved forests, also thorny undergrowth and scrub. **Range** Breeds in the Himalayas from Garhwal east to Arunachal Pradesh, and in n.e. India. Winters in s. India.

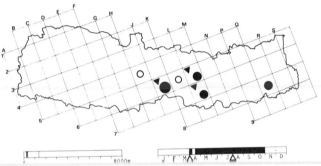

HODGSON'S HAWK-CUCKOO *Hierococcyx fugax*
(*Cuculus fugax*)

Subspecies *nisicolor*. First recorded by B. Hodgson who obtained at least one specimen from the lower hills in April (336,388). The only other record is of one seen at Kosi Tappu on 11 March 1988 (328). Found in broadleaved wooded country (53). **Range** Himalayas from Nepal east to Arunachal Pradesh; n.e. India and Bangladesh.

COMMON HAWK-CUCKOO *Hierococcyx varius* (*Cuculus varius*)

Subspecies *varius*. First recorded by B. Hodgson (388). A common resident from the tarai up to 1000m; rarely found higher. Reported to breed in small numbers in the Kathmandu Valley last century (708), but there are few later records. Proved breeding at Chitwan (296). Like other cuckoos it is silent for much of the non-breeding season and is then easily overlooked. Occurs in lightly-wooded areas including gardens, cultivation and groves. **Range** Throughout the subcontinent.

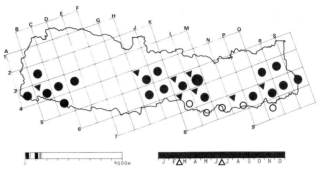

LARGE HAWK-CUCKOO *Hierococcyx sparverioides* (*Cuculus sparverioides*)

Subspecies *sparverioides*. First recorded by B. Hodgson (388). Mainly a fairly common summer visitor between 1830m and 3000m. Found breeding in the eastern hills (Q8) (293). Most birds move south to the Indian peninsula but there are a few winter records: noted at 1800m and 2460m (780), and one was also taken at 1830m in Nawakot District in January (647). One, presumably on passage, was seen at Chitwan on 29 April 1980 (440). Found in broadleaved forests, especially in oaks. **Range** Breeds in the Himalayas from Pakistan east to Arunachal Pradesh and in n.e. India. Winters south to s. India.

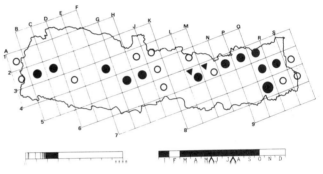

ASIAN EMERALD CUCKOO *Chrysococcyx maculatus*
Emerald Cuckoo (*Chalcites maculatus*)

First recorded by B. Hodgson from the Kathmandu Valley and Bhimpedi, in June, August and September (336,388). A scarce summer visitor. There are three reports from the Kathmandu Valley: a small party seen on 7 September in the early 1950s (635); a specimen taken in May 1959 by the Vishnumati River (247);

and one found in August 1978 at Gokarna (688). The only other records are of singles found in April at Chitwan in 1982 (296,432), and at 1830m near Pokhara (250), and one at Malunga (H6) in September 1988 (575). Nests mid-April to July. Occurs in evergreen, broadleaved forests. **Range** Breeds in the Himalayas from Garhwal east to Arunachal Pradesh, and in n.e. India and Bangladesh.

GREY-BELLIED PLAINTIVE CUCKOO   *Cacomantis passerinus*
Grey-bellied Cuckoo, Indian Plaintive Cuckoo

First recorded by B. Hodgson (388). Occasional. A summer visitor mainly reported between late April and August from the tarai up to 1400m; rare up to 2135m. Probably overlooked because of its resemblance to Black-winged Cuckoo-Shrike, and its silence after breeding. Localities include Dandeldhura and Doti Districts (B3,C3) (657), Chitwan, Kathmandu Valley, upper Arun valley (483), Mechi Zone (R7,R8) (658) and Kosi Tappu. Frequents groves and open forests. **Range** Summers in n. Pakistan and n. India from Kashmir and Mt. Abu east to Bhutan and Meghalaya. Winters south to s. India.

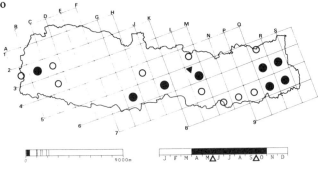

RUFOUS-BELLIED PLAINTIVE CUCKOO   *Cacomantis merulinus*
Plaintive Cuckoo

Subspecies *querulus*. A Hodgson specimen was listed for Nepal by Shelley (724), but it may have originated in India. First definitely recorded by A. Goodwin and S. Gawn who saw one at Chitwan on 21 February 1986 (264,260). The only other record is of one at Kosi Barrage on 9 February 1989 (468). Sometimes considered conspecific with Grey-bellied Plaintive Cuckoo (243). Occurs in well-wooded country (53). **Range** Himalayas from Nepal east to Arunachal Pradesh; n.e. India and Bangladesh.

BANDED BAY CUCKOO   *Cacomantis sonneratii*

Subspecies *sonneratii*. A Hodgson specimen was listed for Nepal by Shelley (724), but it may have originated in India. First definitely recorded by F.M. Bailey from Tribeni (H7) at 75m on 29 December 1935 (62). An uncommon visitor to Chitwan from February to October (296). Mainly single reports from elsewhere. Recently found north of Sunischare (R8) (518,307), Tamaspur (682), lower Arun valley (590), Dharan (561,307,597). Inhabits dense broadleaved forests in the lowlands. **Range** Himalayas from Kumaon east to Arunachal Pradesh; south to Bangladesh and s. India.

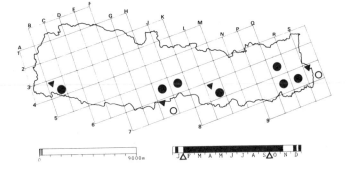

INDIAN CUCKOO *Cuculus micropterus*
Short-winged Cuckoo

Subspecies *micropterus*. First recorded by
B. Hodgson (388). Mainly a summer visitor, although reported to be resident in
the eastern tarai (P8,Q8) (174,293).
Common in spring and summer from
April onwards from the tarai up to 2100m.
Occasionally moves above this altitude.
Occurs at Chitwan (J6,K6) between February and September and arrives in the
Kathmandu Valley in early April. Proved
breeding in both areas (296,629). Frequents forests, well-wooded country and
groves. **Range** Throughout the subcontinent except the arid north-west.

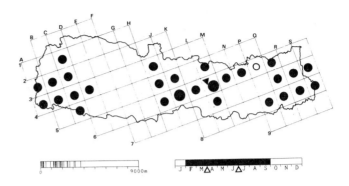

EURASIAN CUCKOO *Cuculus canorus*
Common Cuckoo

First recorded by B. Hodgson (388). A
common summer visitor from 915m to
3800m; uncommon up to 915m from
March to September. Two intergrading
races occur, *C. c. canorus* (c) (96,647,708)
and *C. c. bakeri* (b) (22). The species
occurs in the Kathmandu Valley between
early April and early October (629,708).
Many seen passing through in September
and October (629). Breeding confirmed
at Manangbhot (J4) (512), in the Kathmandu Valley (708), and the upper Mai
valley (S7) (735). Inhabits open wooded
country and secondary growth. **Range**
Breeds in the Himalayas from N.W.F.P.
to Arunachal Pradesh, and in n.e. India.
Winters south to s. India.

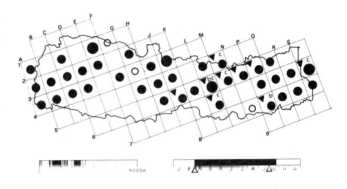

ORIENTAL CUCKOO *Cuculus saturatus*
Himalayan Cuckoo

Subspecies *saturatus*. The species was
described by E. Blyth from Hodgson
specimens taken in Nepal (114,797). Possibly resident in the Himalayas (53), and
reported to descend to lower altitudes in
the foothills and plains in winter (243).
However Nepalese records received are
from the end of March to September.
Common between 1525m and 3050m in
spring and summer from April onwards.
Proved breeding at Godavari (96, 432).
Occurs in open wooded country. **Range**
Breeds in the Himalayas from N.W.F.P.
east to Arunachal Pradesh, and n.e. India.

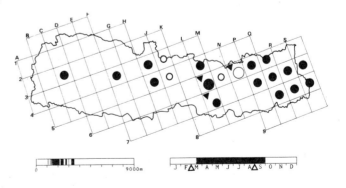

LESSER CUCKOO *Cuculus poliocephalus*
Little Cuckoo, Small Cuckoo

A Hodgson specimen was listed for Nepal by Shelley (724), but it may have originated in India. First definitely recorded by H. Stevens from the upper Mai valley (S7) at about 2135m on 25 May 1912 (741). A summer visitor chiefly occurring between 1500m and 3660m. Common on Sheopuri in spring (243), fairly common at Khaptad (C3) (428), in the middle hills (L5,L6,P6) (559), in Langtang and in the upper Arun valley. Single reports from elsewhere. Possibly under-recorded because of its late arrival in spring. Inhabits dense broadleaved forests. **Range** Breeds

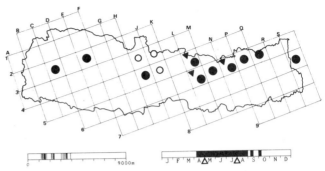

in the Himalayas from Pakistan east to Arunachal Pradesh and n.e. India. Migrates through Bangladesh and the Indian peninsula.

DRONGO-CUCKOO *Surniculus lugubris*

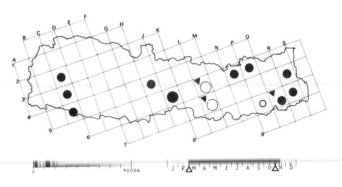

Subspecies *dicruroides*. First recorded by B. Hodgson (382). A local summer visitor mainly occurring up to 1500m. Noted at 2000m at Gopetar (R7) in May (658). A common breeder at Chitwan, where it is reported from April to early November

(296,597). Fairly common in the Kathmandu Valley in spring (243,635). Mainly single reports from elsewhere. Other localities include Khaptad (C3) (428), Bardia, Kosi Tappu, Dharan, and Sukhani to Garuwa (R8). Frequents edges and clearings of forests and groves. **Range** Throughout the subcontinent, except the arid north-west.

COMMON KOEL *Eudynamys scolopacea*
Koel Cuckoo, Asian Koel

Subspecies *scolopacea*, First recorded by B. Hodgson (388). Common throughout up to 1370m. Noted between 1700m and 1800m in the east at Taplejung (R7) (658) and in Dhankuta District (Q7) (613). Reported to be resident at Bardia (192) and in the eastern tarai and foothills

(P8,Q8) (174,293); possibly resident at Sukla Phanta (700). A summer visitor to the Kathmandu Valley chiefly occurring from March to October (417). Uncommon at Chitwan (J6,K6) and only found there from March to September. Occurs in gardens, groves, cultivation and villages. **Range** Throughout the subcontinent.

COMMON KOEL, cont'd ...

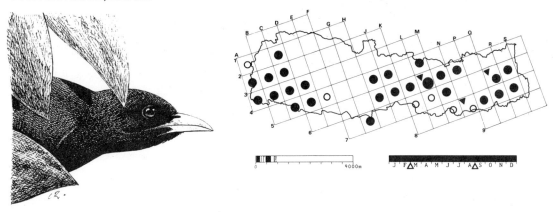

GREEN-BILLED MALKOHA *Phaenicophaeus tristis*
Large Green-billed Malkoha (*Rhopodytes tristis*)

Subspecies *tristis*. First recorded by B. Hodgson (388). Fairly common up to about 700m; uncommon at higher altitudes. Resident at Bardia (192), Chitwan (296), and near Dharan (293). A summer visitor to the Kathmandu Valley where it is chiefly reported from April to September. Breeding confirmed at Chitwan (296). Inhabits dense thickets in forests. **Range** Himalayas from Garhwal east to Arunachal Pradesh, extending south to e. Madhya Pradesh and Bangladesh.

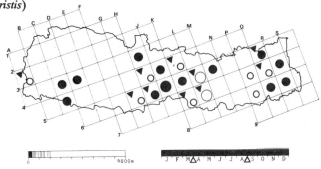

SIRKEER MALKOHA *Phaenicophaeus leschenaultii*
Sirkeer Cuckoo (*Taccocua leschenaultii*)

Subspecies *infuscatus*. First recorded by B. Hodgson (388). Resident up to about 365m. Occasionally seen in the far west at Sukla Phanta and Bardia; uncommon further east. Found in scrub, thorny bushes and acacia trees in dry stony areas. **Range** Throughout the subcontinent.

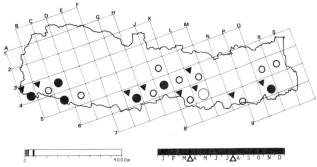

GREATER COUCAL *Centropus sinensis*
Large Coucal, Common Crow-Pheasant

Subspecies *sinensis*. First recorded by B. Hodgson (388). A common and sedentary resident mainly found up to about 365m. Up to three seen in June 1988 at the unusually high altitude of 850m to 900m in Ilam District (R8), including a mating pair (658). Proved breeding at Chitwan (296). Occurs in tall grasslands and thickets near cultivation, gardens and villages. **Range** Throughout the subcontinent.

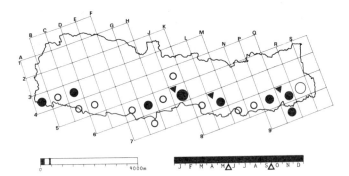

LESSER COUCAL *Centropus bengalensis*
Small Coucal (*Centropus toulou*)

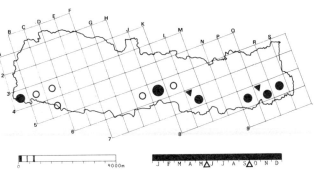

Subspecies *bengalensis*. First recorded by B. Hodgson (388). A local resident and possibly also a summer migrant, chiefly reported up to 365m. Seen several times between 750m and 1400m at Jitpur and Siddhithumka, Ilam District (R8) on 26 June 1988 (658). Fairly common at Chitwan where proved breeding. Numbers are noted to increase there in summer (296). Occasionally reported from elsewhere. Found in large expanses of tall grassland and reedbeds in the lowlands, and in Salima grass with bamboo clumps and scattered trees and bushes (658). **Range** Himalayas from Dehra Dun east to Arunachal Pradesh; n.e. India and Bangladesh south to Orissa; also s.w. India.

BARN OWL *Tyto alba*
Common Barn Owl

Subspecies *stertens*. First recorded by B. Hodgson (385). A local resident. Uncommon in the Kathmandu Valley where it roosts in the roofs of old buildings. Several recent sightings from Durbar Square, Kathmandu. A family group was observed on the roof of Kalimati Durbar in January (247). The only other report is from south of Annapurna in 1977 (762). Crepuscular and nocturnal. Breeds practically all year (53). **Range** Throughout the subcontinent.

GRASS OWL *Tyto capensis*

Subspecies *longimembris*. First reported by R.L. Fleming Sr. who purchased an owlet taken by Tharus, west of the Narayani River, Chitwan in November 1964 (247). Rare and local. Resident at Chitwan (J6,K6) at 225m, where it breeds (296,244); possibly resident at Sukla Phanta (700). Breeds from October to March. Occurs only in tall grasslands. Crepuscular and nocturnal. **Range** Himalayas from Dehra Dun to West Bengal; Assam and Meghalaya; e. and s.w. India.

[ORIENTAL BAY OWL *Phodilus badius*

Subspecies *saturatus*. Only recorded by B. Hodgson who obtained a skin from a shop near Kathmandu (336,388). It is possible the bird may not have originated in Nepal. **Range** Himalayas from Nepal?, Sikkim and Bhutan?; n.e. and s.w. India.]

COLLARED SCOPS OWL *Otus bakkamoena*

First recorded by B. Hodgson (357). A local resident of uncertain status, found between 185m and 1525m. Like other scops owls it is probably under-recorded as it is strictly nocturnal and usually only located by its characteristic calls. Reported as common in the central dun (L7) in 1947 (98), but only one subsequent record (190). Described as common in the Kathmandu Valley in 1949 (635), seen there occasionally in 1970 (240) but with few later records. Proved breeding at Chitwan (296), in Kathmandu in 1986 and 1987 (418) and at Hetaura (98). Two races have been recorded: *O. b. lettia* (l) (98,190) and *O. b. gangeticus* (g) (23,247,807) and it has recently been proposed to treat these as races of two different species (678) on the basis of different calls. However, the situation in the western Himalayas is not resolved and some authorities regard the variation in calls as intraspecific (790). Inhabits mixed forest and groves near cultivation and villages. **Range** Throughout the subcontinent.

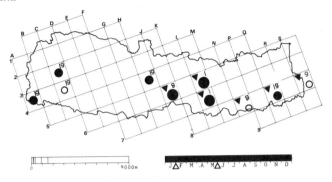

ORIENTAL SCOPS OWL *Otus sunia*
Scops Owl (*Otus scops*)

Subspecies *sunia*. The species was described from Nepal by B. Hodgson (357,797). Mainly a fairly common resident of the tarai and lower hills but occurs up to 1525m (247). Found to be common between Dhangarhi and Nepalganj in March and April 1988 (792). A vagrant taken at Jomosom at 2745m in December (243) is perhaps more likely referable to the Eurasian Scops Owl *O. scops turanicus*. Confirmed breeding at Chitwan (296). Found in forests, secondary growth and groves. **Range** Himalayas from Pakistan east to Arunachal Pradesh; south to s. India.

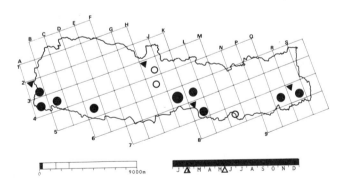

MOUNTAIN SCOPS OWL *Otus spilocephalus*
Spotted Scops Owl

First recorded by B. Hodgson who found it breeding in the Kathmandu Valley (336,388). Resident, mainly found between 1830m and 2590m. Fairly common north-west of Pokhara (H5) and on hills surrounding the Kathmandu Valley. It is likely that two intergrading races occur. Specimens from central Nepal (L6) showed features between *O. s. huttoni* and *O. s. spilocephalus* (98,647). Mainly single records from elsewhere. Inhabits dense evergreen, broadleaved forests. **Range** Himalayas from Pakistan east to Arunachal Pradesh; n.e. India and Bangladesh.

EURASIAN EAGLE OWL *Bubo bubo*
Northern Eagle Owl, Great Horned Owl

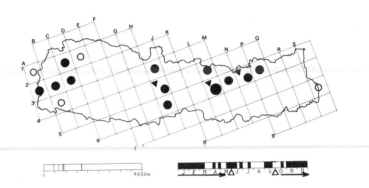

Subspecies *bengalensis*. First recorded by B. Hodgson who found it breeding on Sheopuri (336,357). A local resident occasionally reported from around Pokhara and in the Kathmandu Valley, especially on Nagarjung. Single records from elsewhere. Found as high as 3415m on Machapuchare (244). Frequents wooded country with cliffs or rocky ravines where it roosts during the day. **Range** Throughout the subcontinent.

SPOT-BELLIED EAGLE OWL *Bubo nipalensis*
Forest Eagle Owl

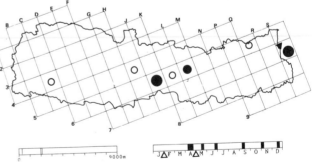

Subspecies *nipalensis*. The species was described from Nepal by B. Hodgson (357,797). Rare and local. Resident at Chitwan (J6,K6) where it breeds (296). Seen a few times on cliffs at Nagarjung (L6). A nestling was taken on 14 April 1912 in the Mai Khola Valley (742). The only other reports are from south of Annapurna in 1977 (762), the Barun valley (Q6) (588) and Gokarna (L6) (418) in 1984, and Bardia (C4) in 1986 (796). Occurs in dense evergreen forests. Nocturnal. **Range** Himalayas from Kumaon to Arunachal Pradesh; n.e. and s.w. India, and Bangladesh.

DUSKY EAGLE OWL *Bubo coromandus*
Dusky Horned Owl

Subspecies *coromandus*. First recorded by B. Hodgson from the tarai and lower hills (336,372). In 1976 found to be a breeding resident, occasionally seen at Kosi Tappu (174,175), but no later reports from there. A few records from Chitwan (J6) between 1984 and 1988 (771,562,792), including an adult photographed with young in February 1984 (196). Breeds December to January. Inhabits wooded areas near water. Semi-diurnal. **Range** Locally throughout the subcontinent.

BROWN FISH OWL *Ketupa zeylonensis*
(*Bubo zeylonensis*)

Subspecies *leschenault*. First recorded by B. Hodgson (363). Mainly a resident found occasionally from the tarai up to 1525m. Breeding confirmed at Hetaura (98) and Gokarna (635). Like other fish-eating birds of prey it is uncommon at Chitwan (296,759). Frequents densely wooded areas near water. Semi-diurnal. **Range** Throughout the subcontinent.

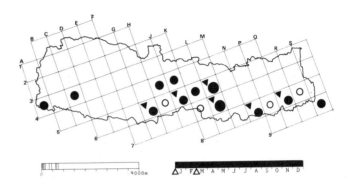

TAWNY FISH OWL *Ketupa flavipes*
(*Bubo flavipes*)

The species was described from Nepal by B. Hodgson who obtained at least six specimens from the lower hills (336,363,797). Very rare, presumably resident. Only three other reports: a bird was obtained at Bhugwada (location unknown) on 30 November 1920 (23). An adult and two juveniles were taken at Hetaura on 18 May and 2 June 1947 (98). Seen at Chitwan in October/November 1978 (759,762). Breeding behaviour is little known, probably December to February. Found in forested ravines near water. Crepuscular and semi-diurnal. **Range** Himalayas from Kashmir to Arunachal Pradesh; n.e. India and Bangladesh.

COLLARED OWLET *Glaucidium brodiei*
Collared Pygmy Owlet

Subspecies *brodiei*. First recorded by B. Hodgson (357). A fairly common, locally distributed resident mainly seen between 1350m and 2900m. Areas include north-west of Pokhara, Langtang, hills surrounding the Kathmandu Valley and the upper Arun and Mai valleys. Inhabits mixed oak forests. Diurnal and calls persistently. **Range** Himalayas from Chitral east to Arunachal Pradesh; n.e. India and Bangladesh.

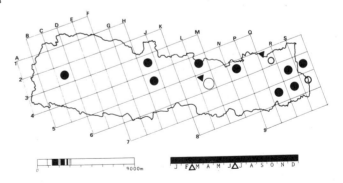

JUNGLE OWLET   *Glaucidium radiatum*
Barred Jungle Owlet

Subspecies *radiatum*. First recorded by B. Hodgson (372). A common resident, mainly occurring from the tarai up to 915m. A few records from north-west of Pokhara (H5) between 1430m and 1600m (451,436,152). Apparently recently extended its range to the Kathmandu Valley; present at Rani Bari all year in 1987 (792). Proved breeding at Chitwan (296) and Hetaura (98). Found in open forests and secondary jungle. Mainly crepuscular. **Range** Himalayas from Himachal Pradesh to Bhutan; south through India to Sri Lanka.

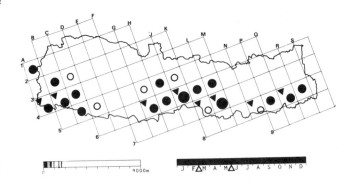

ASIAN BARRED OWLET   *Glaucidium cuculoides*
Barred Owlet

Subspecies *cuculoides*. First recorded by B. Hodgson (372). A common resident, mainly occurring between 245m and 2440m. Proved breeding at Pokhara (326), Chitwan (296) and Hetaura (98). Its altitudinal zone overlaps with that of Jungle Owlet between 160m and 915m. Both species not only breed in the same forests but are also common there (98,296). Frequents open forests. Diurnal. **Range** Himalayas from Murree east to Arunachal Pradesh; n.e. India and Bangladesh.

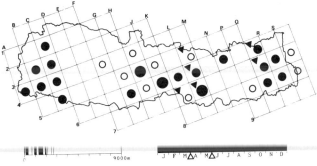

BROWN HAWK OWL   *Ninox scutulata*
Brown Boobook

Subspecies *lugubris*. First recorded by B. Hodgson (370). Resident. Fairly common at Chitwan (296) and occasionally found elsewhere. Breeding behaviour of this race is little known. Three family parties with flying young between 24 July and mid-August in the Kathmandu Valley (792). One in breeding condition was taken at Hetaura on 27 March (190). Inhabits forests and well-wooded areas often near water. Crepuscular and nocturnal. Range Himalayas from Dehra Dun east to Arunachal Pradesh; south to s. India and Bangladesh.

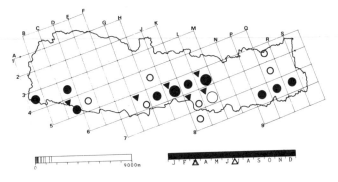

LITTLE OWL *Athene noctua*
Tibet Owlet, Northern Little Owl

Subspecies *ludlowi*. First recorded by O. Polunin at Terengaon (G4) at 4115m on 12 June 1952 (620). Scarce, presumably resident. Occurs in the Tibetan plateau region between 2715m and 4155m. Singles were taken at Terco Phijar (F3) on 8 July and at Tnku, Do Trap (F3) on 23 July 1978 (587). All other records are from Thakkhola (H4): several reports of one or two birds from January to April between 1979 and 1987. Found on stone walls of old buildings and rocky cliffs. Mainly crepuscular and nocturnal. **Range** Baluchistan; Himalayas in N.W.F.P., Baltistan, Ladakh and Nepal.

SPOTTED OWLET *Athene brama*
Spotted Little Owl

Subspecies *indica*. First recorded by B. Hodgson (357). A common resident from the tarai up to 1525m. Breeding confirmed at Majhagaon (A4) (432), northwest of Pokhara (811), Kathmandu (417), Chitwan (296) and Dharan (281). A straggler was collected at 2745m at Khangjung (L5) on 4 September 1949 (619,621). Inhabits villages, towns, ruins and cultivation. Mainly crepuscular and nocturnal. **Range** Throughout the subcontinent.

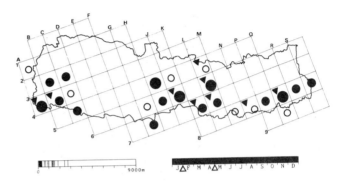

BROWN WOOD OWL *Strix leptogrammica*

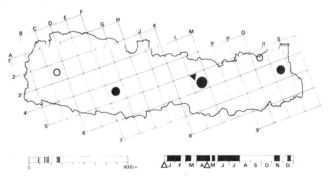

Subspecies *newarensis*. First recorded by B. Hodgson (357). Found between 760m and 2700m. A resident reported occasionally from the Kathmandu Valley. A pair was seen feeding young in May at Rani Bagh (629). Status elsewhere is uncertain; probably under-recorded. Found in west-central Nepal (F5) in 1977 (563), Mai Pokhari (R7) in April 1982 (561), Barun valley (Q6) in November 1984 (588) and at Khaptad (C3) in May 1988 (428). Frequents dense broadleaved forests. Usually nocturnal although a pair was observed feeding young in daylight (629). One flew over Kathmandu chased by a large crow flock in April 1976 (82). **Range** Himalayas from Pakistan east to Sikkim and Arunachal Pradesh?; south through the peninsula.

TAWNY OWL *Strix aluco*
Tawny Wood Owl

First recorded by B. Hodgson (388). Two races possibly occur. *S. a. nivicola* is an uncommon resident. A pair possibly of the race *biddulphi* was seen at Lete (H4) at 2440m on 4 January 1974 (518). This race previously only reported as far east as north of Mussoorie (53). Areas where the species has been recorded include Khaptad (C3), north-west of Pokhara, Langtang, Khumbu and the Arun valley. Probably under-recorded as it is nocturnal and more often heard than seen. Frequents oak, rhododendron and conifer-

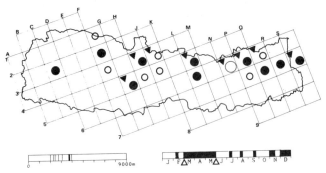

ous forests. **Range** N. Baluchistan and Himalayas from Chitral east to Arunachal Pradesh.

LONG-EARED OWL *Asio otus*

Subspecies *otus*. First recorded by B. Hodgson from the Kathmandu Valley on 20 November (336,372). The only other report is of one taken on the Kakani hills

(L6) at 2000m on 11 November 1962 (190). Nocturnal. **Range** Single breeding records from Baluchistan and Kashmir. Occurs elsewhere in Pakistan and n.w. India.

SHORT-EARED OWL *Asio flammeus*

Subspecies *flammeus*. First recorded by B. Hodgson (372). An uncommon winter visitor and passage migrant. Described last century by Hodgson as the common field owl of the Kathmandu Valley (336) but there is just one later record (98). Several reports from Chitwan and also Kosi Barrage, with a maximum of seven at the latter site on 4 November 1989 (597). A few records from north-west of Pokhara. Singles found on Machapuchare at 3320m on 10 April 1979 and 3260m on 1 October 1979 (244). Found in

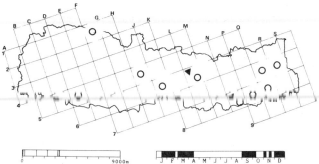

grassland and open scrub country. Diurnal and crepuscular. **Range** Winter visitor throughout the subcontinent.

SAVANNA NIGHTJAR *Caprimulgus affinis*
Franklin's Nightjar

Subspecies *monticolus*. First recorded by B. Hodgson (388). Mainly occurs up to 915m. Movements are unclear. Only two winter records: singles collected at Simery (L7) in January (589) and seen at Chitwan (K6) in February (481).The lack of winter records may be attributed to the species's silence during the non-breeding season. Fairly common at Chitwan (J6,K6) and confirmed breeding there (296). Occasionally seen at Sukla Phanta (700) and a common resident at Bardia (192). Found in small numbers in the central bhabar and dun (K7,L7) (98). Only single records

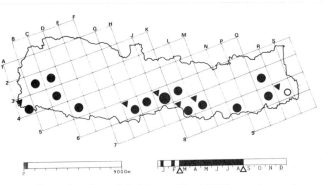

from elsewhere. Inhabits scrubby hillsides and open forest. Crepuscular and nocturnal like other nightjars, **Range** From Punjab and Gujarat east through the subcontinent.

INDIAN NIGHTJAR *Caprimulgus asiaticus*
Little Nightjar, Common Indian Nightjar

Subspecies *asiaticus*. First recorded on 22 March 1961 at Simra Airport (K7) at 105m by R.L. Fleming (234,246). Scarce. Movements are uncertain. Probably under-recorded as its call is not very obvious. Described as resident at Sukla Phanta (700). A few spring records from Chitwan (296,800,172). The only other reports are from Bardia (128,432,202), near Gorsinge (F6) (157), Tilaurakot (G6) (157), and the eastern tarai near Chatra (281,293), Dharan (652) and Kosi Tappu (432). Occurs in open scrub and cultivation in the tarai. **Range** The whole subcontinent east of the Indus Valley.

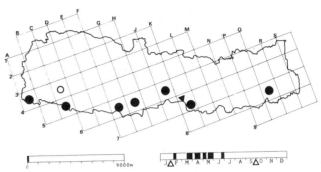

LARGE-TAILED NIGHTJAR *Caprimulgus macrurus*
Long-tailed Nightjar

Subspecies *albonotatus*. First recorded by B. Hodgson (388). Fairly common in forests of the tarai and foothills up to 915m. Movements uncertain. Found at Chitwan (J6,K6) from February/March to October/November. Proved breeding there (296). Reported as resident at Sukla Phanta (700), Bardia (192), Kosi Tappu (174) and elsewhere in the east (P8,Q8) (222) A summer visitor, seen occasionally in the Kathmandu Valley (240); heard as early as 13 March (629) and one collected there on 31 January (589). Hunts in forest clearings. **Range** Himalayas from Kangra to Arunachal Pradesh; south to Bangladesh and s. India, but absent from much of the north-west.

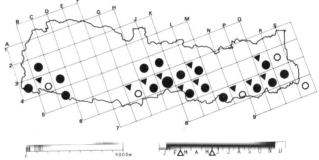

JUNGLE NIGHTJAR *Caprimulgus indicus*
Grey Nightjar

Subspecies *hazarae*. First recorded by B. Hodgson (388). A fairly common resident and partial altitudinal migrant. Regularly found up to 2895m in summer. First heard calling on hills surrounding the Kathmandu Valley in mid-March and probably resident there (632). In winter mainly reported from 180m up to 915m. Birds at Chitwan considered possibly on passage (296). Frequents forest clearings and scrub-covered hillsides. **Range** Himalayas from Hazara to Arunachal Pradesh; n.e. India and Bangladesh; south through Rajasthan to s. India.

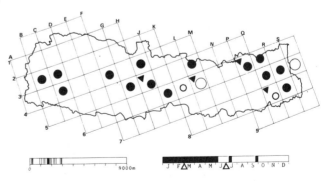

HIMALAYAN SWIFTLET *Collocalia brevirostris*
(*Aerodramus brevirostris*)

Subspecies *brevirostris*. Obtained by B. Hodgson in his later collection (409) but the specimen may have originated in India. First definitely recorded by J. Scully from the Kathmandu Valley on 20 August 1877 (708). A fairly common resident subject to altitudinal movements. Summers up to 4575m. Usually winters between 915m and 2745m and occasionally in the lowlands. Two records from the tarai: in the east (Q8) on 29 June 1975 (293) and at Majhagaon (A4) on 13 May 1982 after storms (432). Gregarious; 2000 estimated over Phewa Tal on 14 January

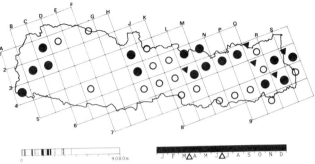

1989 (152). **Range** Himalayas from Himachal Pradesh east to Arunachal Pradesh, and n.e. India.

WHITE-RUMPED NEEDLETAIL *Zoonavena sylvatica*
White-rumped Spinetail Swift (*Chaetura sylvatica*)

First recorded by R.L. Fleming Jr. on 16 March 1972 from Mahendra Rajmarj (J6) (243). Local and uncommon, possibly resident. Regularly seen at Chitwan. Other reports are from Sukla Phanta (432), Bardia (432,162), Nepalganj (627), Majhagaon (A4) (811), Butwal (178),

Tamaspur (206,486,652) and north of Sunischare (59). Movements are poorly known. Noted in winter at Tamaspur and at Chitwan. Breeding habits of the northern population are unknown. Seen at nesthole at Mahendranagar (A4) on 5 March 1981 (811). Hawks insects over lowland forests. **Range** Himalayas in Garhwal, Nepal and Sikkim; Meghalaya and Bangladesh; locally to s.w. India.

WHITE-THROATED NEEDLETAIL *Hirundapus caudacutus*
White-throated Spinetail Swift (*Chaetura caudacuta*)

Subspecies *nudipes*. First recorded by B. Hodgson (352). Status and movements are uncertain. Like other swifts it is possibly under-recorded as it often feeds at high altitude. Some reports received probably refer to White-vented Needletails as the two forms have often been regarded as conspecific (54,243). Areas where reliably seen include Phewa Tal,

Chitwan, Langtang, Kathmandu Valley, Jamuna (R7), Dharan and north of Sunischare. Breeding behaviour is poorly known. Only two winter records: on 31 January 1981 at Hetaura (476) and 11 January 1989 at Birethante (H5) (152), but this subspecies is often considered to be resident. The maximum altitude recorded is 3100m at Khaptad (C3); several reports in April, May and June (657,428). **Range** Himalayas from Hazara to Arunachal Pradesh and n.e. India.

WHITE-THROATED NEEDLETAIL, cont'd ...

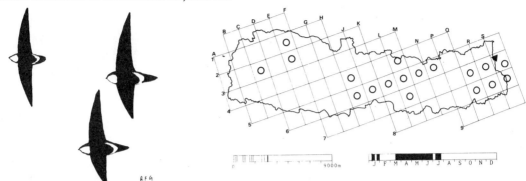

WHITE-VENTED NEEDLETAIL *Hirundapus cochinchinensis*
White-vented Spinetail Swift (*Chaetura cochinchinensis*)

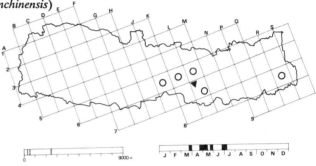

The apparently endemic subspecies *rupchandi* was described by B. Biswas. He observed flocks of about a dozen birds and took specimens on 24 June and 6 July 1947 at Hetaura (98). Its status and movements are poorly known. Probably overlooked because of confusion with White-throated Needletail. Later found near Hetaura in April in 1959 (245) and 1985 (332). Described as rare and possibly resident at Chitwan (296) but several reports received from there with a maximum of 16 seen on 26 April 1982 (432). Four noted flying over Phulchowki at 2440m on 4 May 1980 (440). The only other record is from north of Sunischare in late March 1985 (59). Breeding details are unknown. **Range** Nepal, Meghalaya and Manipur.

COMMON SWIFT *Apus apus*
Black Swift

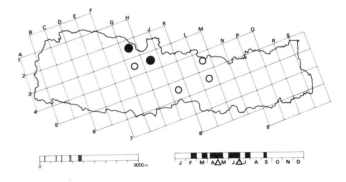

Subspecies *pekinensis*. First recorded by R.L. Fleming Jr. in Dolpo (H3) at 3355m in June 1971 (243). A local summer visitor mainly seen from mid-March to July and in September between 2000m and 3795m. Common in summer north of Annapurna (H4) and fairly common north of Dhaulagiri (G4). The only other records are of four near Syabru (L5) on 16 April 1984 (624), singles over Kathmandu on 31 March 1988 (730) and Kakani (L6) on 13 April 1988 (326), and ten at Chitwan on 18 February 1989 (506). Breeding behaviour is little known. The season is probably May and June in Pakistan and Kashmir. **Range** Summer visitor to Baluchistan, and the Himalayas from Chitral east to Nepal.

[DARK-RUMPED SWIFT *Apus acuticauda*
Khasi Hills Swift, Dark-backed Swift

The species was described from Nepal by T.C. Jerdon from a Hodgson specimen (458,457). However, it is possible that this specimen originated in India. There are no later records. **Range** Breeds in Meghalaya and probably Mizoram.]

FORK-TAILED SWIFT *Apus pacificus*
Pacific Swift, Large White-rumped Swift

Subspecies *leuconyx*. First recorded by B. Biswas near Everest Base Camp at 3600m to 3800m in April 1953 (109). Fairly common, possibly resident. Movements are not fully understood. Winter records received are mainly between 75m and 365m, but noted at 915m at Pokhara in January 1990 (138). In spring and summer seen up to 3800m. Found breeding near Syabru (L5) (612,682, 321,298). On 14 May 1982 after storms about 60 were observed in the tarai at Majhagaon (A4) and 10 at Dhangarhi (432). **Range** Breeds in the Himalayas from Murree east to Arunachal Pradesh, and n.e. India. Winters south to s.w. India.

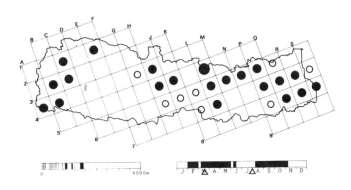

ALPINE SWIFT *Apus melba*

Subspecies *nubifuga*. First recorded by F.M. Bailey at Ramdhuni, Morang District (Q8) on 29 January 1938 (62). Fairly common, probably resident. Movements are little known. Subject to seasonal altitudinal migration and also wanders erratically over long distances when feeding. In summer reported up to 3700m but is mainly found from 75m to 2200m. Most winter records are from the tarai and foothills up to 915m. Possibly resident at Chitwan (296). Hundreds were observed flying round a cliff face by the Rapti River north of Hetaura in February (518). Seen entering cracks in cliff faces at Birethante (H5) in February and near Butwal in June (159). These could have been nesting colonies although the breeding season has been given as May and June (54). Breeding details are poorly known. **Range** Locally throughout the subcontinent.

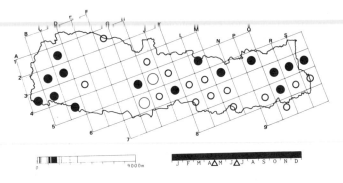

HOUSE SWIFT *Apus affinis*
Little Swift

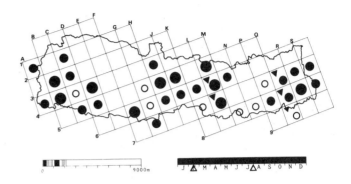

Subspecies *nipalensis*. First recorded by B. Hodgson (352). A common resident seen from 75m to 2100m. Occurs up to 915m throughout the year but withdraws from higher levels in winter. Remains in the Kathmandu Valley from mid-March to mid-November (201). Breeds in the Valley during this period (629,659), but earlier at lower altitudes. Noted entering nests as early as 12 January at Pokhara and 10 February at Hetaura (518). Also proved breeding at Silgadi-Doti (B3) (68), Surkhet (626), Dhangarhi (432), Kapilvastu District (F6) (157), Syabru (L5) (321), north of Pati Bhanjyang (L6) (321), and east of Pokhara (J5) and at Ilam (442). Inhabits towns and villages. **Range** Throughout the subcontinent except the s.e. peninsula.

ASIAN PALM SWIFT *Cypsiurus balasiensis*
(*C. parvus*)

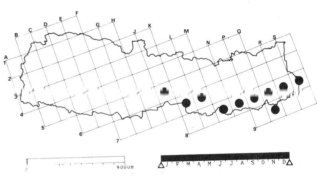

Subspecies *balasiensis*. The first dated record is of five on 7 October 1970, seen by T.P. Inskipp *et al.* at Simra (K7) at 75m (444). An uncommon resident in the tarai, mainly found close to the Indian border. Areas include Birganj (K7), Kosi Barrage, Janakpur (M8), Dharan, Birthamore (R8) and Biratnagar. Occurs as far west as Chitwan where it is a rare visitor (460,813). About 60 seen at Sunischare in February 1987 (463). Inhabits open country and cultivation with scattered palmyra palms. **Range** From Uttar Pradesh and Gujarat east through the whole subcontinent.

CRESTED TREE SWIFT *Hemiprocne coronata*
Crested Swift (*H. longipennis*)

First recorded by B. Biswas at Hetaura on
1 May 1947 (98). A locally common resident usually occurring up to 365m, but
one at Gokarna at 1280m on 22 July 1973
(814) and seen at 760m at Surkhet in
winter (244). Regularly reported from
Dharan, north of Sunischare, Tamaspur,
Simra, Chatra, and also Chitwan where it
breeds (296,432). Uncommon in the west.
Frequents forests. **Range** From Uttar
Pradesh and Gujarat east through the
whole subcontinent.

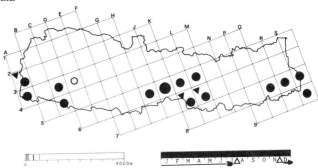

RED-HEADED TROGON *Harpactes erythrocephalus*

Subspecies *hodgsonii*. First recorded by J.
Gould (269) described presumably from a
specimen collected by B. Hodgson. A
local and very uncommon resident which
has declined recently, probably as a result
of habitat loss. Described as not uncommon in the central dun (K7,L7) in 1947
(98), and eight were seen there (L7) in
December 1970 (444). Found breeding at
Godavari at 1830m in 1955 (635). No later
records from these areas. Since 1970 recorded from south of Annapurna (H5)
(768,591), Chitwan (J6,K6), Arun valley
(483,590), Fatehpur (P8) (293), north of
Sunischare and in the lower Mai valley
(S7) (658,307). Inhabits dense,
broadleaved evergreen forests. **Range**
Himalayas from Kumaon east to Arunachal Pradesh; n.e. India and Bangladesh.

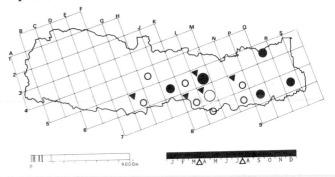

RUDDY KINGFISHER *Halcyon coromanda*

Subspecies *coromanda*. First recorded by
B. Hodgson from the lower hills
(336,388). Scarce and local, probably resident. Recently recorded at Chitwan
(J6,K6) where singles have been seen in
April and May by streams of the Churia
hills (11,67). The only other reports are

from near Hetaura: in May and June 1947 (98) and in
November 1977 (507). Inhabits streams and pools in
shaded, dense, evergreen jungle of the tarai and lower hills.
Probably suffered as a result of habitat loss. Likely to be
overlooked as it is very shy. Breeds March and April. **Range**
Himalayas from Nepal east to Arunachal Pradesh; n.e.
India and Bangladesh.

WHITE-THROATED KINGFISHER *Halcyon smyrnensis*
White-breasted Kingfisher

Subspecies *fusca*. First recorded by B. Hodgson (388). A common resident throughout up to 1000m. Rarely seen above 1800m but one was noted at 3050m in the Langu valley area (F2) in October (330). Most birds at higher altitudes descend in winter. Breeding confirmed at Chitwan (296) and in the Kathmandu Valley (629). Inhabits streams, rivers and pools. Found in a variety of habitats often far from water, such as cultivation, forest edges and gardens. **Range** Throughout the subcontinent.

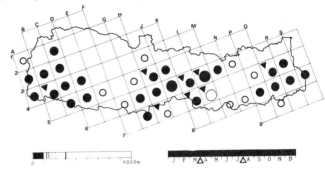

BLACK-CAPPED KINGFISHER *Halcyon pileata*

Vagrant. First recorded by R.L. Fleming Jr. in late September 1974 by the Reu River at Chitwan (218,296). The only other report is from the Mai Khola (R8) at about 300m on 20 April 1981 (559). Mainly occurs near water in coastal areas. **Range** Coasts of Bangladesh and India west to Bombay; locally inland in India.

STORK-BILLED KINGFISHER *Pelargopsis capensis*
Brown-headed Stork-billed Kingfisher (*Halcyon capensis*)

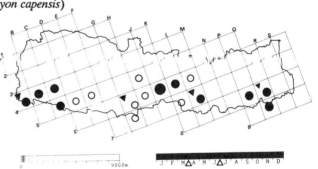

Subspecies *capensis*. First recorded by B. Hodgson (388). A local resident occasionally found up to 760m. Regularly reported from Sukla Phanta, Bardia, Hetaura, Kosi and also Chitwan where proved breeding (296). Seen at the unusually high altitude of 1830m at Godavari on 17 February 1978 (676). Inhabits deeply shaded lakes, slow-moving rivers and streams. **Range** From Dehra Dun and Gujarat east through the whole subcontinent.

[ORIENTAL KINGFISHER *Ceyx erithacus*
Three-toed Kingfisher, Three-toed Forest Kingfisher
Black-backed Kingfisher

Subspecies *erithacus*. The only record is a specimen included in the later collection of B. Hodgson (409), but this may have originated in India. **Range** Himalayas from Nepal(?) east to Arunachal Pradesh; n.e. India and Bangladesh; s.w. India.]

KEY TO THE COLOUR PLATES

PLATE 1 BUSH WARBLERS

1 Yellow-bellied Bush Warbler *Cettia acanthizoides*
2 Pale-footed Bush Warbler *C. pallidipes*
3 Chestnut-crowned Bush Warbler *C. major*
4 Brown-flanked Bush Warbler *C. fortipes fortipes*
5 Brown-flanked Bush warbler *C. f. pallidus*
6 Aberrant Bush Warbler *C. flavolivacea*
7 Grey-sided Bush Warbler *C. brunnifrons*
8 Brown Bush Warbler *Bradypterus luteoventris*
9 Chinese Bush Warbler *B. taczanowskius*
10 Chinese Bush Warbler, May
11 Spotted Bush Warbler *B. thoracicus*
12 Spotted Bush Warbler

PLATE 2 PRINIAS

1 Grey-breasted Prinia *Prinia hodgsoni* winter
2 Grey-breasted Prinia summer
3 Rufous Prinia *P. rufescens* winter
4 Rufous Prinia summer
5 Grey-crowned Prinia *P. cinereocapilla*
6 Graceful Prinia *P. gracilis*
7 Yellow-bellied Prinia *P. flaviventris*
8 Plain Prinia *P. inornata* summer
9 Plain Prinia winter
10 Striated Prinia *P. criniger*
11 Jungle Prinia *P. sylvatica*
12 Hill Prinia *P. atrogularis* winter
13 Hill Prinia summer
14 Ashy Prinia *P. socialis*

PLATE 3 *LOCUSTELLA* AND *ACROCEPHALUS* WARBLERS

1 Thick-billed Warbler *Acrocephalus aedon*
2 Oriental Reed Warbler *A. orientalis* worn
3 Oriental Reed Warbler fresh
4 Black-browed Reed Warbler *A. bistrigiceps*
5 Blunt-winged Warbler *A. concinens*
6 Paddyfield Warbler *A. agricola*
7 Clamorous Reed Warbler *A. stentoreus*
8 Blyth's Reed Warbler *A. dumetorum* fresh spring
9 Blyth's Reed Warbler worn winter
10 Grasshopper Warbler *Locustella naevia*
11 Grasshopper Warbler, streaked
12 Lanceolated Warbler *L. lanceolata*
13 Pallas's Warbler *L. certhiola*

PLATE 4 *PHYLLOSCOPUS* WARBLERS WITH WINGBARS

1 Grey-faced Leaf Warbler *Phylloscopus maculipennis*
2 Pallas's Leaf Warbler *P. proregulus*
3 Yellow-browed Warbler *P. inornatus inornatus*
4 Yellow-browed Warbler *P. i. humei*
5 Orange-barred Leaf Warbler *P. pulcher*
6 Yellow-vented Leaf Warbler *P. cantator*
7 Blyth's Leaf Warbler *P. reguloides*
8 Western Crowned Warbler *P. occipitalis*
9 Greenish Warbler *P. trochiloides viridanus* worn
10 Greenish Warbler *P. t. viridanus* fresh
11 Greenish Warbler *P. t. trochiloides*
12 Green Warbler *P. nitidus* worn
13 Green Warbler fresh
14 Large-billed Leaf Warbler *P. magnirostris*

PLATE 5 *PHYLLOSCOPUS* WARBLERS WITHOUT WINGBARS

1 Slender-billed Warbler *P. tytleri* 1st winter
2 Slender-billed Warbler worn winter
3 Tickell's Warbler (Buff-bellied Warbler) *P. affinis arcanus*
4 Tickell's Warbler *P. a. affinis* fresh autumn
5 Smoky Warbler *P. fuligiventer*
6 Chiffchaff *P. collybita* fresh autumn
7 Dusky Warbler *P. fuscatus*
8 Sulphur-bellied Warbler *P. griseolus*
9 Radde's Warbler *P. schwarzi* 1st winter
10 Radde's Warbler worn winter

PLATES 6 and 7 ROSEFINCHES

1 Dark-breasted Rosefinch *Carpodacus nipalensis*
2 Blanford's Rosefinch *C. rubescens*
3 Pink-browed Rosefinch *C. rhodochrous*
4 Common Rosefinch *C. erythrinus*
5 Dark-rumped Rosefinch *C. edwardsi*
6 Beautiful Rosefinch *C. pulcherrimus*
7 Spot-winged Rosefinch *C. rhodopeplus*
8 Vinaceous Rosefinch *C. vinaceus*
9 White-browed Rosefinch *C. thura*
10 Streaked Rosefinch *C. rubicilloides*
11 Red-fronted Rosefinch *C. puniceus*
12 Great Rosefinch *C. rubicilla*

PLATE 8 BUNTINGS

1. Pine Bunting *Emberiza leucocephalos* male
2. Pine Bunting female
3. White-capped Bunting *E. stewarti* male
4. White-capped Bunting female
5. Chestnut-eared Bunting *E. fucata* female
6. Chestnut-eared Bunting male
7. Rock Bunting *E. cia* female
8 Rock Bunting male
9 Little Bunting *E. pusilla*
10 Rustic Bunting *E. rustica* male
11 Yellow-breasted Bunting *E. aureola* male
12 Yellow-breasted Bunting female
13 Black-faced Bunting *E. spodocephala* female
14 Black-faced Bunting male

Plate 1

Craig Robson '84'

Plate 2

RICHARD GRIMMETT, 84.

Plate 3

Richard Grimmett, 84.

Plate 4

RICHARD GRIMMETT, 84.

Plate 5

RICHARD GRIMMETT NOV, 84.

Plate 6

Plate 7

CR.

Plate 8

BLYTH'S KINGFISHER *Alcedo hercules*
Great Blue Kingfisher

Scarce. The only record is of one seen by T. Nordin and J. Wallander beside the Sabbhaya Khola south of Tumlingtar (Q7) at about 250m on 14 April 1982 (599). Frequents streams in dense lowland forests. **Range** Himalayas from Nepal east to Arunachal Pradesh; n.e. India and Bangladesh.

EURASIAN KINGFISHER *Alcedo atthis*
Common Kingfisher, Small Blue Kingfisher

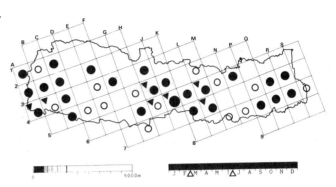

Subspecies *bengalensis*. First recorded by B. Hodgson (388). A fairly common resident up to 1000m; occasionally seen up to 1800m; rare at higher altitudes. The maximum altitude recorded is 3050m at Khaptad (C3) on 24 April 1988 (428). Breeding confirmed at Chitwan (296). Found by streams, rivers, ditches, ponds and lakes in open country. Avoids shady forest. **Range** Throughout the subcontinent.

BLUE-EARED KINGFISHER *Alcedo meninting*
Deep-blue Kingfisher

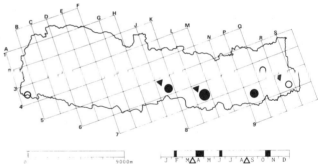

Subspecies *coltarti*. First recorded by B. Biswas who obtained several specimens between 12 and 19 June 1947 at Hetaura (98). Scarce, presumably resident. Very uncommon at Chitwan (296). Only four other confirmed reports: one in Jhapa District (R8) on 17 February 1965 (247) two in Kosi District (P8) on 11 April 1975 (293), one in the lower Arun watershed (Q7) (589), and in Kanchanpur District (A4) in 1985 (470). Occurs by streams in dense shady forest. **Range** Himalayan foothills from Nepal to Arunachal Pradesh; n.e. India south to Orissa; s.w. India.

PIED KINGFISHER *Ceryle rudis*
Small Pied Kingfisher
Indian Pied Kingfisher

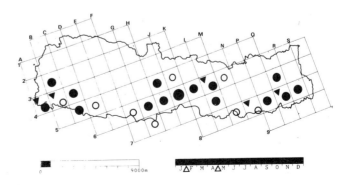

Subspecies *leucomelanura*. First recorded by B. Hodgson (388). A common resident in the tarai and lower hills up to 915m. Breeding confirmed at Chitwan (296). Frequents slow-moving streams, rivers, ponds and lakes in open country. **Range** Throughout the subcontinent.

CRESTED KINGFISHER *Ceryle lugubris*
Large Pied Kingfisher   (*Megaceryle lugubris*)
Himalayan Pied Kingfisher

Subspecies *continentalis*. First recorded
by B. Hodgson (388). A sedentary resident occasionally found between 250m
and 1800m. Reported at the unusually
high altitude of about 3000m in October
1981 in the Dhorpatan valley (573).
Found by rocky, fast-flowing streams in
well-wooded areas; rarely by lakes. **Range**
Himalayas from Kashmir east to Arunachal Pradesh; n.e. India and Bangladesh.

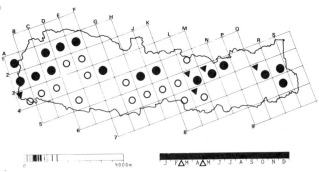

BLUE-BEARDED BEE-EATER *Nyctyornis athertoni*

Subspecies *athertoni*. The species was
described from Nepal by B. Hodgson
(362). An uncommon resident up to
365m, but in the Kathmandu Valley and
surrounding hills it occurs between
1525m and 1980m. Rare at such altitudes
elsewhere. Other areas include Bardia
(192,432), Tamaspur (10,682), Chitwan
(J6,K6), Rapti dun (K7) (486), Dharan
and north of Sunischare. Frequents forest
margins and open forests. **Range** Himalayan foothills from Himachal Pradesh
east to Bhutan; n.e. India and Bangladesh; s.w. India.

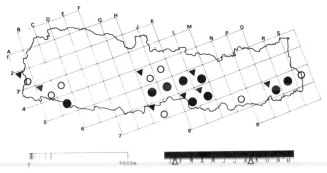

GREEN BEE-EATER *Merops orientalis*
Small Green Bee-eater, Little Green Bee-eater

Subspecies *orientalis*. First recorded by B.
Hodgson (388). A common resident and
summer visitor throughout the tarai,
fairly common in the lower hills up to
620m and uncommon up to 1280m. Birds
noted at 2135m at Ghasa on 23 and 24
April 1982 (207,703) were presumably
migrants. Proved breeding at Chitwan
(296). Inhabits open country with scattered trees and cultivation. **Range**
Throughout the subcontinent.

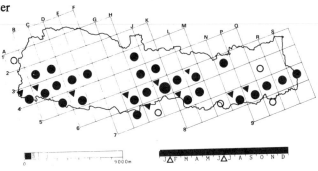

BLUE-TAILED BEE-EATER *Merops philippinus*
(*M. superciliosus*)

Subspecies *philippinus*. First recorded by B. Hodgson (388). A locally, fairly common summer visitor to the tarai. A winter record of one at Chitwan on 19 February 1988 (465). Regularly seen at Sukla Phanta, Chitwan, Tamaspur, Bardia, and Kosi marshes. Occasionally reported up to about 300m and rarely up to 1525m. A large colony was discovered in a gorge where the Bagmati River runs down to the tarai (L7) (245). On 29 March 1978 a flock of 500 to 1000 migrants was seen in n.w. Kapilvastu (F6) (155,157). Favours

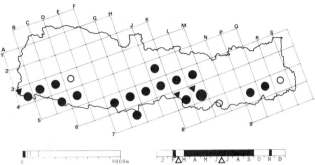

areas near water. **Range** Breeds in n. Pakistan, n. and c. India, and Bangladesh. Winters south to s. India.

CHESTNUT-HEADED BEE-EATER *Merops leschenaulti*

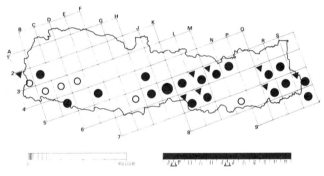

Subspecies *leschenaulti*. First recorded by B. Hodgson (388). Fairly common up to 680m. Mainly a summer visitor although some birds are resident. Chiefly occurs at Chitwan between February and October and proved breeding there (296). A sum-

mer visitor to the Kathmandu Valley arriving in early March. Flocks are regularly seen in Gaucher forest and at Gokarna. Inhabits open broadleaved forests often near water. **Range** Himalayas from Dehra Dun to Arunachal Pradesh; n.e. India and Bangladesh; s.w. India.

INDIAN ROLLER *Coracias benghalensis*
'Blue Jay'

First recorded by B. Hodgson (388). A common resident from the tarai up to 1050m. Rare at higher altitudes. A straggler to the Kathmandu Valley (240). Noted as high as 3655m on 5 August 1950 at Manangbhot (J4) (512). Proved breeding at Chitwan (296). Two races occur: *C. b. benghalensis* (b) (512,647,708), *C. b. affinis* (a) (62,246) and intermediates (ab) (98,482). Frequents cultivation, gardens, groves and open broadleaved forest. **Range** Throughout the subcontinent.

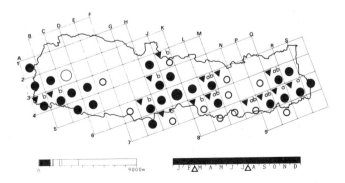

DOLLARBIRD *Eurystomus orientalis*
Broad-billed Roller, Dark Roller

Subspecies *cyanicollis*. First recorded by B. Hodgson (388). A local summer visitor mainly found up to 365m. Common at Chitwan where it breeds (296). Uncommon elsewhere. Areas include Sukla Phanta (432), Bardia (128,192,432), Dharan (561,763,546) and north of Sunischare. Only two reports from the Kathmandu Valley this century (243,444). Inhabits forests and clearings with scattered trees. **Range** Himalayas from Ambala east to Arunachal Pradesh; n.e. India and Bangladesh; s.w. India.

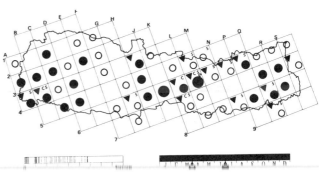

HOOPOE *Upupa epops*

First recorded by B. Hodgson (388). Fairly common. Three subspecies occur. *U. e. ceylonensis* (c) is resident up to about 1500m. Birds breeding at Chitwan (296) and in the Kathmandu Valley (243) are probably this race. *U. e. epops* (e) has been recorded in the Valley, presumably on passage. *U. e. saturata* (s) mainly summers between 1700m and 4400m and descends to the lowlands in winter. Reported on passage: a number were present on Muktinath Himal in September 1954 (419), at Tukche 342 were counted between 5 September and 14 October 1973 (76) and up to 15 a day seen in October in the eastern lowlands and foothills (P8,Q8) (293). Singles in Khumbu in

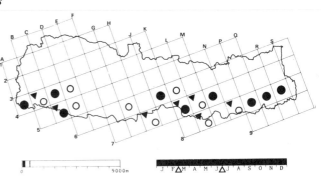

May at 5900m in 1954 (109) and 5200m in 1976 (582), and five between 3800m and 5000m in September and October 1970 (526) were presumably migrants. Frequents open country, lightly wooded areas, cultivation and villages. **Range** Throughout the subcontinent.

INDIAN GREY HORNBILL *Tockus birostris*
Common Grey Hornbill (*Ocyceros birostris*)

Subspecies *pergriseus*. First recorded by B. Hodgson (388). Occasional. A local resident mainly occurring in the tarai. Found up to 760m in the Surkhet valley (244). Subject to local movements depending on fruiting seasons. Areas include Sukla Phanta, Bardia, Kosi Tappu and Ilam District (R8). Rare at Chitwan (296). Inhabits open broadleaved forests, groves, gardens and cultivation wherever fig trees occur. **Range** Most of the subcontinent, but absent from the north-west and the north-east.

RUFOUS-NECKED HORNBILL *Aceros nipalensis*

The species was described from Nepal by B. Hodgson who found it in the lower hills (336,337). There are no later records. Formerly presumably resident inhabiting tall, broadleaved, evergreen forest in the foothills. Little if any suitable habitat remains and the species is probably extinct in Nepal. **Range** Himalayas from Nepal east to Arunachal Pradesh; n.e. India and Bangladesh.

ORIENTAL PIED HORNBILL *Anthracoceros albirostris*
Indian Pied Hornbill (*A. malabaricus, A. coronatus*)

Subspecies *albirostris*. First recorded by B. Hodgson (388). A local resident moving seasonally according to supply, of fruiting trees and small animals. Fairly common at Bardia, north of Sunischare and also Chitwan where proved breeding (296). Occasionally seen at Sukla Phanta and Dharan. Single reports from most other areas. Inhabits broadleaved forests of the lowlands and foothills. It is probably declining due to deforestation. **Range** Throughout most of the subcontinent.

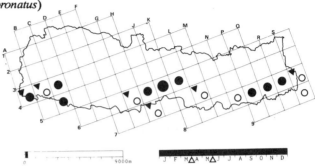

GREAT HORNBILL *Buceros bicornis*
Giant Hornbill, Great Pied Hornbill

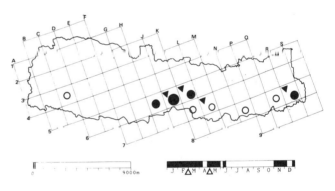

Subspecies *homrai*. First recorded by B. Hodgson (342). A local resident in thick forest of the tarai and duns, subject to seasonal movements. Uncommon at Chitwan (J6,K6) where breeding has been confirmed (296). Only a few recent reports from elsewhere: Bardia (796,750), Tamaspur, near Dharan (484) and north of Sunischare. Observed more frequently in the past: in 1964 and 1965 it was seen 19 times in five localities from Sunischare west to Chitwan (210). Its decline is mainly due to deforestation. **Range** Himalayas from Kumaon east to Arunachal Pradesh; n.e. India and Bangladesh; s.w. India.

GREAT BARBET *Megalaima virens*
Great Hill Barbet, Great Himalayan Barbet

First recorded by B. Hodgson (388). A
common resident mainly occurring between 900m and 2200m. Subject to altitudinal movements. Mainly summers above
1000m. Proved breeding in the hills of the
Kathmandu Valley last century (414).
Two races occur: *M. v. marshallorum* (m)
(245), *M. v. magnifica* (ma) (13,482,
647,659) and intermediates (mma) (98).
Chiefly inhabits temperate forests. **Range**
Himalayas from Murree east to Arunachal Pradesh; n.e. India and Bangladesh.

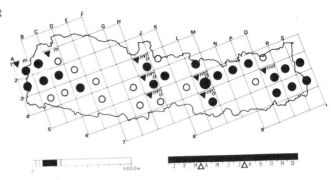

BROWN-HEADED BARBET *Megalaima zeylanica*
Green Barbet

Subspecies *caniceps*. Status and distribution are unclear because of confusion
with Lineated Barbet. First recorded at
Bilauri (A4) at 275m on 5 February 1937
by F.M. Bailey (62). A fairly common
resident at Sukla Phanta (700), and
Bardia (192). Seen at Surkhet (297).
Specimens have been obtained from
Dhangarhi (647), Tikapur (C5) (659),
Gularia (C5) (441), and near Trisuli (L6)
(589). Proved breeding at Birganj (K7) in
April 1987 (752). It has also been reported from Chitwan (11,166) and the
eastern tarai and foothills (P8,Q8) (293),
but further confirmation of its occurrence
there is desirable. Frequents lowland for-

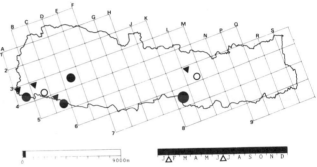

ests and wooded areas near habitation. **Range** Himalayan
foothills from Kangra east to Nepal. N. India from Haryana
east to W. Bengal, and south to s. India.

LINEATED BARBET *Megalaima lineata*

First recorded by B. Hodgson (388). A
common resident. In some localities occurs with Brown-headed Barbet: at
Dhangarhi (647), Surkhet (297) and
Bardia (432). Two races occur. *M. l.
hodgsoni* (h) is reported below 365m. *M. l.
rana* (r) is found up to 915m, and replaces
hodgsoni at higher altitudes in west-central areas (G6) (647). Proved breeding at
Chitwan (296) and in the Trisuli valley
(L6) (517). Occurs in sal forests of the
lowlands and lower foothills. **Range**
Himalayan foothills from Kumaon east to
Arunachal Pradesh; n.e. India and Bangladesh.

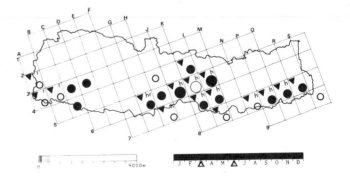

GOLDEN-THROATED BARBET *Megalaima franklinii*

Subspecies *franklinii*. First recorded by E. Blyth from a Hodgson specimen (114). A local resident, seen occasionally between 1500m and 2400m. Formerly recorded more frequently on the hills surrounding the Kathmandu Valley. Proved breeding there last century (336). Described as common in 1947 (98) and in 1970 (240), but recently only reported occasionally from Phulchowki and Sheopuri. Other localities include north-west of Pokhara (H5), Begnas Tal, Langtang, the upper Arun and the upper Kali Gandaki valley, the westernmost limit of the species' range (76). Only single records from elsewhere. Inhabits moist, broadleaved forests. **Range** Himalayas from Nepal east to Arunachal Pradesh; n.e. India and Bangladesh.

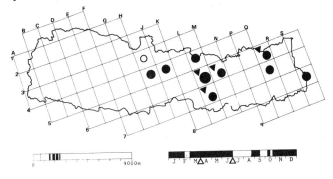

BLUE-THROATED BARBET *Megalaima asiatica*

Subspecies *asiatica*. First recorded by B. Hodgson (388). A common resident from the tarai up to about 1500m. Occasionally seen at higher elevations. In general it is found over a lower altitudinal range than Golden-throated Barbet. Breeding confirmed at Surkhet (626), in the Kathmandu Valley (629), and at Chitwan (296). Frequents open forest, groves near habitation and gardens. **Range** Himalayas from Rawalpindi District east to Arunachal Pradesh; n.e. India and Bangladesh.

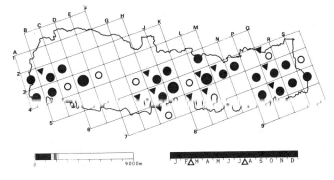

BLUE-EARED BARBET *Megalaima australis*

Subspecies *cyanotis*. First recorded by R.L. Fleming Sr. who obtained specimens north of Bhadrapur (S8) on 7 February 1965 (247). Scarce. Occurs in the far eastern tarai between 120m and 305m. Presumably resident. Only four other reports: from Mechi District (S8), undated (178), one in Kosi District (Q8) on 11 April 1975 (293), four near Sukhani (R8) on 24 March 1981 (442) and one or two near Dharan on 5 April 1986 (546). Inhabits dense tarai forests. Breeds from April to mid-June. **Range** Himalayan foothills from e. Nepal east to Arunachal Pradesh; n.e. India and Bangladesh.

COPPERSMITH BARBET *Megalaima haemacephala*
Crimson-breasted Barbet

Subspecies *indica*. Obtained by B. Hodgson in his later collection (409) but the specimen may have originated in India. First definitely recorded by J. Scully who obtained specimens on 19 June 1877 in the Kathmandu Valley (708). A common resident throughout, up to 915m. Occasionally recorded up to 1830m. Breeding confirmed at Pokhara (442) and in the Kathmandu Valley (243,771), where it is a summer visitor (240,629). Occurs in groves, open wooded areas near villages, cultivation and in gardens. **Range** The whole subcontinent east of the Indus River.

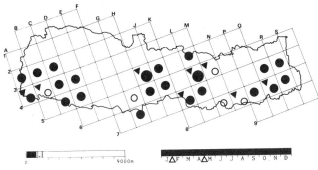

ORANGE-RUMPED HONEYGUIDE *Indicator xanthonotus*
Himalayan Honeyguide, Yellow-rumped Honeyguide

Subspecies *xanthonotus*. First recorded by R.L. Fleming Sr. above Bigu (N6) at 1830m on 24 November 1960 (234,246). Locally distributed. Status uncertain; probably an uncommon resident. Likely to be overlooked because of its drab appearance and slow-moving or inactive behaviour. Mainly reported between 1100m and 3105m. Occurs in the upper Arun valley: near Shunin Oral (483) and fairly common by the Kasuwa Khola (169). Regularly reported from Ghorepani, between Tatopani and Ghasa (H4) and in the upper Langtang Gorge east to Chongdong (L5). Single reports received from elsewhere. Breeding details are poorly known. A female taken on 7 May 1962 at Ting Sang La at 3300m, had laid eggs (190). Noted copulating between 22 April and 19 May 1973 by the Kasuwa Khola at 2195m (169). Frequents steep rocky cliffs above streams and rivers; also dense mixed broadleaved and coniferous forests nearby. Found in the vicinity of bees' nests. **Range** Himalayas from Hazara east to Arunachal Pradesh and n.e. India.

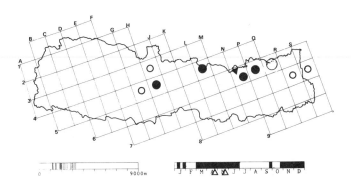

EURASIAN WRYNECK *Jynx torquilla*
Wryneck

First obtained by B. Hodgson in his later
collection (409) but the specimen may
have originated in India. First definitely
recorded by R.L. Fleming Sr. who collected a specimen at Malakheti (B4) at
290m in December 1952 (647). Occasional. A winter visitor up to 915m and
passage migrant. Noted in the Kathmandu Valley in March, April, September, October and December
(240,635,418). Reported on passage in the
upper Kali Gandaki valley: on 2 April
1971 two were noted at Jomosom (450),
and 36 at Tukche between 8 September
and 6 October 1973 (296). One was found
at the unusually high altitude of 3445m on
Machapuchare on 1 May 1980 (244). Two
races have previously been recognised as
occurring (54), but the Eurasian populations are now considered monotypic.
Inhabits secondary growth, scrub, edges
of cultivation and marshes. **Range** Breeds
in the n.w. Himalayas from Pakistan to
Himachal Pradesh. Winters throughout
the subcontinent.

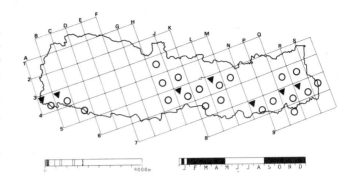

SPECKLED PICULET *Picumnus innominatus*
Spotted Piculet

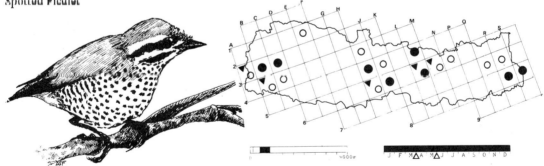

Subspecies *innominatus*. First recorded
by B. Hodgson (367). A resident, mainly
occurring from 915m to 1830m. Fairly
common at Phulchowki, Nagarjung, and
Gokarna in the Kathmandu Valley. Occasionally seen north-west of Pokhara
(H4,H5), and north of Sunischare. Rare at Chitwan (296).
Mainly single reports received from elsewhere. Unobtru-
sive and probably under-recorded. Inhabits broadleaved
forests. **Range** Himalayas from Punjab east to Arunachal
Pradesh; hills of s.w., e. and n.e. India, and Bangladesh.

WHITE-BROWED PICULET *Sasia ochracea*
Rufous Piculet

Subspecies *ochracea*. The species was described from Nepal by B. Hodgson (351,797). Uncommon, presumably resident. Reported from Tamaspur (486,652), Chitwan, Hetaura (98), upper Arun valley (10,482), Dharan, upper Mai valley, and Ilam District (R8). Found as high as 2135m at Mai Pokhari (R7) (561,687). Breeding behaviour is little known. Frequents broadleaved forests, with a preference for bamboo. **Range** Himalayas from Garhwal east to Arunachal Pradesh; n.e. India and Bangladesh.

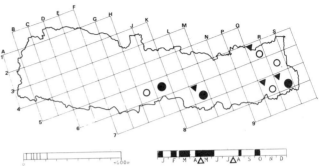

RUFOUS WOODPECKER *Celeus brachyurus*
Brown Woodpecker (*Micropternus brachyurus*)

Subspecies *phaioceps*. First recorded by B. Hodgson (388). A resident, recorded up to 1525m but mainly found below 305m. Occasionally seen at Sukla Phanta (700) and Bardia (192), and uncommon at Chitwan and the eastern tarai (P8,Q8). A rare visitor to the Kathmandu Valley. Single reports received from most other areas. Proved breeding at Chitwan (296) and Hetaura (99). Birds in the west are possibly subspecies *humei*. Inhabits broadleaved forests. **Range** Himalayas from Garhwal and Kumaon east to Arunachal Pradesh; n.e. India, and south through the peninsula.

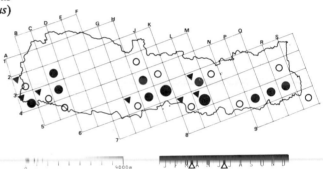

LESSER YELLOW-NAPED WOODPECKER *Picus chlorolophus*
Small Yellow-naped Woodpecker, Lesser Yellownape

First recorded by B. Hodgson (388). A resident, fairly common up to 1750m and rare up to 2135m. Breeding confirmed at Hetaura (98) and in the Kathmandu Valley (708). Two races occur: *P. c. simlae* (s) (647), *P. c. chlorolophus* (c) (98), and intermediates (cs) (98). Found in broadleaved forests. **Range** Himalayas from Haryana east to Arunachal Pradesh; hills of s.w., e. and n.e. India, and Bangladesh.

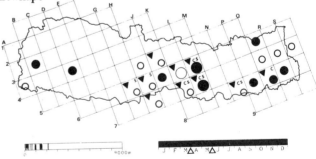

GREATER YELLOW-NAPED WOODPECKER *Picus flavinucha*
Large Yellow-naped Woodpecker, Greater Yellownape

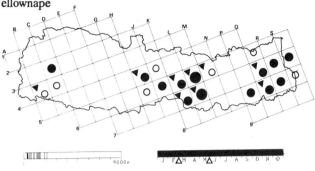

Subspecies *flavinucha.* First recorded by B. Hodgson (367). A resident, fairly common between 305m and 1450m and uncommon up to 2135m. Proved breeding at Bhimpedi (L6) and Hetaura (98). Birds in the west are possibly subspecies *kumaonensis* (54,664). Frequents broadleaved forests. **Range** Himalayas from Garhwal east to Arunachal Pradesh, n.e. India and Bangladesh.

GREY-HEADED WOODPECKER *Picus canus*
Black-naped Green Woodpecker

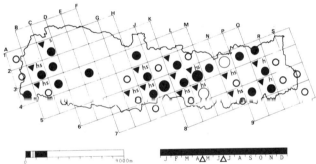

First recorded by B. Hodgson (388). A common resident, chiefly occurring below 2000m. Breeding confirmed at Chitwan (296) and in the Kathmandu Valley (190,708). Two races occur: *P. c. sanguiniceps* (o) (215), *P. c. hessei* (h) (182) and intermediates (hs) (98,647). Inhabits broadleaved forests and favours oaks. **Range** Himalayas from Murree east to Arunachal Pradesh, n.e. and e. India, and Bangladesh.

STREAK-THROATED WOODPECKER *Picus xanthopygaeus*
Small Scaly-bellied Woodpecker (*Picus myrmecophoneus*)
Streak-throated Green Woodpecker

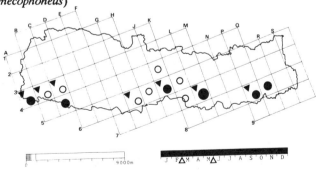

First recorded by B. Hodgson (388). A resident, occasionally seen in the tarai and lower hills up to 465m. Fairly common at Chitwan. Proved breeding at Hetaura (98). There is only one record at a higher altitude: at Begnas Tal at 915m in December 1970 (444). Occurs in secondary growth, open broadleaved forests. **Range** The whole of India from Haryana, central Rajasthan and Gujarat east to Bangladesh.

SCALY-BELLIED WOODPECKER *Picus squamatus*
Large Scaly-bellied Woodpecker, Scaly-bellied Green Woodpecker

Subspecies *squamatus*. A specimen labelled 'Nepal' and presented to the British Museum by E. Hargitt was possibly collected by B. Hodgson. First definitely recorded by F.M. Bailey on 10 October 1935 at Laura Bina (L5) (62). A locally fairly common resident between 1850m and 3700m. Areas include Ghorepani, Ghasa, upper Langtang and Khaptad (C3) where proved breeding (657,428). Scarce east of the Langtang valley. Inhabits coniferous or mixed oak/coniferous forests. **Range** N. Baluchistan and the Himalayas from Chitral east to Darjeeling.

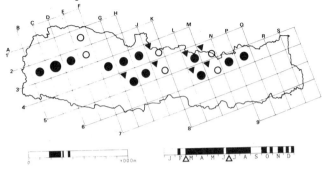

HIMALAYAN FLAMEBACK *Dinopium shorii*
Three-toed Golden-backed Woodpecker, Himalayan Goldenback, Himalayan Golden-backed Woodpecker

Subspecies *shorii*. First recorded by B. Hodgson (388). A local resident found up to 275m. Common at Tamaspur, Chitwan and in the central bhabar and dun (K7,L7). Occasionally seen north of Sunischare, at Sukla Phanta, Bardia and Dharan. Chiefly single reports received from elsewhere. Breeding behaviour is little known. Proved breeding at Chitwan (296,321), and Hetaura (98). Frequents mature lowland forests. **Range** Himalayas from Haryana east to Arunachal Pradesh; n.e. India and Bangladesh; also locally in the hills of the peninsula.

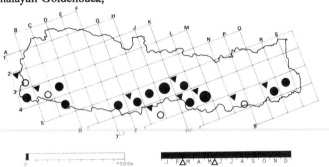

BLACK-RUMPED FLAMEBACK *Dinopium benghalense*
Golden-backed Woodpecker, Black-rumped Goldenback, Lesser Golden-backed Woodpecker

Subspecies *benghalense*. First recorded by B. Hodgson (367). A resident occasionally seen throughout the tarai and dun, below 365m. Fairly common at Sukla Phanta (700), and Bardia (192). Found in groves around villages, open wooded areas, sal forests, and cultivation. **Range** Throughout the subcontinent.

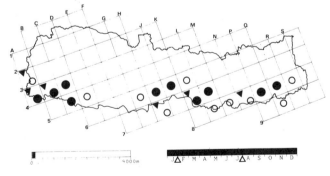

GREATER FLAMEBACK *Chrysocolaptes lucidus*
Greater Goldenback, Greater Golden-backed Woodpecker

First recorded by B. Hodgson (367). A resident, occasionally seen up to 915m, but fairly common at Chitwan and scarce at higher altitudes. Only two records from the Kathmandu Valley (495,612). Proved breeding at Chitwan (296), Simra (98), and Chatra (659). Two races occur: *C. l. sultaneus* (s) (190), *C. l. guttacristatus* (g) (482,574,659), and intermediates (gs) (98). Inhabits forests. **Range** Himalayas from Garhwal east to Arunachal Pradesh; Sri Lanka and the hills of s.w., e. and n.e. India.

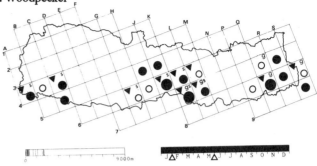

WHITE-NAPED WOODPECKER *Chrysocolaptes festivus*
Black-backed Woodpecker

Subspecies *festivus*. First recorded by R.L. Fleming Sr. at Dhangarhi at 245m on 18 March 1965 (247). An uncommon resident found in the western tarai east to the eastern bank of the Karnali River (432,162). Also reported from Bilauri (A4) (247), Sukla Phanta (432,700) and Bardia (192,432,162). Occurs in light broadleaved forests. **Range** India from Dehra Dun, Rajasthan and Gujarat east to Bengal and from the Oudh tarai, Nepal and Bihar south to Kerala.

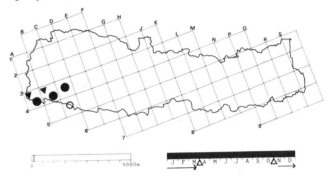

PALE-HEADED WOODPECKER *Gecinulus grantia*

Subspecies *grantia*. Obtained by B. Hodgson in his later collection (409) but this specimen may have originated in India. Scarce, probably a resident. First definitely recorded by S.C. Madge *et al.* who found singles between Garuwa and Sunischare (R8) at 275m on 1 and 3 February 1974 (518). Up to three were seen in the same area on 21 and 22 April 1981 (559). This is the western limit of the species's range. Breeds from March to May. Found in bamboo jungle. **Range** Himalayas from e. Nepal east to Arunachal Pradesh, n.e. India and Bangladesh.

BAY WOODPECKER *Blythipicus pyrrhotis*
Red-eared Rufous Woodpecker

Subspecies *pyrrhotis*. The species was described from Nepal by B. Hodgson (367,797). A local and uncommon resident, mainly found between 1525m and 2500m. Areas include north-west of Pokhara (H5), hills surrounding the Kathmandu Valley, Langtang and the upper Mai valley. Single sightings from other areas. The only low altitude records are of singles at about 150m at Bardia in early February 1990 (202) and at 75m at Sukla Phanta on 12 May 1982 (432), the westernmost record of the species. Proved breeding in the Markhu valley

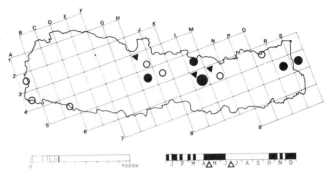

(L6) (99). Possibly overlooked as it inhabits dense forests and thick undergrowth. **Range** Himalayas from Nepal east to Arunachal Pradesh, n.e. India and Bangladesh.

GREAT SLATY WOODPECKER *Mulleripicus pulverulentus*

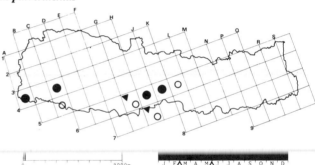

Subspecies *mohun*. First recorded by R.L. Fleming Sr. at Butwal at 275m in February 1952 (647). A local resident; chiefly occurring up to 245m. Occasionally seen at Sukla Phanta (700), Bardia

(192), and Tamaspur. Rare at Chitwan and only three records from elsewhere. Inhabits mature sal forests. **Range** Himalayas from Simla east to Arunachal Pradesh, n.e. India and Bangladesh.

HIMALAYAN WOODPECKER *Dendrocopos himalayensis*
Himalayan Pied Woodpecker (*Picoides himalayensis*)

Subspecies *himalayensis*. First recorded in southern Doti District (B3) in December 1952 by R.L. Fleming Sr. (245). A fairly common resident, subject to altitudinal movements; mainly seen above 2000m. Found east to the Dhorpatan valley (153,499). Proved breeding at Khaptad (C3) in April and May (428). Frequents coniferous and oak/rhododendron forests. **Range** W. Himalayas from Safed Koh east to Nepal.

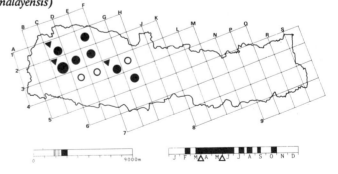

DARJEELING WOODPECKER *Dendrocopos darjellensis*
Darjeeling Pied Woodpecker (*Picoides darjellensis*)

Subspecies *darjellensis*. First recorded by B. Hodgson (388). A fairly common resident, chiefly occurring between 1830m and 3500m. Regularly reported in the upper Kali Gandaki valley, the westernmost limit of the species' range. Found breeding in the upper Mai valley (741,193). Occurs in coniferous and oak/rhododendron forests. **Range** Himalayas from Nepal east to Arunachal Pradesh, and n.e. India.

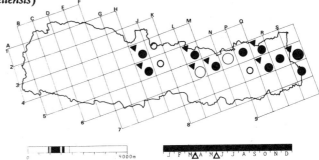

CRIMSON-BREASTED WOODPECKER *Dendrocopos cathpharius*
Crimson-breasted Pied Woodpecker (*Picoides cathpharius*)

Subspecies *cathpharius*. First recorded by E. Blyth from a Hodgson specimen (114). Resident, mainly seen between 1500m and 2750m. Generally found at lower elevations than Darjeeling Woodpecker although their altitudinal ranges overlap. Several reports from the upper Kali Gandaki valley, the westernmost limit of the species's range. Occasionally seen north-west of Pokhara (H4,H5) and in Langtang; uncommon in the Kathmandu and upper Mai valleys. Single records received from most other areas. Found in oak/rhododendron forests. **Range** Hima-

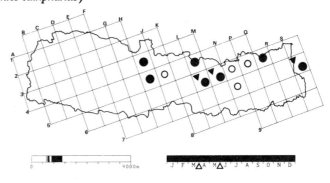

layas from Nepal east to Arunachal Pradesh, and n.e. India.

RUFOUS-BELLIED WOODPECKER *Dendrocopos hyperythrus*
Rufous-bellied Sapsucker (*Hypopicus hyperythrus*)
Rufous-bellied Pied Woodpecker

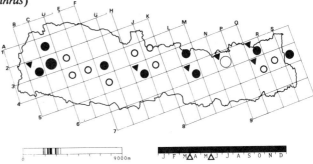

Subspecies *hyperythrus*. First recorded by B. Hodgson (388). A locally fairly common resident, mainly found between 2135m and 3050m. Regularly seen at

Phulchowki, Ghorepani and also Khaptad (C3) where proved breeding (428). Inhabits oak/rhododendron and coniferous forests. **Range** Himalayas from Hazara east to Arunachal Pradesh, n.e. India and Bangladesh.

YELLOW-CROWNED WOODPECKER *Dendrocopos mahrattensis*
Yellow-fronted Pied Woodpecker (*Picoides mahrattensis*)
Mahratta Woodpecker, Yellow-crowned Pied Woodpecker

Subspecies *mahrattensis*. First collected by B. Hodgson (312). An uncommon resident, mainly occurring up to 275m, although found in the eastern tarai and foothills (P8,Q8) to 1500m (293). Noted at the unusually high altitude of 1700m in the upper Arun valley in November 1979 (574). A rare breeding bird at Chitwan (296). Occurs in open wooded areas. **Range** The whole subcontinent east of the Indus River.

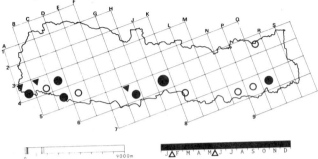

BROWN-FRONTED WOODPECKER *Dendrocopos auriceps*
Brown-fronted Pied Woodpecker (*Picoides auriceps*)

First recorded by B. Hodgson (388). A fairly common resident, found between 1065m and 2440m. Proved breeding at Khaptad (C3) (428) and in the Markhu valley (L6) (98). Two intergrading races occur: *D. a. auriceps* (a) (646,661) and the endemic *D. a. incognitus* (i) (190). Inhabits coniferous and dry broadleaved forests. **Range** N. Baluchistan north to Chitral east through to Nepal.

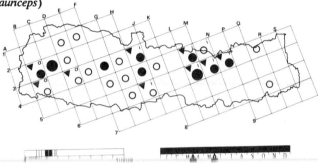

FULVOUS-BREASTED WOODPECKER *Dendrocopos macei*
Fulvous-breasted Pied Woodpecker (*Picoides macei*)

Subspecies *macei*. First recorded by B. Hodgson (388). A common resident from the Modi Khola (H5) eastwards. Occasionally reported from further west. Most frequently seen up to 1830m. Noted at the particularly high altitude of 2745m in the Gandak Kosi watershed (L5) on 23 March 1951 (631). Proved breeding at Chitwan (296). Inhabits broadleaved and broadleaved/coniferous forests and open wooded country. **Range** Himalayas from Murree east to Arunachal Pradesh; n.e. and e. India and Bangladesh.

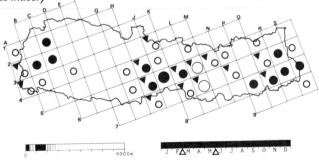

GREY-CAPPED PYGMY WOODPECKER *Dendrocopos canicapillus*
Grey-crowned Pygmy Woodpecker, (*Picoides canicapillus*)
Grey-capped Woodpecker

First recorded by B. Hodgson (388). A resident, mainly found up to 365m. Fairly common from Butwal eastwards. Rarely seen further west. Common at Chitwan and proved breeding there (296,326). An uncommon summer visitor to the Kathmandu Valley (240). Two intergrading races occur: *D. c. mitchelli* (m) (62,247) and *D. c. semicoronatus* (s) (62,247). Inhabits open broadleaved forests. **Range** Himalayas from Murree east to Arunachal Pradesh, n.e. India and Bangladesh.

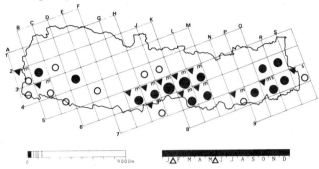

BROWN-CAPPED PYGMY WOODPECKER *Dendrocopos nanus*
Brown-crowned Pygmy Woodpecker, Brown-capped Woodpecker
(*Picoides nanus, Dendrocopos moluccensis*)

Subspecies *nanus*. First recorded by S.D. Ripley from Chisapani (C4) at 225m, and Tikapur (C5) at 150m in January 1949 (659). A resident, most frequent in the west. Fairly common at Sukla Phanta (700), and occasionally seen at Bardia (192). Rare from Chitwan eastwards. Noted in Tilaurakot woods (G6) at 150m in the same area as Grey-capped Pygmy Woodpecker (157). Occurs in light forests, and trees near cultivation in the tarai. **Range** N. India from Haryana, Rajasthan and Gujarat east to Bangladesh, and south through the peninsula.

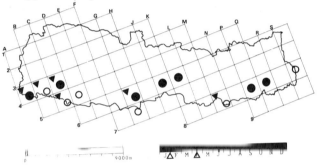

SILVER-BREASTED BROADBILL *Serilophus lunatus*
Hodgson's Broadbill, Collared Broadbill

Subspecies *rubropygius*. Only recorded by B. Hodgson (380). One of his specimens was obtained from the lower hills on 10 January (336). Inhabits evergreen and semi-evergreen jungle up to 1700m. **Range** Himalayas from Nepal east to Arunachal Pradesh; n.e. India and Bangladesh.

LONG-TAILED BROADBILL *Psarisomus dalhousiae*

Subspecies *dalhousiae*. First recorded by B. Hodgson (336,388). Probably resident. Possibly declined; fairly common north of Sunischare but is now scarce and local elsewhere. The only other reports received since 1974 are from south of Annapurna (H5) (762), Phewa Tal, Chitwan, lower Arun watershed (596), Chatra (518) and Hans Pokhari (S8) (193). Described as common in dense forests of the central duns (L6,L7) in 1947 (99), but only one later record from the area: in December 1970 (444). A pair nest-building, and three old nests, found at Bogaytcha north of Sunischare on 29 April 1986 (321). Frequents broadleaved forests of the foothills. **Range** Himalayas from Garhwal east to Arunachal Pradesh; n.e. India and Bangladesh.

LONG-TAILED BROADBILL, cont'd ...

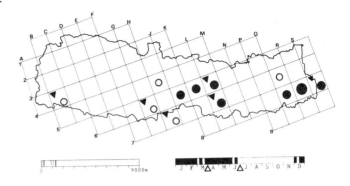

BLUE-NAPED PITTA *Pitta nipalensis*

Subspecies *nipalensis*. The species was described from Nepal by B. Hodgson (371,798). His specimens came from the lower hills and the Kathmandu Valley (336). Scarce and local; probably resident. All later records are from the Valley. Chiefly seen at Godavari at about 1525m. The most recent reports received are from Godavari in January 1983 (402) and Nagarjung in November 1989(675). Breeds from April to August. Occurs in damp gullies in subtropical forests with dense undergrowth. Skulking and easily overlooked, like other pittas. **Range** Himalayas from Nepal east to Arunachal Pradesh; n.e. India and Bangladesh.

HOODED PITTA *Pitta sordida*
Green-breasted Pitta

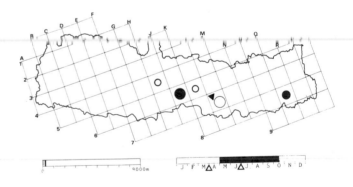

Subspecies *cucullata*. First recorded by E. Blyth from a Hodgson specimen (114). Very locally distributed up to 305m. Described as chiefly resident in the subcontinent (54,664), but only reported from Nepal in summer. Common at Chitwan (J6,K6) from April to October, and proved breeding there (296). The only other reports are from Hetaura in May and June 1947 (99) and in June 1957 (245), Simery (L7) in April 1973 (587), Dharan in May 1976 (293), and south of Annapurna (H5) in 1977 (762). Inhabits damp tropical and subtropical forest with thick undergrowth. **Range** Himalayas from Simla east to Arunachal Pradesh; n.e. India and Bangladesh.

INDIAN PITTA *Pitta brachyura*

First recorded by B. Hodgson (388). A local summer visitor to the lowlands. Common at Chitwan, and proved breeding there (296). Rare at Sukla Phanta (700), and Bardia (128,192,750). The only other report is from the eastern tarai and foothills (Q8), where it is an uncommon passage migrant in May (281,285,293). Inhabits tropical forests with dense undergrowth. **Range** Breeds in the Himalayas from Simla east to Arunachal Pradesh, and south to Rajasthan, Kanara and Bangladesh. Winters in s. India.

INDIAN PITTA, cont'd ...

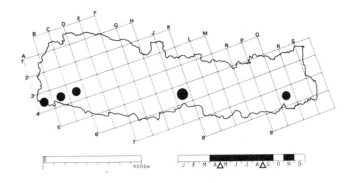

RUFOUS-WINGED BUSHLARK *Mirafra assamica*
Bush Lark, Bengal Bushlark

Subspecies *assamica*. First recorded by B. Hodgson (388). A common resident throughout the tarai. Frequents short grassland, ploughed fields and other dry cultivation. Proved breeding at Chitwan (296). **Range** North-central India from Haryana east to Assam and Bangladesh, and south to s. India.

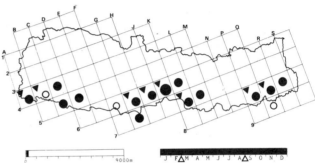

ASHY-CROWNED FINCH LARK *Eremopterix grisea*

First recorded by B. Hodgson (388). A fairly common resident throughout the tarai and up to 730m in the Surkhet valley (244). Occurs in open dry areas including cultivation, stony scrub and ploughed fields. The breeding season is irregular. **Range** Throughout the subcontinent.

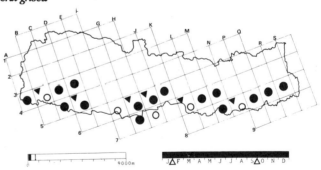

GREATER SHORT-TOED LARK *Calandrella brachydactyla*
Short-toed Lark (*C. cinerea*)

First recorded by B. Hodgson (388). Specimens identified to subspecies have all been *C. b. dukhunensis*, but *C. b. longipennis* possibly occurs. Occasional. Mainly a passage migrant; also a winter visitor. Found with Hume's Short-toed Larks in flocks of up to 1000 in the upper Kali Gandaki valley between 27 September and 14 October 1973 (76). Also seen in mixed flocks in April 1981 at Tukche, Jomosom, and Kagbeni (811). Several records from the Kathmandu Valley, mainly in March, April and October. Also noted in the Kosi marshes in March, April and November, including a flock of about 400 in early March 1989 (172). Noted in winter at Phewa Tal (180), Begnas Tal (325), Chitwan (702), Kalopani (H4) (687), and in the Kathmandu Valley (300). There are two monsoon specimen records: one collected at 5000m at Lobuche (P6) on 17 August 1962 (190) and one in Mustang District (H3) on 11 June 1977 (589). Frequents ploughed fields, open stony, and short grass areas. **Range** Winter visitor throughout the subcontinent.

GREATER SHORT-TOED LARK, cont'd ...

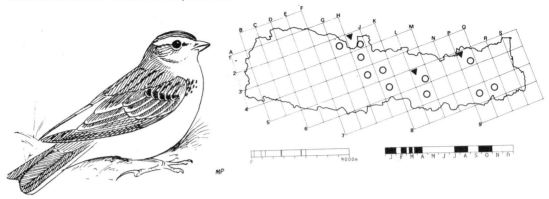

HUME'S SHORT-TOED LARK   *Calandrella acutirostris*

Subspecies *tibetana*. A Hodgson specimen was listed for Nepal by Sharpe (719), but it may have originated from outside Nepal. First definitely recorded by B. Biswas at Phalong Karpo (P6) on 6 May 1954 (109). Common in summer; uncommon in winter and on passage. Reported in spring and autumn from the upper Kali Gandaki valley, in flocks with Greater Short-toed Larks (76,762,811). A few reports of passage migrants in Khumbu (109,558), and in March and April at Kosi Barrage where a maximum of 300 was found in early March 1988 (465). Common in the Dolpo (G3) in summer, and possibly breeds there (224). Also recorded in winter in the Namlang valley

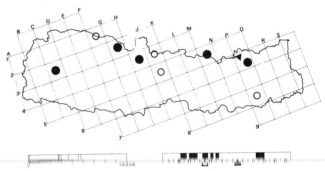

(F2) (447), Khumbu (558) and Kosi Barrage (262). Inhabits open dry stony areas. **Range** Summer visitor to Baluchistan, and the Himalayas from Chitral to Bhutan. Winters from Pakistan east to Bangladesh.

SAND LARK   *Calandrella raytal*
Indian Sandlark

Subspecies *raytal*. Obtained by B. Hodgson in his later collection (315), but the specimen may have originated in India. First definitely recorded by J. Scully in the lowlands in December 1877 (708). A locally common resident. Regularly seen at Tamaspur, Kosi Barrage, and also Chitwan where breeding has been proved (296). Occasionally observed elsewhere. Found on sandy river banks and islands of large rivers in the tarai. **Range** Pakistan, n. India and Bangladesh.

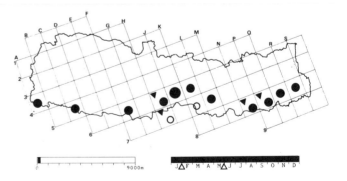

CRESTED LARK *Galerida cristata*

Subspecies *chendoola*. First recorded by B. Hodgson (388). A fairly common resident east to Nepalganj; rare further east. Found in dry fields of the tarai just north of the Indian border. **Range** Pakistan; n. India east to Bihar, and south to Madhya Pradesh.

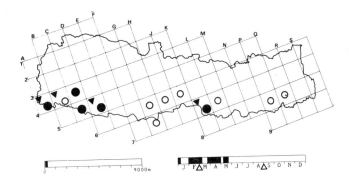

ORIENTAL SKYLARK *Alauda gulgula*
Little Skylark, Small Skylark, Eastern Skylark

First recorded by B. Hodgson (388). A fairly common winter visitor and resident. Three subspecies occur. *A. g. gulgula* (g) is found to 150m and is probably resident (245,246,247). *A. g. inopinata* (i) (99, 240,574,708) and *A. g. lhamarum* (l) (234, 245,659) have been mainly collected in winter between 1280m and 1700m but possibly also breed. The latter race is probably much less common. Birds not subspecifically identified but probably *A. g. inopinata* have been found in summer in the Tibetan plateau region (709,187) and in the Dhorpatan valley (G5) (243,499). A fairly common winter visitor to the Kathmandu Valley. Frequents grassy hillsides, ploughed fields and other cultivation. **Range** Throughout the subcontinent.

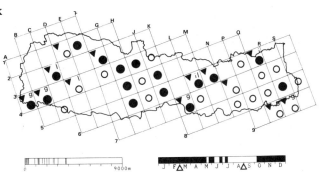

[EURASIAN SKYLARK *Alauda arvensis*

Described as a winter visitor to central Nepal (664) but no definite evidence of its occurrence has been traced. Likely to be confused with the large race of Oriental Skylark *A. gulgula lhamarum*. **Range** Winters in n. Pakistan and n. India east to Uttar Pradesh.]

HORNED LARK *Eremophila alpestris*
Shore Lark

Subspecies *elwesi*. Obtained by B. Hodgson in his later collection (409) but this specimen may have originated from outside Nepal. First definitely recorded by J.O.M. Roberts who collected one at Khangsar (H4) at 4575m on 5 August 1950 (512). Resident and partial altitudinal migrant. Mainly reported between 3965m and 5490m, although one noted at 5900m in summer (620), and one collected in winter as low as 2600m at Mali Dala Jiri (G4) on 2 April 1973 (589). Fairly common in the Dolpo (F3,G3,H3) and in Khumbu. Proved breeding at Khangsar (H4) (512) and at Gokyo (190). Found on barren stony hillsides. **Range** Himalayas from Hazara east to Arunachal Pradesh.

HORNED LARK, cont'd ...

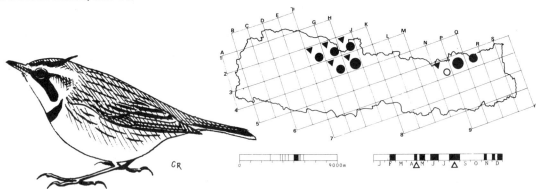

PLAIN MARTIN   *Riparia paludicola*
Sand Martin, Grey-throated Sand Martin, Plain Sand Martin,
Brown-throated Sand Martin

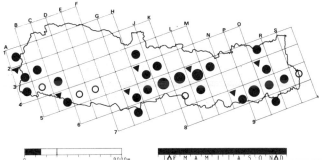

Subspecies *chinensis*. First recorded by B.
Hodgson (352). A common resident up to
1500m, subject to local movements. One
was seen at the unusually high altitude of
2990m near Kagbeni (244). Found breeding at Chitwan (J6,K6) (296,518,481), in
the Kathmandu Valley (518,635), near
Trisuli (L6) (612), and at Kosi Barrage
(442). The breeding season is given as
October to March in the Indian subcontinent (45), but in Nepal it is from February
to November. Frequents rivers and
streams and nests in sandy banks. **Range**
Most of the subcontinent south to 18°N.

SAND MARTIN   *Riparia riparia*
Collared Sand Martin, Bank Swallow

A scarce passage migrant. Most reports
are from 1980 onwards; probably overlooked before this. First collected at Sundar Gundar (Q8) on 15 February 1938 by
F.M. Bailey (62), a bird of the race *R. r.
ijimae*. A flock of 10 to 20 probably of the
race *R. r. diluta* was observed at Kosi
Tappu (Q8) on 20 April 1982 (199,294)
and 2 May 1982 (561). The species has
been reported in April and May from Kagbeni, Jomosom
and Naudanda (811), Chitwan (561), the Kathmandu Valley (440) and Kosi Barrage (483). Recorded between late
September and early November from Rara Lake (68),
Jomosom (76) and Kosi Barrage (327). Only a few other
winter records; from Kosi Barrage (327) and Chitwan (402).
Range Breeds in the Himalayas from N.W.F.P. to Garhwal,
also Bhutan, n.e. India and Bangladesh. Winters south to
Madhya Pradesh.

SAND MARTIN, cont'd ...

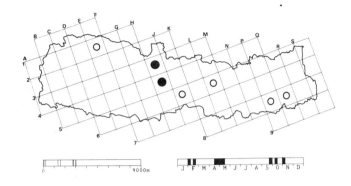

NORTHERN CRAG MARTIN *Ptyonoprogne rupestris*
Crag Martin *(Hirundo rupestris)*

First recorded by B. Hodgson (352). Probably resident, subject to altitudinal movements. The population may also be augmented by winter visitors. Usually found below 2135m in winter, and may occur as high as 4575m in summer. Fairly common north-west of Pokhara (H4,H5). Found breeding in cliffs by the Seti Khola at Pokhara (419), near Ghasa (295), and in walls of houses around Muktinath at 3500m to 3600m (757). A straggler to the Kathmandu Valley, and occasionally reported from elsewhere. Hawks insects near rocky cliffs. **Range** Breeds in the Himalayas from Chitral east to Nepal. Winters south to s. India.

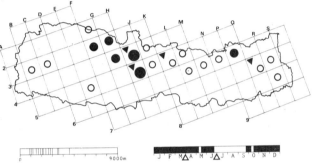

BARN SWALLOW *Hirundo rustica*
Swallow

First recorded by B. Hodgson (352). A common resident and summer visitor, mainly occurring up to 1830m. A straggler was noted in Khumbu at 6400m on 16 May 1975 (580). Chiefly a summer visitor to the Himalayas. Two races occur: *H. r. rustica* (r) (99,482, 647,708) and *H. r. gutturalis* (g), but there is only one record of the latter (99). Proved breeding in Bajhang District (C2) (657), Dandeldhura and Doti Districts (A3,B3,C3) (657, 428,68), Kathmandu streets, north-west of Pokhara (H4,H5) (811), and at Ilam (518). Reported on passage: a total of 321 flew west at Khare (H5) between 20 October and 7 November 1985 (684)

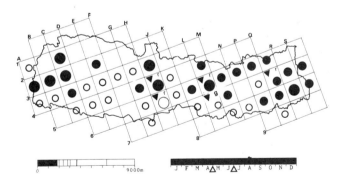

and nearly 500 were seen at 3660m on Machapuchare (244). **Range** Breeds in the Himalayas from Chitral east to Arunachal Pradesh. Winters throughout the subcontinent.

WIRE-TAILED SWALLOW *Hirundo smithii*

Subspecies *filifera*. A Hodgson specimen is listed for Nepal by Sharpe (717) but it may have originated in India. First definitely recorded by R.L. Fleming Sr. near Bhairawa in March 1959 (230). Uncommon and local; possibly resident. Reported from Nepalganj (432,691,811), and Kapilvastu District (F6,G6) (157,792). The only other record is from Mahendranagar (A4) (811). Proved breeding at Nepalganj in March (811). Usually found near water. **Range** Throughout most of the subcontinent.

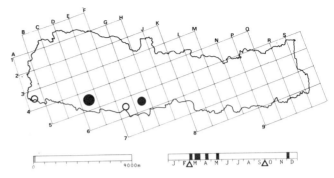

RED-RUMPED SWALLOW *Hirundo daurica*
Striated Swallow

First recorded by B. Hodgson (352). Three races occur. *H. d. nipalensis* (n) is a common resident subject to altitudinal movements. It nests up to 1770m in Dandeldhura and Doti Districts (A3,B3) (657,428,68), at Malunga (H6) (575), Surkhet (626), between Pokhara and Lumsum (G4,H5) (419), Pati Bhanjyang (L6) (440,633), Chitlang (L6) (99), Kathmandu Valley (99,629,708) and Tumlingtar (Q7) (404). In winter descends to between 915m and the tarai. Noted on passage in the Kathmandu Valley in November (436,418) and at Khare (H5) where 13,902 flew west between 20 and 30 Octo-

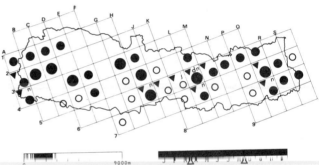

ber 1985 (684). There are only single winter records of *H. d. daurica* (d) (659) and *H. d. japonica* (j) (247). Frequents cultivated open scrub country and upland pastures. **Range** Throughout the subcontinent.

STREAK-THROATED SWALLOW *Hirundo fluvicola*
Indian Cliff Swallow

First recorded by R.L. Fleming and H. Gilston, on 11 April 1975 at Kosi Barrage (243,293). A scarce visitor, reported several times in January: up to 10 were seen at Begnas Tal in 1979 (486,651), three by the Tadi River, Nawakot District in 1980 (L6) (587), and singles at Phewa Tal in 1981 (180), Chobar in 1982 (L6) (73), and Hetaura in 1984 (143). Only three other records: one at Birganj (K7) on 20 August 1973 (77), five at Kosi Barrage on 10 February 1984 (408), and one at Kosi Tappu (Q8) on 22 April 1982 (199,294), the easternmost record of the species. Usually seen with flocks of hirundines

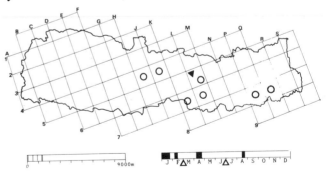

over rivers or lakes. **Range** N. Pakistan, and India east to Madhya Pradesh and e. Nepal.

NEPAL HOUSE-MARTIN *Delichon nipalensis*

Subspecies *nipalensis*. The species was described from Nepal by F. Moore from a Hodgson specimen (409,798) but it may have originated in India. First definitely recorded by H. Stevens from the upper Mai valley (S7) on 28 April 1912 (740). A fairly common resident subject to local altitudinal movements. Usually found up to 3500m in summer but one noted at 3865m at Tengboche (P6) in May (75). Regularly reported in winter between 915m and 2135m, but rare in the lowlands: noted at the particularly low altitude of 160m at Sukla Phanta (700). Occasionally seen on passage in the Kathmandu Valley. Proved breeding near Syabru (L5) (612) and Nundhaki (Q7) (793). Frequents mountain river valleys, grassy ridges and slopes. **Range** Himalayas from Garhwal east to Arunachal Pradesh; n.e. India and Bangladesh.

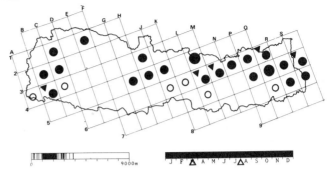

ASIAN HOUSE-MARTIN *Delichon dasypus*
COMMON HOUSE-MARTIN   *D. urbica*

The status and distribution of both species is uncertain as they are often considered conspecific (45,243,664). Birds not specifically identified have been reported between 305m and 4575m. Regularly seen north-west of Pokhara, in Langtang and Khumbu. Proved breeding near Jumla in July (620). On 20 June 1954 "an almost endless stream" was observed passing east over Lumsum (G4) at 1980m, including a flock of 200 birds (419). Many were also seen flying south near Pokhara from 2 to 8 November 1954 (419).

ASIAN HOUSE-MARTIN *Delichon dasypus*

Subspecies *cashmeriensis*. Probably resident, subject to altitudinal movements. First recorded by G. Diesselhorst at Pheriche (P6) at 4250m on 27 August 1962 (190). A nesting colony was found under a huge boulder at Gapte (L5) at 3500m in May (440). Other confirmed records are from Bajhang (C2) (657), north-west of Pokhara (H4,H5), Chitwan (K6) (325), Helambu (L6) (444), Langtang (L5,M5), near Lukla (P6) (769) and Ilam District (442,307). Occurs over grassy slopes and mountain valleys. **Range** Breeds in the Himalayas from Chitral east to Arunachal Pradesh. Winters at lower levels, and occasional records in the plains of n.e. India.

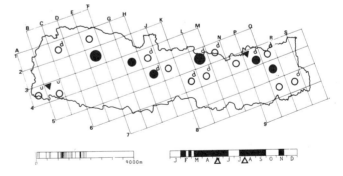

COMMON HOUSE-MARTIN *Delichon urbica*
House Martin

Subspecies *urbica*. Only four definite records, probably of passage migrants. One
was taken by R.L. Fleming near Dhangarhi at 460m on 26 April 1965 (234,247).
The other reports are of ten birds at
Majhagaon (A4) at 150m on 13 May 1982
(432), three over Arung Khola (H6) at
150m in mid-February 1986 (321) and two
between Khare and Suikhet (H5) at about
1470m on 13 February 1989 (506). **Range**
Breeds in the Himalayas from Gilgit east
to Spiti. Winters south to s. India.

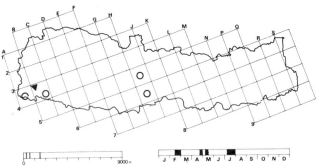

RICHARD'S PIPIT *Anthus novaeseelandiae*
Paddyfield Pipit

First recorded by B. Hodgson (388). Two
races occur. *A. n. richardi* is a winter
visitor and passage migrant, seen occasionally. Regularly reported from Phewa
Tal and Begnas Tal where flocks of up to
35 have been seen. Uncommon at Chitwan, and also in the Kathmandu Valley
where it has been found as early as 19
September (629).

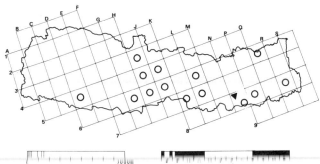

Paddyfield Pipit *A. n. rufulus* is a common
resident up to 1830m, and has been reported up to 2440m in summer (626).
Proved breeding in the Kathmandu Valley (629), at Chitwan (229) and Kosi
(313). The species frequents open grassy
areas and dry cultivation. **Range**
Throughout the subcontinent.

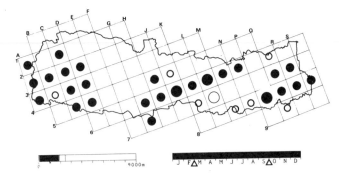

BLYTH'S PIPIT *Anthus godlewskii*

First collected by B. Hodgson (388). A
passage migrant of uncertain status and
distribution. Only specimen records have
been accepted because until recently no
reliable field identification criteria had
been established to separate this species
from Richard's Pipit or Tawny Pipit. Has
been obtained in March and April at
Kathmandu, and at Haraincha (Q8) at
75m (62). Collected in September from
Gumtang (L6) and Kodari (M6) (62);
Langtang at 4115m (621); and Khumbu
between 3800m and 4250m (190). Taken
at Sukipatal (Q6) in October (690) and at
Kathmandu in November (62,190). There
are sight records from Khumbu
(526,559,560), Tukche (811) and several
from Kosi Barrage. **Range** Winters locally
in n.e. India, Bangladesh, and much of the
peninsula south to Kerala. Passage migrant in the e. Himalayas.

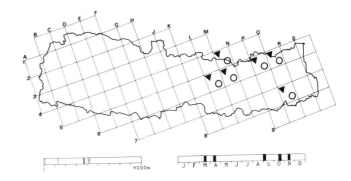

TAWNY PIPIT *Anthus campestris*

Vagrant. First recorded at Chitwan (J6)
on 28 March 1977 by G. Groh (6,634).
Another, probably of this species, was
seen at Sukla Phanta in February 1977
(6,238). The only other records are singles
migrating west at Khare (H5) on 20 and
21 October 1985 (684) and one at Chitwan (K6) on 15 February 1989 (506).
Range Local winter visitor to Pakistan,
India (except the n.e.), and Bangladesh.

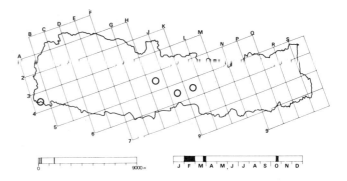

LONG-BILLED PIPIT *Anthus similis*
Brown Rock Pipit

Subspecies *jerdoni*. First collected at
Banbassa (A4) at 150m on 7 January 1937
by F.M. Bailey (62). Scarce, possibly resident. Specimens were also taken at Bilauri (A4) at 275m in December 1952, and
Barmdeo Mandi (A3) at 290m in January
1953 (647). Proved breeding at Silgadi

Doti (B3) at about 1700m; singles noted carrying food at
two sites on 29 May 1988 (438). Seen in song flight at
Dipayal (B3) at 800m on 30 May 1988 (438). Frequents dry
cultivation and grassy and rocky slopes. Breeds from April
to August. **Range** Breeds in the hills of Pakistan, the
Himalayas from N.W.F.P. east to Nepal, and in s.w. India.
Winters east to Bangladesh.

OLIVE-BACKED PIPIT *Anthus hodgsoni*
Hodgson's Pipit, Olive Tree-Pipit, Indian Tree Pipit

First recorded by B. Hodgson (388). Two races occur. *A. h. hodgsoni* (h) is a common resident subject to altitudinal movements. Mainly summers between 2900m and 4000m, occasionally down to 2440m; and winters from about 1980m to 2560m. Confirmed breeding on the Mamche Danda (L6) (640). Birds breeding in the Dhorpatan valley (F4), in June, presumably belonged to this race (499). A specimen was taken at 305m at Amlekhganj (K7) on 7 March 1947 (99). *A. h. yunnanensis* (y) is a common winter visitor up to 2560m. Found on grassy slopes in open forests, and scrub or cultivation with scat-

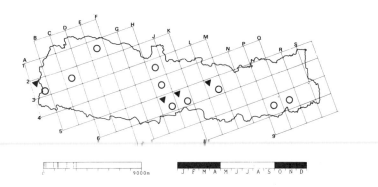

tered trees. **Range** Breeds in the Himalayas from Dharmsala east to Arunachal Pradesh. Winters south to s. India, and east to Bangladesh.

TREE PIPIT *Anthus trivialis*
Brown Tree-Pipit

Subspecies *trivialis*. The first record is a specimen taken at Thankot (L6) on 11 April 1947 by B. Biswas (99). A winter visitor and passage migrant. Mainly recorded since 1979; possibly overlooked before this. Uncommon at Chitwan and Kosi Barrage. Mainly single reports from elsewhere. Frequents cultivation, or open country with scattered trees. **Range** Breeds in the Himalayas from Chitral east to Lahul. Winters throughout the subcontinent.

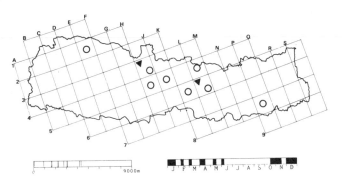

RED-THROATED PIPIT *Anthus cervinus*

First recorded by B. Hodgson in the Kathmandu Valley (336,388). An uncommon winter visitor and passage migrant. Mainly found between October and February, with several reports between March and June, presumably of spring migrants. A few records from fields by Phewa Tal with a maximum of 35 in mid-January 1981 (180). Mainly single reports from elsewhere. A total of 109 migrated west at Khare (H5) between 20 October and 7 November 1985 (684). The maximum altitude recorded is 5180m, above Tukche in December 1949 (647). Winters in wet grassy areas and stubble fields. **Range** Local and uncommon migrant in Pakistan, n.w. India, and Manipur.

ROSY PIPIT *Anthus roseatus*
Rosy-breasted Pipit (*Anthus pelopus*)
Vinaceous-breasted Pipit

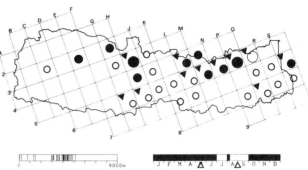

The species was described from Nepal by E. Blyth from a Hodgson specimen (121). A fairly common resident subject to altitudinal movements, and a passage migrant. Mainly summers between 3355m and 5050m, and winters from 760m to 1500m, occasionally down to the tarai. Proved breeding in the upper Kali Gan-

daki valley (811), and at Pheriche (P6) (190). Flocks of up to 50 seen flying up the Kali Gandaki valley on 27 March 1982 (294). A total of 530 was noted at Kosi Tappu in early February 1984, presumably migrants (408). Occurs in summer above the treeline on stony slopes and in alpine meadows. Winters in marshes and cultivation. **Range** Breeds in the Himalayas from Safed Koh east to Arunachal Pradesh. Winters in n. Pakistan, n. India, and Bangladesh.

WATER PIPIT *Anthus spinoletta*
BUFF-BELLIED PIPIT *A. rubescens*

The status and distribution of both species is uncertain as, until recently they were usually considered as conspecific. Birds not specifically identified have been reported between 75m and 2700m in winter and on passage. Several records from Phewa Tal; mainly single reports from elsewhere. Both species inhabit marshes and damp cultivation in winter.

WATER PIPIT *Anthus spinoletta*

Subspecies *blakistoni*. Probably a scarce winter visitor and passage migrant. First definitely recorded by R.L. Fleming Sr. who collected a specimen at Pokhara on 31 December 1963 (247). The only other confirmed records are of singles seen by Phewa Tal on 25 March 1989 (166) and at Kosi Barrage from 3 to 5 February 1990 (256). **Range** Winters locally in Pakistan and n.w. India.

BUFF-BELLIED PIPIT *Anthus rubescens*
Siberian Water Pipit, American Pipit

Subspecies *japonicus*. Probably a scarce winter visitor and passage migrant. A Hodgson specimen was listed for Nepal by Sharpe (717), but it may have originated in India. First definitely recorded by P. Holt at Jomosom at 2715m on 3 and 5 March 1986 (403). The only other confirmed records are of 50 on 23 January by Manora River, Kathmandu Valley (L6); 20 at Phewa Tal on 13 January, about 10 in the Pokhara valley on 14 January and six at Chitwan (K6) on 17 January 1989 (152). **Range** Winters locally in Pakistan; recorded from Darjeeling and Manipur.

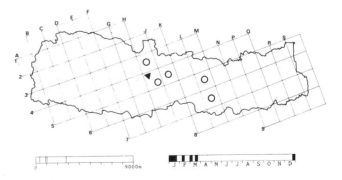

UPLAND PIPIT *Anthus sylvanus*

The species was described from Nepal by B. Hodgson (391,798). He found it breeding in the Kathmandu Valley (336,414). A locally fairly common resident and partial altitudinal migrant. Recorded between 1830m and 2900m in summer, and 1350m to 2000m in winter. Found at Mai Pokhari (R7) on 22 April 1982 (561), the eastern limit of the species's range in the Himalayas. Proved breeding at Pipar (H5) (800). Inhabits steep rocky and grassy slopes. **Range** Himalayas from Pakistan east to e. Nepal.

FOREST WAGTAIL *Dendronanthus indicus* (*Motacilla indica*)

Vagrant. First recorded by K. Curry-Lindahl who saw one by the Rapti River, Chitwan on 30 November 1979 (171). The only other records are of singles seen on 4 April 1984 at Chitwan (694), by Raymond Bridge, Kathmandu on 4 April 1986 (403) and at Chatra (Q8) on 4 October 1987 (792). Usually frequents clearings in broadleaved forest and bamboo jungle. **Range** Winters locally in s.w. and n.e. India, and Bangladesh.

YELLOW WAGTAIL *Motacilla flava*

First recorded by B. Hodgson (388). Occasional. Mainly a winter visitor seen up to 1350m, and a passage migrant. Fairly common at Chitwan (296), where over 2000 Yellow and Citrine Wagtails were seen flying to roost in January 1980 (180). Five races have been recorded, but their distribution and movements are poorly known, and birds subspecifically identified have mainly been spring males. *M. f. beema* (b) occurs on passage and in winter, and is more frequently reported than other races. There are several records of *M. f. thunbergi* (t) in April and May (295,432,440,442,635), single reports of *M. f. melanogrisea* (m) (647), and three of *M. f. leucocephala* (l) (199,294,321). One *M. f. taivana* (a) which is scarce in the subcontinent, was found at Kosi Barrage on 14 March 1981 (442). *M. f. lutea* is

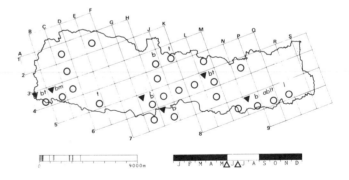

likely to occur. A specimen record of *M. s. simillima* (482) listed in the first edition of this book (435) has been omitted because it is considered unlikely that this far eastern race occurs so far west. The species frequents marshes and damp fields, especially near grazing animals. **Range** Breeds in Ladakh and possibly n. Kashmir. Winters throughout the subcontinent.

CITRINE WAGTAIL *Motacilla citreola*
Yellow-headed Wagtail

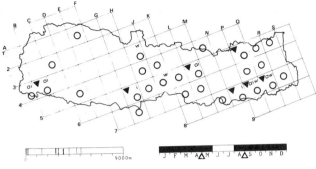

First recorded by B. Hodgson (360). Occasional. Mainly a winter visitor to the lowlands and a passage migrant. Fairly common at Chitwan (296) and Kosi, with a maximum of 60 estimated at the latter place on 2 May 1986 (321). Three races occur. *M. c. calcarata* (a) (62,294,432,

647,428) and *M. c. citreola* (i) (62,432,442,587,647) have been reported on passage and in winter. Only a few records of *M. c. werae* (w), from March to May (294,442,321). Inhabits marshes and wet fields. Prefers wetter areas than Yellow Wagtail. **Range** Breeds in Baluchistan, and in the Himalayas from Chitral east to Spiti. Winters throughout the subcontinent.

GREY WAGTAIL *Motacilla cinerea*
(*M. caspica*)

Subspecies *cinerea*. First recorded by B. Hodgson (388). A common resident subject to altitudinal movements. Mainly summers between 2440m and 4110m, and winters below 365m, but occasionally to 1550m. Proved breeding near Jumla (620), in Langu valley (F2) (330) and along the Marsyangdi and Kali Gandaki Rivers (H4,H5,J5) (757). Migrants noted in the upper Kali Gandaki valley: up to 10 daily between 14 September and 6 October 1973 (76). Occurs by fast-flowing, rocky streams in summer, and slower

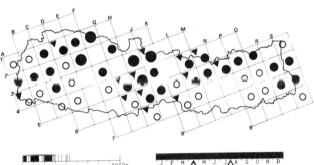

streams in winter. **Range** Breeds in Baluchistan, and the Himalayas from Chitral to Nepal. Winters throughout the subcontinent.

WHITE WAGTAIL *Motacilla alba*
Pied Wagtail

First recorded by B. Hodgson (360). A commmon passage migrant and winter visitor, with one race remaining to breed. Proved breeding in Langu valley (F2) (330). Mainly winters below 1500m. At Sauraha (J6) over 8000 were estimated flying to roost in January 1981 (180). Occasionally reported flying up river valleys on passage. In early November 1954 large numbers passed south over Pokhara daily (419). Migrants noted as high as 5000m at Gorak Shep (P6) (526). Six races occur.

All have been found in the Kathmandu Valley (x) where their status has been studied (635). *M. a. dukhunensis* (d), *M. a. leucopsis* (l), *M. a. personata, M. a. baicalensis* and *M. a. alboides* (a) are regularly seen. The last is also a summer visitor found between 3600m and 4800m (109,190,512). *M. a. ocularis* has only been reported from the Kathmandu Valley on passage (99,240,245,635,708). The species winters in open country near water: marshes, rivers, streams, lakes and wet fields, and summers in the alpine zone. **Range** Breeds in the Himalayas from Gilgit to Arunachal Pradesh. Winters throughout the subcontinent.

WHITE WAGTAIL, cont'd ...

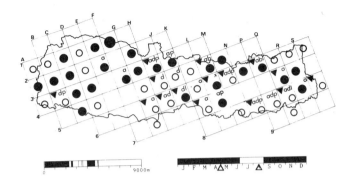

WHITE-BROWED WAGTAIL   *Motacilla maderaspatensis*
Large Pied Wagtail

Obtained by B. Hodgson in his later collection (409) but the specimen may have
originated in India. First definitely recorded by B. Biswas at Thankot (L6) on
10 April 1947 (101). A fairly common
resident throughout the tarai and lower
hills mainly below 915m, and uncommonly up to 1700m. Mainly occurs in the
Kathmandu Valley in summer; scarce in
winter. Proved breeding at Pokhara
(480), Chitwan (296), and in the Kathmandu Valley (009,J10). Frequents
banks of rivers, pools and lakes. **Range**
Locally throughout the subcontinent.

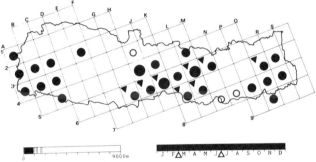

COMMON WOODSHRIKE   *Tephrodornis pondicerianus*
Lesser Wood-Shrike, Indian Wood-Shrike

Subspecies *pondicerianus*. First recorded
by B. Hodgson (375). A locally, fairly
common resident found up to about
455m. Areas include Bardia, Chitwan, the
central dun (K7,L7) and the eastern lowlands (Q8,R8). Proved breeding at Chitwan (296), and Hetaura (99). Inhabits
dry scrub and lightly wooded areas.
Range Throughout most of the subcontinent.

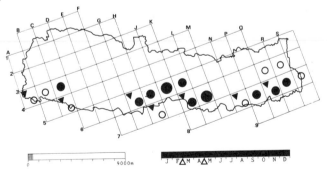

LARGE WOODSHRIKE *Tephrodornis gularis*
(*T. virgatus*)

Subspecies *pelvica*. First recorded by B. Hodgson (375). A locally fairly common resident up to 365m. Areas include Tamaspur, Chitwan, and north of Sunischare. A straggler to the Kathmandu Valley. Occurs in broadleaved forests and well-wooded country, but prefers wetter areas than the Common Woodshrike. **Range** Himalayan foothills from Nepal east to Arunachal Pradesh; n.e. India and Bangladesh; s.w. India.

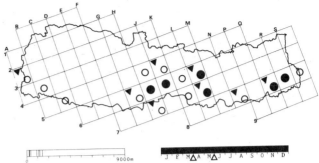

BAR-WINGED FLYCATCHER-SHRIKE *Hemipus picatus*
Pied Wood-shrike

Subspecies *capitalis*. First recorded by B. Hodgson (388). A common resident up to 1830m subject to some altitudinal movements. Chiefly a summer visitor to the Kathmandu Valley. Breeding confirmed at Chitwan (440). Frequents open broadleaved forests. **Range** Himalayan foothills from Simla east to Arunachal Pradesh; south to s. India and Bangladesh.

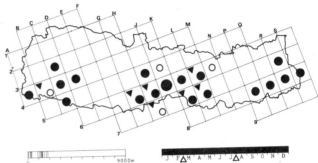

BLACK-HEADED CUCKOO-SHRIKE *Coracina melanoptera*

Subspecies *sykesi*. First recorded by B. Biswas at Hetaura on 21 May 1947 (99). Scarce. Subject to seasonal movements; mainly seen in spring and summer in the lowlands, but is possibly under-recorded. As breeding does not start until June most birds probably do not arrive until late spring. A few reports from Chitwan between March and the monsoon (772,730,562,810); also in December 1989 (138). Single records from elsewhere: Birganj (K7) in 1973 (587), Chapagaon forest (L6) at 1430m in February 1978 (301), Simra in February 1979 (486), Bardia and Kosi Tappu in May 1982 (432), north of Sunischare in January 1985 (142) and Dharan in November 1989 (597). A male was seen carrying nesting material on 15 April 1977 at Birtamod

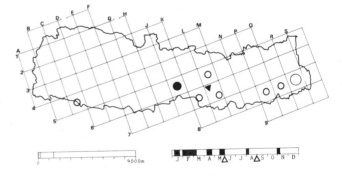

(R8) (243). Occurs in open broadleaved forests and secondary growth. **Range** Himalayan foothills from Himachal Pradesh east to West Bengal, and south to Kutch and Bangladesh.

BLACK-WINGED CUCKOO-SHRIKE *Coracina melaschistos*
Dark Cuckoo-Shrike, Dark Grey Cuckoo-Shrike

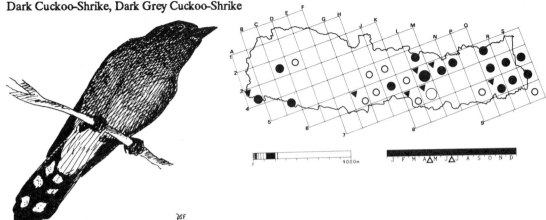

Subspecies *melaschistos*. The species was described from Nepal by B. Hodgson (374,798). A resident subject to altitudinal movements. Occasionally found up to 915m throughout the year, and up to 2200m in summer. Seen between February and mid-October in the Kathmandu Valley (635), and proved breeding there (635, 659). Occurs in open forests and groves. **Range** Breeds in the Himalayas from Murree to Arunachal Pradesh, and in n.e. India. Winters south to Karnataka and Bangladesh.

LARGE CUCKOO-SHRIKE *Coracina macei*
Black-faced Cuckoo-shrike (*C. novaehollandiae*)

Subspecies *nipalensis*. First recorded by B. Hodgson (374,798). A common resident up to 2135m. Generally descends from higher elevations in winter, although it has been found at 1525m. Inhabits secondary growth and open wooded country. **Range** Himalayan foothills from Rawalpindi east to Arunachal Pradesh; south to s. India and Bangladesh.

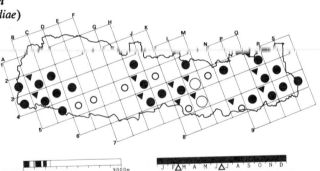

SCARLET MINIVET *Pericrocotus flammeus*

Subspecies *speciosus*. First recorded by B. Hodgson (388). A common resident up to 2200m, possibly subject to altitudinal movements. Breeding confirmed at Chitwan (296). Frequents broadleaved and coniferous forests. **Range** Himalayas from Murree to Arunachal Pradesh; also locally south in the hills to s. India.

SCARLET MINIVET, cont'd ...

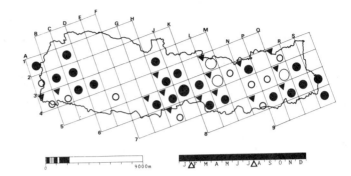

SHORT-BILLED MINIVET   *Pericrocotus brevirostris*

Subspecies *brevirostris*. First recorded by
B. Hodgson (388). Scarce, probably resident. Found between 1005m and 2745m.
Very similar to the Long-tailed Minivet;
the two species were long confused in the
literature and not separated until 1914.
Collected in the Langtang valley (L5)
(619,621), at Deorali, (L6) (99), Jiri (N6)
(190,196), near Jamuna (S7) (246), and in
the upper Arun valley (10). Other confirmed localities include south of Annapurna (J5), the Kathmandu Valley,
Sangure ridge (Q8) and Dharan. The only
published breeding information for the
species is of one taken in breeding condition at Deorali at 1495m on 29 April 1947
(99), and a pair nest-building above

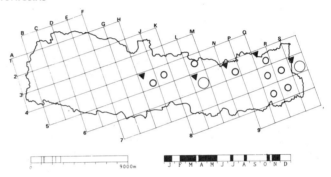

Hanga Tham at about 2140m on 27 April 1986 (321,323).
Inhabits open broadleaved forests and forest edges. **Range**
Himalayas from Naini Tal east to Arunachal Pradesh, and
n.e. India.

LONG-TAILED MINIVET   *Pericrocotus ethologus*

The species was first collected by B.
Hodgson; this was confirmed by the recent location of specimens in the British
Museum (Natural History). A common
resident subject to altitudinal movements. Most frequent in summer between
1200m and 2400m, and in winter between
245m and 2135m. Recorded at 3965m at
Khangsar in August (512). Found breeding at Rara Lake (626) and in the Kathmandu Valley (440,629,659,708). Two
races occur: *P. e. laetus* (l) (247), *P. e.
favillaceus* (f) (512,647), and intermediates (fl) (99,109,647,659). Frequents forests, trees at edges of cultivation and
groves. **Range** Breeds in the Himalayas

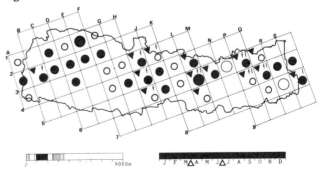

from N.W.F.P. east to Arunachal Pradesh; n.e. India and
Bangladesh. Winters south to Madhya Pradesh and Orissa.

GREY-CHINNED MINIVET *Pericrocotus solaris*
Yellow-throated Minivet

Subspecies *solaris*. First recorded by B. Hodgson (388). Scarce, presumably resident and found between 250m and 2075m. Occasionally seen on the lower slopes of Phulchowki. Other records are from north-west of Pokhara (223,309), Chitwan (K6) (11), Chapagaon forest (L6) (243), Deorali (L6) (99), Num (Q6) (587), Trisuli valley (L6) (794), north of Sunischare (142) and the far eastern hills (Q8,R8) (223). Noted at Ulleri (H5) in March 1982 (207,561); the most westerly records for the species. Occurs in damp broadleaved forests. Its breeding behav-

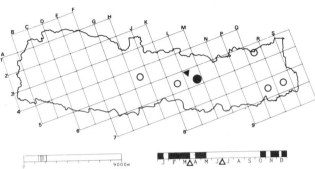

iour is little known. **Range** Himalayas from Nepal east to Arunachal Pradesh, and n.e. India.

SMALL MINIVET *Pericrocotus cinnamomeus*

A Hodgson specimen was listed for Nepal by Sharpe (714), but it may have originated in India. First definitely recorded by F.M. Bailey from Tribeni (H7) at 75m on 8 February 1936 (62). A resident, occasionally seen throughout the lowlands up to 290m. Breeding confirmed at Chitwan (296). The eastern race *P. c. vividus* has been collected in the far western tarai (A4,B4) (647), but Ripley considered his western specimens were intermediates between this race and *P. c. peregrinus* (46, 659,664). Frequents more open wooded areas than other minivets. **Range** Throughout most of the subcontinent.

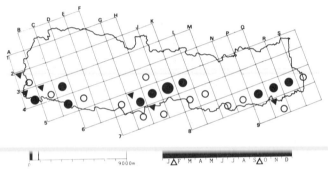

ROSY MINIVET *Pericrocotus roseus*

Subspecies *roseus*. First recorded by B. Hodgson (388). Locally distributed. Status uncertain, possibly resident. Seen in winter at Bardia (192), Chitwan (180,460) and at Dharan (597), but all other records are from March to May. Occasionally seen at Chitwan and a few sightings from Tamaspur. Only single reports received from elsewhere: at Barmdeo Mandi (A3) (247), Kanchanpur District (A4) (470), Bardia (192), south of Annapurna (J5) (762), Hetaura (190), Kosi District (P8) (293), Dharan (597), Kosi Tappu (328), and north of Sunischare (442). Inhabits broadleaved forest and open wooded country. **Range** Breeds

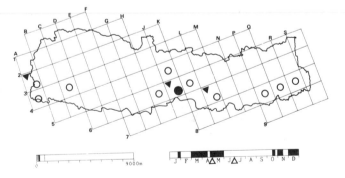

in the Himalayas from N.W.F.P. to Arunachal Pradesh, and in n.e. India. Winters south to Maharashtra.

STRIATED BULBUL *Pycnonotus striatus*
Striated Green Bulbul

Subspecies *striatus*. First recorded by B. Hodgson (388). A local resident, with some altitudinal movements, found between 1500m and 2650m. Reported at Ulleri (H5) on 22 July 1978 (688), the most westerly record of the species. Occasionally seen between Dhampus and Landrung (H5), on Phulchowki, and in the Trisuli (L5), Arun and Mai valleys. Breeding behaviour is little known. Taken in breeding condition on 6 May 1947 at Bhimpedi at 1220m (99). Frequents damp, broadleaved, evergreen forests. **Range** Himalayas from Nepal east to Arunachal Pradesh, and n.e. India.

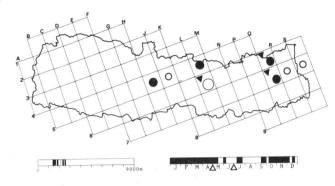

BLACK-CRESTED BULBUL *Pycnonotus melanicterus*
Black-headed Yellow Bulbul

Subspecies *flaviventris*. First recorded by B. Hodgson (388). Resident. Common up to 800m in Mechi Zone (R7,R8) (658). Elsewhere occasionally seen up to 365m, uncommon up to 915m and rare to 1525m. Breeding confirmed at Chitwan (296) and Hetaura (99). Inhabits moist forests with dense undergrowth and thick secondary jungle. **Range** Himalayas from Simla east to Arunachal Pradesh, and e. and s.w. India.

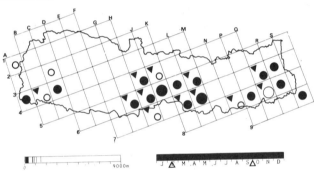

RED-WHISKERED BULBUL *Pycnonotus jocosus*

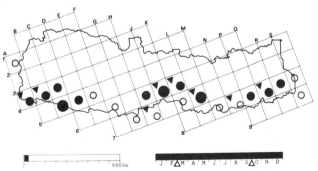

Subspecies *pyrrhotis*. First recorded by B. Hodgson (388). A locally common and sedentary resident, reported up to 455m. An abundant breeding bird at Chitwan (296), and also found breeding at Bardia (432) and Hetaura (99). Occurs in scrub jungle and open forest. Prefers damp habitats. **Range** Lowlands below the Himalayas from Punjab east to Arunachal Pradesh; also most of India, except the north-west, and Bangladesh.

WHITE-CHEEKED BULBUL   *Pycnonotus leucogenys*

Subspecies *leucogenys*. First recorded by
B. Hodgson (388). Mainly a common resident between 350m and 2400m. Abundant in some areas up to 1830m. Occasionally found down to 250m and up to
3050m. Confirmed to breed at Chitwan
(296), in the Kathmandu Valley (708),
and at Hetaura (99). Frequents secondary
growth, scrub jungle, and cultivation.
Range Himalayan foothills from Chitral
east to Arunachal Pradesh; Pakistan and
n.w. India.

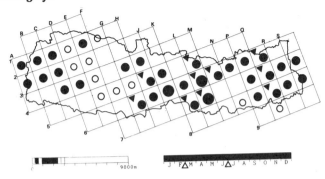

RED-VENTED BULBUL   *Pycnonotus cafer*

Subspecies *bengalensis*. First recorded by
B. Hodgson (388). A common resident
from the tarai up to 1500m, occasionally
seen up to 2135m. Abundant in some
areas. Found breeding at Dipayal (B3)
(68), in the Kathmandu Valley
(336,629,708), at Chitwan (296) and
Hetaura (99). Frequents gardens, secondary scrub and light broadleaved forests.
Range Himalayas from N.W.F.P. east to
Arunachal Pradesh; south throughout the
subcontinent.

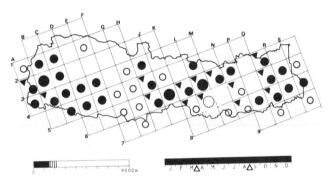

WHITE-THROATED BULBUL   *Criniger flaveolus*

Subspecies *flaveolus*. The species was
described by J. Gould (783), the locality
of the type later given as Nepal (479). It
was collected by B. Hodgson (388). Locally distributed, probably resident, up to
455m. Fairly common north of Sunischare. A few records from Hetaura, but
none since 1970. Found rarely at Chitwan
(J6,K6) (296,481), the westernmost locality for the species. The only other reports
are from Amlekhganj (K7) in 1947 (101),
the eastern tarai (P8) in 1975 (293) and
Hans Pokhari Danda (S8) in 1989 (193).
Inhabits undergrowth in dense,
broadleaved, evergreen forests. **Range**
Himalayas from Nepal east to Arunachal
Pradesh; n.e. India and Bangladesh.

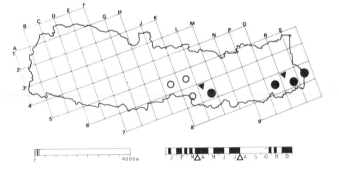

MOUNTAIN BULBUL *Hypsipetes mcclellandii*
Rufous-bellied Bulbul (*H. virescens*)

Subspecies *mcclellandii*. First recorded by B. Hodgson (388). A fairly common resident subject to altitudinal movements, most frequently seen between 1830m and 2135m. Proved breeding at Bhimpedi (99), and in the Kathmandu Valley (336,708). Inhabits forests and secondary growth. **Range** Himalayas from Mussoorie east to Arunachal Pradesh; n.e. India and Bangladesh.

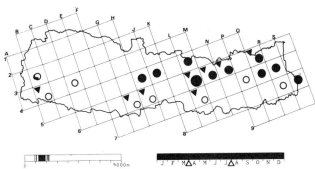

ASHY BULBUL *Hypsipetes flavalus*
Brown-eared Bulbul

Subspecies *flavalus*. The species was described from Nepal by E. Blyth from a Hodgson specimen (798,118), but it may have originated in India. First definitely recorded by B. Biswas at Hetaura on 3 May 1947 (99). A resident, occasionally seen between 305m and 1525m. Rare in the Kathmandu Valley. Occurs in forests and dense secondary growth. **Range** Himalayan foothills from between Simla and Mussoorie east to Arunachal Pradesh.

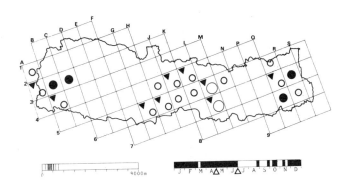

BLACK BULBUL *Hypsipetes leucocephalus*
Grey Bulbul (*H. madagascariensis*)

Subspecies *psaroides*. First recorded by B. Hodgson (388). A common resident between 305m and 2600m, most frequent between 1830m and 2135m. Abundant in some areas. Some birds apparently descend to the foothills in winter, but also found at 2700m on hills surrounding the Kathmandu Valley (629). Occasionally seen at Chitwan and confirmed to breed there (296). Frequents forests. **Range** Himalayas; also s.w. India, n.e. India and Bangladesh.

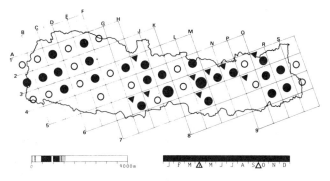

COMMON IORA *Aegithina tiphia*
Iora

Subspecies *tiphia*. First recorded by B. Hodgson (388). Common up to 365m, occasionally seen up to 1900m. A summer visitor to the Kathmandu Valley. Breeding confirmed at Chitwan (296), Gaucher forest (L6) (243), Hetaura (96) and near Dhankuta (Q7) (446). Inhabits open broadleaved forests and scrub jungle. **Range** Himalayas from N.W.F.P. east to Arunachal Pradesh; also all of India except for the north-west; Bangladesh.

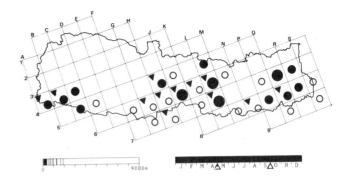

GOLDEN-FRONTED LEAFBIRD *Chloropsis aurifrons*

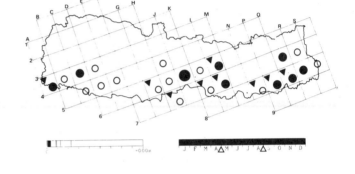

Subspecies *aurifrons*. First collected by B. Hodgson (114). A fairly common resident up to 365m; uncommon up to 915m, and rare above this altitude. Subject to altitudinal movements. Scarce in the Kathmandu Valley, but sometimes seen on the western slopes of Nagarjung (243) and noted on Phulchowki in January 1984 (418). Breeding confirmed at Chitwan (296). Occurs in broadleaved forests. **Range** Himalayas from Garhwal east to Arunachal Pradesh; also south to Bangladesh, e. and s.w. India.

ORANGE-BELLIED LEAFBIRD *Chloropsis hardwickii*

Subspecies *hardwickii*. The species was described from Nepal by Jardine and Selby (449). Resident, subject to some altitudinal movements, and mainly recorded between 1300m and 2135m. Occurs over a higher altitudinal zone than Golden-fronted Leafbird. Fairly common on Phulchowki and occasionally reported from other areas. Favours broadleaved evergreen forests. **Range** Himalayas from Simla east to Arunachal Pradesh; south to Bangladesh.

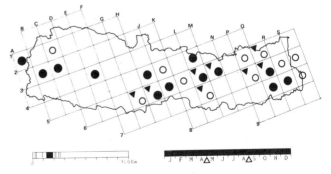

ASIAN FAIRY BLUEBIRD *Irena puella*

Subspecies *sikkimensis*. First recorded north-west of Sunischare at 335m on 1 January 1965 by R.L. Fleming Sr. (247). Local, presumably resident. Mainly found in dense, moist forest near water up to 365m. Fairly common north of Sunischare. Described as an uncommon resident in Morang District (Q8) in 1976 (293). Found at Hetaura in December 1971 (405) and March 1978 (507). The only other record is from Hans Pokhari Danda (S8) in May 1989. Its overall nesting season is from January to June. **Range** Himalayas from Nepal east to Arunachal Pradesh, and south to Bangladesh; also s.w. India.

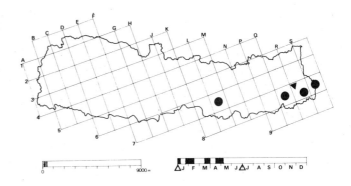

BOHEMIAN WAXWING *Bombycilla garrulus*

Subspecies *garrulus*. First recorded by R.L. Fleming Jr. who saw a party of four at Thare Pati, Helambu (L5) at 3660m on 16 December 1967 (211). The only other record is of five seen together below Pisang (J4) at 3050m on 17 March 1985 (332). **Range** Irregular vagrant to the Himalayas and Pakistan.

WHITE-BREASTED DIPPER *Cinclus cinclus*
Dipper, White-throated Dipper

Subspecies *cashmeriensis*. First recorded by O. Polunin in upper Langtang (M5), between 3355m and 3660m, in summer 1949 (621). A resident between 3500m and 4800m. Subject to some altitudinal movements. Fairly common in the Tibetan plateau region, also reported from Langtang (L5,M5) (195,621,656), Khumbu (P6) (299), Taplejung District (S6) (194), Topke Gola (R6) (487), and also the upper Ladka Khola valley (R6) (537) and Tak Do Trap (F3) (587) where proved breeding. Seen at the particularly low altitude of 2590m at Tukche in March

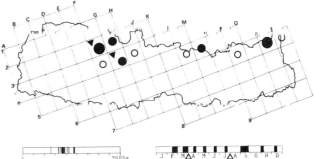

1982 (598). Frequents rocky, fast-flowing waters. **Range** Himalayas from the Kagan valley east to Bhutan and probably Arunachal Pradesh.

BROWN DIPPER *Cinclus pallasii*

Subspecies *tenuirostris*. First recorded by B. Hodgson (388). A common resident between 915m and 3100m, occasionally seen up to 4960m in summer. Usually found at lower elevations than White-breasted Dipper, although the two species have been seen in the same localities where their altitudinal ranges overlap.

Confirmed to breed between 1525m and 3600m at Khaptad (C3) (428), Kawa (D2) and Barikot (E4) (620), Chankeli (626), Dhorpatan (G5) (153), Langtang (517,771), north-west of Pokhara (H4,H5) (82,811,812,480,111), Sundarijal (L6) (635), Naubise (L6) (321,734) and Mai valley (R8,S7) (740,307). Occurs on mountain streams. **Range** Himalayas from Ladakh east to Arunachal Pradesh.

BROWN DIPPER, cont'd ...

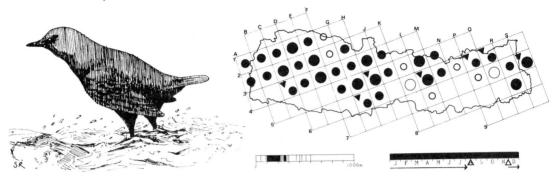

NORTHERN WREN   *Troglodytes troglodytes*
Wren, Winter Wren

Subspecies *nipalensis*. First recorded by
B. Hodgson (388). A fairly common resident subject to altitudinal movements.
Chiefly occurs between 2500m and
4700m, but noted at 5300m in Khumbu
(314), and at 2135m at Ghasa (H4) in
February 1982 (770). Regularly winters
up to 3050m and probably occurs higher.
Found among rocks and dwarf scrub; also
on rocky slopes above the treeline. **Range**
Himalayas from N.W.F.P. east to Arunachal Pradesh.

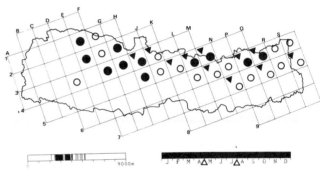

MAROON-BACKED ACCENTOR   *Prunella immaculata*

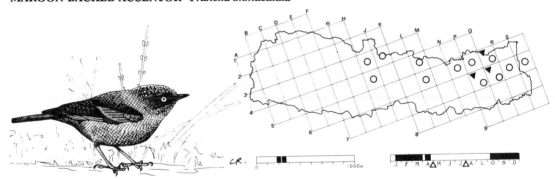

The species was described from Nepal by
B. Hodgson (391,798). A winter visitor,
mainly occurring between 1830m and
2700m. Found west to Ghasa (H4), the
westernmost locality for the species.
Regularly reported from the upper Mai
and upper Kali Gandaki valleys, and occasionally from
Ghorepani and the Arun valley. Several records from the
hills surrounding the Kathmandu Valley, Langtang, and
Tamur valley. Mainly single reports from elsewhere. Occurs
in damp forests and forest clearings. **Range** Himalayas from
Nepal east to Arunachal Pradesh.

RUFOUS-BREASTED ACCENTOR   *Prunella strophiata*

The species was described from Nepal from a Hodgson specimen (114). A fairly common resident subject to altitudinal movements. Chiefly summers above 3500m; found as high as 4930m in Khumbu. Mainly winters between 1600m and at least 3650m. Two races occur: *P. a. strophiata* (s) and *P. s. jerdoni* (j) (647). Found in upland pastures with scattered bushes in winter; rhododendron and dwarf juniper scrub near the treeline in summer. **Range** Himalayas from Pakistan to Arunachal Pradesh.

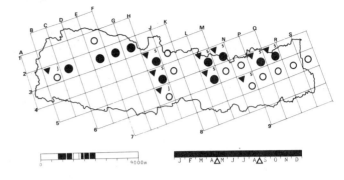

BROWN ACCENTOR   *Prunella fulvescens*

Subspecies *sushkini*. First recorded by R.L. Fleming Sr. from Jomosom in December 1949 (647). An altitudinal migrant, common in the Tibetan plateau region. Summers up to 4880m, and seen nest-building in June at 4270m (243). Winters from 2300m up to at least 3800m. Fairly common in winter in Thakkhola (H4). The unusually high number of 103 was counted there between Kalopani and Muktinath in December 1984 (58). Found in low scrub on dry rocky hillsides. **Range** Himalayas from Hunza to Sikkim.

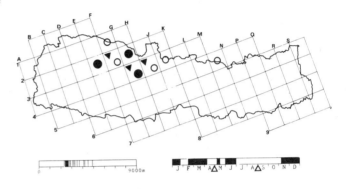

BLACK-THROATED ACCENTOR   *Prunella atrogularis*

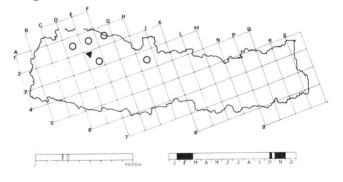

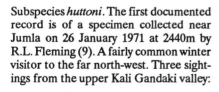

Subspecies *huttoni*. The first documented record is of a specimen collected near Jumla on 26 January 1971 at 2440m by R.L. Fleming (9). A fairly common winter visitor to the far north-west. Three sightings from the upper Kali Gandaki valley: from Jomosom in March 1981 (559), Kalopani in October 1984 (145) and Marpha in November 1985 (298), the most easterly records in the Himalayas. Occurs among bushes in cultivation. **Range** Winters in the Himalayas from Hunza to Nepal.

ROBIN ACCENTOR   *Prunella rubeculoides*

The species was described from Nepal by F. Moore from a Hodgson specimen (409,798) and listed for Nepal in Hodgson's later collection (276), but the specimens may have originated in India. First definitely recorded by R.L. Fleming Sr. from Jomosom at 2805m in December 1949 (647). A fairly common altitudinal migrant between 2655m and 5000m. Summers at higher altitudes than other accentors, mainly over 4500m. Confirmed to breed at Gokyo at 4800m (190). Seen as high as Everest base camp at 5485m in May 1976 (582). Fairly common in winter between Marpha at 2655m and Muktinath at 3795m. Reported at 3960m in Khumbu in February 1954 (86), and found to be common there up to 4880m in

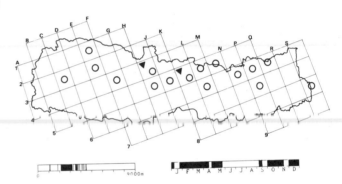

November 1987 (558). May occur higher in winter. In summer inhabits dwarf willows and Caragana scrub near streams or pools. Winters in dry, stony areas. **Range** Himalayas from Baltistan and Ladakh east to Bhutan, and probably Arunachal Pradesh.

ALTAI ACCENTOR   *Prunella himalayana*
Rufous-streaked Accentor

Obtained by B. Hodgson in his later collection (409) but the specimen may have originated in India. First definitely recorded by R.L. Fleming Sr. from Jomosom at 2805m in December 1949 (647). A fairly common winter visitor, chiefly occurring between 2135m and 4270m. Noted as low as 1340m at Rukum (location unknown) on 25 March 1982 (244). A late record in mid-May from Gosainkund, at 4300m (243,440). Feeds on grassy hillsides. **Range** Winter visitor to the Himalayas from N.W.F.P. east to Arunachal Pradesh.

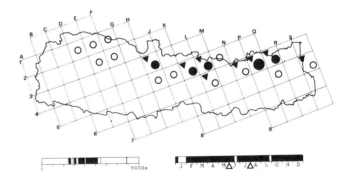

ALPINE ACCENTOR   *Prunella collaris*

Subspecies *nipalensis*. First collected by B. Hodgson (114). Occasional. A resident subject to altitudinal movements. Chiefly summers over 4200m; noted as high as 7900m on Mt Everest (49). Confirmed to breed in Khumbu from 4900m to 5000m (190). Winters between 2440m and 3795m, and probably higher. Noted in Khumbu at 4930m in November (453). Inhabits rocky alpine pastures and scree slopes, and also occurs in winter near villages. **Range** Himalayas from N.W.F.P. to Arunachal Pradesh.

GOULD'S SHORTWING   *Brachypteryx stellata*

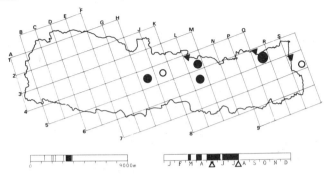

Subspecies *stellata*. The species was described by J. Gould (272) from a specimen collected by C.V. Eccles. This is labelled "Nepal, 10,000'" (798), but it is often ascribed to Sikkim (664,716). First definitely recorded in the upper Mai Valley (S7) at 2135m on 8 April 1912 by H. Stevens (740). Scarce and very locally distributed; probably a resident, subject to altitudinal movements. Summers near Gapte cave at 3505m where the maximum

of seven was seen on 22 May 1982 (199,682). Found breeding in the upper Arun valley in late June 1973 (167), but there are no other published breeding records for the species (48). The only other reports received are from the upper Mai valley in March 1961 (246), upper Arun valley in July and October 1973 (10), south of Annapurna (H5,J5) in May 1974 (259) and 1977 (762), and in Gaucher forest (L6) in July 1977 (301). Inhabits rhododendron and juniper shrubberies. **Range** Himalayas from Kumaon east to Arunachal Pradesh.

[RUSTY-BELLIED SHORTWING   *Brachypteryx hyperythra*

A specimen in the Hancock Museum, Newcastle-upon-Tyne, U.K. is labelled solely 'Nepal', but no further details are known (322).]

WHITE-BROWED SHORTWING   *Brachypteryx montana*

Subspecies *cruralis*. First recorded by B. Hodgson (388). A very uncommon resident subject to altitudinal movements. Summers from 2560m to 3660m at localities including Pipar (H5) (475,499), the Gosainkund trail (L5) (633,652), the upper Arun (483) and upper Mai valleys (440,561,264,321), and the hills surrounding the Kathmandu Valley. Reported in the non-breeding season between 245m and 2375m from areas including Phewa Tal (622,403), south-west of Annapurna (H5) (746,702), Phulchowki (152), Arung Khola (H6) (486,652), Chitwan (759) and Barun valley (588). Frequents damp oak and rhododendron forests with dense undergrowth near streams. **Range** Himalayas from Garhwal east to Arunachal Pradesh.

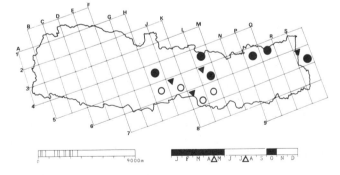

LESSER SHORTWING *Brachypteryx leucophrys*

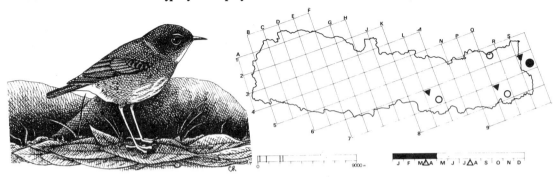

Subspecies *nipalensis*. Obtained by B. Hodgson in his later collection (409,798) but the specimen may have originated in India. First definitely recorded by H. Stevens from the upper Mai Valley (S7) at 2135m on 3 and 8 April 1912 (740). Scarce, presumably a resident, subject to altitudinal movements. Recorded from 250m to 2135m between January and April: from Ilam District (R8) (undated) (223), Tarahara (Q8) in February 1971 (589), north of Sunischare in April 1986 (264), the upper Arun valley in March 1987 (769), Simery (L7) in February 1988 (589), east of Ilam bazaar (R8) in January and March 1988 (658) and Hanga Tham in March 1988 (465). Inhabits thick undergrowth in damp forests, and secondary jungle often near streams. **Range** Himalayas from Garhwal and east Nepal east to Arunachal Pradesh.

SIBERIAN RUBYTHROAT *Luscinia calliope*
Eurasian Rubythroat (*Erithacus calliope*)

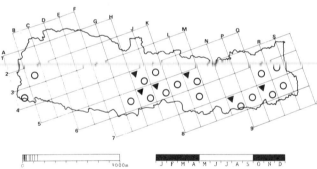

First recorded by B. Hodgson (388). A winter visitor and passage migrant, found occasionally up to 1370m. Probably overlooked because of its skulking behaviour. Inhabits thick undergrowth, wet ravines and long grass often near water. **Range** Winters in the Himalayas from Nepal east to Arunachal Pradesh; south to Rajasthan, Andhra Pradesh and Bangladesh.

BLUETHROAT *Luscinia svecica*
(*Erithacus svecicus*)

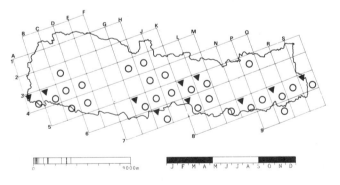

First recorded by B. Hodgson (388). Mainly a fairly common winter visitor and passage migrant up to 915m. Noted on passage at about 3445m on 28 September 1972 in Khumbu (474), at Tukche between 14 September and 10 October 1973 (76) and at Khaptad (C3) on 1 May 1988 (428). Two specimens from the eastern tarai (Q8) were *L. s. pallidogularis* (62), but no others have been subspecifically identified. Skulks in damp ravines, scrub, reeds, tall grass and cultivation near water. **Range** Winters throughout the subcontinent.

WHITE-TAILED RUBYTHROAT   *Luscinia pectoralis*
Himalayan Rubythroat   (*Erithacus pectoralis*)

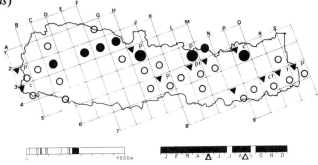

First recorded by B. Hodgson (388). Occasional. Three races occur. *L. p. pectoralis* (p) is a resident subject to altitudinal movements. Summers in west and central areas. Breeding confirmed at Manangbhot (H4) between 3960m and 4570m (512), and at 3300m at Thare Pati (L5) (48). A few winter records from 275m to 1340m east to Jhapa District (S8) (247). *L. p. confusa* (c) is a resident subject to altitudinal movements. Found breeding in Khumbu between 4200m and 4800m (190) and wintering in the foothills (62). Only two records of *L. p. tschebaiewi* (t): in winter and on passage (246). Inhabits dwarf rhododendron and juniper shrubberies and Caragana scrub above the treeline in summer; dense scrub in winter. **Range** Himalayas from Baltistan east to Arunachal Pradesh.

INDIAN BLUE ROBIN   *Luscinia brunnea*
Blue Chat   (*Erithacus brunneus*)

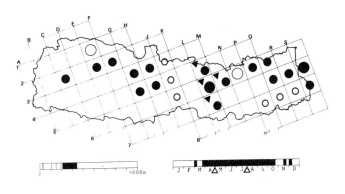

Subspecies *brunnea*. The species was described from Nepal by B. Hodgson (371,798). Mainly a fairly common summer visitor, arriving in April. Common at Khaptad (C3) (657,428). Breeds above 2135m, most frequently between 2440m and 3355m. Proved breeding on Sheopuri (243,635) and in the Mai valley (740).

Occasionally seen in the lowlands on passage in spring. A male on 5 March 1982 at Chitwan (77) was possibly an early migrant. Found in winter at Thare Pati (L5) in November 1970, and the Rapti dun (L7) in December 1970 (444). Skulks in dense undergrowth in damp forests. **Range** Breeds in the Himalayas from Pakistan to Arunachal Pradesh. Winters in s. India and occasionally in the Himalayan foothills.

SIBERIAN BLUE ROBIN   *Luscinia cyane*
(*Erithacus cyane*)

Vagrant. The only record is of an adult male seen on 29 November 1985 at Nagarjung, Kathmandu Valley, at about 1450m by R. Roberts (677). **Range** Straggler to W. Bengal and Manipur.

ORANGE-FLANKED BUSH-ROBIN *Tarsiger cyanurus*
Red-flanked Bluetail   (*Erithacus cyanurus*)

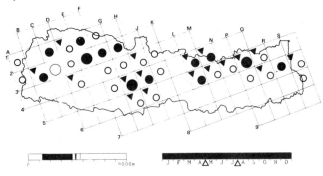

Subspecies *rufilatus*. First recorded by B.
Hodgson (391,798). A common resident
subject to altitudinal movements. Mainly
summers between 3000m and 4000m, and
winters from 1370m to 2745m. Proved
breeding at Dori Lekh (E3) (626),
Khumjung (P6) (190) and in the
Dhorpatan valley (G5) (499). Inhabits the
understorey and bushes at clearing edges
in broadleaved and coniferous forests.
Range Breeds in the Himalayas from
N.W.F.P. east to Arunachal Pradesh.
Winters south to n.e. India.

GOLDEN BUSH-ROBIN   *Tarsiger chrysaeus*
(*Erithacus chrysaeus*)

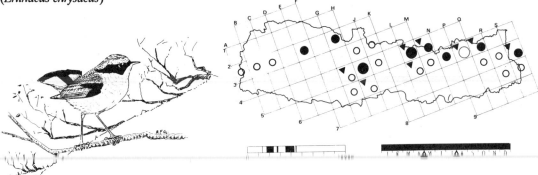

Subspecies *chrysaeus*. The species was
described from Nepal by B. Hodgson
(391,798). A resident subject to altitudinal movements: most frequent in summer
between 3500m and 4200m, and in winter
from 1700m and 2800m. Fairly common
north-west of Pokhara (H5), Langtang
(L5,M5) and in the Arun and upper Mai

valleys; occasionally seen elsewhere. Confirmed breeding
south of Annapurna (H5) (499) and in the Gandak-Kosi watershed (L5) (633). Frequents dense shrubberies of birch,
rhododendron and juniper above the treeline, and rocky
slopes with scattered shrubs in summer; thick undergrowth
in evergreen forests, or secondary scrub, in winter. **Range**
Himalayas from Hazara east to Arunachal Pradesh, and n.e.
India.

WHITE-BROWED BUSH-ROBIN   *Tarsiger indicus*
(*Erithacus indicus*)

Subspecies *indicus*. First recorded by B.
Hodgson (388). A resident subject to altitudinal movements. Occasionally seen in
summer between 3000m and 4000m, and
in winter from 2100m to 3050m. Noted at
the unusually low altitude of 915m at

Phewa Tal in February 1988 (262). Found breeding south of
Annapurna (H5) (499). Occurs in dense shrubberies of fir,
birch, rhododendron and juniper, and in bushes at forest
edges. **Range** Himalayas from Garhwal east to Arunachal
Pradesh, and n.e. India.

WHITE-BROWED BUSH-ROBIN, cont'd ...

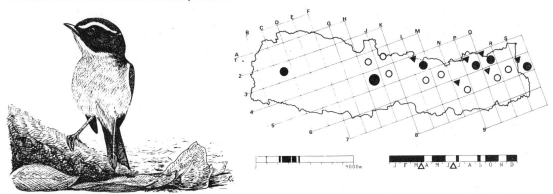

RUFOUS-BREASTED BUSH-ROBIN   *Tarsiger hyperythrus*
Rufous-bellied Bush Robin   (*Erithacus hyperythrus*)

First collected by B. Hodgson (388). An altitudinal migrant, presumably resident. Occasionally found in summer between 3200m and 4200m, and in winter from 2135m to 3050m. Described as very scarce in the Himalayas in 1973 (48) and there were only four Nepalese records up to 1978, but its population has apparently increased recently. Regularly found in spring near Gapte cave at about 3505m since 1979 (L5) with a maximum of ten birds on 30 May 1982 (207). Pairs were seen feeding young there in May in 1979 (651,652), 1980 (440) and 1982 (207). Young just able to fly were seen on 3 June at 3200m in Helambu (244). The nest and eggs are undescribed (48). Regularly reported in winter from north-west of Pokhara, especially from Ghorepani

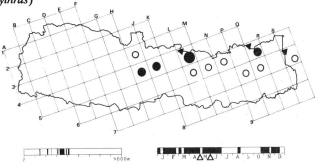

(H5). Chiefly single records from elsewhere. Found at Kabre (H4) at about 1500m in January 1983, the western limit of the species's range. Inhabits edges and clearings of dwarf birch and rhododendron forest, especially near streams. **Range** Breeds in the Himalayas from Nepal east to Arunachal Pradesh. Winters south to n.e. India.

ASIAN MAGPIE-ROBIN   *Copsychus saularis*
Magpie Robin, Robin Dayal

Subspecies *saularis*. First recorded by B. Hodgson (360). A commmon resident up to 1525m and occasionally found up to 2000m. Subject to some local movements. Occurs in the Kathmandu Valley throughout the year, but surprisingly only reported at Chitwan from March to October (296). Proved breeding in these areas and at Hetaura (100). A female with a brood patch was mist-netted as high as 3050m at Chankheli on 7 July 1979 (626). Inhabits villages, towns, gardens, groves, open dry broadleaved forests, and secondary growth. **Range** Most of the subcontinent, except parts of the arid north-west.

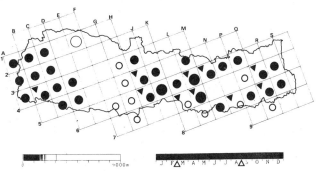

WHITE-RUMPED SHAMA   *Copsychus malabaricus*
Shama

Subspecies *indicus*. First recorded by B.
Hodgson (388). A resident, mainly occurring up to 365m. The maximum altitude
reported is 500m in Ilam District (R8) in
April (658). Common at Chitwan where
proved breeding (296); fairly common
near Dharan and north of Sunischare; occasionally seen elsewhere. Frequents
undergrowth in broadleaved forests.
Range Himalayan foothills from Kumaon
east to Arunachal Pradesh, and south to
e. Madhya Pradesh and the Eastern
Ghats; also in w. and s.w. India.

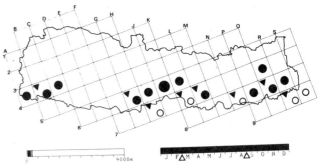

RUFOUS-BACKED REDSTART   *Phoenicurus erythronotus*
Eversmann's Redstart

First recorded at Jomosom at 2805m in
December 1949 by R.L. Fleming Sr.
(647). A winter visitor. Fairly common at
Rara Lake in February (243), occasionally seen at Jumla and regularly seen but
uncommon in the upper Kali Gandaki
valley. Noted at Pisang (J4) at 3300m on
15 November 1981 (553), the most easterly record of the species in the Himalayas. Found amongst scrub and on stone
walls bordering fields in dry habitats.
Range Winters in n. Baluchistan, and the
Himalayas from N.W.F.P. east to Nepal.

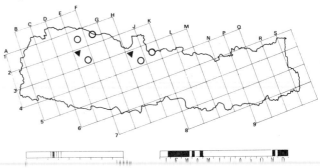

BLUE-CAPPED REDSTART   *Phoenicurus caeruleocephalus*
Blue-headed Redstart

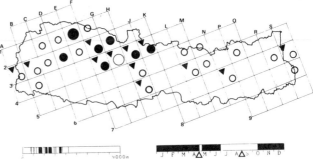

BLUE-CAPPED REDSTART, cont'd ...

First recorded by B. Hodgson (388). A resident subject to altitudinal movements. Fairly common in the breeding season in the north-west, from the upper Kali Gandaki valley (H4) westwards. Occasionally seen further east to the Kathmandu Valley and Langtang, and scarce in east Nepal. Mainly summers between 2900m to 4270m, and winters between 1370m and 2900m. Noted at the unusually low altitude of 800m at Dipayal (B3) in February 1988 (68). Proved breeding at Rara Lake (620). Summers on rocky ground in juniper and open conifer forests and winters in open forests and scrub. **Range** Himalayas from N.W.F.P. east to Bhutan.

BLACK REDSTART *Phoenicurus ochruros*

Subspecies *rufiventris*. First recorded by B. Hodgson (388). An altitudinal migrant. Common in summer in the Tibetan steppe region between 2560m and 5700m. Mainly winters in the tarai and foothills up to about 700m. Proved breeding at Chharkabhotagaon (G3) (620), in Khumbu (190), and in the upper Kali Gandaki valley (811). Migrants were noted in the upper Kali Gandaki valley in September and October 1973: a peak of about 100 occurred on 10 October (76). Inhabits grasslands above the treeline in summer; stony areas, thin scrub, and cultivation in winter. **Range** Breeds in the Himalayas from N.W.F.P. east to Sikkim. Winters south throughout the subcontinent.

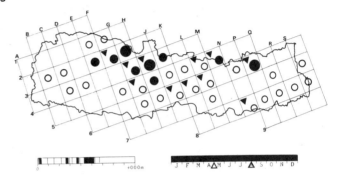

HODGSON'S REDSTART *Phoenicurus hodgsoni*

The species was first collected by B. Hodgson from the Kathmandu Valley (336,388) and described by F. Moore (409,798). A winter visitor seen occasionally, mainly from 760m to 2800m, but common in the Kathmandu and upper Kali Gandaki valleys. Noted at 150m in south-east Nepal (302). Late migrants seen at Ghora Tabela (L5) on 30 April and 1 May 1981 (517), above Muktinath at 5030m in May 1978 (301), and at Pheriche (P6) at 4240m on 23 April 1982 (207). Frequents grass areas interspersed with bushes, dry cultivation, and open forests. **Range** Winters in the Himalayas from Naini Tal east to Arunachal Pradesh; and n.e. India and Bangladesh.

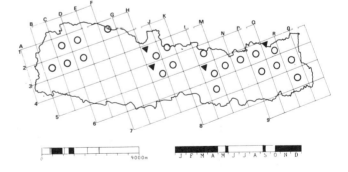

BLUE-FRONTED REDSTART   *Phoenicurus frontalis*

First recorded by B. Hodgson (388). A common altitudinal migrant. Chiefly summers between 3350m and 4900m, and winters between 1000m and 3050m, but noted as low as 455m in the south-east (302). Proved breeding in Khumbu, at Kyangjin (M5) (199), in the Dolpo (G3) (243) and north-west of Pokhara (300). Inhabits open rhododendron, birch and juniper shrubberies and stony slopes above the treeline in summer. Winters in fields and open forest. **Range** Breeds in the Himalayas from N.W.F.P. east to Arunachal Pradesh. Winters south to n.e. India and Bangladesh.

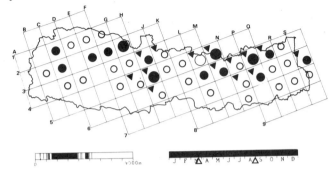

WHITE-THROATED REDSTART   *Phoenicurus schisticeps*

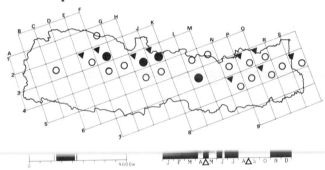

The species was described from Nepal by J.E. and G.R. Gray from a Hodgson specimen (277,798). A high altitude resident subject to relatively small altitudinal movements. Occasionally seen in summer between 3050m and 4200m and in winter between 2500m and 3050m, but noted at 3965m in January on Gosainkund ridge (244). Recorded at Khaptad (C3) on 16 March 1989 (68), the western limit of the species's range. Common between Kalopani and Jomosom in winter. Its breeding behaviour is little known. Frequents open shrubberies on rocky slopes. **Range** Himalayas from w. Nepal east to Arunachal Pradesh.

GULDENSTADT'S REDSTART   *Phoenicurus erythrogaster*
White-winged Redstart

Subspecies *grandis*. Obtained by B. Hodgson in his later collection (409) but the specimen may have originated in India. First definitely recorded by R.L. Fleming Sr. from Jomosom at 2805m in December 1949 (647). An altitudinal migrant occurring at high elevations. Found between 2650m and 3965m in winter and probably higher; in summer mainly between 4900m and 5600m. Fairly common between Tukche and Muktinath in winter, uncommon elsewhere. Other localities include Jumla, Manang, Langtang and also Khumbu, where proved breeding (190). Inhabits the dry alpine zone in summer; stony pastures, rocky moraines and scrubby areas in winter. **Range** Himalayas from Chitral east to Arunachal Pradesh.

GULDENSTADT'S REDSTART, cont'd ...

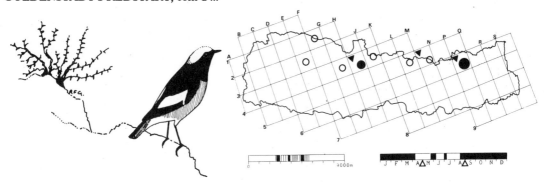

PLUMBEOUS REDSTART *Rhyacornis fuliginosus*

Subspecies *fuliginosus*. First recorded by B. Hodgson (388). A common resident subject to altitudinal movements. Winters between 75m and 2560m; most frequently between 1000m and 1800m. Summers mainly between 1525m and 3750m; uncommonly up to 4420m. Proved breeding in the Kathmandu Valley (629) and at Sukipatal (Q6) (12). Frequents fast-flowing rocky streams. **Range** Breeds in the Himalayas from N.W.F.P. east to Arunachal Pradesh, and in n.e. India. Winters south to Bangladesh

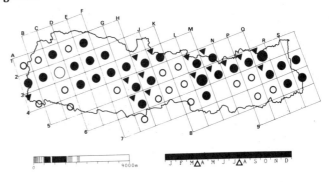

WHITE-BELLIED REDSTART *Hodgsonius phoenicuroides*
Hodgson's Shortwing

Subspecies *phoenicuroides*. The species was described from Nepal by J.E. and G.R. Gray from a Hodgson specimen (277,798). A summer visitor, occasionally seen between 2900m and 4270m. Breeding confirmed in the Dhorpatan valley (G5) (499), and in upper Manang (H4) (757). A scarce winter visitor to the foothills, with only two records received: from Bardia (192) and Marek (G6) at 915m (247). Summers in birch, rhododendron and juniper shrubberies near the treeline; winters in thick undergrowth and forest edges. **Range** Himalayas from the Indus River east to Arunachal Pradesh.

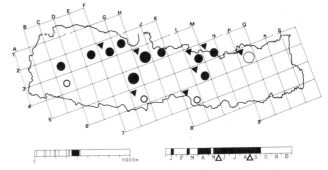

WHITE-TAILED ROBIN   *Cinclidium leucurum*
White-tailed Blue Robin

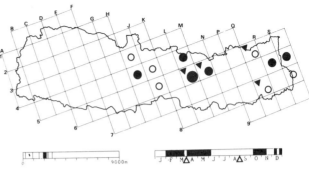

The species was described from Nepal by B. Hodgson (391). A local and uncommon resident subject to altitudinal movements. Summers between 1900m and 2745m, and mainly winters below 915m. Seen near Lete (H4) at 2440m on 16 November 1979, the westernmost record of the species (206). Summers on Phul-

chowki and also Sheopuri, where proved breeding (635). A rare winter visitor to Chitwan and Phewa Tal. Single records received from most other areas. Probably overlooked because of its secretive behaviour. Frequents undergrowth in dense, damp forest, often near streams. **Range** Himalayas from Nepal east to Arunachal Pradesh; n.e. India and Bangladesh.

[BLUE-FRONTED ROBIN   *Cinclidium frontale*
Blue-fronted Long-tailed Robin

Subspecies *frontale*. Obtained by B. Hodgson in his later collection (109) but the specimen may have originated in India. The only other report is of a bird,

probably of this species, singing at Phulchowki on 28 and 30 April 1979 (171). Inhabits wet subtropical forest. **Range** Himalayas in Nepal?, Sikkim and Darjeeling.]

GRANDALA   *Grandala coelicolor*
Hodgson's Grandala

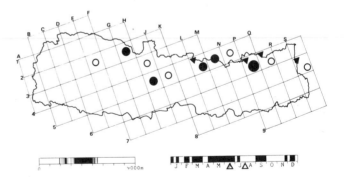

GRANDALA, cont'd ...

The species was described from Nepal by B. Hodgson (386,798). A locally fairly common, high altitude resident, subject to altitudinal movements. Summers between 3900m and 5500m. Winters mainly between 3000m and 3960m, occasionally

PURPLE COCHOA *Cochoa purpurea*

The species was described from Nepal by B. Hodgson (347). He found it in the lower hills, and also in breeding condition in the northern hills on 20 May (336). Scarce, presumably resident. The only recent reports are from Sukipatal, upper Arun valley (Q6) at 2135m on 6 November 1973 (12) and the Mai valley: found near Hanga Tham at 2255m on 14 May 1970 (9) and on 20 September 1978 (301), and near Ilam (R8), also in 1978 (178). Only three other records of singles: on Sheopuri ridge on 21 May 1921 (423), at 2135m in the same area between 1942 and 1945 (733), and at Bhimpedi on 10 May

GREEN COCHOA *Cochoa viridis*

The species was described from Nepal by B. Hodgson (347,798). He obtained at least four specimens from the lower hills in June (336). There are no later records. In India frequents undergrowth in damp, dense broadleaved evergreen forests in tropical and subtropical zones. **Range** Himalayas in Kumaon, Nepal, Darjeeling and Sikkim; possibly Bhutan and Arunachal Pradesh; and n.e. India.

COMMON STONECHAT *Saxicola torquata*
Collared Bushchat, Stonechat

First recorded by B. Hodgson (388). Common. Three races occur. Their status and distribution are not fully understood. *S. t. maura* (m) is a winter visitor of uncertain status (62,619,682). *S. t. przevalskii* (p) is mainly a common winter visitor up to 1500m and a passage migrant. It also breeds in the Tibetan plateau region above 2745m (243,620). *S. t. indica* (i) is a common resident subject to altitudinal movements. It summers between 365m and 2895m. This subspecies proved

descending in bad weather: recorded as low as 1950m near Ghandrung (H5) on 18 March 1989 (166). Regularly reported from Gosainkund, Kyangjin (M5), Dole to Gokyo (P6) and, in severe winters, from the upper Kali Gandaki valley. Proved breeding in Khumbu (190). Frequents rocky slopes and stony alpine meadows. **Range** Himalayas from Kashmir east to Arunachal Pradesh.

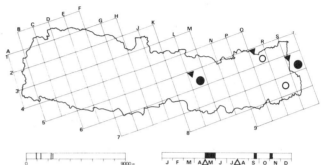

1947 (100). Breeds from early May to mid-June. Inhabits damp, dense broadleaved, evergreen forests of the tropical and lower temperate zones. **Range** Himalayas from Kumaon east to Arunachal Pradesh, and n.e. India.

BROWN ROCK CHAT *Cercomela fusca*

Scarce. First recorded by R.L. Fleming who collected a specimen at Kosi Barrage on 12 March 1969 (244). The only other confirmed record is of a pair breeding at Hariaun, Sarlahi District (L7); the parents were feeding young in August 1989 and four or five individuals were seen afterwards (494). There is also an undated sighting from Bhairawa that possibly relates to this species (244). Found amongst buildings in open country. **Range** Resident in n.e. Pakistan; n.w. and central India.

breeding in the Kathmandu Valley (659), and at Hetaura (100). The species has also been confirmed to breed in Doti District (B3,C3) (428) and at Pokhara (326). Thousands of birds not subspecifically identified were noted passing through the Valley between 5 and 14 April 1948, but no large scale return migration was observed in autumn (629). Common in the upper Kali Gandaki valley in September and October (76), and very common at Kosi Barrage in winter and early spring, presumably on passage. Frequents open country and cultivation with scattered bushes. **Range** Breeds in n. Baluchistan, and the Himalayas from Chitral east to Arunachal Pradesh. Winters south throughout the subcontinent.

COMMON STONECHAT, cont'd ...

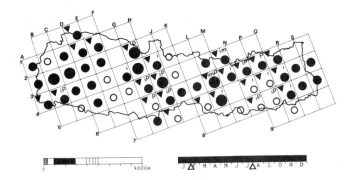

WHITE-TAILED STONECHAT *Saxicola leucura*
White-tailed Bushchat

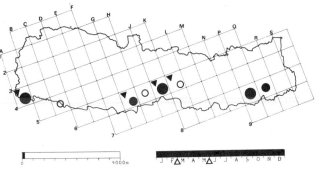

First recorded at Bilauri (A4) at 275m on
28 January 1937 by F.M. Bailey (62). A
local resident of the lowlands. Fairly
common at Sukla Phanta, Chitwan, and
Kosi Barrage. Proved breeding at Chitwan (56,296,111) and north of Kosi Barrage (294), and at Sukla Phanta (432).
Single reports from elsewhere. There are
two doubtful records from the Kathmandu Valley in April (243); the species
has not been recorded above 700m elsewhere in its range. Inhabits reeds and tall
grassland often in wet areas. **Range** Pakistan and n. India east to n.e. India and
Bangladesh.

HODGSON'S BUSHCHAT *Saxicola insignis*
White-necked Bushchat

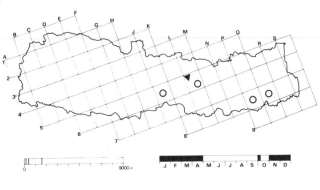

HODGSON'S BUSHCHAT, cont'd ...

A Hodgson specimen was listed for Nepal by J.E. and G.R. Gray (277,798) but this apparently originated in India (413). First definitely recorded by R.L. Fleming south of Kosi Barrage on 11 April 1975 (186,293). It is an uncommon winter visitor there, observed between November and late April. Only single reports from two other localities: two immature males collected along the Manora River (L6) at 1380m on 9 October 1982 (589), and one seen at Meghauli (J6) on 23 March 1986 (403). The maximum of over 10 was recorded at the Barrage on 17 and 18 March 1982 (541). Found in tall grasses, tamarisk, and reeds by the river. **Range** Winters in n. India from Ambala east to Assam.

PIED BUSHCHAT *Saxicola caprata*

Subspecies *bicolor*. First recorded by B. Hodgson (388). Common from the tarai up to 915m; fairly common to 1400m, and occasionally seen up to 2440m in summer but noted at 2665m at Marpha (H4) in March (111). Most birds occurring above 1400m descend to the foothills in winter. Proved breeding at Chitwan (296), Sukla Phanta (432,750), and also in the Kathmandu Valley (756). Nest-building has been observed as early as 1 February at Chitwan (180). Frequents cultivation and open country with sparse scrub. **Range** Throughout the subcontinent.

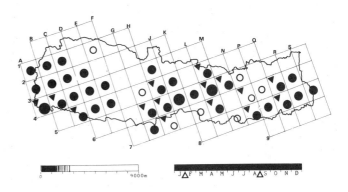

JERDON'S BUSHCHAT *Saxicola jerdoni*

Vagrant. The only records are of a male on 11 May 1975, and another male with a possible juvenile on 19 June 1976, seen by R.C. Gregory-Smith at Kosi Barrage (293). Found in reedbeds. **Range** Himalayas from Nepal east to Arunachal Pradesh, and south to e. Bihar and Bangladesh.

GREY BUSHCHAT *Saxicola ferrea*
Dark-grey Bush Chat

Subspecies *ferrea*. The species was described from Nepal by J.E. and G.R. Gray from a Hodgson specimen (277,798). A fairly common altitudinal migrant. Summers between 1500m and 3355m, most frequently above 1800m. Chiefly winters between 915m and 2125m. It is a rare winter visitor to the tarai. Breeding confirmed on Sheopuri (635) and in Doti District (C3) (438). Inhabits secondary growth, forest edges, and scrub-covered hillsides. **Range** Breeds in the Himalayas from N.W.F.P. east to Arunachal Pradesh, and in n.e. India. Winters south to the plains of n. India and Bangladesh.

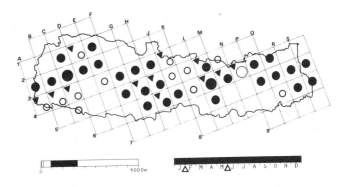

ISABELLINE WHEATEAR *Oenanthe isabellina*

First recorded by the Manora River, Kathmandu Valley at 1280m on 16 November 1968 (9), and twice seen in the same area in April by R.L. Fleming (243). A scarce passage migrant. One was observed by New Road, Kathmandu at 1370m on 13 March 1982 (811). The only other records are from the upper Kali Gandaki valley in March 1982, between 2440m and 2590m: singles were reported from Tukche on 18 March (207,561), and on 27 March at Lete (294) and Kalopani (199). Found in dry cultivation. **Range** Breeds in n. Baluchistan, and in the Himalayas in N.W.F.P. Winters in Pakistan and n.w. India.

NORTHERN WHEATEAR *Oenanthe oenanthe*
Wheatear

Subspecies *oenanthe*? Vagrant. The only record is of an adult male seen on 1 April 1983 at Meghauli (J6) by C. Byers and A. Adams (140). Another record of an *Oenanthe* species seen at Kyangjin (M5) on 18 April 1984 (624) was previously incorrectly ascribed to this species in the first edition of this book (435). **Range** Vagrant to Pakistan, n.w. India and Nepal.

PIED WHEATEAR *Oenanthe pleschanka*

Vagrant. The only record is of one, probably a first year male, seen at Tukche at 3890m on 11 January 1908 by T. Andrews (59). **Range** Breeds in the Himalayas from N.W.F.P. east to Lahul; migrant in n. Baluchistan; vagrant elsewhere in the subcontinent.

DESERT WHEATEAR *Oenanthe deserti*

Subspecies *oreophila*. A scarce but regular summer visitor and passage migrant. First recorded by R. Jarman and W. Howard at Tukche on 1 April 1971 (450). Subsequently reported several times in the upper Kali Gandaki valley between Marpha and Jomosom, between 2650m and 2715m, from mid-March to mid-June. Collected in the Dolpo (G3,H3) in June (243,587) and seen at Rara Lake (127). The only other reports are of singles, presumably on passage, at Chitwan in April 1981 (296), in the Yamdi Khola valley (H5) in March 1985, and at Khaptad (C3) in May 1988 (428,68). Inhabits dry semi-desert country. **Range** Breeds in n. Baluchistan, and the Himalayas from Kashmir east to c. Nepal. Winters south through Pakistan and n. India.

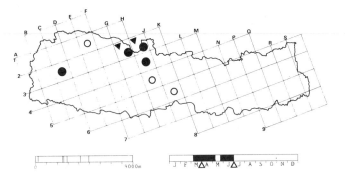

VARIABLE WHEATEAR *Oenanthe picata*
Eastern Pied Wheatear

Scarce. First recorded by P. Hagen at Birendranagar, Surkhet valley (D4) at 760m on 3 December 1979; it remained until February 1980 and the species was seen in the same area in subsequent winters (244). The only other record is of one seen at Chisapani Gorge, Bardia (C4) on 13 February 1988 (731). **Range** Breeds in n. Baluchistan and north to Gilgit. Winters in Pakistan and n.w. India.

WHITE-CAPPED REDSTART *Chaimarrornis leucocephalus*
White-capped River Chat (*Thamnolaea leucocephala*)
River Chat

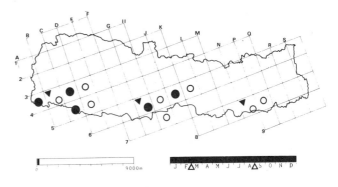

First recorded by B. Hodgson (388). A common altitudinal migrant. Mainly summers between 1830m and 5100m. Proved breeding in Khumbu (197). Winters most frequently between 915m and 1525m; occasionally up to 2590m, and in the foothills from 245m to 915m. Occurs on rocks in rushing streams. Often found at considerable distances from water in summer in the alpine zone. **Range** Himalaya from N.W.F.P. east to Arunachal Pradesh, and n.e. India.

INDIAN ROBIN *Saxicoloides fulicata*
Indian Chat

Subspecies *cambaiensis*. First recorded by B. Hodgson (388). A local resident reported up to 760m and most often from the west. Uncommon at Sukla Phanta, Bardia and Nepalganj, and rare at Chitwan (J6,K6). Mainly single reports received from other areas. Inhabits sparse scrub in dry stony areas and edges of cultivation. **Range** Throughout the subcontinent.

BLUE-CAPPED ROCK-THRUSH *Monticola cinclorhyncha*
Blue-headed Rock-Thrush

First recorded by B. Hodgson (388). A
summer visitor, occasionally seen between early April and early October from
1200m up to 2135m. Proved breeding at
Silgadi Doti (B3) (438), in the Trisuli
valley (L5,L6) (440,517), and Ilam District (R8) (658). Inhabits coniferous forests and rocky slopes with scattered trees.
Range Breeds in the Himalayas from
N.W.F.P. east to Arunachal Pradesh, and
in n.e. India. Winters mainly in s.w. India
and Assam.

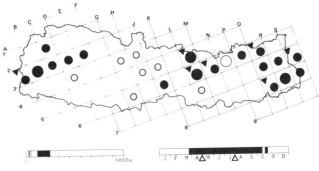

CHESTNUT-BELLIED ROCK-THRUSH *Monticola rufiventris*

First recorded by B. Hodgson (388). A
fairly common resident subject to some
altitudinal movements. Mainly summers
between 1800m and 3400m, but recorded
up to 4460m at Gosainkund (543). Winters between 915m and 2380m, but is most
frequent between 1800m and 2135m.
Found breeding in the upper Mai valley
(740). Frequents coniferous and
broadleaved forests. **Range** Breeds in the
Himalayas from Murree east to Arunachal Pradesh, and in n.e. India. Winters
south to Bangladesh, and rarely in the
plains of n. India.

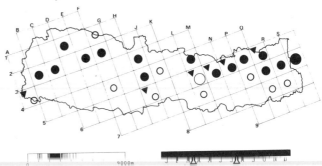

BLUE ROCK-THRUSH *Monticola solitarius*

Subspecies *pandoo*. First recorded by B.
Hodgson (388). An altitudinal migrant.
Occasionally seen in summer in the
Trans-Himalayan region between 2590m
and 4880m and in winter from the tarai up
to 1400m. Confirmed to breed at Manang
(757), and in Dolpo District (G3) (243). A
male near Naudanda (H5) on 22 December 1973, showing characters of the race
M. s. philippensis (518), forms the first
record of the race for the subcontinent.
However, birds showing features intermediate between *M. s. pandoo* and *M. s.
philippensis* have been recorded from
Assam and Meghalaya (49). Summers in
open rocky areas or on steep cliffs and

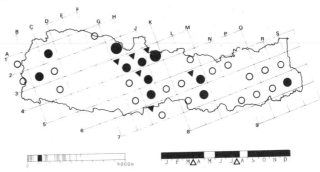

winters along streams or amongst old buildings. **Range**
Breeds in n. Baluchistan, and in the Himalayas from
N.W.F.P. east to west-central Nepal. Winters throughout
the subcontinent.

BLUE WHISTLING THRUSH *Myiophoneus caeruleus*
Whistling Thrush *(Myiophonus caeruleus)*

Subspecies *temminckii*. First recorded by B. Hodgson (388). A common resident subject to vertical movements. Chiefly summers between 1500m and 3100m, but noted at 4800m in Khumbu on 15 May 1954 (109); winters from the tarai up to 2745m. Found breeding in the Dhorpatan valley (499), Solu (P6) (109) and the Trisuli valley (L5) (771). Occurs along streams and rivers in forested areas. Favours gorges and ravines. The upper limit of its summer range usually coincides with the treeline. **Range** Breeds in n. Baluchistan, the Himalayas from Chitral east to Arunachal Pradesh, and in n.e. India and Bangladesh. Winters in the foothills and rarely in the adjacent plains.

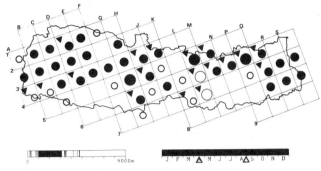

PLAIN-BACKED MOUNTAIN THRUSH *Zoothera mollissima*
Plain-backed Thrush

Subspecies *mollissima*. First recorded by E. Blyth from a Hodgson specimen (114). A fairly common altitudinal migrant, wintering between 1500m and 2400m. Chiefly summers between 3000m and 4000m. Juveniles were taken on 28 and 29 July 1964 between 3900m and 3930m near Tarke Gyang (M5) (247). Its breeding behaviour is poorly known. Inhabits fir forests and open grassy slopes near the treeline in summer; broadleaved and coniferous forests in winter. **Range** Himalayas from Hazara east to Arunachal Pradesh, and n.e. India.

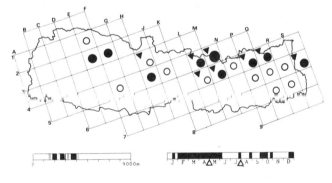

LONG-TAILED MOUNTAIN THRUSH *Zoothera dixoni*
Long-tailed Thrush

First recorded by B. Hodgson breeding at Jahar Powah, Kathmandu Valley (336). An altitudinal migrant, occasionally seen in winter between 1500m and 2700m, and in summer from 2100m to 4250m. Breeding also confirmed near Jumla (620), Tarke Gyang (M5) (247) and at Chandabari (L5) (321). Occurs in forests of birch, fir or juniper near the treeline in summer; thick forests, often near streams in winter. **Range** Himalayas from the Sutlej River east to Arunachal Pradesh, and n.e. India.

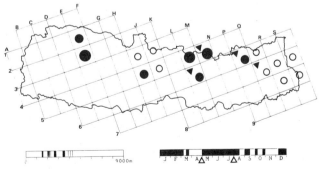

SCALY THRUSH   *Zoothera dauma*
Speckled Mountain Thrush, White's Thrush,
Golden Mountain Thrush

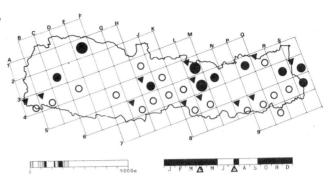

Subspecies *dauma*. First recorded by B.
Hodgson (388). A partial migrant. Fairly
common in summer between 2320m and
3540m. Found breeding in Langtang
(199), on Sheopuri (243), and at
Chankheli (627). Common between 275m
and 1500m in winter, when numbers are
augmented by migrants from elsewhere.
Inhabits thick forests with dense undergrowth, often near streams. **Range**
Breeds in the Himalayas from Murree
east to Arunachal Pradesh, and in n.e. and
s.w. India. Winters south to Madhya
Pradesh and Bangladesh.

LONG-BILLED THRUSH   *Zoothera monticola*
Large Long-billed Thrush, Large Brown Thrush

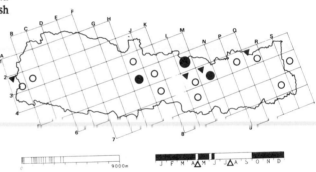

Subspecies *monticola*. First recorded by
B. Hodgson (388). A resident subject to
altitudinal movements. Occasionally seen
in winter between 915m and 2500m;
rarely at lower altitudes. Reported in
summer between 2285m and 3850m.
Proved breeding in Langtang (264). In
habits the forest floor in dense, damp
forests, usually near streams. **Range**
Breeds in the Himalayas from Kulu east
to Arunachal Pradesh, and in n.e. India.
Winters south to Bangladesh.

DARK-SIDED THRUSH   *Zoothera marginata*
Lesser Long-billed Thrush, Lesser Brown Thrush

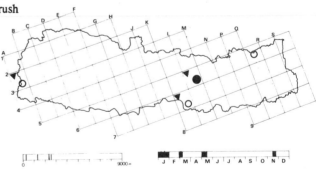

Scarce. First collected by B. Biswas on 8
March 1947 at Amlekhganj (K7) at 305m.
He also obtained two on 5 and 10 May
1947 at Bhimpedi (100). A specimen
taken at Barmdeo Mandi (A3) at 290m in
January 1953 (647) is the westernmost
record of the species. The only other record is of one at Shyaksila Toten, Barun
valley (Q6) at 2195m on 22 November
1984 (588). Frequents the forest floor in
damp forests near streams. **Range** Himalayas from Nepal east to Arunachal
Pradesh; n.e. India and Bangladesh.

PIED GROUND THRUSH *Zoothera wardii*
Pied Thrush

First recorded by B. Hodgson, who found it breeding in the Kathmandu Valley (388,414). An uncommon summer visitor, mainly found between 1500m and 2400m. One seen at Ghasa at about 2040m at the early date of 26 February (403). Regularly seen in the Trisuli valley between Ramche and Dhunche (L5). Other localities include Khaptad (C3), between Surkhet and Dailekh (D4), north-west of Pokhara (H4,H5), Phulchowki and the lower Arun valley. Found breeding near Bokejunda, Trisuli valley (L5) (440,652), Khaptad (C3) (68) and near Syabru (L5) (294). Single reports from most other areas. Occurs in open forests and in thick undergrowth along streams. **Range** Breeds in the Himalayas from the Kulu valley east to Arunachal Pradesh, and in n.e. India. Migrates through India to winter in Sri Lanka.

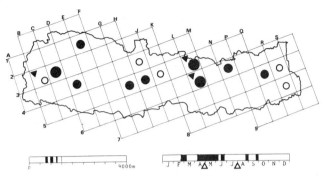

ORANGE-HEADED GROUND THRUSH *Zoothera citrina*
Orange-headed Thrush

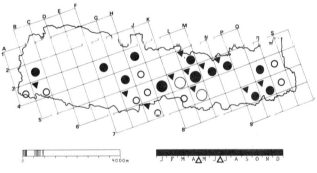

Subspecies *citrina*. First recorded by B. Hodgson (388). A fairly common partial migrant. Mainly a summer visitor occurring from mid-April to early October, between 250m and 1830m. Found breed- ing at Chitwan (296) and at Rani Bagh (L6) (629). Some birds winter in the tarai and dun. Noted at 915m at Pokhara in January 1990 (138). Found in damp forests, often in wet ravines. **Range** Breeds in the Himalayas from Chamba east to Arunachal Pradesh, and in Bangladesh, and n.e., e., and s. India. Winters throughout e. India and Bangladesh.

TICKELL'S THRUSH   *Turdus unicolor*
Indian Grey Thrush

First recorded by B. Hodgson (388).
Mainly a fairly common summer visitor
occurring between April and the end of
October from 1500m to 2450m. Confirmed breeding at Gaucher forest (L6)
(629) and in the lower Arun valley (Q7)
(446). Several winter reports from the
lowlands at Chitwan and Sukla Phanta
(700). One seen north-west of Pokhara
(H5) on 5 January (152). In summer inhabits open broadleaved forests with
little undergrowth. **Range** Breeds in the
Himalayas from N.W.F.P. east to Nepal
and probably Sikkim. Winters east to
Arunachal Pradesh, and south to Andhra
Pradesh and Bangladesh; and also in n.
Baluchistan.

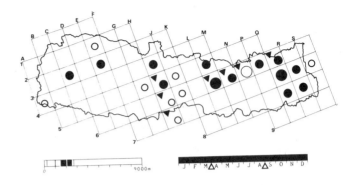

WHITE-COLLARED BLACKBIRD   *Turdus albocinctus*

First recorded by B. Hodgson (388). A
fairly common resident subject to altitudinal movements. Winters between
1525m and 3000m, mainly above 2100m
but singles noted at about 250m near
Dharan on 24 January 1981 (180) and at
Chitwan (J6) on 5 March 1989 (810).
Chiefly summers between 2400m and
3445m. Found breeding in the Dhorpatan
valley (499). Frequents broadleaved and
coniferous forests, especially edges and
clearings. **Range** Himalayas from
Chamba east to Arunachal Pradesh, and
n.e. India.

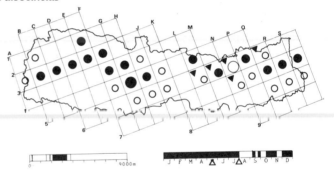

GREY-WINGED BLACKBIRD   *Turdus boulboul*

First recorded by B. Hodgson who found
it breeding at Jahar Powah (L6)
(336,388). A common altitudinal migrant.
Chiefly summers between 2100m and
2745m, but found at 3300m at Bigu on 16
May 1962 (190). Breeding confirmed in
the Hongu valley (P6) (109) and on
Sheopuri (243). Mainly winters between
1400m and 1980m, occasionally descending as far as the tarai. Summers in damp
broadleaved forests, preferring thicker
habitat than White-collared Blackbird.
Winters in open, wooded country. **Range**
Breeds in the Himalayas from Murree

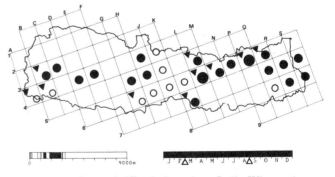

east to Arunachal Pradesh, and n.e. India. Winters down to
the adjacent plains, rarely further south.

EURASIAN BLACKBIRD *Turdus merula*
Common Blackbird, Blackbird

Subspecies *maximus*. First recorded in Jumla District on 11 August 1952 by O. Polunin (620). Mainly an erratic visitor in winter and spring. Chiefly observed between 3305m and 4800m, although also found in the tarai in January (243). An invasion occurred in April and May 1978, when described as fairly common in Sagarmatha National Park (243), and also seen at Jumla and Langtang (M5) (243). There are also several records from Thakkhola (H4), Langtang (L5,M5) and Khumbu. Mainly single reports from elsewhere. Favours juniper shrubberies above the treeline. **Range** Himalayas from N.W.F.P. east to Arunachal Pradesh; hills of peninsular India.

CHESTNUT THRUSH *Turdus rubrocanus*
Grey-headed Thrush

The species was described from Nepal by J.E. and G.R. Gray from a Hodgson specimen (277,798). An uncommon and erratic winter visitor; possibly breeds. Most records received are from December to March between 2000m and 2745m. Mainly seen north-west of Pokhara, on the hills surrounding the Kathmandu Valley and upper Arun and upper Mai valleys. Chiefly single reports from other areas. Two races recorded, *T. r. rubrocanus* (r), and one record of *T. r. gouldii* (63). Found in winter in open wooded country on fruiting trees. **Range** Breeds in the Himalayas from Safed Koh east to Sikkim. Winters south to n.e. India.

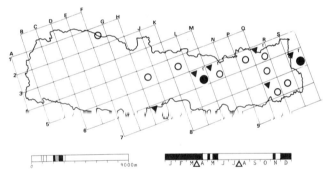

KESSLER'S THRUSH *Turdus kessleri*
White-backed Thrush

A scarce and erratic winter visitor. First recorded by T. Robinson who saw a male on 26 January 1986 above Namche Bazaar (P6) at about 3445m (680). Three later sightings in Khumbu (P6) during the same winter (680,558). Several records from Khumbu (P6) between 17 November and 31 December 1988, including over 20 on 21 November at Tongaba Phortse Dangbe (453,456) and over 15 at Shomare on 19 December (596). The only other report received is of 35 to 40 on 16 February 1989 at Kyangjin (M5) at about 3600m (70). Found in mixed birch and rhododendron forest, juniper and *Berberis* shrubberies, and in potato fields. **Range** Vagrant to Sikkim and Nepal.

EYE-BROWED THRUSH   *Turdus obscurus*
Dark Thrush

A Hodgson specimen was listed from
Nepal by Seebohm (710) but it may have
originated in India. First definitely recorded by E. Cronin who netted one in
1973 in the Arun valley (exact location
unknown) (243). A scarce winter visitor
found between 1500m and 2300m. One to
two also seen at Danda Bazaar (Q8) on 6
October 1978 (155), Gokarna on 20 December 1978 (486,651,652), Hanga Tham
on 22 December 1979 (206) and on 28
April 1986 (321), above Syabru (L5) on 23
April 1985, two sightings in the lower
Arun valley in January 1990 (256), and
one at Basantpur (Q7) in March 1990
(256). There is also a record from 2300m
on 18 May (locality and year unknown)
(49). **Range** Winters in n.e. India and
Bangladesh.

DUSKY THRUSH   *Turdus naumanni*

Subspecies *eunomus*. First collected by B.
Hodgson from the Kathmandu Valley on
10 and 29 January (113,336). A scarce
winter visitor found between 915m and
2850m. Reported from Gokarna on 4
February 1979 (486,651,652), and on 26
April 1982 (157). The large numbers reported in spring 1948 at Nagarjung (629)
have not been repeated and are open to
doubt. Singles showing intermediate features of *T. n. eunomus* and *T. n. naumanni* were found near Jomosom from 27
March to 1 April 1983 (56) and at Jolbari
(R7) on 19 January 1989 (307). Recorded
from the upper Kali Gandaki valley at
Lete on 22 to 24 January 1979 (486,
651,652), Marpha on 27 April 1981 (811),
Kalopani on 10 and 11 March 1982

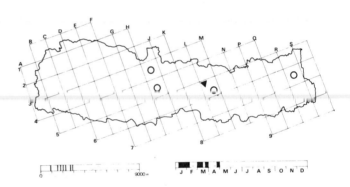

(207,561) and at Jomosom on 6 March 1986 (403). The only
other reports are from Phewa Tal on 5 March 1986 (55) and
above Ghorepani on 27 April 1987 (484). Records are
mainly of single birds. Frequents forest edges and scrub.
Range Winters in n.e. India.

DARK-THROATED THRUSH   *Turdus ruficollis*
Black-throated Thrush, Red-throated Thrush

First recorded by B. Hodgson (388). A
common winter visitor. Two subspecies
occur: Black-throated Thrush *T. r. atrogularis* from the tarai up to 4200m, and Red-
throated Thrush *T. r. ruficollis* mainly at
higher altitudes from 2400m to 3900m.
Arrives in the Himalayas in October and
descends to lower altitudes during the

winter. Noted in the Kathmandu Valley by mid-November,
but not usually seen at Chitwan and the eastern foothills
(Q8) until February (293). Most birds leave Nepal by the
end of April. Frequents grassy slopes, forest edges and
forests. **Range** Winters in the Himalayas from N.W.F.P.
east to Arunachal Pradesh, and south to Sind, Madhya
Pradesh, and Bangladesh.

DARK-THROATED THRUSH, cont'd ...

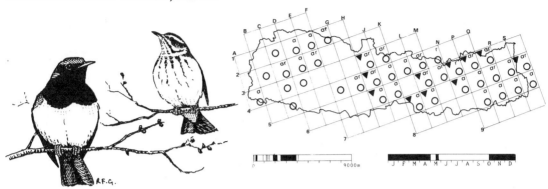

MISTLE THRUSH   *Turdus viscivorus*

Subspecies *bonapartei*. A Hodgson specimen was listed for Nepal by Seebohm
(710) but it may have originated in India.
First definitely recorded by R.L. Fleming
Sr. who collected a specimen east of
Rupal (A3) at 2225m on 9 April 1965
(247). A fairly common resident subject
to altitudinal movements, and reported
east to Machapuchare (244). Mainly
summers between 2400m and 3800m, and
winters between 2135m and 3050m. Inhabits coniferous and broadleaved forests
in summer, and open grassy slopes and
forest edges in winter. **Range** N. Baluchistan, and the Himalayas from N.W.F.P.
east to Nepal.

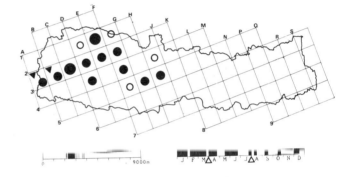

LITTLE FORKTAIL   *Enicurus scouleri*

Subspecies *scouleri*. First recorded by B.
Hodgson (388). A fairly common resident
subject to some altitudinal movements.
Summers chiefly between 1830m and
4000m, and winters between 900m and
1830m. Found breeding in the upper Kali
Gandaki valley (811) and in Jumla District (620). Frequents rushing rocky
streams, often near waterfalls, and in
winter also on slower moving waters.
Range Himalayas from N.W.F.P. east to
Arunachal Pradesh; n.e. India and Bangladesh.

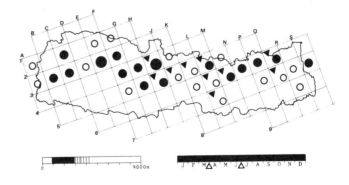

BLACK-BACKED FORKTAIL   *Enicurus immaculatus*

The species was described from Nepal by
B. Hodgson (360). A resident occasionally found up to 1370m from west-central
areas eastwards; few records from the
west. Fairly common and confirmed to
breed at Chitwan (296); also found breeding at Hetaura (100). Occurs on fast-flowing streams in damp broadleaved forest.
Range Himalayas from Garhwal east to
Arunachal Pradesh; n.e. India and Bangladesh.

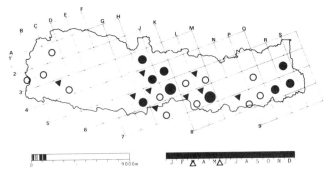

SLATY-BACKED FORKTAIL   *Enicurus schistaceus*

The species was described from Nepal by
B. Hodgson (360, 798). Mainly an uncom-
mon resident between 900m and 1675m.
Fairly common on the Modi Khola and
Bhurungdi Khola near Birethante. Other
localities include the lower Arun and upper Mai valleys, and
north of Sunischare. Mainly single reports from elsewhere.
Frequents large fast-flowing rocky streams and lakes.
Range Himalayas from Kumaon east to Arunachal
Pradesh; n.e. India and Bangladesh.

SPOTTED FORKTAIL   *Enicurus maculatus*

First recorded by B. Hodgson (360). A
fairly common resident, mainly summering between 1370m and 3100m. Some
birds descend from higher elevations in
winter but others remain up to at least
2745m. Proved breeding at Hetaura
(100). Two races occur: *E. m. maculatus*
(m) (100,109,190,647), and *E. m. guttatus*
(g) (246,736). Inhabits rocky streams in
forests,and shady ravines, avoiding rivers
and lakes. **Range** Himalayas from
N.W.F.P. east to Arunachal Pradesh; n.e.
India and Bangladesh.

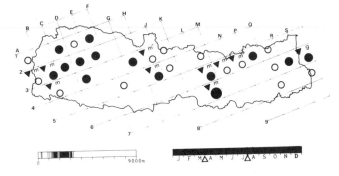

CHESTNUT-HEADED TESIA   *Tesia castaneocoronata*
Chestnut-headed Ground Warbler

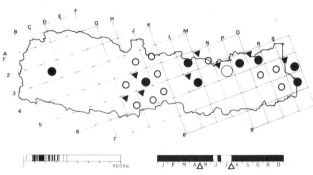

Subspecies *castaneocoronata*. The species was described by E. Burton, probably from Nepal (139). First definitely recorded by B. Hodgson (371). A fairly common resident subject to altitudinal movements. Summers between 2135m

and 4000m, most frequently from 2440m to 3300m. Mainly winters between 800m and 1830m, but descends to lower altitudes at Chitwan, where it is a rare visitor (296). Proved breeding at Phulchowki (771). Frequents thick undergrowth in broadleaved forest. **Range** Himalayas from Kulu east to Arunachal Pradesh; n.e. India and Bangladesh.

GREY-BELLIED TESIA   *Tesia cyaniventer*
Dull Slaty-bellied Ground Warbler, Slaty-bellied Ground Warbler

The species was described from Nepal by B. Hodgson (371,798). Occasional. An altitudinal migrant. Summers mainly between 1525m and 2440m, and winters from 1830m down to the foothills, and rarely to the tarai. Found breeding in Langtang Gorge (L5) (682). Occurs in tangled undergrowth in thick forest near small streams; favours ravines in summer, and shady broadleaved forest in winter. **Range** Himalayas from Garhwal east to Arunachal Pradesh; n.e. India and Bangladesh.

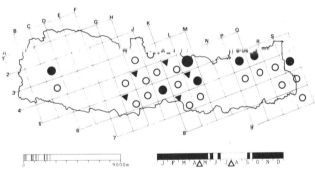

SLATY-BELLIED TESIA   *Tesia olivea*

Scarce, probably resident. The species was discovered in Nepal by H.S. Nepali in the Arun valley (Q6,Q7) between 1000m and 1700m. First recorded at Hururu on 30 August 1986 and later seen on 31

August at Num and on 21 September at Khandbari (590). Frequents dense undergrowth in damp, broadleaved, evergreen forest. **Range** Himalayas from e. Nepal east to Arunachal Pradesh; n.e. India.

PALE-FOOTED BUSH WARBLER *Cettia pallidipes*
Blanford's Bush Warbler

Subspecies *pallidipes*. First definitely recorded at Simra on 4 March 1947 by B.
Biswas (102). A local resident. Fairly
common at Chitwan (J6,K6). Chiefly
single reports from elsewhere. It is shy
and skulking as are other bush warblers,
and is probably overlooked as it is more
often heard than seen. Inhabits tall
grasses and bushes at forest edges. **Range**
Himalayas from Dehra Dun east to Arunachal Pradesh, and n.e. India.

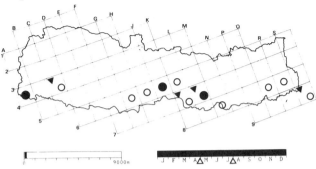

BROWN-FLANKED BUSH WARBLER *Cettia fortipes*
Strong-footed Bush Warbler (*C. montana*)

The species was described from Nepal by
B. Hodgson (391,798). An altitudinal
migrant whose seasonal movements are
uncertain. Found between about 1400m
and 2135m in December (307) and between 1800m and 3200m in summer.
Reported to be fairly common in spring in
the upper Arun valley (483); several records from the upper Mai valley (R7,R8)
and near Ilam (R8) (246,658,307); also
reported from Hans Pokhari (S8) (183). It
is rare further west: single records from
Dandeldhura District (A3) (317), south
of Annapurna (J5) (762), and the
Dhorpatan valley (499). Two races occur:
C. f. fortipes (f) (246), and *C. f. pallida* (p)

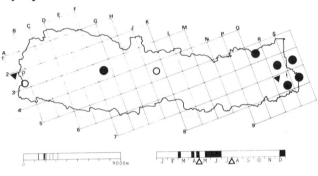

(247). Frequents dense undergrowth in forest and favours
damp ravines. **Range** Himalayas from Kashmir east to
Arunachal Pradesh; n.e. India and Bangladesh.

CHESTNUT-CROWNED BUSH WARBLER *Cettia major*
Large Bush Warbler

Subspecies *major*. The species was described from Nepal by T. Horsfield and F.
Moore from a specimen included in
Hodgson's later collection (409,798) but
this may have originated in India. The
first dated records are of several pairs
found breeding by J.M. Thiollay between
3550m and 3680m on Lamjung Himal
(J5) on 16 and 18 June 1977 (762). A
scarce altitudinal migrant. Its breeding
behaviour is poorly known. Found on
Machapuchare (H5) at 3415m on 13 October 1979 (499). A scarce winter visitor
to the lowlands: at Chitwan (J6,K6) from
October to April, also two trapped near
Kosi Barrage in March (243), and noted

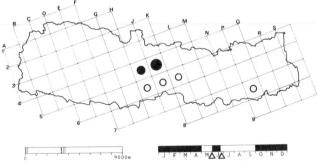

at Tamaspur in December 1979 (681). Summers in thorny
scrub at rhododendron forest edges, and winters in
reedbeds. **Range** Himalayas from Garhwal east to Arunachal Pradesh, and n.e. India.

ABERRANT BUSH WARBLER   *Cettia flavolivacea*

Subspecies *flavolivacea*. The species was described from Nepal by B. Hodgson (798,118). A common resident subject to altitudinal movements. Mainly summers between 2440m and 3600m, and winters between 915m and 1830m. A rare winter visitor, recorded at lower altitudes at Tamaspur and Chitwan. Frequents shrubberies and also bushes at forest edges and in clearings. **Range** Himalayas from Garhwal east to Arunachal Pradesh, and n.e. India.

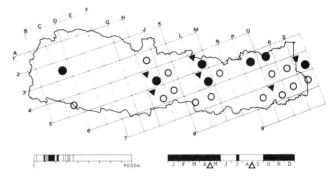

YELLOW-BELLIED BUSH WARBLER   *Cettia acanthizoides*
Hume's Bush Warbler, Verreaux's Bush Warbler

Subspecies *brunnescens*. Collected by B. Hodgson who confused it with Brown-flanked Bush Warbler; the specimens have now been correctly identified in the British Museum (Natural History). Scarce, probably resident. All other records are from spring and summer between 2000m and 3660m. Collected on the Singalila Ridge (S7) at 3050m on 29 April 1912 (738), on Walung ridge (Q6) at 2000m on 12 March 1959 (482), and on the northern slopes of Sheopuri at 2590m on 30 March 1969 (9). Two singing males were found in July 1973 above Tukche between 3150m and 3250m (529). Fairly common at Khaptad (C3): at least 11 singing birds found between 21 and 27 May 1988 at about 2700m (428). One seen

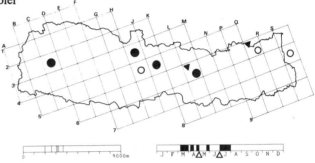

in Annapurna Sanctuary (H5) on 3 April 1987 (463). Noted near Sheopuri summit: in May 1986 (578) and on 16 April 1988 (438). Inhabits ringal bamboo but also found in scrub above Tukche (529). **Range** Himalayas from Garhwal east to Arunachal Pradesh.

GREY-SIDED BUSH WARBLER   *Cettia brunnifrons*
Rufous-capped Bush Warbler

Subspecies *brunnifrons*. The species was described from Nepal by B. Hodgson (391,798). A common altitudinal migrant. Summers chiefly between 2745m and 4000m, and winters between 915m and 2135m, uncommon at lower altitudes down to 215m. Noted as low as 75m on 16 January 1989 at Kosi Tappu (596). Found breeding on the hills north of the Kathmandu Valley (635), and at Khumjung (P6) (190). Occurs in rhododendron and barberries at forest edges in summer, and in tall grass and dense undergrowth in winter. **Range** Breeds in the Himalayas

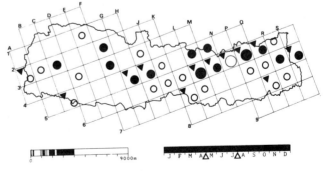

from the Pir Panjal range east to Arunachal Pradesh. Winters down to the foothills, and the plains of n.e. India.

SPOTTED BUSH WARBLER   *Bradypterus thoracicus*

Subspecies *thoracicus*. The species was
described from Nepal by E. Blyth, from a
Hodgson specimen (118). A scarce altitudinal migrant. Only two summer records.
A nest with eggs was found at 3850m on
Lamjung Himal (J5) on 22 July 1977
(541). Noted to be common in June up to
3350m on the ridge west of Mardi valley,
Machapuchare (H5) and proved breeding there (499,244). One seen near Tatopani (H4) at 1220m on 15 April 1977 was
presumably a migrant (243). All other
reports are from the lowlands in winter or
spring: rare at Kosi Barrage and Chitwan
(J6,K6), and single records from San
Pakwa (Q8) on 2 March 1938 (62), Bhorli
(N8) in December 1953 (647), and Sukla
Phanta on 4 and 5 May 1982 (432). Inhab-

its rhododendron and juniper shrubberies above the
treeline in summer, reedbeds and tall grass in winter. **Range**
Breeds in the Himalayas from Kashmir east to Arunachal
Pradesh. Winters down to the foothills, and the plains of
n.e. India.

CHINESE BUSH WARBLER
Bradypterus tacsanowskius

Subspecies *tacsanowskius*. Vagrant. First
recorded on 20 February 1938 at
Haraincha (Q8) by F.M. Bailey (62).
Subsequently single birds were found
north of Sunischare on 25 February 1961
(234,246), and at Kosi Barrage on 13
March 1981 (442). Winters in reedbeds.
Range Rare winter visitor to Nepal and
Bhutan.

BROWN BUSH WARBLER   *Bradypterus luteoventris*

Subspecies *luteoventris*. Vagrant. The species was described
from Nepal by B. Hodgson (391,798). He obtained specimens from the northern hills (336). The other records from
Sukla Phanta (432), listed in the first edition of this book
(435), are now considered unacceptable. **Range** Himalayas
from Nepal east to Arunachal Pradesh, and n.e. India.

BRIGHT-CAPPED CISTICOLA   *Cisticola exilis*
Golden-headed Cisticola, Golden-headed Fantail Warbler

Subspecies *tytleri*. First recorded at Dhangarhi in December 1952 by R.L. Fleming
Sr. (647). Very local, probably resident.
Fairly common at Sukla Phanta
(432,700), and at Sukebhar, Chitwan.
Four were seen near Damak (R8) in
December 1978 (134). Several records
from Kosi Barrage including a maximum
of six on 4 March 1988 (465). The only
other record is of four seen at Biratnagar
airport in December 1989 (256). Inhabits
tall grassland in the tarai. **Range** Kumaon
and the Nepal tarai east to Arunachal
Pradesh; n.e. and s.w. India, and Bangladesh.

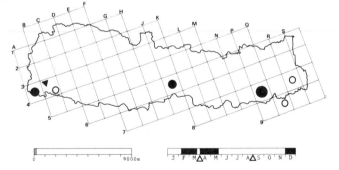

ZITTING CISTICOLA *Cisticola juncidis*
Fan-tailed Warbler, Fantail Cisticola,
Streaked Fantail Warbler

Subspecies *cursitans*. First collected by B.
Hodgson (115). A fairly common resident
and summer visitor up to 1350m, locally
up to 1900m. Found in the Kathmandu
Valley from March to October (244).
Proved breeding there (629) and at Chitwan (770). A common summer visitor to
the eastern tarai from March to October
(293). Frequents paddyfields, tall grass
and reedbeds. **Range** Throughout the
subcontinent.

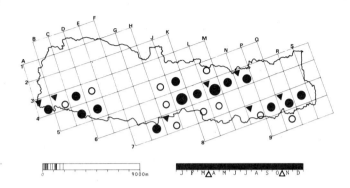

GRACEFUL PRINIA *Prinia gracilis*
Fulvous-streaked Prinia, Streaked Wren-Warbler

First definitely recorded at Tribeni (H7)
at 75m on 19 January 1936 by F.M. Bailey
(62). A very local resident in the tarai.
Fairly common along the Karnali River
(C4) (192,243) and south of Kosi Barrage,
where several pairs were proved breeding
(321). Rare at Chitwan (296). Also recorded from Bilauri (A4) (62), Haraincha
(Q8) (62), Bardia District (D5) (162),
Kosi Tappu (327) and Chatra (245). The
last record is referable to *P. g. stevensi* but
the race involved in all other records is
unknown. Found in tall grass along sandy
river beds in the tarai. **Range** Pakistan
and n. India east to Bangladesh.

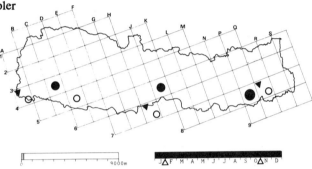

PLAIN PRINIA *Prinia inornata*
Plain Wren-Warbler (*P. subflava*)

First recorded by B. Hodgson (391). A
resident seen occasionally throughout the
tarai. Two subspecies occur: *P. i. fusca* (f)
(647) and *P. i. terricolor* (t) (659). Like
other prinias it is probably under-recorded because of field identification difficulties. Inhabits tall grass and reedbeds
at edges of cultivation and sal forests.
Range Throughout the subcontinent.

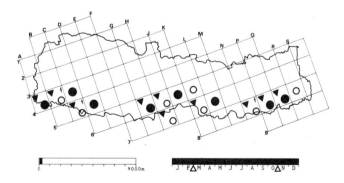

ASHY PRINIA *Prinia socialis*
Ashy Wren-Warbler

Subspecies *stewarti*. Obtained by B. Hodgson in his later collection (409) but the specimen may have originated in India. First definitely recorded by F.M. Bailey at Bilauri (A4) on 9 February 1937 (62). A resident, occasionally seen throughout the tarai. Frequents tall grass and reedbeds at the edges of cultivation, sal forests and rivers. Prefers wetter habitats than Plain Prinia. **Range** Throughout most of the subcontinent.

[RUFOUS PRINIA *Prinia rufescens*
Rufescent Prinia, Beavan's Wren-Warbler

A Hodgson specimen was listed for Nepal by Sharpe (716), but it may have originated in India. Reported from Chitwan (315,703), but further confirmation is needed. Occurs in tall grassland or light grass patches under groves of broadleaved trees (48). **Range** Himalayas from Darjeeling east to Arunachal Pradesh; Orissa, n.e. India and Bangladesh.]

GREY-CROWNED PRINIA *Prinia cinereocapilla*
Hodgson's Wren-Warbler, Grey-capped Prinia

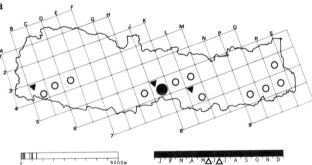

The species was described from Nepal by F. Moore from a specimen in Hodgson's later collection (409,798) but it may have originated in India. First definitely recorded by R.L. Fleming Sr. at Badamachli (B4) at 460m in December 1952 (647). A local resident, mainly found between 75m and 1065m, but noted as high as 1600m in the eastern hills (Q8) (293). Fairly common and confirmed breeding at Chitwan (J6,K6) (296). Described as common in the central dun (L7) in 1947 (102) but just one later record from there. Only a few reports from other areas, including Bardia (C4) (162), Tamaspur (206,681), Trisuli (L6) (180), and Ilam District (681,794). Little is known of its breeding habits. Frequents bushes in forest clearings and secondary growth; more arboreal than other prinias. **Range** Himalayan foothills from Kumaon east to Bhutan; Assam in n. Cachar.

GREY-BREASTED PRINIA *Prinia hodgsonii*
Hodgson's Prinia, Ashy Wren-Warbler,
Franklin's Wren-Warbler

Subspecies *rufula*. First collected by B.
Hodgson (115). A fairly common resident
in the tarai, bhabar and dun up to 400m,
occasionally seen up to 1200m, and locally
up to 1750m. Proved breeding at Chitwan
(296). Found in bushes at the edges of
forest and cultivation. **Range** Throughout
the subcontinent.

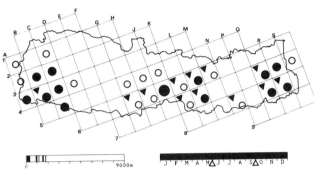

YELLOW-BELLIED PRINIA *Prinia flaviventris*
Yellow-bellied Wren-Warbler

Subspecies *flaviventris*. Obtained by B.
Hodgson in his later collection (409) but
the specimen may have originated in India. First definitely recorded by F.M.
Bailey at Bilauri (A4) on 5 February 1937
(62). A local resident. Fairly common at
Sukla Phanta, Kosi marshes, Tamaspur,
and also Chitwan (J6,K6), where found
breeding (296). Single records from elsewhere. Occurs in tall grassland along riverbeds, and in reedbeds. **Range** Pakistan
and n.w. India; foothills of the Himalayas
from Nepal east to Arunachal Pradesh;
n.e. India and Bangladesh.

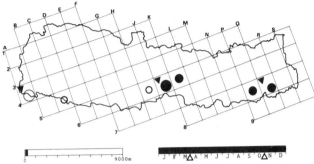

STRIATED PRINIA *Prinia criniger*
Brown Hill Prinia, Brown Hill Warbler

Subspecies *criniger*. The species was described from Nepal by B. Hodgson
(359,798). A common resident. Summers
chiefly between 1220m and 2300m, and
winters between 915m and 2135m. Noted
as low as 75m at Kosi Tappu on 3 March
1988 (327). Confirmed breeding at
Nagarjung (635). Inhabits hillsides
amongst scrub and grass, also terraced
cultivation. **Range** The hills of Pakistan;
Himalayas from Murree east to Arunachal Pradesh; n.e. India and Bangladesh.

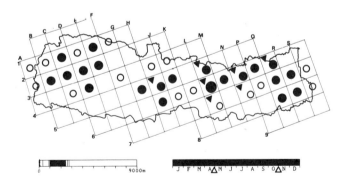

JUNGLE PRINIA *Prinia sylvatica*
White-tailed Prinia, Jungle Wren-Warbler

Subspecies *gangetica*. First definitely recorded at Banbassa (A4) at about 75m on 11 January 1937 by F.M. Bailey (62). A resident, occurring in the far western tarai. Occasionally seen at Sukla Phanta (432,700), Dhangarhi (647) and Bardia (192,432). Reported from Chitwan (296,762), but its occurrence there requires further confirmation. Inhabits scrub and tall grass in open dry areas. **Range** Himalayan foothills from Jammu east to W. Bengal; south to Bangladesh and s. India.

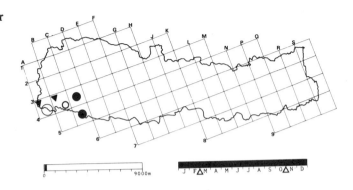

HILL PRINIA *Prinia atrogularis*
Black-throated Hill Prinia, Black-throated Hill Warbler

Subspecies *atrogularis*. Obtained by B. Hodgson in his later collection (409) but the specimen may have originated in India. First definitely recorded by H. Stevens from the Mai valley (S7) in April 1912 (738). A resident, seen occasionally in the far east. Regularly reported from the Mai valley (R7,S7), several records from Ilam District (R8) and Hans Pokhari (S8); also noted by the Mewa Khola, Taplejung District (R7) (243). One was recorded between Mure and Hurure, Arun valley (Q6) on 13 June 1988 (537), the western limit of the species's range. Found in scrub and grass on hill-

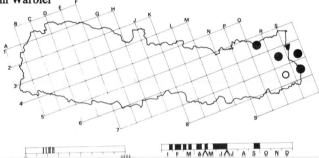

sides, and terraced cultivation between 1400m and 2500m. **Range** Himalayas from Nepal east to Arunachal Pradesh; n.e. India and Bangladesh.

LARGE GRASS WARBLER *Graminicola bengalensis*

First recorded at Bilauri (A4) at 270m on 2 February 1937 by F.M. Bailey (62); also collected there in December 1952 and January 1953 (647). A very local resident. Occasionally seen, and possibly breeds at Chitwan (296). The record from Kosi Barrage listed in the first edition of this book (435) has been withdrawn, but the species has been reported from there in November 1989 (597). The only other report is of two at Sukla Phanta on 4 May 1982 (432), the western limit of the species's range. Found in tall grass and reeds in the tarai. Skulking and probably overlooked. **Range** Nepal, n.e. India and Bangladesh.

COMMON TAILORBIRD *Orthotomus sutorius*
Tailor Bird

Subspecies *patia*. First recorded by B. Hodgson (388). A common resident from 75m to 1830m. Confirmed to breed at Chitwan (296) and in the Kathmandu Valley (629,708). Inhabits gardens and bushes at the edges of cultivation, and broadleaved forests. **Range** Throughout the subcontinent.

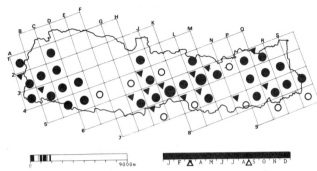

[MOUNTAIN TAILORBIRD
Orthotomus cuculatus
Golden-headed Tailorbird

Subspecies *coronatus*. A specimen has been listed as originating in Nepal, but no other details are known (716). Described as obtained by B. Hodgson (48) but not included in the catalogues (276,277,388). **Range** Himalayas from Darjeeling east to Arunachal Pradesh; n.e. India and Bangladesh.]

PALLAS'S WARBLER *Locustella certhiola*
Pallas's Grasshopper Warbler

Subspecies *rubescens*. Vagrant. First recorded by F.M. Bailey who collected a specimen by the Kosi River in the tarai on 12 February 1937 (62,108). One was also seen there on 17 March 1982 (606) and two on 7 April 1986 (403). The only other record is of one seen by the Bagmati pools, Kathmandu Valley on 26 October 1989 (256). Winters in reedbeds. All *Locustella* warblers are very skulking, especially in winter, and are probably overlooked. **Range** Winters in n.e. India and Bangladesh.

LANCEOLATED WARBLER *Locustella lanceolata*
Streaked Grasshopper Warbler

Vagrant. First recorded by F.M. Bailey who collected a specimen from the eastern tarai at San Pakwa (Q8) on 23 February 1938 (62,108). The only other records are of singles seen at Sukla Phanta on 2, 4 and 5 May 1982 (432), Chitwan on 19 April 1983 (56) and on 4 March 1986 (514), and Kosi Barrage in late January 1987 (594). A specimen from the Babai River, originally identified as this species (243), has been redetermined as a Grasshopper Warbler by the Chicago Field Museum (9). Found in tall grassland in

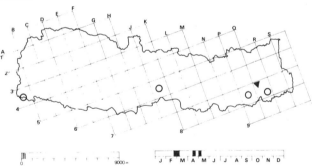

Nepal; also inhabits low vegetation in paddy stubbles (664). **Range** Winters in n. and n.e. India, and Bangladesh.

GRASSHOPPER WARBLER *Locustella naevia*

Subspecies *straminea*. Vagrant. A specimen was obtained from the Babai River, Bardia District (D5) in April 1972 by R.L. Fleming (9,243). Only three other records: one ringed on 11 April 1976 at Kosi

Barrage (287,293), another seen there on 8 April 1983 (56), and one or two at Chitwan (J6) on 13 April 1985 (59). Frequents tall grass and reedbeds. **Range** Winters locally throughout the subcontinent.

BRISTLED GRASS WARBLER   *Chaetornis striatus*

First definitely recorded by R.L. Fleming Jr. who saw one singing by the Rapti River, Chitwan (J6) on 24 April 1986 (227). A minimum of five birds was found in the same area between 6 and 13 May 1986, including one nest-building on the latter date (763,324,321). Found in riverine grassland. **Range** Punjab in Pakistan; most of India, but very locally distributed; Bangladesh.

STRIATED MARSH WARBLER   *Megalurus palustris*
Striated Warbler

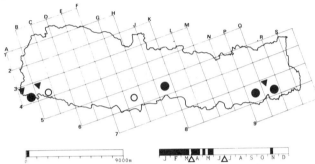

First recorded from the Kosi River on 15 February 1938 by F.M. Bailey (62). Local, probably resident. Common at Kosi Tappu (P8,Q8): a maximum of 30 was reported there on 31 May 1982 (432). Fairly common at Kosi Barrage, a rare resident at Chitwan, and also reported from Belatari (G6) (587), Sukla Phanta (432), Dhangarhi (647), and Emelie (A4) (647). Inhabits tall, damp grassland and reedbeds. **Range** Pakistan in the Punjab, east to n.e. India and Bangladesh.

BLACK-BROWED REED WARBLER
Acrocephalus bistrigiceps
Schrenck's Sedge Warbler

Subspecies *bistrigiceps*. Vagrant. There are three records, all of single birds in the Kosi marshes in winter. First seen on 19 January 1981 by J. Hall (300). Subsequently found there on 17 March 1982 (770), and 23 February 1983 (66). Found in tall grass and reedbeds. Like other *Acrocephalus* warblers it is skulking and easily overlooked, especially in winter. **Range** Recorded in winter in Ladakh (once), Nepal (rare), Calcutta, and n.e. India.

BLUNT-WINGED WARBLER   *Acrocephalus concinens*
Blunt-winged Paddyfield Warbler, Swinhoe's Reed Warbler

Subspecies *haringtoni*? Status uncertain, only three confirmed records received. Possibly overlooked because of its similarity to Paddyfield Warbler. First recorded on 10 February 1965 north-west of Bhadrapur (R8) at 230m by R.L. Fleming Sr. (234,247). Later reported along the Vishnumati River, Kathmandu Valley in March and November (243). Found in tall grasses, reedbeds and willows along river banks. **Range** Breeds in the Himalayas from the Kagan valley east to Kashmir; Assam. Winter quarters poorly known, but recorded from the Bengal duars and Bangladesh.

PADDYFIELD WARBLER   *Acrocephalus agricola*

Obtained by B. Hodgson in his later collection (409) but the specimen may have originated in India. First definitely recorded by F.M. Bailey from Sundar Gundar, Morang District (Q8) on 7 February 1938 (62). A local winter visitor to the tarai. Fairly common at Kosi Barrage, but scarce at Chitwan. It has been recorded from the Kathmandu Valley (629,687,403), but requires further confirmation. Only single records from elsewhere. It is possible that some reports should be referred to the Blunt-winged Warbler because the two species are easily confused. Frequents reed-beds and tall damp grassland. **Range** Breeds in n. Baluchistan. Winters throughout the subcontinent.

PADDYFIELD WARBLER, cont'd ...

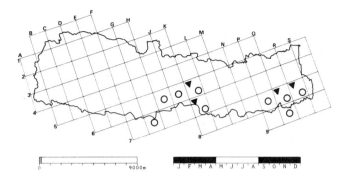

BLYTH'S REED WARBLER *Acrocephalus dumetorum*

First recorded by B. Hodgson (388). A fairly common winter visitor and passage migrant, most frequent in winter up to 1525m, but noted on passage up to 2900m. Reported in the Kathmandu Valley, and in the eastern tarai and foothills (P8,Q8) (293), between October and May. Inhabits bushes at the edges of cultivation and forests and in gardens. **Range** Winters throughout the subcontinent.

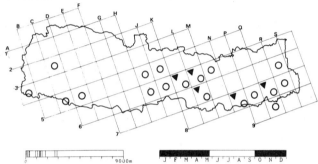

CLAMOROUS REED WARBLER *Acrocephalus stentoreus*
Indian Great Reed Warbler

Subspecies *brunnescens*. First recorded by B. Hodgson (388). A local winter visitor and passage migrant, occurring chiefly in the tarai. Occasionally seen at Kosi Barrage, found at Kosi Tappu (481,327), rare at Chitwan, and only single records from other areas. Singles were collected at Balaju (L6) at 1340m on 26 December 1966 (591) and on 12 September 1970 (589). Some records should perhaps be referred to the Oriental Reed Warbler as the two species are easily confused. Occurs in reeds, wet grassland, and bushes in

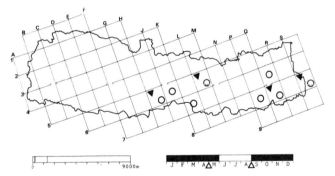

damp areas. **Range** Breeds in Pakistan, Kashmir, and sporadically in the Indian peninsula.

ORIENTAL REED WARBLER *Acrocephalus orientalis*
Eastern Great Reed Warbler (*A. arundinaceus*)
Great Reed Warbler

Vagrant. The only record is of one collected near Biratnagar (Q9) at about 75m on 9 March (year unknown) by R.L. Fleming (243). The record from Kosi Barrage given in the first edition of this book (435) has been withdrawn. Possibly overlooked because of similarity to Clamorous Reed Warbler. Found in reedbeds and wet rice fields. **Range** Winters in n.e. India.

THICK-BILLED WARBLER *Acrocephalus aedon*
(*Phragamaticola aedon*)

Subspecies *aedon*. Obtained by B. Hodgson in his later collection (409) but the specimen may have originated in India. First definitely recorded by R.L. Fleming at Trisuli Bazaar (L6) on 14 November 1956 (245). An uncommon winter visitor regularly reported between 75m and 1500m. Areas include Pokhara, Kathmandu Valley, Hetaura, and Chatra (Q8). Occurs in tall grass and scrub along wooded streams and forest edges, also in gardens and at the edges of cultivation. **Range** Winters from Rajasthan and Gujarat east to n.e. India and Bangladesh.

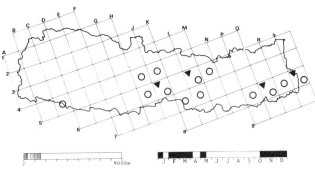

BOOTED WARBLER *Hippolais caligata*
Booted Tree Warbler

Subspecies *caligata*. First recorded by B. Hodgson (388,710). A scarce winter visitor and passage migrant reported between January and April. The subsequent records are of one collected at Beltar (L6) at 550m on 5 January 1974, singles seen at Tamaspur on 7 and 9 April 1981 (559), at Meghauli (J6) on 24 March 1982 (770), Kagheni at 2810m on 5 April 1982 (812), Kosi Barrage on 18 April 1982 (199,294) and on 13 February 1984 (408), Kosi Tappu on 9 February 1984 (408), and at Sauraha (J6) on 17 March 1986 (403). Found in deciduous scrub and bushes at edges of cultivation in dry habitats; fa-

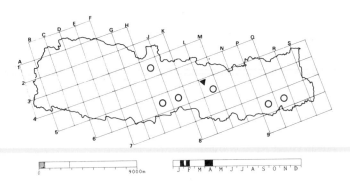

vours acacias. **Range** Breeds in Pakistan. Winters locally throughout the subcontinent, except n.e. India.

ORPHEAN WARBLER *Sylvia hortensis*

Subspecies *jerdoni*. Vagrant. First recorded in spring 1975 at Sukla Phanta by R.L. Fleming Sr. (238). Later the same year a probable was noted at Dharan (Q8) on 13 June (293), and one was seen at Chitwan on 11 November (141). The only other record is of one seen at Kosi Tappu on 9 March 1989 (193). Found in bushes and forest edges in the tarai and bhabar. **Range** Breeds in n. Baluchistan, and in the Himalayas in N.W.F.P. Winters east to Bihar, and south to s. India.

LESSER WHITETHROAT *Sylvia curruca*

Subspecies *blythi*. First recorded on 30 October 1957 at Phewa Tal by R.A. Paynter Jr. (663). An uncommon winter visitor and passage migrant, regularly seen in winter up to 1500m, at localities including Pokhara, Tamaspur, the Kathmandu Valley and Chitwan where the maximum of nine was seen in mid-February 1989 (506). Birds noted at about 2750m in the upper Kali Gandaki valley in March (594) and September (76), and at Hanga Tham at about 2135m in March (193) were presumably on passage. Frequents scrub and undergrowth. **Range** Breeds in n. Baluchistan, and in the Himalayas from N.W.F.P. east to Kashmir. Winters east to West Bengal, and south to s. India.

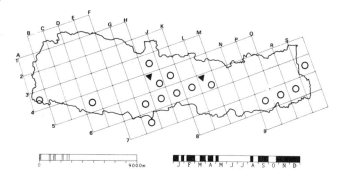

GOLDEN-SPECTACLED WARBLER *Seicercus burkii*
Yellow-eyed Warbler, Black-browed Flycatcher-Warbler

Subspecies *burkii*. First recorded by B. Hodgson (388). A common altitudinal migrant. Mainly summers between 2400m and 3800m and winters from 2135m down to 250m, occasionally to 150m. Breeding confirmed at Phulchowki (190). Found in undergrowth in broadleaved and coniferous forests and in rhododendron shrubberies above the treeline. **Range** Himalayas from Murree east to Arunachal Pradesh.

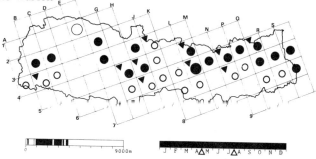

GREY-CHEEKED WARBLER *Seicercus poliogenys*
Grey-cheeked Flycatcher-Warbler

Obtained by B. Hodgson in his later collection (409) but the specimen may have originated in India. First definitely recorded by H. Stevens from the Singhalila ridge (S7) at 3100m in April and May 1912 (738). Scarce, probably resident. There are a few records from Phulchowki. Reported in Kathmandu (635) but its presence there requires confirmation. Noted in the upper Manang valley (J4) (762) in mid-July 1977, the western limit of the species's range. The only other records are from the upper Mai valley (S7) at 2440m on 10 March 1961 (246), Milke Danda (Q7) at 3200m in October 1978 (155,156,301) and in Mechi Zone (R8,S7)

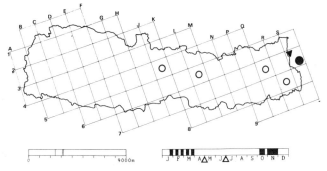

on 25 January 1985 (142) and on 30 March 1989 (193). Inhabits bamboo and dense undergrowth in damp, evergreen, broadleaved forests. **Range** Himalayas from Nepal east to Arunachal Pradesh.

[WHITE-SPECTACLED WARBLER *Seicercus affinis*
Allied Flycatcher-Warbler

The species was described from Nepal by F. Moore from a specimen included in Hodgson's later collection (409,798) but it may have originated in India. There are no other records. Inhabits dense, damp evergreen, broadleaved forests. **Range** Himalayas from Nepal east to Arunachal Pradesh.]

CHESTNUT-CROWNED WARBLER *Seicercus castaniceps*
Chestnut-crowned Flycatcher-Warbler

Subspecies *castaniceps*. The species was described from Nepal by B. Hodgson (798,118). A resident subject to altitudinal movements. Occasionally seen between 1800m and 2750m in summer; and between 1000m and 2285m in winter, although sometimes down to 250m. Inhabits broadleaved forests. **Range** Himalayas from Corbett east to Arunachal Pradesh.

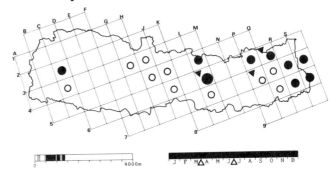

GREY-HOODED WARBLER *Seicercus xanthoschistos*
Grey-headed Flycatcher-Warbler

The species was described from Nepal by J.E. and G.R. Gray from a Hodgson specimen (277,798). A common resident subject to altitudinal movements. Summers between 1000m and 2750m. Some birds remain at the highest elevations during winter, but most descend to between 2000m and 750m; rarely down to 245m. Found breeding in the upper Kali Gandaki (811), west of Pamdur (H5) (153), and on the hills surrounding the Kathmandu Valley (629). Two intergrading races occur: *S. x. albosuperciliaris* (a), and *S. x. xanthoschistos* (x). Feeds in the lower canopy and in tall bushes in coniferous and broadleaved forests. **Range** Himalayas from N.W.F.P. east to Arunachal Pradesh.

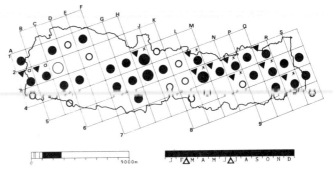

BROAD-BILLED WARBLER *Tickellia hodgsoni*
Broad-billed Flycatcher-Warbler (*Abroscopus hodgsoni*)

Subspecies *hodgsoni*. The species was described from Nepal by F. Moore from a specimen included in Hodgson's later collection (409,798) but it may have originated in India. First definitely recorded by H.S. Nepali from Shyaksila Toten, Barun valley (Q6) at 2195m on 22 November 1984 (588). The only other record is of one seen at Tashigaon, upper Arun valley (Q6) at about 2300m on 5 September 1986 (590). Inhabits moist broadleaved forest with bamboo. **Range** Himalayas from Nepal east to Bhutan and possibly Arunachal Pradesh.

RUFOUS-FACED WARBLER *Abroscopus albogularis*
White-throated Warbler, White-throated Flycatcher-Warbler

Subspecies *albogularis*. The species was described from Nepal by F. Moore from a specimen included in Hodgson's later collection (409,798) but this may have originated in India. There are only two definite records, both from the eastern tarai and lower foothills in Ilam District (R8): an undated record by R.L. Fleming (223), and three seen south of Ilam on 18 March 1982 at about 305m (794). Scarce, presumably resident. Breeds from early April to June. Frequents bamboo and scrub jungle. **Range** Himalayas from Nepal east to Arunachal Pradesh; n.e. India and Bangladesh.

YELLOW-BELLIED WARBLER *Abroscopus superciliaris*
Yellow-bellied Flycatcher-Warbler

Subspecies *flaviventris*. Obtained by B. Hodgson in his later collection (276) but the specimen may have originated in India. First definitely recorded by B. Biswas on 11 May 1947 at Hitaura, and proved breeding there (102). A resident subject to altitudinal movements, mainly seen between 245m and 1525m. Fairly common in the upper Mai valley (R7), and from Garuwa north to Ilam. Uncommon at Chitwan where it is possibly only a winter visitor. Found on Phulchowki in March (476) and a pair noted courtship feeding at 1700m on Nagarjung in May (556). Single reports received from other areas. Found on the hills around Pokhara in mid-August 1977 (H5) (762) and at Phewa Tal on 6 February 1989 (673), the

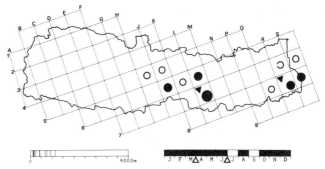

most westerly records of the species. Breeding confirmed at Hetaura (102). The maximum altitude recorded is at 2285m, above Hanga Tham on 23 December 1979 (206). Inhabits bamboo in damp, broadleaved forests, often near streams. **Range** Himalayas from Nepal east to Arunachal Pradesh; n.e. India and Bangladesh.

BLACK-FACED WARBLER *Abroscopus schisticeps*
Black-faced Flycatcher-Warbler

Subspecies *schisticeps*. The species was described from Nepal by J.E. and G.R. Gray from a Hodgson specimen (277,798). A local resident found between 1525m and 2700m. Probably descends from higher altitudes in winter. Fairly common on Phulchowki and Sheopuri; occasionally seen north-west of Pokhara (H5), and in Langtang (L5) where proved breeding north of Syabru (321). Single records received from elsewhere. Found at Khaptad (C3), the only locality in the west (428). Frequents damp forests, especially in moss-covered trees, bamboo, and thick undergrowth. **Range** Himalayas from Garwhal east to Bhutan and possibly Arunachal Pradesh; also n.e. India.

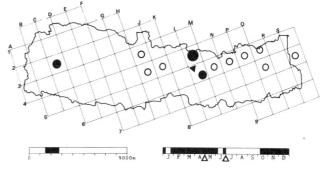

YELLOW-VENTED WARBLER *Phylloscopus cantator*
Yellow-throated Leaf Warbler, Black-browed Leaf Warbler,
Yellow-faced Leaf Warbler

A Hodgson specimen was listed for Nepal
by Seebohm (710) but it may have originated in India. First definitely recorded
by R.L. Fleming who collected one north-
west of Bhadrapur (S8) at 305m on 8
February 1965 (247). Uncommon and
very locally distributed. Reported between November and early April in the
far eastern tarai and foothills, between
250m and 600m. Regularly seen between
Sukhani and Chisapani (R8). The only
other records are of one near Dharan
(Q8) on 25 December 1978 (134), and one
or two near Tumlingtar (Q7) on 13 April
1982 (599). Found in Sikkim at 2000m
(738), and possibly occurs at a similar
altitude in eastern Nepal. Breeds from
the end of April to June. Frequents the
lower storey of broadleaved forests,
among bushes and bamboo. **Range**
Himalayas from Nepal east to Bhutan;
n.e. India.

BLYTH'S LEAF WARBLER *Phylloscopus reguloides*
Crowned Leaf Warbler, Blyth's Crowned Warbler

Subspecies *reguloides*. First collected by
B. Hodgson (114). A common resident
subject to altitudinal movements. Summers from 1980m up to 3800m; chiefly
between 2440m and 3050m. Mainly winters below 1500m, although it has been
found up to 2750m. Found breeding at
Khaptad (C3) (428), in the Dudh Kosi
valley (P6) (109), and on the hills surrounding the Kathmandu Valley (635).
Inhabits broadleaved and coniferous forests in summer; forest edges, bushes and
open forests in winter. **Range** Breeds in
the Himalayas from Murree east to Arunachal Pradesh, and in n.e. India. Winters
down to the adjacent plains and south to
Bangladesh.

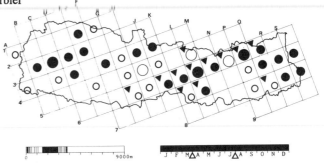

WESTERN CROWNED WARBLER *Phylloscopus occipitalis*
Large Crowned Leaf Warbler

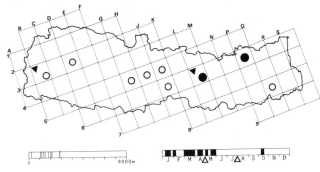

A Hodgson specimen was listed for Nepal by Seebohm (710) but it may have originated in India. First definitely recorded by F.M. Bailey from Godavari (L6) on 17 April 1938 (62). An uncommon spring passage migrant and rare winter visitor; possibly breeds. Described as fairly common in the west between 1800m and 1990m in spring and summer (243), but only three other reports received from there (464,573,438). Chiefly recorded between March and May in the Kathmandu Valley and surrounding hills, and at Chitwan. Described as a common winter visitor to Chitwan (296), but this requires confirmation. The maximum of ten was seen there on 14 March 1983 (513). Only a few other winter records received: in January from Begnas Tal (408) and Godavari (320), and in February from Kosi Tappu (408); and also one in October from Dhorpatan (573). Found in broadleaved and coniferous forests. **Range** Breeds in the Himalayas from Kohat east to Kumaon. Winters in the Indian peninsula, possibly east to Bangladesh.

SLENDER-BILLED WARBLER *Phylloscopus tytleri*
Tytler's Leaf Warbler

Scarce. Status uncertain; possibly a passage migrant or else a summer visitor. First recorded by R.L. Fleming Sr. who collected one south of Rupal, Dandeldhura District (A3) at 2135m on 9 April 1965 (234,247). The only other records are from Khaptad (C3), where one was seen on 20 April at 2500m, and also noted between 22 and 29 April at 3050m, with a maximum of five on 28 April (428). Found in oak/rhododendron forest (243) and in shrubberies at forest edges (428). **Range** Breeds in the w. Himalayas in Gilgit, Hazara and Kashmir. Winters in the Indian peninsula, but few records.

CR.

GREEN WARBLER *Phylloscopus nitidus*
Yellowish-breasted Warbler (*P. trochiloides nitidus*)

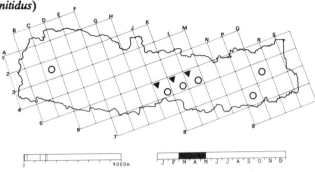

A Hodgson specimen was listed for Nepal by Seebohm (710) but may have originated in India. First definitely recorded by J. Scully in April 1877 from the Kathmandu Valley (708). A scarce and local spring migrant, reported between March and mid-May, chiefly in the second half of April. There are several reports from the Kathmandu Valley and surrounding hills, between 1500m and 2135m. The only other records are from Khaptad (C3) at 2100m (428), Gorlekharka (Q7) (546); also the lowlands between 75m and 305m, at Chitwan (440,111), the Rapti dun (K6) (190), Narayangarh (J6) (647), and Kosi

Barrage (559). Found in broadleaved trees in forests and forest edges. **Range** Winters in s. India, and recorded on passage from Pakistan east to Nepal and Calcutta.

GREENISH WARBLER *Phylloscopus trochiloides*
Dull Green Leaf Warbler

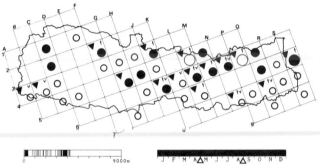

First collected by B. Hodgson (114). Two subspecies occur. *P. t. viridanus* (v) is a common winter visitor up to 1830m and a passage migrant. *P. t. trochiloides* (t) is a common summer visitor between 2440m and 4270m; chiefly between 2900m and 3900m. Found breeding at Kalapokhari (S7) (530). Passage birds presumably move through very quickly as there are only a few reports, chiefly from April to early May, and from mid-September to early October. Surprisingly, there are only a few winter records. Summers in broadleaved and coniferous forests or bushes near the treeline, and winters in

open wooded areas and gardens. **Range** Breeds in the Himalayas from Kohat east to Arunachal Pradesh, and n.e. India. Winters throughout India and Bangladesh.

LARGE-BILLED LEAF WARBLER *Phylloscopus magnirostris*

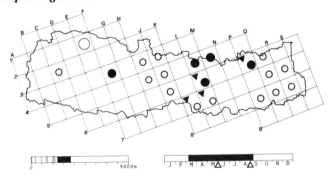

LARGE-BILLED LEAF WARBLER, cont'd ...

First recorded by B. Hodgson (388). A summer visitor; possibly also occurs in winter. Likely to be confused with Greenish Warbler especially in winter. Mainly summers between 2440m and 3600m. There are several records of passage migrants from Chitwan and the central region (L6,L7,K7) in March, April, August and September. Reported in winter between 75m and 2750m at Phewa Tal (300), Ghorepani (309), Chitwan (408), Hetaura (121), Kosi Barrage (622), Kathmandu Valley (309,518) and Mai valley (R7) (307) but further confirmation of its occurrence in winter is desirable. Occurs in broadleaved trees near streams in summer. **Range** Himalayas from N.W.F.P. east to Bhutan and presumably Arunachal Pradesh. Winters in southern and n.e. India.

ORANGE-BARRED LEAF WARBLER *Phylloscopus pulcher*
Buff-barred Warbler

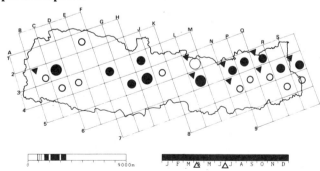

The species was described from Nepal by E. Blyth from a Hodgson specimen (118). A common altitudinal migrant. Summers between 2440m and 4265m, chiefly from 3500m to 4000m. Winters between 915m and 3050m and possibly higher. One was noted at the unusually low level of 75m in January 1978 at Janakpur (M8) (302).

Two intergrading races occur: *P. p. pulcher* (p) and *P. p. kangrae* (k). Found breeding in the Kathmandu Valley (313), Khumjung (P6) (190), the Gandak Kosi watershed (L5) (633) and Gapte (682). Frequents broadleaved forests and also shrubberies of fir, birch, juniper and rhododendron above the treeline in summer. **Range** Breeds in the Himalayas from Kishtwar east to Arunachal Pradesh, and in n.e. India. Winters at lower elevations in the same hills.

GREY-FACED LEAF WARBLER *Phylloscopus maculipennis*
Ashy-throated Warbler

GREY-FACED LEAF WARBLER, cont'd ...

Subspecies *maculipennis*. The species was described from Nepal by E. Blyth (125,798), but it may have originated in India. The species was collected by B. Hodgson, but not separated from Pallas's Leaf Warbler. First definitely recorded by H. Stevens from the upper Mai valley (S7) at 2745m in April 1912 (738). A fairly common resident subject to altitudinal movements. Chiefly summers between 2440m and 3500m, and winters between 2900m and 1525m, rarely down to 915m. Little is known of its breeding behaviour. Confirmed breeding at Khaptad (C3) (428), south of Annapurna (H5) (814) and on Phulchowki (636). Occurs in broadleaved and broadleaved/coniferous forests in summer; broadleaved forests and secondary growth in winter. **Range** Himalayas from Kashmir east to Arunachal Pradesh, and probably n.e. India.

PALLAS'S LEAF WARBLER *Phylloscopus proregulus*
Yellow-rumped Leaf Warbler, Lemon-rumped Warbler, Pallas's Warbler

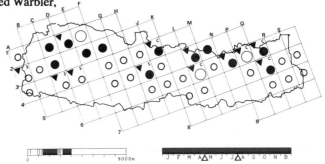

First recorded by B. Hodgson (388). A common altitudinal migrant. Mainly summers between 2750m and 4000m, and winters between 275m and 2750m, chiefly from 1400m to 2000m. Two intergrading races occur: *P. c. simlaensis* (s) and *P. c. chloronotus* (c) (798). Found in broadleaved and coniferous forests and also in fir and birch shrubberies above the treeline in summer. **Range** Breeds in the Himalayas from N.W.F.P. east to Arunachal Pradesh. Winters in the foothills and adjacent plains south to Bangladesh.

YELLOW-BROWED WARBLER *Phylloscopus inornatus*
Plain Leaf Warbler, Inornate Warbler

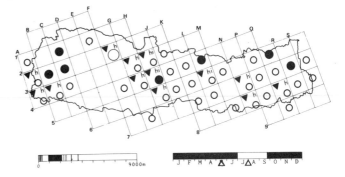

First recorded by B. Hodgson (388). Two races occur. *P. i. inornatus* (i) is an uncommon winter visitor and passage migrant from March to mid-April, and from mid-October to early November. Found in the Kathmandu Valley (628,635), near Pokhara (628) and at Tukche (527). *P. i. humei* (h) is a common resident and abundant passage migrant. Summers between 2800m and 3660m; fairly common in winter below 2135m, and rare up to 2560m. Breeds in coniferous forests and winters in open broadleaved woods and secondary scrub. **Range** Breeds in the Himalayas from N.W.F.P. east to Nepal; probably also in Arunachal Pradesh. Winters south to Belgaum and Bangladesh.

RADDE'S WARBLER *Phylloscopus schwarzi*

Vagrant. One was found north of Charali (Q8) at 150m on 25 December 1979 by R. Fairbank (206). The only other records are of singles seen at Pokhara on 4 and 5 March 1983 (794) and on 4 March 1986 (55). The species frequents undergrowth and bushes in winter. **Range** Vagrant in n.w. India and Nepal.

DUSKY WARBLER *Phylloscopus fuscatus*
Dusky Leaf Warbler

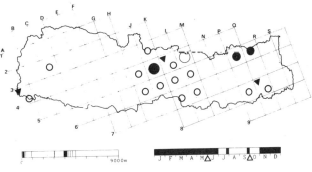

First recorded by B. Hodgson (391). A winter visitor, occasionally seen up to 1600m. Most birds appear in mid-October and remain to the end of March. Common at Kosi Barrage. Two races occur: *P. f. weigoldi* (w) (234,247), and *P.*

f. fuscatus (f) (102,190,647,659). Inhabits bushes, hedges and long grass, especially near water. Probably overlooked because of its skulking behaviour. **Range** Winters in the Himalayan foothills from Nepal east to Arunachal Pradesh and south to Rajasthan and Bangladesh.

SMOKY WARBLER *Phylloscopus fuligiventer*
Smoky Willow Warbler

Subspecies *fuligiventer*. The species was described from Nepal by B. Hodgson (391,798). Mainly an uncommon altitudinal migrant. Breeding behaviour is poorly known. Reported in summer between 3900m and 5000m: described as common and found breeding on Lamjung Himal (J5) between 3900m and 4200m in June (757,762); also seen between Gapte Cave and Gosainkund and noted carrying food there in late May (321); seen in Khumbu in June and July (48,190,474) and in the Barun valley (Q6) in September (590). Regularly reported in winter below 915m at Sukla Phanta, Phewa Tal, Tamaspur, Chitwan, and Kosi Barrage. Noted as high as 3200m in November at Barapakhari, Lamjung District (J4) (589). Three birds at Khaptad (C3) at about 3050m in April and May were presumably passage mi-

grants. Summers in dwarf juniper shrubberies and other low bushes above the treeline, and winters in dense undergrowth near water. **Range** Breeds in Nepal, n. Sikkim and Bhutan. Winters in the adjacent foothills and plains from Corbett east to Arunachal Pradesh, and in n.e. India.

SULPHUR-BELLIED WARBLER *Phylloscopus griseolus*
Olivaceous Leaf Warbler

First recorded in Kathmandu by F.M.
Bailey on 13 April 1938 (62,108). A scarce
passage migrant and winter visitor.
Mainly reported in April, presumably on
passage. Described as common in Bardia
District (C5) in early April 1972 (9,243).
Singles were seen below Naudanda (H5)
on 5 April 1982 (199,294), and at Chitwan
on 12 and 15 April 1983 (56). The only
other records are from the lower Langtang valley on 21 August 1949 (619), and
at Tamaspur on 4 December 1979 (206).
Winters in rocky areas. **Range** Breeds in
the w. Himalayas from N.W.F.P. east to
Gilgit. Winters in n. Pakistan and n. India.

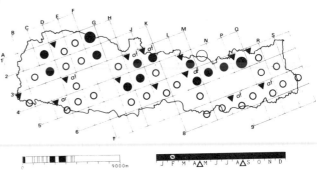

TICKELL'S WARBLER *Phylloscopus affinis*
Buff-bellied Leaf Warbler (*P. subaffinis*)
Buff-throated Warbler

First recorded by B. Hodgson (388). Two
races occur. *P. a. arcanus* (ar) is a scarce
winter visitor (659). *P. a. affinis* (af) is a
common altitudinal migrant. Mainly
summers between 3355m and 4880m, and
winters in the tarai; occasionally also in
the lower hills up to 1190m. Proved
breeding in the Langu valley (F1) (110)
and in Khumbu (190). A common migrant on the hills surrounding the Kathmandu Valley, in March, April and September (635), and in the upper Kali Gandaki valley in September and October
(76,526). Occurs in willow and other
shrubs in summer; bushes and secondary

growth in well-wooded areas in winter. **Range** Breeds in the
Himalayas from Gilgit east to Sikkim. Winters in e., n.e. and
s. India and in Bangladesh.

CHIFFCHAFF *Phylloscopus collybita*
Brown Leaf Warbler

Subspecies *tristis*. First collected by B.
Hodgson (277). A winter visitor occasionally seen up to 1370m. Seen at higher
altitudes, presumably on passage: near
Chumo (P6) at 2800m in May (75), Hanga
Tham at about 2135m in March (549),
and several reports from the upper Kali
Gandaki valley between 2560m and
2800m, from mid-March to mid-April,
and from late September to early October. Winters in bushes, secondary growth
and light forest. **Range** Winters in Paki-

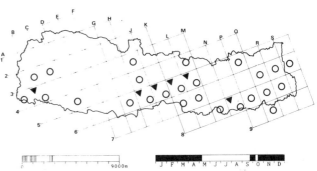

stan, in n. India south to Maharashtra and Bengal, and in
Bangladesh.

GOLDCREST *Regulus regulus*

A Hodgson specimen was listed for Nepal by Gadow (253,798) but it may have originated in India. First definitely recorded by H. Stevens on the Singhalila ridge (S7) on 25 January 1912 (738). A resident, subject to altitudinal movements. Occasionally found between 2200m and 3050m in winter, and up to 4000m in summer. Proved breeding at Khumjung (P6) (190). The intermediate *R. r. sikkimensis/himalayensis* (hs) and *R. r. sikkimensis* (s) have been recorded. Occurs in coniferous forest. **Range** Himalayas from N.W.F.P. east to Arunachal Pradesh.

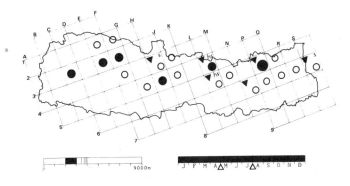

STOLICZKA'S TIT-WARBLER *Leptopoecile sophiae*
White-browed Tit-Warbler

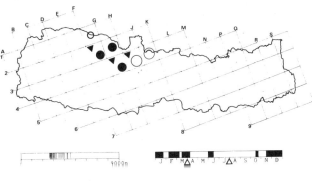

Subspecies *obscura*. First recorded above Jomosom in December 1949 at 3600m by R.L. Fleming Sr. (647). A resident, occasionally seen between 2700m and 4575m throughout the year, in the trans-Himalayan region. Found in dwarf juniper and Caragana shrubs above the treeline in semi-desert areas. **Range** Tibetan facies north of the Himalayas in Baltistan, Gilgit and Ladakh east to Nepal.

LARGE NILTAVA *Niltava grandis*
(*Muscicapa grandis*)

Subspecies *grandis*. First recorded by B. Hodgson (388). A locally distributed resident. Occurs between 1525m and 2850m and is probably subject to seasonal movements. One at Ghorepani on 14 March 1983 is the most westerly record of the species (148). Uncommon on Annapurna, in the upper Mai valley (R7,S7) and on Phulchowki in winter, and single records from elsewhere. Inhabits dense, damp, broadleaved forests, especially near streams. **Range** Himalayas from Nepal east to Arunachal Pradesh; n.e. India.

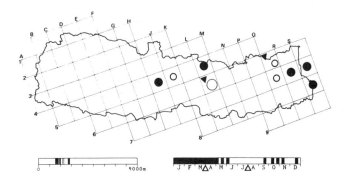

SMALL NILTAVA   *Niltava macgrigoriae*
(*Muscicapa macgrigoriae*)

Subspecies *macgrigoriae*. First recorded by B. Hodgson (369). A fairly common resident subject to altitudinal movements. Winters between 270m and 1400m, and summers up to 2200m. Locally common north-west of Pokhara (H5) and in the Kathmandu Valley and surrounding hills. Proved breeding on Phulchowki (763,792). Inhabits bushes near streams, edges of tracks and clearings in broadleaved forest. **Range** Himalayas from Mussoorie east to Arunachal Pradesh; n.e. India.

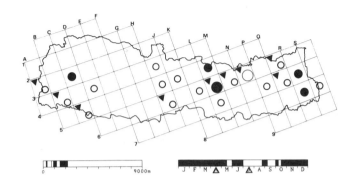

RUFOUS-BELLIED NILTAVA   *Niltava sundara*
Beautiful Niltava   (*Muscicapa sundara*)

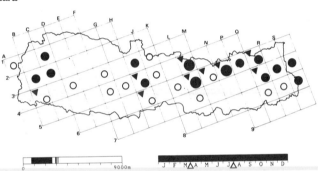

Subspecies *sundara*. The species was described from Nepal by B. Hodgson (369). A common resident subject to altitudinal movements. Chiefly winters between 800m and 1830m, and summers between 2135m and 3200m. Proved breeding near Syabru (L5) (682), at Thodung (N6) (190) and on Phulchowki (792). Frequents bushes and undergrowth in broadleaved forests and secondary growth. **Range** Breeds in the Himalayas from Murree east to Arunachal Pradesh, and in n.e. India. Winters in the foothills and adjacent plains south to Bangladesh.

PALE-CHINNED FLYCATCHER   *Cyornis poliogenys*
Brooks' Flycatcher   (*Muscicapa poliogenys*)

Subspecies *poliogenys*. Collected by B. Hodgson, but confused with Bluethroated Flycatcher; the specimens have now been correctly identified in the British Museum (Natural History). A resident, mainly seen up to 455m. Found at Butwal and Dobhan (G6) in January 1950 (647), and Tilaurikot woods (G6) in 1978 (157), the most westerly records for the species. Common at Chitwan and north of Sunischare where proved breeding (296,321); also common at Dharan and Tamaspur and occasionally seen elsewhere. Inhabits bushes and undergrowth in broadleaved forests. **Range** Himalayas from Nepal east to Arunachal Pradesh; n.e. India, Bangladesh and the E. Ghats.

PALE-CHINNED FLYCATCHER, cont'd ...

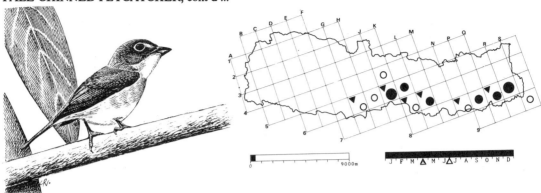

PALE BLUE FLYCATCHER *Cyornis unicolor*
(*Muscicapa unicolor*)

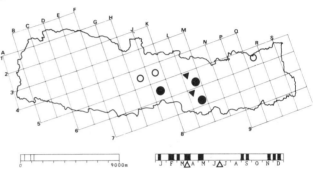

Subspecies *unicolor*. First recorded at Hetaura and Bhimpedi between 4 and 16 May 1947 by B. Biswas. One of the specimens was a female with eggs (103). Scarce; presumably a resident, subject to seasonal altitudinal movements. Little is known of its breeding habits. Regularly reported from Phewa Tal. The only other records are from the Rapti dun (L7) in December 1970 (444), south of Annapurna (J5) in 1977 (762), upper Arun valley in September 1986 (590), Chitwan in March 1987 (552) and April 1989 (193), Godavari in March 1986 (514) and Nagarjung (L6) in November 1989 (256).

Found in damp subtropical broadleaved forests. **Range** Himalayas from Garhwal east to Arunachal Pradesh; n.e. India and Bangladesh.

BLUE-THROATED FLYCATCHER *Cyornis rubeculoides*
Blue-throated Blue Flycatcher (*Muscicapa rubeculoides*)

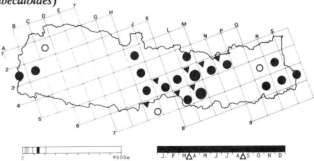

Subspecies *rubeculoides*. First recorded by B. Hodgson (369). A partial migrant. Mainly a summer visitor between about 365m and 1500m but noted at 2100m at Bigu (N6) (190). Fairly common and breeds in the Kathmandu Valley (635). Occasionally reported in summer from elsewhere. Confirmed breeding at Hetaura and Bhimpedi (103). Rarely recorded in winter at localities in the lower foothills, including Chitwan and north of Sunischare. Frequents open forests and groves. **Range** Breeds in the Himalayas from Kashmir east to Arunachal Pradesh, and in n.e. India and Bangladesh. Winters south to s. India.

HILL BLUE FLYCATCHER   *Cyornis banyumas*
Large-billed Blue Flycatcher   (*Muscicapa banyumas*)

Subspecies *magnirostris*. A Hodgson specimen was listed for Nepal by Sharpe (714), but it may have originated in India. First definitely recorded by D. Lowndes who collected one from Thangja, Marsiyangdi valley (J4) at 2590m on 20 August 1950 (512). A male was seen in the same valley at about 1250m on 1 May 1984 (158). These are the most westerly records for the species. Found on Makalu Base Camp trek (Q6) at about 3350m on 6 and 11 May 1982 (244) and at Nagarjung (L6) on 31 December 1988 and 1 January 1989 (69). Reported fom Godavari in winter (73,587), but further confirmation is desirable. Found in dense humid broadleaved forest, especially in ravines. Little is known of the altitudinal distribution and seasonal movements of the Himalayan population. **Range** Himalayas from Nepal east to Arunachal Pradesh; n.e. India.

TICKELL'S BLUE FLYCATCHER   *Cyornis tickelliae*
Tickell's Red-breasted Blue Flycatcher   (*Muscicapa tickelliae*)

Subspecies *tickelliae*. Obtained by B. Hodgson in his later collection (409) but the specimen may have originated in India. First definitely recorded by R.L. Fleming Sr. from Butwal at 275m in February 1950 (647). Scarce, status and movements uncertain. Described as fairly common at Sukla Phanta in winter and possibly resident (700), and a resident seen occasionally at Bardia (192,432,162). The only other reports are from Dhangarhi in December 1952 (647),the eastern foothills (Q8) in April 1975 (293), Luxmighat (G6) in March 1978 (157), and Chitwan in autumn 1978 (763), in March and April 1980 (440,474) and in October

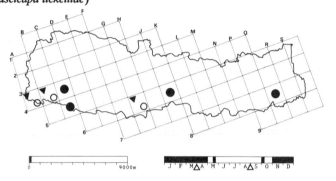

1986 (135). Inhabits open dry broadleaved forests. **Range** The Indian peninsula east of a line from Kutch to Mussoorie; n.e. India and Bangladesh.

PYGMY BLUE FLYCATCHER   *Muscicapella hodgsoni*

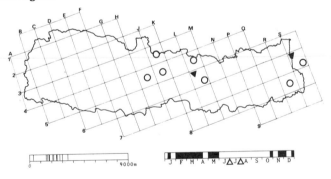

PYGMY BLUE FLYCATCHER, cont'd ...

Subspecies *hodgsoni*. The species was described from Nepal by F. Moore, from a specimen included in Hodgson's later collection (409,798) but it may have originated in India. First definitely recorded by H. Stevens in the upper Mai valley (S7) on 21 March 1912 (739). Scarce and local, probably resident. Seasonal altitudinal movements are uncertain. Summers between 2100m and 3500m, and winters between about 305m and 3500m. Found near Ghorepani on 19 March 1982 (57) and 31 March 1986 (264), the most westerly records of the species. Reported between March and October in Manang (762), south of Annapurna (H5) (300,559), (J5) (762), below Thare Pati (L5) (141), on Phulchowki, in the upper Mai valley (442), and from Godavari ravines and north of Sunischare in winter. Its breeding habits are little known. Found in dense, damp broadleaved forests. **Range** Himalayas from Nepal east to Arunachal Pradesh; n.e. India.

VERDITER FLYCATCHER *Muscicapa thalassina*

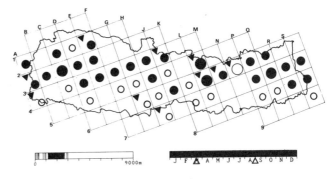

Subspecies *thalassina*. First recorded by B. Hodgson (388). A partial migrant; common in summer, occasionally seen in winter. Mainly a summer visitor between 1200m and 2625m, and sparsely up to 3000m. Proved breeding at Khaptad (C3) (428), in Langtang (682), in the Kathmandu Valley and on the surrounding hills (432,440,629,659), at Bhimpedi (103), and north of Dhankuta (Q7) (446). Some birds remain in the tarai and foothills up to 350m in winter. Occurs in open forests, especially of broadleaved trees. **Range** Breeds in the Himalayas from the Indus valley east to Arunachal Pradesh, and in n.e. India. Winters south throughout India and Bangladesh.

FERRUGINOUS FLYCATCHER *Muscicapa ferruginea*
(*M. rufilata*)

The species was described from Nepal by B. Hodgson (391,798). Scarce, probably only a summer visitor. Summers between 2000m and 3300m. Records at lower altitude are probably of migrants. Seen at Lete (H4) at 2440m on 6 May 1981, the most westerly record of the species (811). Mainly found in the east; localities where reported recently include north-west of Pokhara (H5) (655,82,111), Khumbu (559,463), upper Arun valley (483), Barun valley (Q6) (590), upper Mai valley (R7) (561), Ilam (770) and Hans Pokhari (S8) (193,183). Frequents humid, broadleaved

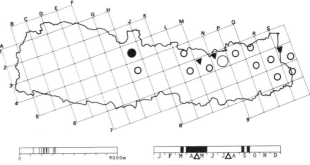

forests, especially of oak. **Range** Himalayas fom Nepal east to Arunachal Pradesh; n.e. India.

ASIAN SOOTY FLYCATCHER *Muscicapa sibirica*
Sooty Flycatcher, Dark-sided Flycatcher

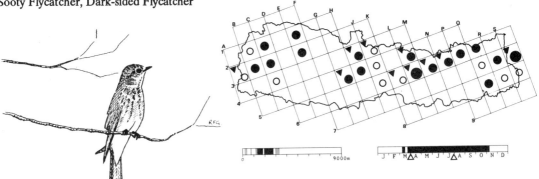

Subspecies *cacabata*. First recorded by B. Hodgson (388). A fairly common summer visitor between 2000m and 3300m. Seen at lower altitudes on passage. Breeds on the north face of Sheopuri (243) and in the upper Mai valley (S7) (741). There is a winter record of one at Begnas Tal on 27 December 1981 (300). Occurs in the canopy of open broadleaved and coniferous forest, or in clearings. **Range** Himalayas from Safed Koh east to Arunachal Pradesh; n.e. India.

RUFOUS-TAILED FLYCATCHER *Muscicapa ruficauda*

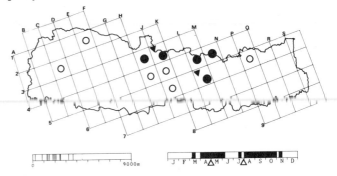

First recorded at Kathmandu on 19 April 1935 by F.M. Bailey (62). An uncommon summer visitor and passage migrant. Summers between 2440m and 3655m. Localities include the upper Kali Gandaki valley (509), Manangbhot (J4) (512), south of Annapurna (J5) (765), and Langtang (L5,M5) (199,682,321). Reported occasionally on passage in April and May in the Kathmandu Valley, and rarely at Chitwan in April, September and October. There are only two records from the east (155,301,474), and further confirmation of its occurrence there is desirable. Summers in fir, birch and oak forests. **Range** Breeds in the Himalayas from Safed Koh east to central Nepal. Winters in s.w. India.

BROWN-BREASTED FLYCATCHER *Muscicapa muttui*

Vagrant. First recorded by S. Vyas who saw one at Rani Bari, Kathmandu Valley at about 1330m on 6 September 1987 (792). The only other record is of one seen at Chatra at about 135m on 4 October 1987 (792). Found in thickets near water and in forest undergrowth. **Range** Breeds in n.e. India and possibly in Sikkim; winters in s.w. India and Sri Lanka.

ASIAN BROWN FLYCATCHER   *Muscicapa latirostris*
Brown Flycatcher   (*M. dauurica*)

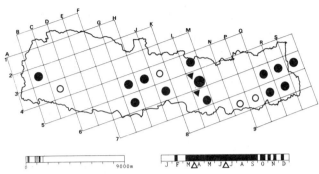

Subspecies *latirostris*. First recorded by B. Hodgson (388). Mainly an uncommon passage migrant and summer visitor, rare in winter. Breeds between 1000m and 1550m. Occasionally reported from the Kathmandu Valley between April and September and found breeding in Gaucher forest (243). There are a few spring and autumn records, presumably of passage migrants, from Chitwan, and north of Sunischare, and mainly single reports from elsewhere. Noted in winter in the Kathmandu Valley (78,444), at Chitwan (296), and in the eastern tarai (P8) (293). Inhabits open broadleaved forest. **Range** Breeds in the Himalayas from Chamba east to Bhutan; also in the Vindhya Range, and the W. Ghats. Winters in s. and e. India, and Bangladesh.

SAPPHIRE FLYCATCHER   *Ficedula sapphira*
Sapphire-headed Flycatcher   (*Muscicapa sapphira*)

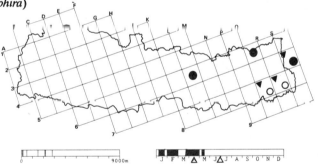

Subspecies *sapphira*. Obtained by B. Hodgson in his later collection (409) but the specimen may have originated in India. First definitely recorded by H. Stevens in the upper Mai valley at about 2135m on 4 and 11 April 1912 (741). Scarce, possibly resident. Subject to altitudinal movements. Seen in the upper Arun valley at 2800m in May 1981 (483). Found in the eastern lowlands from January to March: at Chatra (Q8) at 150m in 1949 (659) and 1974 (518), and in the lower Mai valley (R8) in 1961 (246), 1985 (59) and 1989 (549,307). A male, probably on passage, seen at Nagarjung on 31 May 1982 (540), forms the most westerly record for the species. Reported near Ghandrung (H5) (243), but confirmation of its occurrence so far west is desirable. Inhabits damp, evergreen, broadleaved forest. Its breeding behaviour is little known. **Range** Himalayas from Nepal east to Bhutan and possibly Arunachal Pradesh; n.e. India.

SLATY-BLUE FLYCATCHER *Ficedula tricolor*
(*Muscicapa leucomelanura*)

Subspecies *tricolor*. The species was described from Nepal by B. Hodgson
(391,798). A common altitudinal migrant.
Mainly summers between 3050m and
4000m. Winters between 160m and
2135m but most frequently between 245m
and 1525m. The race *F. t. minuta* is described as occurring in Nepal (450), but
no records have been located. Inhabits
shrubberies above the treeline in summer; bushes, tall grass and forest undergrowth in winter. **Range** Himalayas from
the Indus River east to Arunachal
Pradesh; n.e. India.

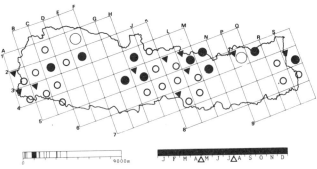

ULTRAMARINE FLYCATCHER *Ficedula superciliaris*
White-browed blue Flycatcher (*Muscicapa superciliaris*)

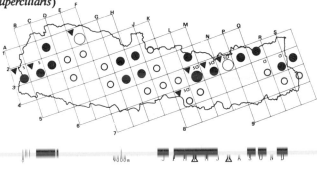

First recorded by B. Hodgson (388).
Common. Mainly a summer visitor from
late February to late October. Found in
the breeding season between 1800m and
3200m, but chiefly from 2000m to 2500m.
Proved breeding on Sheopuri (440,682).
There are a few winter records up to

1500m: localities include Dana (H4) (439), Naudanda (H5)
(309), and the Kathmandu Valley (622). Two intergrading
races occur: *M. s. aestigma* (a) and *M. s. superciliaris* (s).
Occurs in broadleaved forests, especially of oaks. **Range**
Breeds in the Himalayas from Kohat east to Arunachal
Pradesh, and in n.e. India. Winters south to Karnataka and
Bangladesh.

LITTLE PIED FLYCATCHER *Ficedula westermanni*
(*Muscicapa westermanni*)

Subspecies *collini*. First recorded by B.
Hodgson (388). An uncommon altitudinal migrant. Summers between 1200m
and 3000m, and winters between 275m
and at least 915m. A nest was found in the
Dhorpatan valley at 2990m (499); seen
carrying food on 17 May at Thulokobang

(H5) (800) and collected in breeding condition at Chitlang
(L6) in April (103). There is no other published breeding information for this subspecies. Taken at Barmdeo Mandi
(A3) at 300m in January 1953, the most westerly record of
the species (647). **Range** Breeds in the Himalayas from
Nepal east to Arunachal Pradesh, and in n.e. India. Winters
south to Madhya Pradesh and Bangladesh.

LITTLE PIED FLYCATCHER, cont'd ...

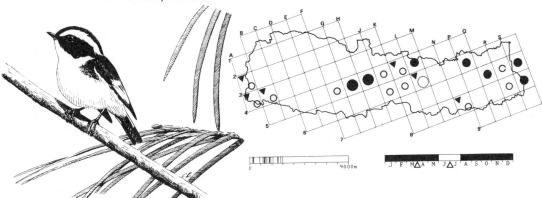

SLATY-BACKED FLYCATCHER *Ficedula hodgsonii*
Rusty-breasted Blue Flycatcher (*Muscicapa hodgsonii*)

First recorded by B. Biswas on 20 March 1947 at 1495m at Thankot, Kathmandu Valley (103). A scarce and local altitudinal migrant. Caught at Phematan, Barun valley (Q6) at 3450m before the monsoon in 1973 (71). All other reports are between 245m and 2000m in winter and early spring. Described as fairly common in the Kathmandu Valley during winter and early spring in 1955 (635); now a scarce but regular visitor to Godavari. A few records from north of Sunischare and single reports from elsewhere. Found below Ghasa on 24 February 1986, the most westerly record for the species (403). Found in fir forests in summer and in damp broadleaved forests in winter. **Range** Himalayas from Nepal east to Arunachal Pradesh; n.e. India.

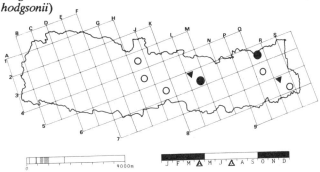

SNOWY-BROWED FLYCATCHER *Ficedula hyperythra*
Rufous-breasted Blue Flycatcher (*Muscicapa hyperythra*)

Subspecies *hyperythra*. First recorded by B. Hodgson (388). An altitudinal migrant. Occasional. Summers between 2000m and 2440m, and sometimes up to 3000m. Winters between 275m and about 1525m. Proved breeding on the hills surrounding the Kathmandu Valley (635). Rare at Chitwan between September and April (296). Found in the lower storey of humid broadleaved forests with dense growth. **Range** Himalayas from Kumaon east to Arunachal Pradesh; n.e. India.

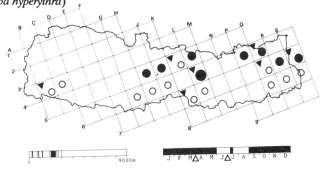

WHITE-GORGETTED FLYCATCHER *Ficedula monileger*
(*Muscicapa monileger*)

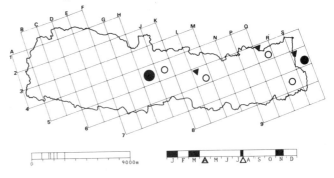

Subspecies *monileger*. The species was described from Nepal by B. Hodgson (391). Scarce, presumably resident. An adult and a juvenile were found at Lumle (H5) at 1550m on 25 July 1973 (814); also seen at Ghandrung on 2 November 1979 (813). These form the two westernmost records for the species. Altitudinal movements within Nepal are poorly known. Other reports are from Phewa Tal (460), south of Annapurna (J5) (762), Sheopuri (587), Godavari (647), Kathmandu Valley (486), Arun valley (441), Barun valley (Q6) (588), the upper Mai valley (741) and north of Sunischare (142). Found in dense undergrowth in damp, broadleaved

forest. Breeding of the race occurring in Nepal is undescribed but probably is the same as in the eastern race. **Range** Himalayas from Nepal east to Arunachal Pradesh; n.e. India.

ORANGE-GORGETTED FLYCATCHER *Ficedula strophiata*
Rufous-gorgetted Flycatcher (*Muscicapa strophiata*)

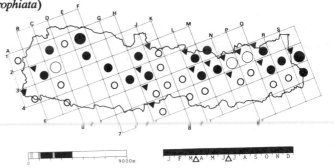

Subspecies *strophiata*. The species was described from Nepal by B. Hodgson (369). A common altitudinal migrant. Mainly summers between 2440m and 4000m, and winters between 915m and 1830m, but seen uncommonly up to 2135m and down to 245m. Confirmed breeding in the Mai valley (741) and at Chankheli (626). Found in broadleaved and coniferous forests. **Range** Breeds in the Himalayas from Kangra east to Arunachal Pradesh, and in n.e. India. Winters in the foothills and south to Bangladesh.

KASHMIR FLYCATCHER *Ficedula subrubra*
Kashmir Redbreasted Flycatcher (*Muscicapa subrubra*)

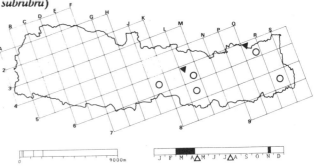

KASHMIR FLYCATCHER, cont'd ...

First recorded in Kathmandu on 10 April 1953 by D. Proud (635). A scarce visitor, mainly reported on passage in spring. Status uncertain. Several reports of singles in March and April 1982: at Sauraha (J6) (682), Pashupatinath (199,208), Gokarna (599), Hetaura (682,770), and north of Birtamod (R8) (794). Also reported in April at Sauraha (J6) in 1985 (313) and 1986 (403). Only two autumn records: from Godavari in October 1970 (444) and Sukipatal (Q6) in November 1973 (441). Found twice in the Kathmandu Valley in winter: at Swayambhunath in December 1964 (589) and at Godavari in February 1980 (523). Frequents open broadleaved forest. **Range** Breeds in the w. Himalayas in Kashmir and the Pir Panjal range. Winters in Sri Lanka. Vagrant east to Bhutan.

RED-BREASTED FLYCATCHER *Ficedula parva*
Red-throated Flycatcher (*Muscicapa parva*)

Subspecies *albicilla*. First recorded by B. Hodgson (388). A common winter visitor from the tarai up to 1830m. Mainly occurs between late September and late April in the Kathmandu Valley (635), at Chitwan (296), and in the eastern tarai and foothills (P8,Q8) (293). Noted on autumn passage: at Tukche, at 2590m, where one or two were seen from 4 to 16 September 1973 (76), and in Langtang at 2320m on 31 October 1980 (516). Found in bushes, groves and scrub at edges of cultivation. **Range** Winters throughout the subcontinent.

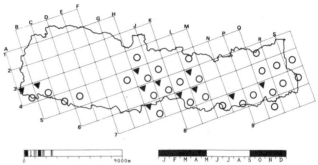

GREY-HEADED FLYCATCHER *Culicicapa ceylonensis*

Subspecies *pallidior*. First recorded by B. Hodgson (388). A very common partial migrant. Summers between 1200m and 3100m, but most frequent from 1500m to 2400m. Found breeding in the central region (L6) (103,659), at Chitwan (296), in the Hongu valley (P6) (109), and north of Dhankuta (Q7) (446). Some birds remain in winter from 75m up to 1800m. **Range** Breeds in the Himalayas from the Indus valley east to Arunachal Pradesh, and in s.w. and c. India. Winters in n. Pakistan, much of India, and in Bangladesh.

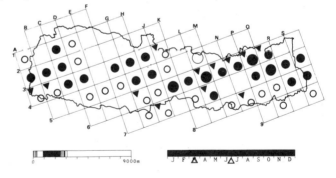

YELLOW-BELLIED FANTAIL   *Rhipidura hypoxantha*

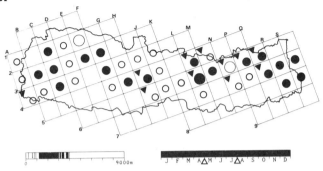

First recorded by B. Hodgson (388). A very common resident, subject to altitudinal movements. Chiefly summers between 2440m and 4000m. Winters between 200m and 1800m, but seen occasionally up to 2560m and down to 760m. Proved breeding on Phulchowki (792).

Noted as low as 245m at Chitwan in February 1981 (300,656) and December 1986 (325). Found in the lower canopy of broadleaved and coniferous forests and shrubberies of birch, fir and rhododendron above the treeline. **Range** Himalayas from the Chenab River east to Arunachal Pradesh; n.e. India and Bangladesh.

WHITE-THROATED FANTAIL   *Rhipidura albicollis*

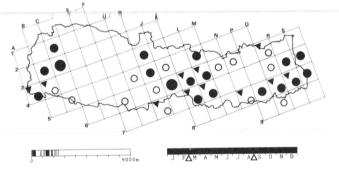

First recorded by B. Hodgson (388). A fairly common resident up to 1500m, and occasionally seen up to 2440m. Usually descends from the highest altitudes in winter but noted at 2135m in February (243). Common at Chitwan where it breeds (296); also proved breeding in Doti District (C3) (438). Inhabits ravines and shady areas in broadleaved forests. Although the western race *R. a. canescens* is given as extending to w. Nepal (47), specimens of *R. a. albicollis* have been collected throughout (62,647). **Range** Himalayas from Murree east to Arunachal Pradesh; n.e. India, Bangladesh and the Indian peninsula from Mt. Abu southwards.

WHITE-BROWED FANTAIL *Rhipidura aureola*

Subspecies *aureola*. Obtained by B. Hodgson in his later collection (409), but the specimen may have originated in India. First definitely recorded by F.M. Bailey from Tribeni (H7) at 75m on 19 December 1935 (62). Chiefly an uncommon resident throughout the lowlands up to 275m. Occasionally found at Chitwan, and single records received from most other areas. Frequents undergrowth and bushes near the ground, in more open and drier forests than White-throated Fantail. **Range** Himalayan foothills from the Indus River east to the Bhutan duars; south through most of the subcontinent.

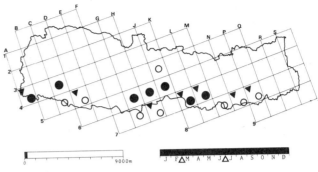

ASIAN PARADISE FLYCATCHER *Terpsiphone paradisi*
Paradise Flycatcher

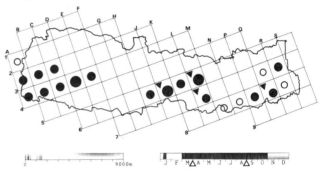

Subspecies *leucogaster*. First recorded by B. Hodgson (388). A summer visitor, mainly seen from the tarai up to 1525m. Noted at 1850m at Yangnam (R7) in April (658). There is a winter record of one at Soktim (R8) in January (142). A common breeder at Chitwan (J6,K6) where it occurs from March to October (296). Found to be fairly common and breeding at Dailekh (D4) in June 1979 (626). Last century described as breeding very commonly in the Kathmandu Valley (708), but only a few recent reports, including a pair breeding at Nagarjung in July 1987 (792). Chiefly single reports from elsewhere. Found in open forests, groves and gardens. **Range** N. Baluchistan, and the Himalayan foothills from N.W.F.P. east to Arunachal Pradesh; n.e. India, Bangladesh, and the Indian peninsula from Kathiawar southwards.

BLACK-NAPED MONARCH *Hypothymis azurea*
Black-naped Flycatcher (*Monarcha azurea*)

Subspecies *styani*. First recorded by B. Hodgson (388). A local resident, occasionally seen in the tarai and lower foothills up to 365m. Breeding confirmed at Chitwan (296) and Hetaura (103). Other localities include Sukla Phanta (700), Bardia (162), Tamaspur, the central dun (K7,L7), and the eastern lowlands, especially north of Sunischare (P8,Q8,R8). Found in the middle storey of broadleaved forests. **Range** India south and east of a line from Kutch to Dehra Dun; Bangladesh.

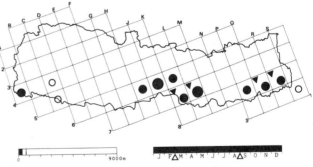

PUFF-THROATED BABBLER *Pellorneum ruficeps*
Spotted Babbler

Subspecies *mandellii*. First recorded by B. Hodgson (388). A resident chiefly occurring up to 915m; rare up to 1675m. Does not appear to move seasonally. Common at Tamaspur and Chitwan (J6,K6), fairly common in the eastern tarai and foothills (P8,Q8,R8), and occasionally seen at Begnas Tal, Phewa Tal and in the lower Arun valley. Scarce in the Kathmandu Valley (300,635) and few records from the west. Inhabits bushy undergrowth of broadleaved forests, heavy scrub and secondary growth. **Range** Himalayan foot-

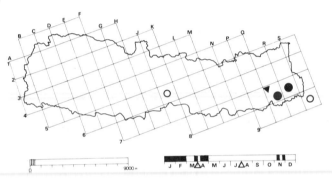

hills from Kangra east to Arunachal Pradesh; n.e. India, and the hills of peninsular India.

ABBOTT'S BABBLER *Trichastoma abbotti*

Subspecies *abbotti*. Obtained by B. Hodgson in his later collection (409) but the specimen may have originated in India. First definitely recorded by S.D. Ripley from Chatra at 150m in February 1949 (659). A very local resident occurring between 75m and 275m. Common north of Sunischare where the maximum of 15 was heard on 24 March 1981 (442). Found again at Chatra in 1957 (245). The only other records are from Dharan in 1986 (763), Kosi Tappu in 1987 (328), Charkose Ban (S9) in 1989 (164), and Chitwan in 1978 (762) and 1989 (597), the westernmost locality for the species. Breeds from April to July. Frequents

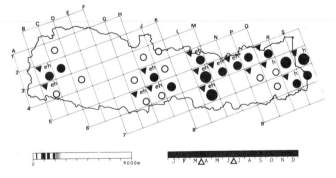

tangled thickets, especially at forest edges along stream banks. **Range** Himalayan foothills from Nepal east to Arunachal Pradesh; n.e. India and Bangladesh.

RUSTY-CHEEKED SCIMITAR-BABBLER *Pomatorhinus erythrogenys*

First recorded by B. Hodgson (359). A common and sedentary resident, mainly seen between 305m and 2135m and occasionally up to 2440m. Confirmed breeding on the hills surrounding the Kathmandu Valley (336,708), at Hetaura and Bhimpedi (101), Taplejung (R7) (687), and in the Mai valley (S7) (737). The race *P. e. haringtoni* (h) (246,587,737) and intermediates between *P. e. erythrogenys* and *P. e. haringtoni* (eh) (62,101,621,647) have been collected. Found in thick scrub and undergrowth at forest edges, secondary jungle, bushy hillsides, and bushes at field edges. **Range** Himalayas from the Jhelum River east to Arunachal Pradesh; n.e. India and Bangladesh.

WHITE-BROWED SCIMITAR-BABBLER *Pomatorhinus schisticeps*
Slaty-headed Scimitar-Babbler (*P. horsfieldii*)

Subspecies *schisticeps*. The species was described from Nepal by B. Hodgson (359,798). A sedentary resident, occasionally seen between 245m and 915m, and rarely up to 1500m. Breeding confirmed at Hetaura (78) and Chitwan (296). Found in dense scrub, secondary jungle, and undergrowth in forests. **Range** Himalayas from Kangra east to Arunachal Pradesh; n.e. India and Bangladesh.

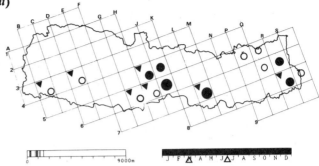

STREAK-BREASTED SCIMITAR-BABBLER *Pomatorhinus ruficollis*
Rufous-necked Scimitar-Babbler

The species was described from Nepal by B. Hodgson (359,798). A fairly common resident betweeen 1500m and 2590m, which is not known to migrate altitudinally. Two intergrading races have been recorded: *P. r. godwini* (g) (246,574,659) and *P. r. ruficollis* (r) (62,101,190, 621,647,708). Inhabits thick undergrowth and dense, scrub-covered hillsides. **Range** Himalayas from Kumaon east to Arunachal Pradesh; n.e. India and Bangladesh.

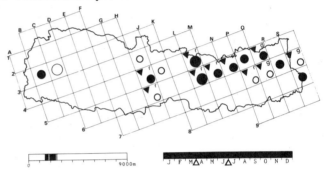

CORAL-BILLED SCIMITAR-BABBLER *Pomatorhinus ferruginosus*

Subspecies *ferruginosus*. Obtained by B. Hodgson in his later collection (409) but the specimen may have originated in India. The only other report is of a dozen sightings from the Arun valley in 1973 (243). Occurs in dense undergrowth and bamboo jungle. **Range** Himalayas from Nepal east to Arunachal Pradesh; n.e. India.

SLENDER-BILLED SCIMITAR-BABBLER   *Xiphirhynchus superciliaris*

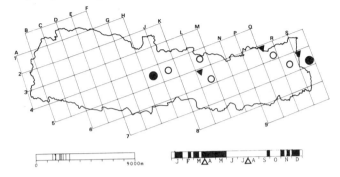

Subspecies *superciliaris*. Although listed as obtained in Nepal by B. Hodgson in his later collection (409), these specimens may have originated in India (716). First definitely recorded by H. Stevens from Kalipokhari (S7) between 2440m and 3050m in April and May 1912 (737). A few later reports received from the upper Mai valley (S7). A scarce resident which probably migrates altitudinally. Found near Tirkedhunge (H5) at 1500m on 29 January 1979 (486,652) and on 10 March 1981 (476), the westernmost locality for the species. The only other records are from south of Annapurna (H5,J5), above Syabru (L5) (321), below Ghora Tabela (L5) (70), on the north face of Sheopuri (9,243), at Sukipatal (Q6) (10) and in the Barun valley (588). Inhabits bamboo and thick undergrowth in damp broadleaved forests. **Range** Himalayas from Nepal east to Arunachal Pradesh; n.e. India and Bangladesh.

[LONG-BILLED WREN-BABBLER   *Rimator malacoptilus*

Subspecies *malacoptilus*. Obtained by B. Hodgson in his later collection (409,716) but the specimen may have originated in India. Inhabits forest undergrowth and dense scrub (46). **Range** Himalayas from Nepal east to Arunachal Pradesh; n.e. India.]

GREATER SCALY-BREASTED WREN-BABBLER   *Pnoepyga albiventer*
Scaly-breasted Wren-Babbler

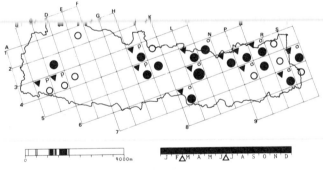

The species was described from Nepal by B. Hodgson (391,798). A fairly common resident subject to altitudinal movements. Usually summers between 2440m and 4000m. Winters between 275m and 2285m, but mainly between 1000m and 2440m. Two intergrading races occur: *P. a. pallidior* (p) (647,659) and *P. a. albiventer* (a) (101, 246,574,647). Inhabits dense undergrowth in damp broadleaved forests, particularly near streams and in ravines; also boulder-strewn slopes and forest edges. **Range** Himalayas from Duala Dhar east to Arunachal Pradesh; n.e. India.

LESSER SCALY-BREASTED WREN-BABBLER *Pnoepyga pusilla*
Brown Wren-Babbler, Pygmy Wren-Babbler

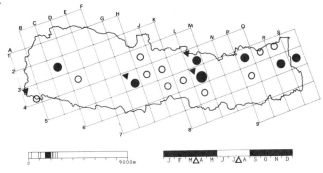

Subspecies *pusilla*. The species was described from Nepal by B. Hodgson (391,798). A resident subject to altitudinal movements. Breeds over a lower altitudinal range than the previous species, although their ranges overlap between 2440m and 2590m. Occasionally seen between 1500m and 2590m in summer, and between 915m and 1770m in winter; rarely down to 275m. Breeds near the rim of Sheopuri (243). Collected at Ainthpur (A4) in January 1953 (469), the western limit of its range. Habitat is similar to that of Greater Scaly-breasted Wren-Babbler. **Range** Himalayas from Nepal east to Arunachal Pradesh; n.e. India and Bangladesh.

SPOTTED WREN-BABBLER *Spelaeornis formosus*

Scarce, presumably resident. The only record is of one heard by R.L. Fleming Jr. north-west of Shyaksila Toten, Barun valley (Q6) at 1785m on 12 November 1984 (588,226). Frequents damp rhododendron forest with thick ferns and mossy rocks (46). **Range** Himalayas from e. Nepal east to Arunachal Pradesh; n.e. India and Bangladesh.

RUFOUS-THROATED WREN-BABBLER *Spelaeornis caudatus*
Tailed Wren-Babbler

Obtained by B. Hodgson in his later collection (409) but the specimen may have originated in India. First definitely recorded by R.L. Fleming in the upper Mai valley (S7) at 2195m on 10 March 1961 (246). Subsequently regularly reported from the same area. A scarce and very local resident found between 2135m and 2440m. The only other records are from Paniporua (R7) on 18 April 1988 (537), and from Shyaksila Toten, Barun valley (Q6) on 24 November 1985 (588), the most westerly locality of the species. Frequents damp dense broadleaved forests among thick undergrowth and moss-covered boulders. Its breeding habits are poorly known. **Range** Himalayas from Nepal east to Arunachal Pradesh.

[LONG-TAILED WREN-BABBLER   *Spelaeornis longicaudatus*

Mistakenly listed for Nepal, instead of the
previous species, by Fleming (234) and
this error was repeated by Ripley (664).]

RUFOUS-CAPPED BABBLER   *Stachyris ruficeps*
Red-headed Babbler

Subspecies *ruficeps*. Obtained by B.
Hodgson in his later collection (409) but
the specimen may have originated in India. First definitely recorded by H. Stevens who found it breeding commonly in
the upper Mai valley (S7) in April 1912
(737). A fairly common resident in the far
east; possibly subject to altitudinal seasonal movements. Regularly seen subsequently in the Mai valley, and also the
Arun valley watershed, probably the
western limit of its range. Reported as far
west as Lumle (H4) (814), but further
evidence of its presence in the area is
required, as this would be a considerable
westward extension of its range. A record

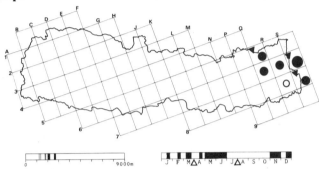

from Sheopuri (733) is also not acceptable. Frequents
bamboo and dense undergrowth in humid, broadleaved forests. **Range** Himalayas from Nepal east to Arunachal
Pradesh; n.e. India and Orissa.

BLACK-CHINNED BABBLER   *Stachyris pyrrhops*

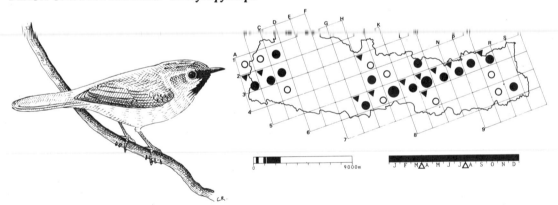

The species was described from Nepal by
E. Blyth from a Hodgson specimen
(115,798). A resident, fairly common east
to the Tamur valley; rare further east. A
sighting in Ilam District (R8) in summer
1989 (658) is the easternmost record for

the species. Found throughout the year from 245m to
2440m, but most frequently above 915m. Birds at higher
altitudes sometimes descend in winter. Proved breeding in
the Kathmandu Valley (336) and at Chitwan (296). Found
on the ground, or in low undergrowth, in secondary and
open forest. **Range** Himalayas from Murree east to Nepal.

GOLDEN BABBLER *Stachyris chrysaea*
Golden-headed Babbler

Subspecies *chrysaea*. The species was described from Nepal by E. Blyth from a Hodgson specimen (115,798). Scarce and very local, probably resident. Recorded between 1800m and 2440m. Several records from south of Annapurna, and also from south of Machapuchare (H5), the western limit of the species's range. The only other records are an undated one from the upper Mai valley (S7) (223) and from Tashigaon, upper Arun valley on 5 September 1986 (590). Breeds from April to July. Inhabits bamboo and dense undergrowth in humid, broadleaved forests. **Range** Himalayas from Nepal east to Arunachal Pradesh; n.e. India and Bangladesh.

GREY-THROATED BABBLER *Stachyris nigriceps*
Black-throated Babbler

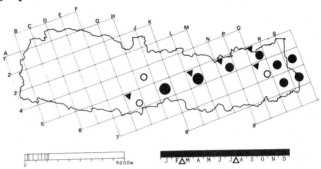

Subspecies *nigriceps*. The species was described from Nepal by E. Blyth from a Hodgson specimen (115). Occasional. A local resident subject to some altitudinal movements. Chiefly summers between 1220m and 2000m, and winters between 245m and at least 1830m. Mainly seen east of the Kathmandu Valley, rare further west. Areas include Phulchowki and the Mai Valley (R8,S7). Collected at Ranibas (G6) at 760m in January 1952 (647), the western limit of the species's range. Confirmed breeding at Chitwan (296), Godavari (190) and as early as 12 March at Bhimpedi (101). Occurs in undergrowth and bamboo thickets in damp broadleaved forests. **Range** Himalayas from Nepal east to Arunachal Pradesh; n.e. India.

TAWNY-BELLIED BABBLER *Dumetia hyperythra*
Rufous-bellied Babbler

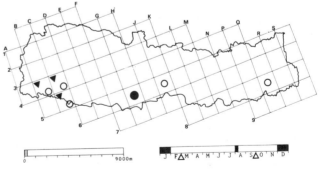

Subspecies *hyperythra*. First recorded at Chisapani (C4) at 305m, and at Tikapur (C5) at 75m in December 1948, by S.D. Ripley (659). He described the species as common in the area but it has not been reported there subsequently. Scarce, probably resident. Found in the tarai between 75m and 305m. Collected at Dhangarhi in December 1952 (647); rare at Chitwan (296). The only other records are of 12 in the eastern tarai (Q8) in January 1975 (293) and one north of Butwal on 1 August 1978 (159). Inhabits thorny scrub and tall grass of the lowlands. **Range** S. Rajasthan east through Simla and the Nepal tarai to Bangladesh, and south through the peninsula to s. India.

STRIPED TIT-BABBLER *Macronous gularis*
Yellow-breasted Tit-Babbler

Subspecies *rubricapilla*. First recorded by
B. Hodgson (388). A resident from the
tarai up to 760m. Common from central
areas eastwards, and occasionally seen
further west. Found at Barmdeo Mandi
(A3) in January 1953 at 290m (647), and
at Sukla Phanta in May 1982 (432), the
western limits of the species's range. Confirmed breeding at Chitwan (296) and
Hetaura (101). Frequents both open and
dense broadleaved forests. **Range** Himalayan foothills from Nepal east to Arunachal Pradesh; e. and n.e. India, and
Bangladesh.

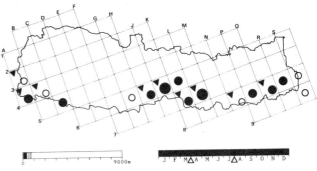

CHESTNUT-CAPPED BABBLER *Timalia pileata*
Red-capped Babbler

Subspecies *bengalensis*. First recorded by
B. Hodgson (388). A locally common resident. Reported at Barmdeo Mandi (A3)
at 290m in January 1953 (647), the westernmost record of the species. Frequent
at Chitwan (J6,K6) where breeding has
been confirmed (296). A few records
from Tamaspur, but only single reports
from elsewhere. Forages amongst tall
grass, reedbeds, and damp scrub jungle in
the lowlands. **Range** Himalayan foothills
from Nepal east to Arunachal Pradesh;
n.e. India and Bangladesh.

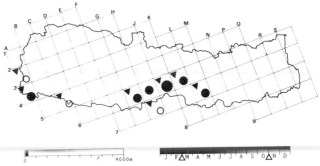

YELLOW-EYED BABBLER *Chrysomma sinense*

Subspecies *sinense*. First recorded by B.
Hodgson (388). A local resident from the
tarai up to 365m. Fairly common at Chitwan (J6,K6) and occasionally seen at
Sukla Phanta and Bardia (C4,C5). Only
single records from elsewhere. Occurs in
bushes, sugarcane fields, reeds and tall
grass. **Range** Throughout most of the
subcontinent, absent from parts of the
arid north-west.

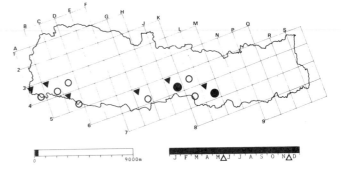

GREAT PARROTBILL *Conostoma aemodium*
(*C. oemodium*)

The species was described from Nepal by
B. Hodgson (383,798) who collected it
from Gosainkund (L5) (336). Uncommon, probably resident. Occurs between
2700m and 3660m, and shows little, if any,
seasonal movement. Observed as high as
3355m in late January (243). Recorded a
few times at Khaptad (C3) (245,657,428),
the most westerly records of the species.
Regularly reported from north-west of
Pokhara, especially above Ghorepani.
Other localities where found recently
include the upper Kali Gandaki valley
(159,546), Surkhe (P6) (595), upper Arun
valley (10,483,589) and Singhalila ridge
(S7) (549). Inhabits bamboo. Its breeding

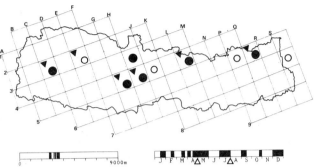

behaviour is poorly known. Probably under-recorded be-
cause it tends to remain out of sight in the undergrowth.
Range Himalayas from Nepal east to Bhutan and probably
Arunachal Pradesh.

BROWN PARROTBILL *Paradoxornis unicolor*
Brown Suthora

Subspecies *unicolor*. The species was
described from Nepal by B. Hodgson
(386). Uncommon and very local, probably resident. Recorded between 2590m
and 3050m from October to May. There
are several reports from the upper Mai
valley, below Machapuchare, at Pipar,
and near Ghorepani, the westernmost
locality for the species. The only other
records are from the Tinjure ridge (Q7) at
2895m in February 1949 (659) and from
Surkhe (P6) in December 1986 (595). Its
breeding behaviour is little known. A
female with enlarged ovaries was collected in the upper Mai valley at 2925m
on 19 May 1970 (9,243). Inhabits bamboo.
Range Himalayas from Nepal east to
Arunachal Pradesh.

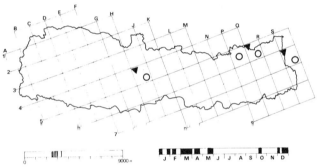

BLACK-BREASTED PARROTBILL *Paradoxornis flavirostris*
Gould's Parrotbill

Subspecies *flavirostris*. The species was
described from Nepal by J. Gould from a
Hodgson specimen (267,798). Although
not included in the catalogues of
Hodgson's collections (276,277, 388), a

specimen was subsequently listed as collected in the Nepal
tarai (716). There are no later records. Frequents dense
thickets of reeds, high grass and bamboo, from the plains up
to 1900m (664). **Range** Himalayas from Nepal east to
Arunachal Pradesh; n.e. India and Bangladesh.

FULVOUS PARROTBILL *Paradoxornis fulvifrons*
Fulvous-fronted Parrotbill, Fulvous-fronted Suthora

Subspecies *fulvifrons*. The species was described from Nepal by B. Hodgson (388,798). Uncommon and locally distributed, probably resident. Not known to move altitudinally with the seasons. Seen above Ghorepani on 2 April 1982 (199,294); the western limit of the species's range. There are a few records from the Modi Khola valley (H5), but the only other recent reports are from Pipar (499), Syabru (L5) (656), between Ghat and Kharke (P6) (769), and the upper Arun valley (10,483,589). Frequents bamboo. Probably breeds in June and July, but its nest has still not been found. **Range** Himalayas from Nepal east to Arunachal Pradesh.

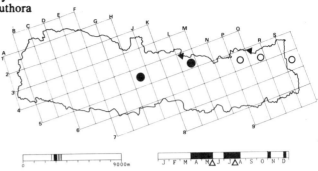

BLACK-THROATED PARROTBILL *Paradoxornis nipalensis*
Nepal Parrotbill, Orange Suthora

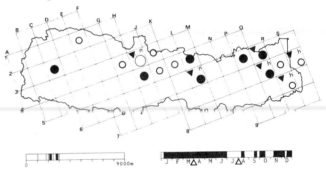

The species was described from Nepal by B. Hodgson (378,798). A resident, mainly found between 2000m and 3000m, but noted a few times as low as 1050m near Birethante (518,594,142). Occasionally reported from the Kali Gandaki valley eastwards. Only two localities from the west: at Chankheli (627) and common at Khaptad (657,428). Two races have been recorded: *P. n. humii* (h) (659) and *P. n. nipalensis* (n) (246,527,647). *P. h. garhwalensis* may occur in the west. Breeding behaviour is poorly known. A pair seen copulating in mid-March above Ghasa (321). Frequents bamboo and thick undergrowth in oak forests. **Range** Himalayas from Garhwal east to Arunachal Pradesh; n.e. India.

[RUFOUS-HEADED PARROTBILL *Paradoxornis ruficeps*
Greater Red-headed Parrotbill, Red-headed Parrotbill

Subspecies *ruficeps*. Obtained by B. Hodgson in his later collection (409) but the specimen may have originated in India. There are no other records. Inhabits bamboo, dense thickets of reeds and mixed grasses, and scrub growth from the plains up to 1400m (664). **Range** Himalayas from Nepal east to Arunachal Pradesh; n.e. India and Bangladesh.]

SPINY BABBLER *Turdoides nipalensis*

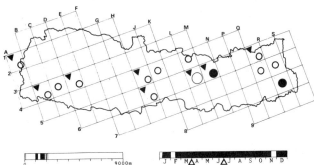

The only endemic species of bird in Nepal. The species was described from Nepal by B. Hodgson (359,798). A resident, subject to altitudinal movements. Found occasionally between 1500m and 2135m in summer, and between 915m and 1830m in winter. Regularly seen from Pokhara north-westwards (H5) and on the hills surrounding the Kathmandu Valley, particularly near Tokha Sanitorium. Noted as far east as Ilam District (R8) (658) and west to Baitidi (A2) (587). It may occur west into India, but there are no definite records. Inhabits dense, secondary scrub, particularly away from cultivation, where the undergrowth is usually thicker. Probably under-recorded as it is difficult to observe, and is more often heard than seen. **Range** Nepal.

COMMON BABBLER *Turdoides caudatus*

Subspecies *caudatus*. First collected by J.A. Propst near Nepalganj airport in 1973 (243) and subsequently found to be fairly common in the area (243,464). Very locally distributed, probably resident. Occurs in the tarai near the Indian border. Seen in 1978 in Tilaurakot woods (G6) (155,157). The only other records are from Sanauli (G7) on 21 March 1959 (230) and near Lumbini (G7) (750). Frequents dry cultivation and scrub. **Range** Throughout the subcontinent, except Orissa, W. Bengal and n.e. India.

STRIATED BABBLER *Turdoides earlei*

Subspecies *earlei*. First recorded by B. Hodgson (388). Resident. Locally common in the eastern tarai and dun (P8,Q8), particularly on Kosi marshes; also at Chitwan where proved breeding (296). Uncommon elsewhere. Occurs in tall grass and reed-beds in the lowlands. **Range** The plains of the Indus, Ganges, and Brahmaputra River systems.

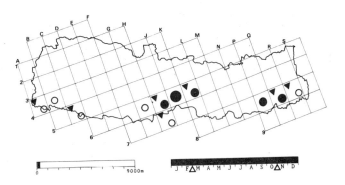

SLENDER-BILLED BABBLER *Turdoides longirostris*

The species was described from Nepal by
F. Moore from a specimen included in B.
Hodgson's later collection (409,798) but
it may have originated in India. First definitely recorded by T.P. and C. Inskipp
near Tiger Tops, Chitwan (J6) on 28 April
1980 (440). Very local, probably resident.
It is fairly common at Chitwan (296), and
was probably overlooked previously.
There are no records from elsewhere.
Frequents tall grass and reeds, especially
near water. Usually remains hidden in
the vegetation. **Range** From Oudh and
the Nepal tarai east to Arunachal
Pradesh; n.e. India and Bangladesh.

LARGE GREY BABBLER *Turdoides malcolmi*

First recorded on the India-Taulihawa
road (F7) at 105m on 10 August 1978
(155,157) by J. Cox Jr. Later seen in the
same area (777), and nearby at Bhairawa
on 27 January 1982 (770). Locally distributed and presumably resident. Occasionally found in the tarai near the Indian
border. The only other records are on 9
and 11 January 1980 at Kalapani, by the
Babai Khola near Ghurai (E6,F6) in
January 1981 (576), from the Babai Khola
crossing near Gularia (C5) on 22 May
1982 (432), and near Lumbini (G7) in
February 1989 (749). Feeds on the ground
or in low vegetation, in open dry scrub
country and cultivation. **Range** India
from Punjab east to Uttar Pradesh, and
south to Tamil Nadu.

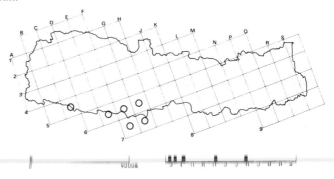

JUNGLE BABBLER *Turdoides striatus*

Subspecies *striatus*. First recorded by B.
Hodgson (388). A fairly common resident
mainly occurring between 75m and
1220m. Found at 1500m in Doti District
(B3) (68). Not known to move altitudinally. Found in gardens, cultivation and
secondary scrub. **Range** Throughout
most of the subcontinent.

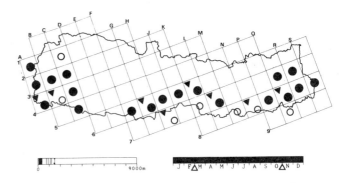

WHITE-THROATED LAUGHING-THRUSH *Garrulax albogularis*

Subspecies *albogularis*. The species was described from Nepal by B. Hodgson (353). A common resident, subject to altitudinal movements. Summers chiefly between 1800m and 2440m ; occasionally up to 3500m. Winters between 1220m and at least 2255m. Proved breeding on the hills surrounding the Kathmandu Valley (708). Inhabits both dense forest and open secondary growth. **Range** Himalayas from Murree east to Arunachal Pradesh; n.e. India.

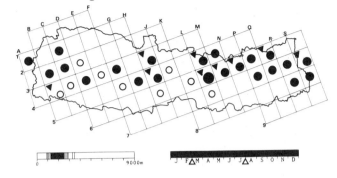

WHITE-CRESTED LAUGHING-THRUSH *Garrulax leucolophus*

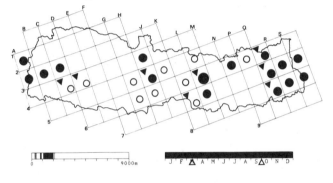

Subspecies *leucolophus*. First recorded by B. Hodgson (388). A common resident occurring mainly between 800m and 1980m. Uncommon down to 305m, and up to 2135m. Possibly shows some sea-sonal movements. Confirmed breeding at Godavari (190). Frequents broadleaved evergreen forests; also secondary growth. **Range** Himalayas from Chamba east to Arunachal Pradesh; n.e. India and Bangladesh.

LESSER NECKLACED LAUGHING-THRUSH *Garrulax monileger*
Necklaced Laughing-thrush

Subspecies *monileger*. The species was described from Nepal by B. Hodgson (353,798). Mainly an uncommon resident from the tarai up to 915m. Found at Marek (G6) at 915m in January 1950 (647), the westernmost record of the species. Localities where regularly reported include Begnas Tal, Pokhara, Chitwan and north of Sunischare. Only two records from the Kathmandu Valley this century (629,652). Occurs in dense broadleaved forests. **Range** Himalayas from Nepal east to Arunachal Pradesh; n.e. India and Bangladesh.

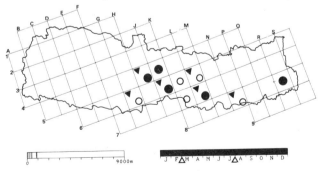

GREATER NECKLACED LAUGHING-THRUSH   *Garrulax pectoralis*
Large Necklaced Laughing-thrush, Black-gorgetted Laughing-thrush

Subspecies *pectoralis*. The species was described from Nepal by B. Hodgson (353). A local resident occurring between 75m and 1220m. A few records at Pokhara (208,519,142), the westernmost locality for the species. Fairly common north of Sunischare, uncommon at Chitwan (J6,K6) and mainly single reports from elsewhere. Uncommon near the western limit of its range. Only one record from the Kathmandu Valley this century (629). Found breeding at Hetaura (101). Inhabits dense broadleaved forests. **Range** Himalayas from Nepal east to Arunachal Pradesh; n.e. India and Bangladesh.

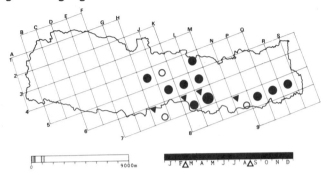

STRIATED LAUGHING-THRUSH   *Garrulax striatus*

First recorded by B. Hodgson (388). A locally common resident between 1200m and 2850m; most frequent between 1500m and 2750m. Possibly shows some altitudinal movements. Regularly seen at Khaptad (C3), north-west of Pokhara (H5), in Langtang, in the Arun and upper Mai valleys, and on Sheopuri and Phulchowki. Two subspecies have been recorded: *G. s. vibex* (v) (101,190,482), and *G. s. sikkimensis* (s) (482,659). Frequents dense broadleaved forests. **Range** Himalayas from Kulu east to Arunachal Pradesh and n.e. India.

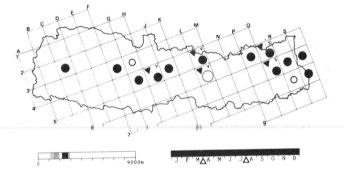

VARIEGATED LAUGHING-THRUSH   *Garrulax variegatus*

Subspecies *variegatus*. First recorded by B. Hodgson (388). A resident, possibly subject to some seasonal movements. Occurs between 2100m and 4100m. Common in west and central areas east to upper Langtang (M5). Scarce in Helambu (L5) and further east. Collected at Ting Sang La between 3400m and 3500m on 3 and 7 May 1962 (190), the most easterly records for the species. Proved breeding in the Dhorpatan valley (F4,G5) (499). Found in coniferous and broadleaved forests with thick undergrowth and rhododendrons above the treeline. **Range** Himalayas from Kohat, Chitral and Gilgit east to Nepal.

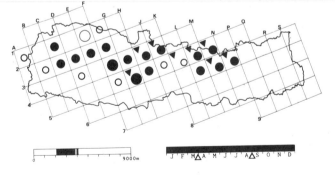

RUFOUS-CHINNED LAUGHING-THRUSH *Garrulax rufogularis*

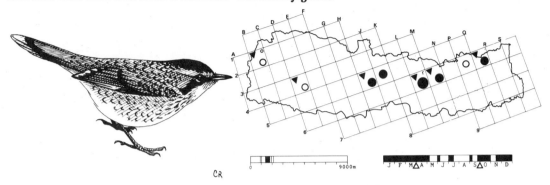

First recorded by B. Hodgson (353). A locally distributed resident, possibly making some altitudinal movements. Occasionally seen between 915m and 1675m; rare up to 2135m. Regularly reported from Pokhara and hills to the north-west (H5); also from hills surrounding the Kathmandu Valley. Mainly single reports from elsewhere. Confirmed to breed at Bhimpedi (101), and on Jahar Powah (L6) (336). Two intergrading races occur: *G. r. occidentalis* (o) (245) and *G. r. rufogularis* (r) (101,647). Found in broadleaved forests. **Range** Himalayas from Murree east to Arunachal Pradesh; n.e. India and Bangladesh.

SPOTTED LAUGHING-THRUSH *Garrulax ocellatus*
White-spotted Laughing-thrush

First recorded by B. Hodgson (388). A locally, fairly common and sedentary resident; chiefly found between 2135m and 3660m. Regularly seen at Khaptad (C3), Ghorepani, Ghasa, Langtang, and in the Arun and upper Mai valleys. Little is known of its breeding behaviour. Two nests with young were found at Thodung (N6), at 2850m and 3100m, on 30 May and 3 June 1962 (190). Also collected in breeding condition at Jiri (N6) and Thodung, between 3000m and 3200m in May and June (190). Two intergrading races occur: *G. o. griseicauda* (g) (246) and *G. o. ocellatus* (o) (246,621,647,737). Frequents open mixed forest with undergrowth, and rhododendron shrubberies. **Range** Himalayas from Garhwal east to Arunachal Pradesh.

GREY-SIDED LAUGHING-THRUSH   *Garrulax caerulatus*

Subspecies *caerulatus*. The species was
described from Nepal by B. Hodgson
(353,798). A locally distributed resident,
occasionally seen between 1370m and
2745m. Regularly reported from Phulchowki, the upper Arun valley (Q6)
(690,590), the eastern hills (Q7,R8) (223),
and on Sheopuri where proved breeding
(243). Noted south of Annapurna (J5) at
about 1500m in June 1977 (762), the most
westerly record of the species. Inhabits
dense, humid, broadleaved forests.
Range Himalayas from Nepal east to
Bhutan and probably Arunachal Pradesh;
n.e. India.

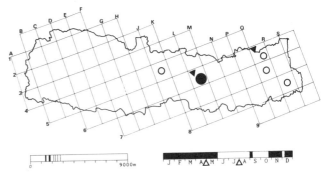

RUFOUS-NECKED LAUGHING-THRUSH   *Garrulax ruficollis*

First recorded by B. Hodgson (277). A
very local resident. Fairly common near
Tiger Tops, Chitwan where breeding has
been proved (296). The only other records are from Tamaspur, the western
limit of its range. Found in thick undergrowth in dense,
broadleaved forest at about 275m. Breeds from March to
August. **Range** Himalayas from Nepal east to Arunachal
Pradesh; n.e. India and Bangladesh.

STREAKED LAUGHING-THRUSH   *Garrulax lineatus*

Subspecies *setafer* or *lineatus* if *setafer* is
considered invalid (647). First recorded
by B. Hodgson (353,798). A resident,
subject to some altitudinal movements.
Common in the Langtang valley (L5) and
further west. Occasionally seen in the
Kathmandu Valley and eastwards. Summers chiefly between 2440m and 3905m,
and winters from 1065m up to at least
2745m. Found breeding on the hills surrounding the Kathmandu Valley in May
and June (190,336,708) and at Junbesi
(P6) (190). Inhabits secondary scrub, forest edges, bushes at roadsides, and edges
of cultivation. **Range** Hills of Pakistan,
and the Himalayas from Chitral east to
Arunachal Pradesh.

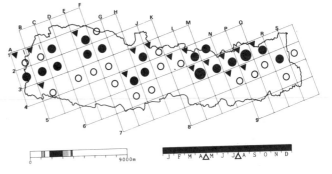

BLUE-WINGED LAUGHING-THRUSH *Garrulax squamatus*

First recorded by B. Hodgson who found it breeding in the central region (353,414). A scarce resident between 1220m and 2440m. One was seen at Karuwa (H5) on 27 April 1984, the most westerly locality for the species (623). Other recent reports are from Phulchowki, the lower Marsyangdi Khola (J5) (126,142), the upper Arun (10,574), Barun (588) and upper Mai valleys (142) and Hans Pokhari (S8) (559). Proved breeding on Sheopuri (247). Skulks in dense undergrowth in humid, broadleaved, evergreen forests. **Range**

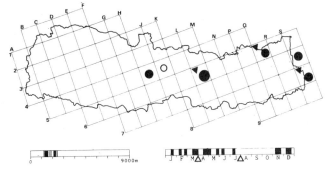

Himalayas from Nepal east to Arunachal Pradesh; n.e. India.

SCALY LAUGHING-THRUSH *Garrulax subunicolor*
Plain-coloured Laughing-thrush

Subspecies *subunicolor*. The species was described from Nepal by E. Blyth (114,798) from a Hodgson specimen. Local, probably resident. Occurs between 1500m and 3450m, and possibly descends from higher levels in winter. Fairly common in the upper Arun and upper Mai valleys. Occasionally reported from the Modi Khola valley and Pipar (H5). Found north of Ghasa (H4) at 2075m on 16 May 1984 (158), the westernmost record for the species. Single reports from elsewhere. Frequents thick undergrowth in damp, broadleaved, evergreen forests. **Range** Himalayas from Nepal east to Arunachal Pradesh.

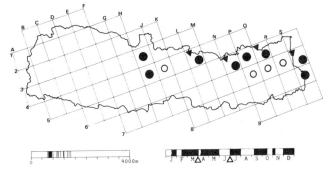

BLACK-FACED LAUGHING-THRUSH *Garrulax affinis*

The species was described from Nepal by E. Blyth from a Hodgson specimen (114,798). A common resident subject to altitudinal movements. Summers mainly between 2750m and 4000m, and locally as high as 4600m. Descends from higher levels in winter, occasionally down to 1830m. Regularly seen west to the upper Kali Gandaki valley. Recorded near Bundi Pass, Jumla District (E3) on 19 May 1985 (160), the western limit of the species's range. Confirmed breeding in Khumbu (190) and Langtang (771). Two races occur: *G. a. affinis* (a), *G. a. bethelae* (b), and intermediates (ab). Occurs in bushes in broadleaved, coniferous and

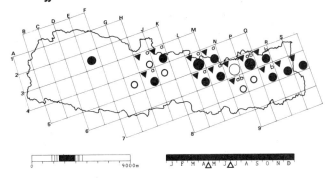

mixed forests, and shrubberies above the treeline. **Range** Himalayas from Nepal east to Arunachal Pradesh.

CHESTNUT-CROWNED LAUGHING-THRUSH *Garrulax erythrocephalus*
Red-headed Laughing-thrush

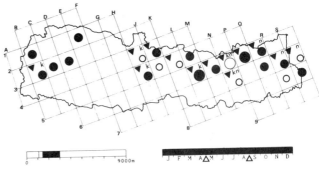

First recorded by B. Hodgson (388). A common resident subject to altitudinal movements. Summers chiefly between 1800m and 3000m. Mainly winters between 1800m and at least 2750m, and occasionally down to 1100m. Proved breeding in the Kathmandu Valley (101,190). Two races occur: *G. e. kali* (k), *G. e. nigrimentum* (n) and intermediates (kn). Frequents dense undergrowth in broadleaved forests. **Range** Himalayas from Changla Gali and Murree east to Arunachal Pradesh; n.e. India.

RED-FACED LIOCICHLA *Liocichla phoenicea*
Crimson-winged Laughing-thrush

Subspecies *phoenicea*. The species was described from Nepal by J. Gould (268), probably from a Hodgson specimen. Recorded by Hodgson (277), but there are no later records. Occurs in dense undergrowth in evergreen forests, and at field edges, from 900m to 1800m (46). **Range** Himalayas from Nepal east to Arunachal Pradesh; n.e. India and Bangladesh.

SILVER-EARED MESIA *Leiothrix argentauris*

Subspecies *argentauris*. The species was described from Nepal by B. Hodgson (378,798). Local, probably a sedentary resident. Recorded mainly between 365m and 1220m, but occasionally down to 205m and up to 1830m. Regularly seen in Ilam District (R8), but few recent reports from elsewhere: at Bardia (162), near Bandipur (H5) (329), south of Annapurna (J5) (762), near Narayanghat (J6) (7), Tribeni (Q8) (446) and Hans Pokhari (S8) (193). Frequents bushes in evergreen broadleaved forests and shady ravines. **Range** Himalayas from Garhwal east to Arunachal Pradesh; n.e. India and Bangladesh.

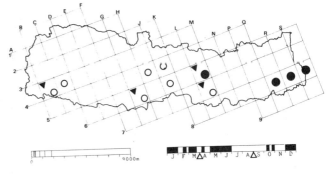

RED-BILLED LEIOTHRIX *Leiothrix lutea*
Pekin Robin

Subspecies *calipyga*. First recorded by B. Hodgson (378). A fairly common resident subject to slight altitudinal movements. Occurs mainly between 1220m and 2440m, but occasionally seen down to 915m and up to 2745m. Found breeding on Sheopuri (414,632). Inhabits thick undergrowth and wooded ravines in moist broadleaved forests. **Range** Himalayas from Pakistan, in the Punjab, east to Arunachal Pradesh; n.e. India.

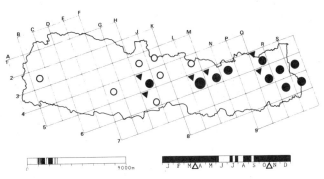

FIRE-TAILED MYZORNIS *Myzornis pyrrhoura*

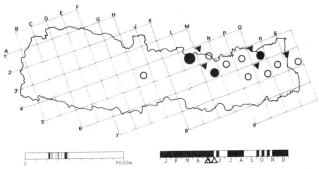

The species was described from Nepal by E. Blyth from a Hodgson specimen (114,798). A locally distributed resident, subject to some altitudinal movements. Found between 2135m and 3950m, and up to at least 2745m in winter (659). Occurs mainly from Langtang (L5) eastwards. Noted north-west of Pokhara (H5) at about 2000m in early August 1977 (762), the westernmost record for the species. Regularly seen near Gapte cave (L5), and in the upper Arun and upper Mai valleys. Its breeding behaviour is poorly known. The nest of the species was first described from the Gandak-Kosi watershed (L5) at 3660m, where a pair was feeding young in late May 1961 (639). Three nests under construction were found at Gapte (L5) at 3505m on 21 May 1982 (294,682). Inhabits mossy forests of juniper and rhododendron; also bamboo thickets. **Range** Himalayas from Nepal east to Arunachal Pradesh.

CUTIA *Cutia nipalensis*
Nepal Cutia

Subspecies *nipalensis*. The species was described from Nepal by B. Hodgson (348). Very locally distributed, probably resident. Favours an altitudinal zone of 2100m to 2300m. Possibly shows some altitudinal movements, but noted up to at least 2285m in February (647). Found as low as 1095m at Birethante in December 1984 (142). Regularly recorded on Phulchowki; occasionally seen in the upper Mai and Modi Khola valleys, but only two records from elsewhere. The nest has not been described. Feeds in the canopy of dense oak and on moss-covered trunks in humid, broadleaved evergreen forests. **Range** Himalayas from Kumaon east to Arunachal Pradesh; n.e. India.

CUTIA, cont'd ...

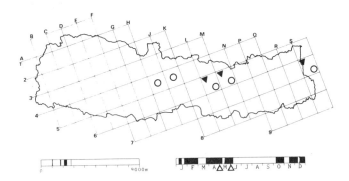

BLACK-HEADED SHRIKE-BABBLER *Pteruthius rufiventer*
Rufous-bellied Shrike-Babbler

First definitely recorded from Nepal by R.L. Fleming Sr. at Jiri (N6) at 2500m on 19 November 1960 (246). Specimens in B. Hodgson's later collection have been described as Nepalese (409), but may have originated in India (276). A scarce and local resident, mainly reported between 2135m and 2500m. A few reports from south of Annapurna, and also south of Machapuchare where found up to 3230m on 23 April 1979 (244). Noted twice near Ghandrung (H5) (746,436), the most westerly locality for the species. The only other records are from the upper Arun valley in 1973 (10,441), Barun valley (Q6) in 1984 (588), upper Mai valley (S7) in 1983 (148) and 1989 (307), and

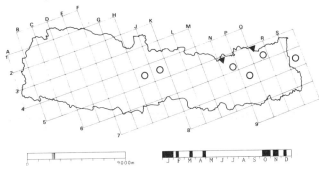

west of Banam (P7) in 1986 (546). Its seasonal movements and breeding habits are unknown. Frequents dense mossy, humid, broadleaved evergreen forests. It moves sluggishly and is easily overlooked. **Range** Himalayas from Nepal east to Arunachal Pradesh; n.e. India.

WHITE-BROWED SHRIKE-BABBLER *Pteruthius flaviscapis*
Red-winged Shrike-Babbler

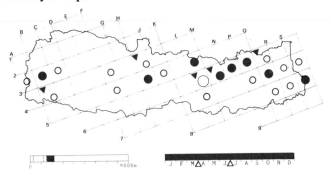

WHITE-BROWED SHRIKE-BABBLER, cont'd ...

Subspecies *validirostris*. First recorded by B. Hodgson (388). A fairly common resident subject to some altitudinal movements. Summers chiefly between 1800m and 2200m. Winters mainly between 1500m and 2135m, but wanders down to 1200m, and one record at 305m at Badalmachi (B4) in December 1952 (647). Inhabits broadleaved forests, favouring oaks. **Range** Himalayas from Murree east to Arunachal Pradesh; n.e. India.

GREEN SHRIKE-BABBLER   *Pteruthius xanthochloris*

The species was described from Nepal by J.E. and G.R. Gray from a Hodgson specimen (277,798). A resident, occasionally found between 2135m and at least as high as 3050m throughout the year. May descend from the higher altitudes in winter. Regularly reported north-west of Pokhara (H4,H5), in Langtang, and on the hills surrounding the Kathmandu Valley. Two races occur: *P. x. occidentalis* (o) (245), and *P. x. xanthochloris* (x) (647). Frequents broadleaved and coniferous forests. **Range** Himalayas from Murree east to Arunachal Pradesh; n.e. India.

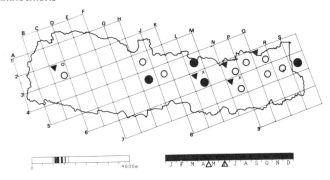

BLACK-EARED SHRIKE-BABBLER   *Pteruthius melanotis*
Chestnut-eared Shrike-Babbler

Subspecies *melanotis*. The species was described from Nepal by B. Hodgson (395). A resident, subject to altitudinal movements. Occasional and locally distributed. Summers between 1800m and 2440m, but mainly above 2135m. Winters mainly between 1500m and 2000m, but recorded at 305m on 12 January 1981 south of Ilam (300). Regularly seen north-west of Pokhara (H5), on the hills surrounding the Kathmandu Valley, and in the upper Arun, Barun and upper Mai valleys (R7,S7). Reported a few times from Ghorepani, the western limit of the species's range. Breeding behaviour is

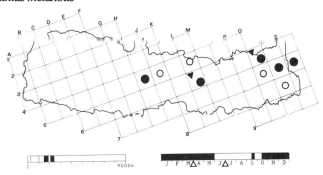

little known. Found in humid, broadleaved evergreen forests. **Range** Himalayas from Nepal east to Arunachal Pradesh; n.e. India and Bangladesh.

WHITE-HOODED BABBLER   *Gampsorhynchus rufulus*
White-headed Shrike-Babbler

Subspecies *rufulus*. Scarce. Obtained by B. Hodgson in his later collection (409) but the specimen may have originated in India. First definitely recorded by R.L. Fleming who saw one north of Bhadrapur (S8) at 600m in February 1965 (247). The only other record received is of five seen at Soyang, Ilam District (R8) at about 1400m on 17 January 1989 (694). Occurs in secondary jungle, and in undergrowth of evergreen forest (664). **Range** Himalayas from Nepal east to Arunachal Pradesh; n.e. India and Bangladesh.

RUSTY-FRONTED BARWING *Actinodura egertoni*
Spectacled Barwing

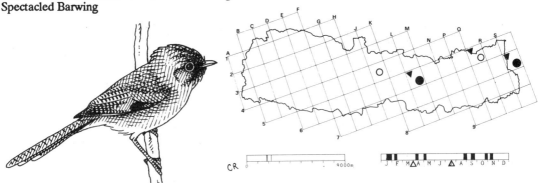

Subspecies *egertoni*. The species was described by J. Gould from a specimen presented by P.G. Egerton from Nepal (267,798). Scarce and local, presumably resident. Reported between 1785m and 2255m. Found south of the Lamjung Himal (J5) in October 1976 (474) and in 1977 (762), the most westerly records for the species. Uncommon in the upper Mai valley. The only other reports are from Chitlang in April 1947 (101), Walung forest (Q6) in January 1959 (482), Barun valley (Q6) in 1984 and upper Arun valley in 1986 (590). Frequents dense thickets in humid, broadleaved evergreen forest. **Range** Himalayas from Nepal east to Arunachal Pradesh; n.e. India.

HOARY BARWING *Actinodura nipalensis*

The species was described from Nepal by B. Hodgson (353,798). A fairly common resident subject to some altitudinal movements. Most frequently seen between 1980m and 3000m, but occasionally up to 3500m and down to 1500m. Noted up to at least 2750m in winter (647). Fairly common at Khaptad (C3) (657,428,68), the western limit of the species's range. Little is known of its breeding behaviour. Collected in breeding condition between 15 May and 3 June 1962 at Bigu, Jiri, and Thodung (N6), between 2900m and 3200m (190). Seen nest-building on Sheopuri on 16 April 1988 (438) and at Kutumsang (L5) at about 2470m on 18 May 1988 (771). Forages in mossy oak and rhododendron forests. **Range** Himalayas from Nepal east to Bhutan.

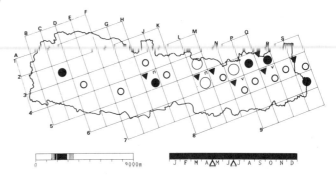

BLUE-WINGED MINLA *Minla cyanouroptera*

Subspecies *cyanouroptera*. The species was described from Nepal by B. Hodgson (378,798). A fairly common resident, subject to some altitudinal movements. Winters mainly between 1000m and 1830m, but occasionally up to 2285m. Summers up to 2440m, and rarely to 2750m. Proved breeding at Hans Pokhari (S8) (193). Found in bushes and tangled undergrowth in dense forest. **Range** Himalayas from Naini Tal east to Arunachal Pradesh; n.e. India and Bangladesh.

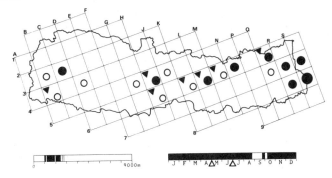

CHESTNUT-TAILED MINLA *Minla strigula*
Bar-throated Minla, Bar-throated Siva

The species was described from Nepal by B. Hodgson (378,798). A common resident subject to altitudinal movements. Summers chiefly between 2440m and 3750m. Winters mainly between 1400m and 2745m, but noted at 1035m at Birethante (H5) in February 1982 (770). Proved breeding on Sheopuri and Phulchowki (243). Two subspecies occur: *M. s. simlaensis* (si) (247), and *M. s. strigula* (s). Chiefly inhabits broadleaved forests, especially of oak. **Range** Himalayas from Kangra east to Arunachal Pradesh; n.e. India.

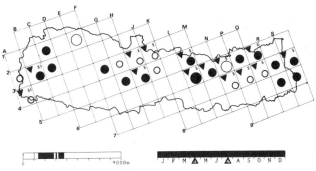

RED-TAILED MINLA *Minla ignotincta*

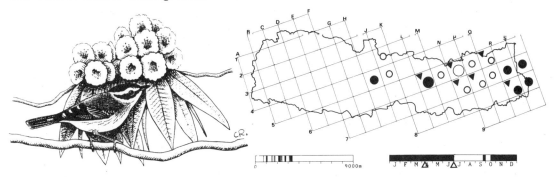

Subspecies *ignotincta*. The species was described from Nepal by B. Hodgson (378,798). An altitudinal migrant; probably resident. Common in the far east, and occasionally seen elsewhere. Reported from Ghorepani (206,439), the westernmost locality for the species. Summers mainly between 1830m and 3400m, and winters between 760m and at least 2285m. Little is known of its breeding behaviour. Collected in breeding condition at Thodung and Jiri (N6), between 3100m and 3400m, on 24 and 30 May 1962 (190). Frequents damp, dense broadleaved, evergreen forests, especially of oak. **Range** Himalayas from Nepal east to Arunachal Pradesh; n.e. India and Bangladesh.

GOLDEN-BREASTED FULVETTA *Alcippe chrysotis*
Golden-breasted Tit-Babbler

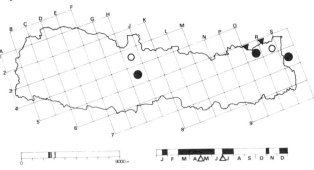

Subspecies *chrysotis*. The species was described from Nepal by E. Blyth from a Hodgson specimen (116). Hodgson found it breeding in the central region in May and June (414). Its breeding habits have not been recorded since. Very local, probably resident. Found between 2435m and 3050m. Common in the upper Modi Khola valley (H5), occasionally seen in the upper Mai valley and uncommon south of Annapurna. Only two other records received: collected in April 1984 at Yanjua Dhoja (R6) (589) and at Pahakhola (Q6) in June 1988 (537). Noted north of Ghasa on 3 March 1986 (321), the most westerly record for the species. Frequents bamboo. **Range** Himalayas from Nepal east to Arunachal Pradesh; n.e. India.

[YELLOW-THROATED FULVETTA *Alcippe cinerea*
Dusky-green Tit-Babbler

Obtained by B.Hodgson in his later collection (409) but the specimen may have originated in India. Reported at Godavari in April 1948 (629), but confirmation of its occurrence there is desirable. No later records. Found in deep evergreen forest (47). **Range** Himalayas from Sikkim east to Arunachal Pradesh; n.e. India and Bangladesh.]

RUFOUS-WINGED FULVETTA *Alcippe castaneceps*
Chestnut-headed Tit-Babbler

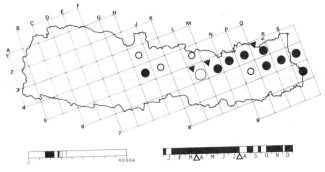

Subspecies *castaneceps*. The species was described from Nepal by B. Hodgson (378,798). A common resident subject to some altitudinal movements. Summers mainly between 1825m and 2745m but noted at the particularly high altitude of 3505m at Gapte cave in May 1982 (682). Winters from 1525m up to at least 2745m. A few records from the upper Kali Gandaki valley, the western limit of the range of the species. Occurs in thick undergrowth in moist broadleaved forests. **Range** Himalayas from Nepal east to Arunachal Pradesh; n.e. India and Bangladesh.

WHITE-BROWED FULVETTA *Alcippe vinipectus*
White-browed Tit-Babbler

The species was described from Nepal by B. Hodgson (378,798). A common resident subject to some altitudinal movements. Summers usually between 2400m and 4200m. Winters between 2135m and 3000m, but rarely down to 1525m. Proved breeding at Khaptad (C3) (68), in Langtang (771), Khumbu (190), and on Nangi Danda (L6) (636). Two races occur: *A. v. vinipectus* (v) (62), and *A. v. chumbiensis* (c) (647). Inhabits bushes in broadleaved and coniferous forests, and shrubberies of birch, juniper and rhododendron. **Range** Himalayas from Dharmsala east to Bhutan, and possibly Arunachal Pradesh; n.e. India.

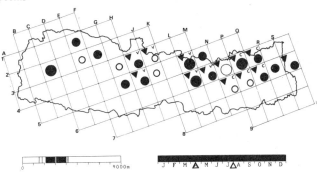

NEPAL FULVETTA *Alcippe nipalensis*
Nepal Babbler, Nepal Quaker Babbler

Subspecies *nipalensis*. The species was described from Nepal by B. Hodgson (378,798). A resident subject to altitudinal movements. Winters chiefly between 245m and 1830m, and summers up to 2285m. Common on the hills surrounding the Kathmandu Valley, but uncommon elsewhere. Reported from north west of Pokhara (H5), Chitwan (J6,K6) and Mechi Zone (R7,R8,S7,S8). Single records from elsewhere. Found breeding on Phulchowki (101,629,659), and on Sheopuri (243). Noted near Narsinghkanda (C4) on 15 November 1985 (162), the westernmost record of the

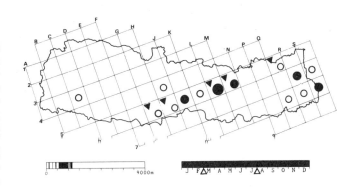

species. Frequents dense undergrowth in damp forests. **Range** Himalayas from Nepal east to Arunachal Pradesh; n.e. India and Bangladesh.

RUFOUS-BACKED SIBIA *Heterophasia annectans*
Chestnut-backed Sibia

Subspecies *annectans*. Scarce, presumably resident. First seen near Mai Pokhari (R7) at 2135m on 17 and 18 September 1978 by S. LeClerq, R. DeWitt and R.L. Fleming Jr. (178,243). The only other records are from the same area near Phidim (R7) at 1450m on 10 November 1978 (155,301) and at Hanga Tham at 2650m on 27 March 1989 (193). Breeds in May and June. Occurs in dense, humid, broadleaved evergreen forest (664). **Range** Himalayas from Nepal east to Arunachal Pradesh; n.e. India.

BLACK-CAPPED SIBIA   *Heterophasia capistrata*

First recorded by B. Hodgson (381). A
common resident subject to altitudinal
movements. Chiefly summers between
1980m and 3000m, and winters between
1050m and 2750m. Noted at 850m in
December in Mechi Zone (658) and at
3400m at Ting Sang La in May (190).
Proved breeding at Godavari (190).
Three races occur: *H. c. capistrata* (c)
(247), *H. c. nigriceps* (n) (101,482,
619,647,798) and *H. c. bayleyi* (b) (647).
Forages in broadleaved forests, especially
of oaks. **Range** Himalayas from Murree
east to Arunachal Pradesh.

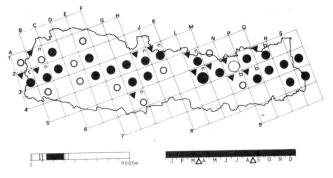

LONG-TAILED SIBIA   *Heterophasia picaoides*

Subspecies *picaoides*. The species was
described from Nepal by B. Hodgson
(381,798). He found it in the tarai and
lower hills (336). Described as tolerably
common about Nimboatar (L7) in winter
1877 (708). There are no other confirmed
records. Frequents forest clearings, and
open scrub with large trees (47). **Range**
Himalayas from Nepal east to Arunachal
Pradesh; n.e. India.

WHITE-NAPED YUHINA   *Yuhina bakeri*
Chestnut-headed Yuhina

Obtained by B. Hodgson in his later collection (409) but the specimen may have
originated in India. First definitely recorded by R.L. Fleming who collected
one from Hans Pokhari Danda (S8) at
1525m on 18 February 1969 (9) and de-
scribed the species as fairly common (243). The only other
record is of one seen at the same locality on 8 April 1989
(193). Breeds from April to July. Frequents humid evergreen forest. **Range** Himalayas from Nepal east to Arunachal Pradesh; n.e. India and Bangladesh.

Two records of Rufous-vented Yuhina (109,647,659) have been wrongly listed as this species (47,101,664).

WHISKERED YUHINA   *Yuhina flavicollis*
Yellow-naped Yuhina

The species was described from Nepal by
B. Hodgson (356,798). A common resident subject to some altitudinal movements. Summers chiefly between 1830m
and 2745m, and winters between 800m
and 2745m. Proved breeding in the cen-
tral region (414) and on Sheopuri (243). Two races occur: *Y.
f. flavicollis* (f) (62,101,659), and *Y. f. albicollis* (a)
(247,647,659). Found in bushes and lower branches of
mainly broadleaved forests. **Range** Himalayas from Himachal Pradesh east to Arunachal Pradesh; n.e. India and
Bangladesh.

WHISKERED YUHINA, cont'd ...

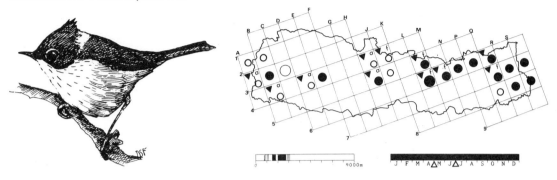

STRIPE-THROATED YUHINA   *Yuhina gularis*

Subspecies *gularis*. The species was described from Nepal by B. Hodgson (356,798). A common resident subject to altitudinal movements. Summers mainly between 2435m and 3700m; winters between 1700m and 3050m, rarely down to 1400m. Breeding behaviour is little known. Collected in breeding condition between 14 and 27 May 1962 at Bigu and Harkhate Gairi (N6) between 3200m and 3300m (141). Inhabits forests of pure broadleaves and mixed with conifers. **Range** Himalayas from Garhwal east to Arunachal Pradesh and n.e. India.

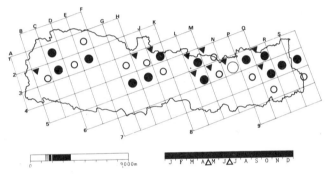

RUFOUS-VENTED YUHINA   *Yuhina occipitalis*

Subspecies *occipitalis*. The species was described from Nepal by B. Hodgson (356,798). A common resident subject to altitudinal movements. Summers between 2400m and 3600m, most frequently between 3050m and 3400m; winters from 1830m to at least 2745m. Found breeding on Nangi Danda (L6) (636), and in the Gandak-Kosi watershed (L5) (633). Occasionally seen in the upper Kali Gandaki valley, the western limit of the species's range. Records from the west near Rara (627) and Jumla (620), which are given in the first edition of this book (435), are now considered unacceptable. Frequents broadleaved forests. **Range** Himalayas from Nepal east to Arunachal Pradesh.

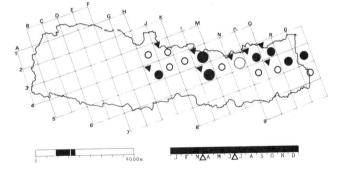

BLACK-CHINNED YUHINA *Yuhina nigrimenta*

Subspecies *nigrimenta*. The species was described from Nepal by B. Hodgson (392,798). Scarce, probably resident. Reported between 610m and 1500m. Altitudinal movements are poorly understood. Recently recorded from Khaptad (C3) (428), Surkhet (D4) (297), south of Annapurna (H5,J5) (762,142), the Arun valley (Q6,Q7) (10,596,769), Sangure ridge (Q8) (293), and below Ilam (59). Frequents the lower storey of broadleaved evergreen forests. **Range** Himalayas from Garhwal east to Arunachal Pradesh; n.e. India and Bangladesh.

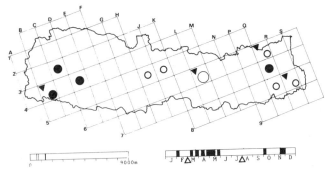

WHITE-BELLIED YUHINA *Yuhina zantholeuca*
(*Y. xantholeuca*)

Subspecies *zantholeuca*. The species was described from Nepal by B. Hodgson (115,798). A local resident, subject to large and poorly understood altitudinal movements. Recorded between 180m and 2285m, mainly below 1650m. Its breeding zone is uncertain but most frequently reported between 1300m and 1600m. Common in the Kathmandu Valley, and fairly common at Chitwan (J6,K6) where it is possibly resident (296). Occasionally seen west to Pokhara District (H5). Collected south of Dandeldhura (B4) on 24 April 1965 (247), the

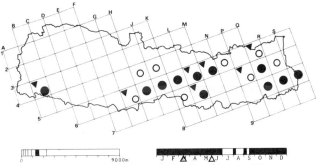

most westerly record of the species. Found in clearings and forest edges. **Range** Himalayas fom Nepal east to Bhutan; n.e. India and Bangladesh.

BLACK-BROWED TIT *Aegithalos iouschistos*
Rufous-fronted Tit

Subspecies *iouschistos*. The species was described from Nepal by E. Blyth from a Hodgson specimen (116,798). A resident, occasionally found between 2590m and 3700m throughout the year. Three noted on Phulchowki at about 2400m on 31 October 1989, the first for the Kathmandu Valley (256). Collected above Dana (H4) at 2590m on 21 December 1963 (247) and seen between Kalopani and Tukche (H4) on 9 December 1984 (58), the most westerly records of the species. The nest was first described in Ilam District at 2745m in May (243). Also confirmed breeding at Ghora Tabela (L5) (812) in May, at Thodung (N6)

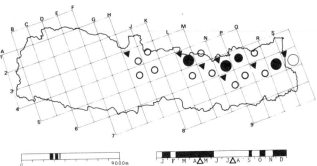

(190), near Jaubari (R7) (12) and in the upper Mai valley (R7) (704). Frequents the lower storey of broadleaved and hemlock forests. **Range** Himalayas from Nepal east to Arunachal Pradesh.

WHITE-THROATED TIT *Aegithalos niveogularis*

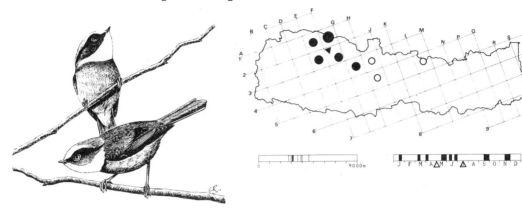

First definitely recorded near Jumla in mid-May 1952 by O. Polunin (620). Probably resident. Found between 2800m and 3550m. Its movements in Nepal are poorly understood. Occasionally seen in the north-west, including Rara (E2), Jumla (E3) and the Dolpo (F3). Common in the Langu valley (F2) where proved breeding (330). There are three reports from Ghorepani: on 12 March 1981 (559), and on 19 and 23 November 1981 (146); also one from Kalopani (H4) at 2560m on 19 March 1984 (787). Only one record from farther east: a pair at Gosainkund on 3 April 1979 at about 2750m (474), a considerable range extension for the species. Inhabits bushes in mixed birch and coniferous forests, and shrubberies near the treeline. **Range** Himalayas from the Kagan valley east to Nepal.

BLACK-THROATED TIT *Aegithalos concinnus*
Red-headed Tit

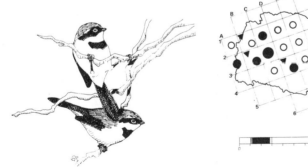

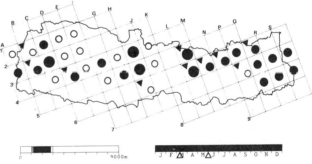

Subspecies *iredalei*. First recorded by B. Hodgson (388). An abundant resident. Occurs mainly between 1400m and 2700m throughout the year, but occasionally found down to 1065m, and up to 3000m. Proved breeding at Khaptad (C3) (428), north-west of Pokhara (H4,H5) (811), on Phulchowki (440), and in Langtang (440). Inhabits broadleaved or mixed broadleaved/coniferous forests. **Range** N. Baluchistan; Himalayas from N.W.F.P. east to Arunachal Pradesh; n.e. India.

YELLOW-BROWED TIT *Sylviparus modestus*

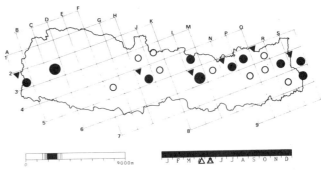

Subspecies *modestus*. The species was described from the Himalayas by E. Burton (139), the type locality later defined as Nepal by Baker (64). A resident subject to some altitudinal movements. Generally fairly common, from the Kali Gandaki valley eastwards, and common in some areas. Usually summers between 2135m and 2800m, and occasionally up to 3250m; winters between 1500m and 2800m. Noted at 4265m in the Gandak-Kosi watershed (732), but confirmation of its occurrence at such high altitude is desirable. Little is known of its breeding habits. The nest was first described from Phulchowki at 2380m on 4 May 1968, when the parents were feeding young (215). Another nest with young was found on Phulchowki on 2 May at 2000m (510,651). A nest with eggs was discovered on 25 April at 2410m during a trek to Ganesh Himal (215). Noted feeding flying young at Khaptad (C3) on 19 May (428) and carrying food on Phulchowki in mid-May (556). Occurs in broadleaved forests and favours oaks. **Range** Himalayas from Kashmir east to Arunachal Pradesh; n.e. India.

GREY-CRESTED TIT *Parus dichrous*
Brown Crested Tit

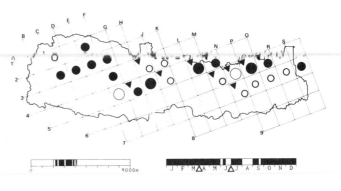

Subspecies *dichrous*. The species was described from Nepal by E. Blyth from a Hodgson specimen (116,798). A resident subject to some altitudinal movements. Chiefly summers between 2745m and 4200m, and winters from 2000m up to
3655m, but seen at 4270m in February in Khumbu (558). Proved breeding at Pipar (H5) (800), in the Gandak-Kosi watershed (L5) (633), and at Khumjung (P6) (190). Frequents broadleaved, coniferous and mixed forests. **Range** Himalayas from Kashmir east to Arunachal Pradesh.

RUFOUS-NAPED TIT *Parus rufonuchalis*
Simla Black Tit   (*P. rubidiventris rufonuchalis*)
Rufous-naped Black Tit

First definitely recorded by F.M. Bailey at Tullo Silki (D2) on 6 June 1936 (62). Fairly common, probably resident; subject to some altitudinal movements. Summers between 2700m and 4000m. Its winter altitudinal range in Nepal is poorly known. Occasionally found in the upper Kali Gandaki valley, the eastern limit of the species's range. Proved breeding at Tukche (528). Frequents coniferous and oak/rhododendron forests. **Range** N. Baluchistan; Himalayas from N.W.F.P. east to Nepal.

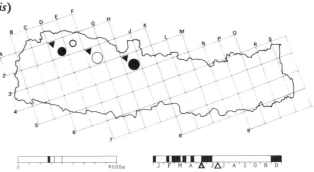

RUFOUS-VENTED TIT *Parus rubidiventris*
Rufous-breasted Black Tit, Rufous-bellied Crested Tit
Sikkim Black Tit, Rufous-vented Black Tit

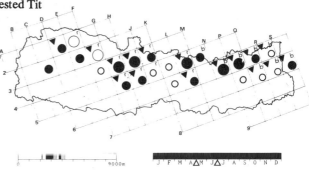

The species was described from Nepal by E. Blyth (121). A common resident, subject to some altitudinal movements. Summers chiefly between 3050m and 4250m. May descend in winter, occasionally down to 2135m, but noted as high as 4270m in February in Khumbu (558). Breeding confirmed at Dhorpatan (G5) (528), above Tukche (528), in the Gandak-Kosi watershed (L5) (633), at Thodung (N6) (528) and at Khumjung (P6)

(190). Two races occur: *P. r. rubidiventris* (r), and *P. r. beavani* (b). It has been suggested that the Bhote Kosi (M6) marks the division between the races (528), but *beavani* has been found just west of there in upper Langtang (M5) (195,243,509). A specimen of nominate *rubidiventris* from near Jiri (N6) (525) was possibly a stray, and confirmation of its occurrence there regularly is needed. Frequents coniferous forests, and mixed conifer and birch forests; also rhododendron shrubberies. **Range** Himalayas from Tehri Garhwal east to Bhutan and probably to Arunachal Pradesh; n.e. India.

SPOT-WINGED TIT *Parus melanolophus*
Crested Black Tit, Spot-winged Black Tit

First definitely recorded by O. Polunin
above Maina (E4) on 6 April 1952 (620).
A common resident, probably subject to
altitudinal movements. Summers between 2200m and 3700m; wintering altitudes are poorly known. Found east to the
Namlang and Langu valleys (F2)
(447,330) and at Ringmo (F3) where
proved breeding (528). Hybridises with
Coal Tit further east (x). Birds showing
slight introgression with the latter species
have been found breeding and collected
near Tarakot (F4), at Thankur (G4) and
Dhorpatan (G5) (528). Hybrids have also
been collected near Dhorpatan (G5)
(528). Sightings of the species as well as
hybrids have been reported further east

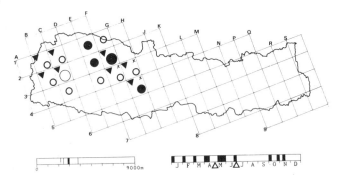

from Ghorepani (305,476), and in the upper Kali Gandaki
valley (207,559, 546,480), but confirmation of its occurrence
in these areas is needed. Favours conifers, but also frequents mixed forest. **Range** Himalayas from N.W.F.P. east
to Nepal.

COAL TIT *Parus ater*

Subspecies *aemodius*. First recorded by
B. Hodgson (388,798). A fairly common
resident subject to some altitudinal movements. Summers chiefly between 2800m
and 4000m, occasionally down to 2440m
and up to 4250m. Winters mainly between
2500m and at least 3050m, but noted at
4370m in February in Khumbu (P6) (558)
and rarely down to 1830m. Found breeding in the Gandak-Kosi watershed (L5)
(633) and at Thodung (N6) (528). Hybrids
(x) with Spot-winged Black Tit have been
collected near Dhorpatan (G5) (528), and
specimens showing introgression with

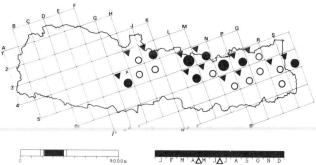

that species have been collected near Dhaulagiri (H4)
(528). Frequents coniferous forests and dwarf junipers
above the treeline. **Range** Himalayas from Nepal east to
Bhutan.

GREAT TIT *Parus major*
Grey Tit

Subspecies *nipalensis*. First recorded by
B. Hodgson (378,798). A common resident subject to some altitudinal or local
movements. Frequent up to 1525m, occasionally seen up to 1800m, and rare at
higher elevations. Noted as high as 3050m
at Rara on 23 June 1979 (626). Proved
breeding in Doti District (B3,C3) (438)
and at Chitwan (296). Inhabits open forest, groves, cultivation and gardens; favours broadleaved trees. **Range** N. Baluchistan; Himalayan foothills from
N.W.F.P. east to Arunachal Pradesh; n.e.
India and Bangladesh; peninsular India.

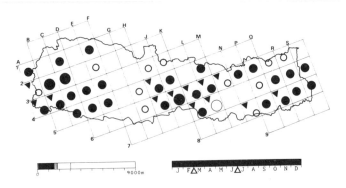

GREEN-BACKED TIT *Parus monticolus*

Subspecies *monticolus*. First recorded by
B. Hodgson (388). A common resident
subject to altitudinal movements. Frequent between 1370m and 3100m, and occasionally seen up to 3660m. Replaces
Great Tit altitudinally, chiefly breeding
above 1525m, and wintering below
2745m. Proved breeding at Khaptad (C3)
(428), near Dhankhuta (Q7) (446), and in
the Trisuli valley (L5) (517). Occurs in
both dense and light forests; prefers
moister habitat than that occupied by
Great Tit. **Range** Himalayas from
N.W.F.P. east to Arunachal Pradesh; n.e.
India.

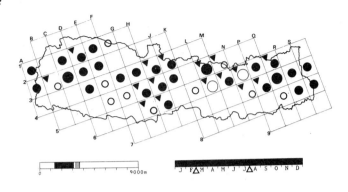

BLACK-LORED TIT *Parus xanthogenys*
Yellow-cheeked Tit

Subspecies *xanthogenys*. First recorded
by B.Hodgson (388). A common resident
subject to altitudinal movements. Breeds
mainly between 1500m and 2300m, and
winters between 915m and 2135m. Noted
at the exceptional altitudes of 75m near
Simra in January 1981 (309), at 2925m in
the Dhorpatan valley (G5) in June 1981
(499) and at 2700m at Rara in July 1989
(68). Common in the Arun valley uncommon further east. Seen with Yellow-
cheeked Tits at Chisapani (R8) on 14
January 1989 (307). Breeding confirmed
at Khaptad (C3) (428), on the hills surrounding the Kathmandu, Chitlang and
Markhu valleys (104,517), and at Pati

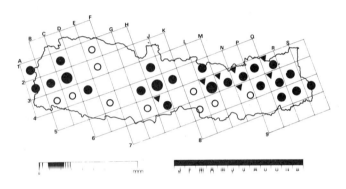

Bhanjyang (L6) (771). Found in open forests, groves, and
edges of dense forest. **Range** Himalayas from Murree east
to Darjeeling; hills of the Indian peninsula.

YELLOW-CHEEKED TIT *Parus spilonotus*
Black-spotted Yellow Tit

Subspecies *spilonotus*. Obtained by B.
Hodgson in his later collection (409) but
the specimen may have originated in India. First definitely recorded by H. Stevens in the upper Mai valley at about
2400m on 28 March 1912 (737). Uncommon and very local, probably resident.
Chiefly recorded between 1980m and

2440m in the upper Mai valley near Hanga Tham between
January and April. Two seen with Black-lored Tits at the
exceptionally low altitude of 450m at Chisapani (R8) on 14
January 1989 (307). Breeds from the end of March to the
end of June. Altitudinal movements in Nepal are not
known. Frequents open oak forests. **Range** Himalayas from
Nepal east to Arunachal Pradesh; n.e. India.

SULTAN TIT *Melanochlora sultanea*

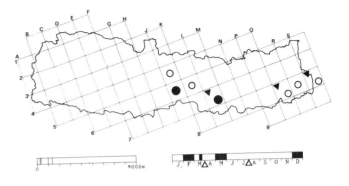

Subspecies *sultanea*. The species was described from Nepal by B. Hodgson who obtained specimens from the lower hills (336,378, 798). Scarce, probably resident. Described as fairly common in December 1877 between Hetaura and Nimboatar (L7) (708). The only later report from the area is one collected at Hetaura on 24 May 1947 (104). Found at Rupa Tal (J5) in 1977 (587), the most westerly record for the species. Also reported from Chatra (Q8) in February 1949 (659), near Shantinagar (S8) on 20 February 1969 (9), north of Sunischare on 17 March 1982 (794) and a few recent reports from the Churia hills at Chitwan (J6,K6) (481,11,67). Frequents broadleaved forests. **Range** Himalayan foothills from Nepal east to Arunachal Pradesh; n.e. India and Bangladesh.

VELVET-FRONTED NUTHATCH *Sitta frontalis*

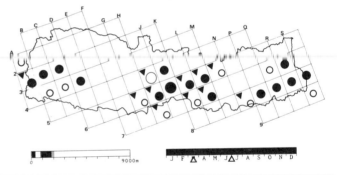

Subspecies *frontalis*. First recorded by B. Hodgson (351). Mainly a fairly common resident found between 75m and 2015m, most frequent up to 1000m. No altitudinal movements have been reported. Common at Chitwan where proved breeding (296). Inhabits broadleaved forests, especially those of sal. **Range** Himalayas from Dehra Dun east to Arunachal Pradesh; n.e. India and Bangladesh; locally throughout the Indian peninsula.

WHITE-CHEEKED NUTHATCH *Sitta leucopsis*

Subspecies *leucopsis*. First definitely recorded by the Lulo Khola (F3) at 4575m on 30 June 1952 by O. Polunin (620). Probably resident. Found between 2745m and 4575m. Altitudinal movements in Nepal are unknown. Described as fairly common in the north-west (243) and as common in the Langu valley (F2) (330). Other localities include Rara Lake (159,68) and the Dolpo. Singles near Tarakot (F4) on 3 June 1973 (589) and on 20 April 1974 (153) are the most easterly records of the species. Inhabits coniferous forests. **Range** Himalayas from N.W.F.P. east to Nepal.

WHITE-CHEEKED NUTHATCH, cont'd ...

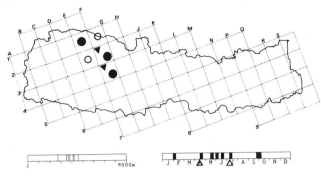

WHITE-TAILED NUTHATCH *Sitta himalayensis*

Subspecies *himalayensis*. First recorded by B. Hodgson (351). A common resident subject to some altitudinal movements. Occurs chiefly between 1800m and 3050m. Sometimes descends in winter, rarely down to 915m. Confirmed breeding at Khaptad (C3) (428), Ghorepani (82), on the Mamche Danda (L6) (633), on Phulchowki (632) and in Mechi Zone (R7) (658). Chiefly inhabits broadleaved forests. **Range** Himalayas from Chamba east to Arunachal Pradesh; n.e. India.

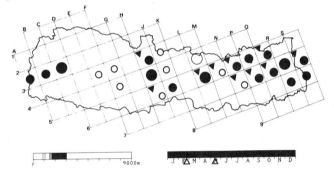

CHESTNUT-BELLIED NUTHATCH *Sitta castanea*

First recorded by B. Hodgson (388). A common resident from the tarai up to 1830m. No altitudinal movements have been reported. Confirmed breeding in Doti District (C3) (438), the Kathmandu Valley (517), and at Chitwan (296). Three races are recorded: *S. c. castanea* (ca) (247,659), *S. c. almorae* (a) (190,647), *S. c. cinnamoventris* (ci) (482) and intermediates between the two latter races (ac) (104). Mainly frequents broadleaved forests and groves. **Range** Himalayas from Chakrata east to Arunachal Pradesh; n.e. India and Bangladesh; locally in n., c., and s.w. India.

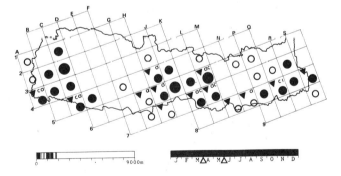

KASHMIR NUTHATCH *Sitta cashmirensis*
Eurasian Nuthatch (*S. europaea*)

Variously regarded as a subspecies of *S. europaea* (243,664) or *S. castanea* (784); here treated as a separate species pending results of further studies. Found between 2400m and 3505m. First definitely recorded on 12 May 1952 at Sialgari (E3) at 2895m by O. Polunin (620). Fairly common in the north-west, probably resident. Altitudinal movements in Nepal are poorly known. Found in oak, spruce and pine forests. **Range** N. Baluchistan; Himalayas from N.W.F.P. east to Nepal.

WALLCREEPER *Tichodroma muraria*

Subspecies *nepalensis*. First recorded by B. Hodgson (388). Fairly common. Mainly reported in winter when found over a wide altitudinal range from 245m to over 5000m. Noted at 5730m in Khumbu in mid-March 1975 (605). Uncommon at Chitwan from October to March (296). Confirmed breeding in Khumbu (190) and in the Dhauligiri area (G4) (526). Frequents gorges and cliffs, especially above streams. **Range** Breeds in the Himalayas from Safed Koh east to Arunachal Pradesh. Winters down to the foothills, and in the plains south to Rajasthan.

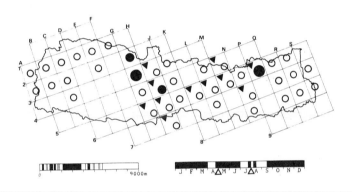

BROWN-THROATED TREECREEPER *Certhia discolor*
Sikkim Treecreeper

Subspecies *discolor*. A Hodgson specimen was listed for Nepal by Gadow (253) but it may have originated in India. First definitely recorded by S.D. Ripley at Godavari in November 1948 (659). A resident subject to some altitudinal movements. Summers chiefly between 2000m and 2750m, occasionally up to 3050m. Sometimes descends in winter down to 1800m, but has been found at 3050m in December (243). One collected at the exceptionally low altitude of 305m at Badalmachi (B4) in December 1952 (647) is the most westerly record of the species. Fairly common on Phulchowki, uncommon elsewhere. Breeding habits are poorly known. Taken in breeding condition at Godavari at 2000m on 9 March

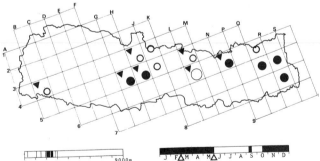

1962 (190). Frequents broadleaved forests. The four Nepalese treecreepers all occur in the central Himalayas (H4,H5). Each species has been found to inhabit different overlapping altitudinal belts and forest formations (533). **Range** Himalayas from Nepal east to Arunachal Pradesh; n.e. India.

BAR-TAILED TREECREEPER *Certhia himalayana*
Himalayan Treecreeper

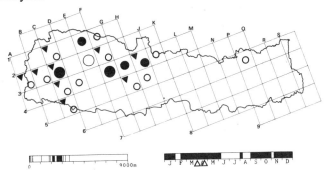

Subspecies *himalayana*. A Hodgson specimen was listed for Nepal by Gadow (253) but it may have originated in India. First definitely collected by S.D. Ripley at the exceptionally low altitude of 75m at Tikapur (C5) in December 1948 (659). A fairly common resident subject to some altitudinal movements. Summers mainly between 2900m and 3660m; in winter sometimes descends to 1800m, and occasionally down to 305m. Regularly reported east to the upper Kali Gandaki valley. Four were seen below Pisang (J4) on 28 March 1985 (451); the most easterly record in the Himalayas. A nest was found on 9 April 1974 in the Pelma Khola valley (F4) (153). Noted feeding young on 8 May 1988 at Khaptad at 3050m (C3) (428), and carrying nest material on 9 May 1985 at 2740m near Bumra (E3) (163). Breeding behaviour for this subspecies was previously unrecorded. Frequents coniferous and rhododendron forests. **Range** N. Baluchistan, and the Himalayas from N.W.F.P. east to Nepal.

RUSTY-FLANKED TREECREEPER *Certhia nipalensis*
Nepal Treecreeper

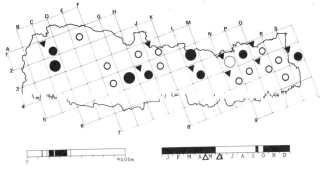

The species was described from Nepal by E. Blyth from a Hodgson specimen (798,118). A fairly common resident, subject to some altitudinal movements. Summers chiefly between 2550m and 3660m, and winters between 1830m and at least 3505m. Breeding behaviour is poorly known. A nest was found on 4 May 1970 at Dhorpatan (G5) at 3400m (527); seen feeding young on 21 May 1982 at Gapte cave (L5) at 3505m (199); and flying in and out of a crevice in an oak in the upper Langtang valley on 30 April 1982 (517). Taken in breeding condition at Ting Sang La (N6) between 3000m and 3400m on 7 May and 2 June 1962 (190). Inhabits oak, also mixed coniferous and broadleaved forests. **Range** Himalayas from Kumaon east to Arunachal Pradesh.

EURASIAN TREECREEPER *Certhia familiaris*
Northern Treecreeper, Common Treecreeper

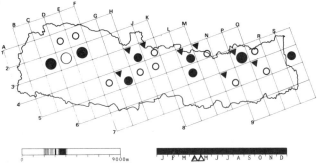

Subspecies *mandellii*. First definitely recorded at Chilung Pati (L5) at 2895m on 9 September 1935 by F.M. Bailey (62). A fairly common resident, subject to some altitudinal movements. Mainly summers between 3000m and 4100m, and winters from 2000m up to at least 3655m. Breeding behaviour of this subspecies is little known. Observed nest-building on 19 April 1952 in an old fir stump at Punga Lekh (D3) at 3355m (620). Juveniles collected at 3950m and 4200m in Khumbu in late June 1962, were found to be independent (190). Seen feeding young in a nest hole at 3250m on Dori Lekh (E3) on 9 May 1985 (163), and one recently fledged young bird was seen at 2800m at Khaptad (C3) on 21 May 1988 (428). Occurs in coniferous and birch forests. **Range** Himalayas from Gilgit east to Arunachal Pradesh.

FIRE-CAPPED TIT *Cephalopyrus flammiceps*

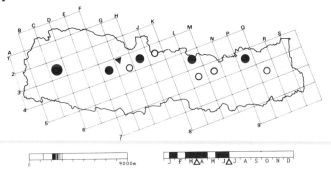

A specimen listed as "Nepal Purchased", but with no other details is the first notice of the species (253). First definitely recorded by J. Martens from Myandi Khola, Muri (G4) at 2100m on 26 March 1970 (527). Status in Nepal is uncertain; a scarce resident but also a very uncommon and erratic visitor. Proved breeding at Khaptad (C3) with flying young seen in May (657,428). Mainly recorded between 2135m and 3000m. Several recent reports from the upper Kali Gandaki valley in March and April, and a few from the Kathmandu Valley and surrounding hills between January and March. An influx in 1982 from February to May: in the Kathmandu Valley (73), Khumbu (599), Syabru (L5) (199), and in the upper Kali Gandaki valley with a maximum of over 12 near Lete (703). Single records from elsewhere. Two races have been recorded: *C. f. flammiceps* (664) and *C. f. olivaceus* (253,664,789). Frequents broadleaved and mixed forests, favouring maples. **Range** Himalayas from Gilgit east to Bhutan.

RUBY-CHEEKED SUNBIRD *Anthreptes singalensis*
Rubycheek

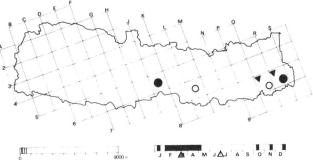

Subspecies *rubinigentis*. First recorded at Chatra in February 1949 by S.D. Ripley (659). Very locally distributed, probably resident. Uncommon north of Sunischare and rare at Chitwan (296), the most westerly locality for the species. Described as uncommon in the eastern tarai in 1976 (293). The only other records are from near Dharan on 8 February 1969 (9) and Hetaura on 9 October 1970 (444,450). Breeds from mid-March to June. Reported up to 455m in open forests or forest clearings; favours evergreens. **Range** Himalayas from Nepal east to Arunachal Pradesh; n.e. India and Bangladesh.

PURPLE SUNBIRD *Nectarinia asiatica*

Subspecies *asiatica*. First recorded by B.
Hodgson (366). A resident, common
from the tarai up to at least 365m, mainly
a summer visitor above 900m. In the
Kathmandu Valley chiefly occurs between June and mid-November, with a
few overwintering. Confirmed breeding
in the Kathmandu Valley (708), and at
Chitwan (296). Found in flowering shrubs
and trees in open forests and gardens.
Range Throughout the subcontinent.

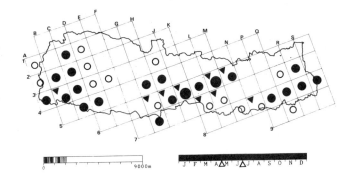

MRS GOULD'S SUNBIRD *Aethopyga gouldiae*

Subspecies *gouldiae*. A Hodgson specimen was listed for Nepal by Gadow (254)
but it may have originated in India. first
definitely recorded by F.M. Bailey at
Kodari (M6) on 27 May 1937 (62). An
uncommon resident, subject to altitudinal
movements. Summers chiefly between
2500m and 3655m, and winters between
1830m and at least 2700m. Breeding confirmed above Dhunche (L5) (195). Regularly seen north-west of Pokhara
(H4,H5), in Langtang, the upper Mai
valley (S7) and on Phulchowki. Frequents
rhododendrons in oak and coniferous
forests. **Range** Himalayas from the Sutlej
valley east to Arunachal Pradesh; n.e.
India and Bangladesh.

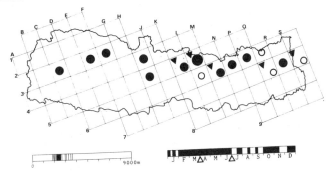

GREEN-TAILED SUNBIRD *Aethopyga nipalensis*
Nepal Sunbird

The species was described from Nepal by
B. Hodgson (366,798). A common resident subject to altitudinal movements.
Summers chiefly between 1830m and
3000m, occasionally up to 3505m. Mainly
winters between 915m and 2745m but
collected as low as 305m at Tari (N8) in
December 1953 (647). Two intergrading
races occur: *A. n. horsfieldi* (h) (647,659),
A. n. nipalensis (n) (104,190,512,
647,659,741) and intermediates (hn)
(647). Found in oak and rhododendron
and mixed broadleaved forests. **Range**
Himalayas from Mussoorie east to Arunachal Pradesh; n.e. India and Bangladesh.

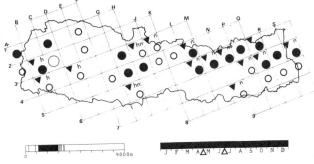

BLACK-THROATED SUNBIRD *Aethopyga saturata*
Black-breasted Sunbird

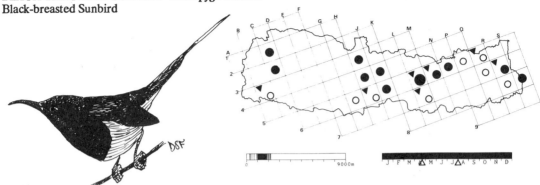

Subspecies *saturata*. The species was described from Nepal by B. Hodgson (366,798). A resident, subject to some altitudinal movements. Occasionally found between 1000m and 1830m, and up to 2200m in summer. Descends from higher levels in the coldest weather, infrequently down to 305m. Confirmed breeding in the Chitlang valley (L6) (104). Inhabits flowering bushes in open forests, and the edges of dense forest. **Range** Himalayas from Murree east to Arunachal Pradesh; n.e. India and Bangladesh.

CRIMSON SUNBIRD *Aethopyga siparaja*
Scarlet-breasted Sunbird, Yellow-backed Sunbird

Subspecies *seheriae*. First recorded by B. Hodgson (366). A resident, subject to some altitudinal movements. Fairly common up to 915m, occasionally seen up to 1200m, and scarce up to 1800m. Withdraws from higher levels in cold weather. Confirmed breeding at Amlekghanj (K7) (104), and Chitwan (296). Found in flowering shrubs in light forests, groves and gardens. **Range** Himalayas from Kangra east to Arunachal Pradesh; n.e. India and Bangladesh; hills of the n.e. peninsula and W. Ghats.

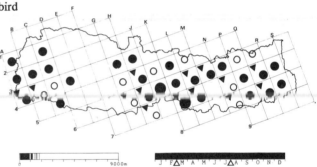

FIRE-TAILED SUNBIRD *Aethopyga ignicauda*
Fire-tailed Yellow-backed Sunbird

Subspecies *ignicauda*. The species was described from Nepal by B. Hodgson (366,798). A fairly common resident subject to altitudinal movements. Summers at higher altitudes than Green-tailed Sunbird, mainly between 3000m and 4000m. Winters chiefly between 1050m and 2135m, but has been found up to 2895m. Proved breeding at Gosainkund (L5) (771). Inhabits rhododendron bushes above the treeline and open coniferous forest. **Range** Himalayas from Garhwal east to Arunachal Pradesh; n.e. India and Bangladesh.

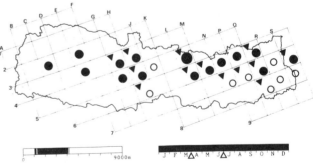

LITTLE SPIDERHUNTER *Arachnothera longirostra*

Subspecies *longirostra*. First recorded at Kankaimukh near the Mechi River (S8) at 150m on 21 February 1961 by R.L. Fleming Sr. (234,246). Scarce and very local, probably resident. Subsequently found north of Sunischare (R8) (243) including one on 16 November 1978 (155) and three in mid-January 1989 (307). A scarce resident at Chitwan, near Tiger Tops (296), the most westerly record of the species. Breeds from March to September. Frequents wild bananas in damp broadleaved evergreen forests along streams, between 75m and 305m. **Range** Himalayas from Nepal east to Arunachal Pradesh; n.e. India and Bangladesh; W. and E. Ghats.

STREAKED SPIDERHUNTER *Arachnothera magna*

Subspecies *magna*. The species was described from Nepal by B. Hodgson (366,798). Probably resident, locally distributed. Mainly found in the tarai and lower hills up to 450m, but two were trapped at 2135m in the Arun valley (243). Fairly common north of Sunischare and uncommon elsewhere. Found at Chitwan, the most westerly locality of the species this century. Inhabits broadleaved evergreen forests with dense undergrowth, favouring wild bananas. Usually feeds in the canopy. **Range** Himalayas in the Sutlej valley (not since 1868), and from Nepal east to Arunachal Pradesh; n.e. India and Bangladesh.

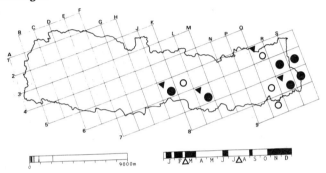

THICK-BILLED FLOWERPECKER *Dicaeum agile*

Subspecies *agile*. First recorded by J. Scully in July and August (1876 or 1877) in the Kathmandu Valley (708). A resident below 800m, mainly a summer visitor at higher elevations. Occasionally seen in the Kathmandu Valley up to 2135m between May and October, and at Sukla Phanta where breeding has been confirmed (432). Uncommon elsewhere. Inhabits broadleaved forests and groves. **Range** Himalayan foothills from Rawalpindi east to Arunachal Pradesh, and south to Kerala and Bangladesh.

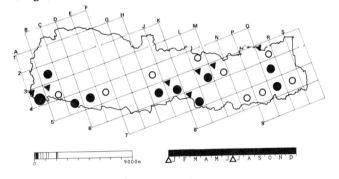

YELLOW-VENTED FLOWERPECKER *Dicaeum chrysorrheum*

Subspecies *chrysochlore*. Obtained by B. Hodgson in his later collection (409) but the specimen may have originated in India. First definitely recorded by R.L. Fleming Jr. in 1974 near Dhankuta along the Tamur River (Q8) at 245m (216,243). Scarce and very local, probably resident.

Reported from north of Sunischare: in March and April in 1977 (178), 1981 (559), 1982 (207,561) and 1987 (205). The only other records are from Chitwan in March in 1985 and 1989 (67), the western limit of the species's range. Breeds from April to July. Seen in mistletoes in open forests and forest edges. **Range** Himalayan foothills from Nepal east to Arunachal Pradesh; n.e. India and Bangladesh.

YELLOW-BELLIED FLOWERPECKER *Dicaeum melanoxanthum*

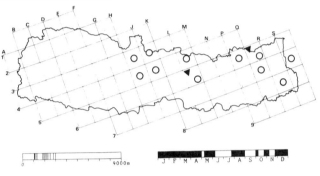

The species was described from Nepal by E. Blyth from a Hodgson specimen (114,798). Locally distributed, probably resident. Seasonal movements are poorly understood. Found between 2400m and 3000m in summer, and from 1050m to at least 1550m in winter. Occasionally seen in the Kathmandu Valley and surrounding hills in winter, uncommon elsewhere. Breeding behaviour is unknown. Frequents flowering and fruiting trees in open broadleaved forest and forest clearings. **Range** Himalayas from Almora east to Arunachal Pradesh; n.e. India.

PALE-BILLED FLOWERPECKER *Dicaeum erythrorhynchos*
Tickell's Flowerpecker

Subspecies *erythrorhynchos*. First recorded by B. Hodgson (388). A resident, occasionally found throughout the tarai and lower foothills up to 305m. Sight records from the Kathmandu Valley at 1400m in summer (50,629,664,814) are unacceptable. The species is easily confused with Plain Flowerpecker, particularly the immatures which all have pale bills. Inhabits groves and open broadleaved forest. **Range** Himalayas from Dharmsala east to Arunachal Pradesh; n.e. India and Bangladesh; Indian peninsula.

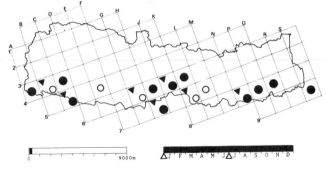

PLAIN FLOWERPECKER *Dicaeum concolor*
Plain-coloured Flowerpecker

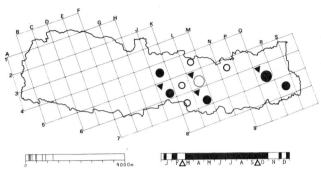

Subspecies *olivaceum*. A Hodgson specimen was listed for Nepal by Sharpe (717)
but it may have originated in India. First
definitely recorded by S.D. Ripley at
Nagarjung (L6) in April 1947 (659). Locally distributed, presumably resident.
Occurs mainly between 305m and 1525m.
Noted as high as 2500m above the Trisuli
valley (L5) on 31 October 1980 (516).
Fairly common north of Sunischare, and
in the Kathmandu Valley from mid-
March to the end of September (635), but
uncommon elsewhere. Proved breeding
at Tumlingtar (Q7) (546). Found in
broadleaved forest edges and groves.
Range Himalayas from Nepal east to
Arunachal Pradesh; n.e. India and Bangladesh; s.w. India.

FIRE-BREASTED FLOWERPECKER *Dicaeum ignipectus*
Buff-bellied Flowerpecker

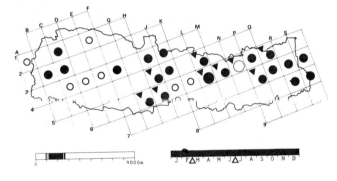

Subspecies *ignipectus*. The species was
described from Nepal by E. Blyth from a
Hodgson specimen (114,798). A common
resident subject to altitudinal movements. Summers mainly between 1830m
and 2700m, and winters between 915m
and 2285m. A scarce winter visitor to
Chitwan. Proved breeding in the Chitlang
valley (L6) and Kathmandu Valley (104).
Frequents broadleaved forests. **Range**
Himalayas from Kashmir east to Arunachal Pradesh; n.e. India.

SCARLET-BACKED FLOWERPECKER *Dicaeum cruentatum*

Subspecies *cruentatum*. Obtained by B.
Hodgson in his later collection (315) but
the specimen may have originated in India. First definitely recorded from Ilam
District (R8) at the exceptionally high
altitude of 2135m (undated) (223,243).
Scarce and very local, probably resident.

The only other record is of a male and two females seen at
Dharan at 305m on 21 April 1979 (651,652). These are the
westernmost records of the species. Breeds from April to
August. Frequents broadleaved forests. **Range** Himalayan
foothills from Nepal east to Arunachal Pradesh; n.e. India
and Bangladesh.

ORIENTAL WHITE-EYE *Zosterops palpebrosus*
White-eye, Indian White-eye

Subspecies *palpebrosus*. First recorded by
B. Hodgson (388). A very common resident, subject to some altitudinal movements. Occurs up to 1370m throughout
the year; probably only a summer visitor
at higher altitudes up to 2440m. Breeding
confirmed at Chitwan (296,432) and in
the Kathmandu Valley (629,708). Inhabits undergrowth in open forests, groves
and gardens. **Range** Throughout the subcontinent, except parts of the extreme
north-west.

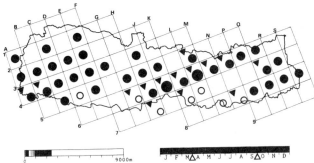

MAROON ORIOLE *Oriolus traillii*

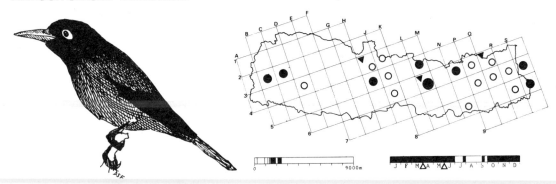

Subspecies *traillii*. First recorded by B.
Hodgson (348). A locally fairly common
resident, subject to some seasonal movements. Regularly seen on the hills surrounding the Kathmandu Valley, north-
west of Pokhara (H5) and at Khaptad
(C3) (428); few reports from elsewhere.

Summers mainly between 1500m and 2440m, and winters
between 1200m and 1800m. Noted at Chitwan in November
1981 (296). Breeding confirmed at Bhimpedi (105). Inhabits dense broadleaved forests. **Range** Himalayas from
Himachal Pradesh east to Arunachal Pradesh; n.e. India
and Bangladesh.

BLACK-HOODED ORIOLE *Oriolus xanthornus*
Black-headed Oriole

Subspecies *xanthornus*. First recorded by
B. Hodgson (388). A resident, subject to
local seasonal movements. Common in
the tarai and lower foothills below 365m,
uncommon up to 915m, and rare at higher
altitudes. A straggler to the Kathmandu
Valley (240). Breeding confirmed at Chitwan (296) and Hetaura (105). Inhabits
open broadleaved forests and groves.
Range Himalayas from Himachal
Pradesh east to Arunachal Pradesh, and
south to Kerala, Kutch and Bangladesh.

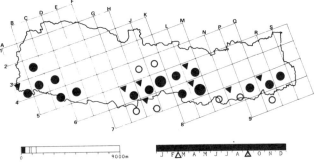

SLENDER-BILLED ORIOLE   *Oriolus tenuirostris*
Black-naped Oriole   (*O. chinensis*)

First recorded by J. Scully on 1 February 1877 in the Kathmandu Valley (708). He found it to be fairly common in the Valley from October to March, but it has only been recorded a few times subsequently, between January and April (222,243, 301,629). Scarce. Status is uncertain, probably a winter visitor. Other recent confirmed records are from north of Dhumre (J5) (652), Chitwan (151,296), Dharan (628), Hetaura (262), Tumlingtar (Q7) (574,587), upper Mai valley (R7) (321), Kosi Tappu (408) and north of Sunischare (658,549). Found in trees in open country and groves. **Range** Breeds

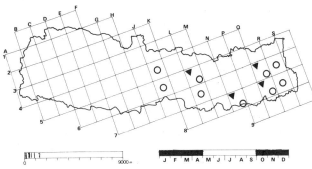

in the Himalayas from Bhutan east to Arunachal Pradesh and in Meghalaya. Winters west to Nepal and Bombay, and south to Kanyakumari.

EURASIAN GOLDEN ORIOLE   *Oriolus oriolus*
Golden Oriole

Subspecies *kundoo*. First recorded by B. Hodgson (388). A summer visitor from the tarai up to 1830m. Common at Chitwan from March to October (296), occasionally seen elsewhere. Found in the Kathmandu Valley and surrounding hills between mid-April and the end of November (629,635). Breeding confirmed in the Valley (629) and near Dhankhuta (Q7) (446). Inhabits groves, trees at the edges of cultivation, and open wooded country. **Range** Breeds in Pakistan, in the Himalayas from N.W.F.P. east to Nepal,

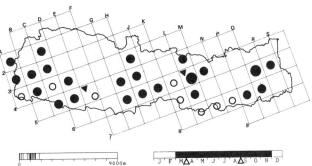

and south to Karnataka. Winters throughout the peninsula east to Bengal.

BROWN SHRIKE   *Lanius cristatus*

Subspecies *cristatus*. First recorded by B. Hodgson (375). A winter visitor and passage migrant, occurring mainly below 1525m. Fairly common from central Nepal (K7,L6) eastwards, uncommon further west. One seen at Syang (H4) at about 2700m on 29 January 1983 showed the characters of *lucionensis* (748). Noted, presumably on passage: in the upper Kali Gandaki valley at 2560m from 13 September to 5 October 1973 (76), and in mid-March 1982 (207); also at Tarnga (P6) at 4000m in mid-October 1970 (526), and between Khinza and Those (N6) at 2700m on 3 May 1982 (207). Frequents open forest, forest clearings and edges,

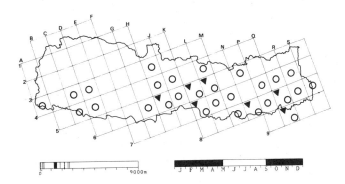

secondary scrub, and hillsides with scattered bushes. **Range** Winters throughout the subcontinent, except parts of the north-west.

ISABELLINE SHRIKE *Lanius isabellinus*
Pale Brown Shrike   (*L. collurio isabellinus*)

Subspecies *isabellinus*. First recorded by
J. Scully who collected a specimen on 15
August 1875 which is held in the British
Museum (Natural History). The speci-
men is not listed by Gadow (253) or by
Scully (708). Vagrant. The only other

records are of singles seen at Meghauli (J6) on 28 December 1984 and at Sunischare on 28 January 1985 (142); also at
Kosi Barrage on 30 January 1987, and photographed at
Phewa Tal on 3 March 1986 (55). Frequents dry open scrub
country. **Range** Winters in Pakistan and n.w. India.

BAY-BACKED SHRIKE *Lanius vittatus*

Subspecies *vittatus*. First recorded by B.
Hodgson (388). Mainly an uncommon
winter visitor and passage migrant, but
regular sightings in summer and winter at
Surkhet (D4) (244). Winters chiefly between 75m and 335m. Singles noted, presumably on passage, at Marpha at 2600m
in September 1973 (76), at Kagbeni at
2810m in April 1982 (812), and north of
Manang (J4) at the exceptionally high
altitude of 3965m in July 1988 (194). Inhabits open, dry bushy areas, and edges of
cultivation. **Range** Pakistan and India
from the w. Himalayan foothills, east
to Bengal and south to s. India.

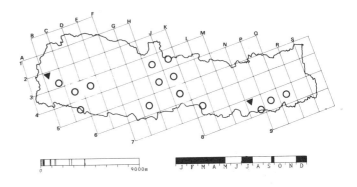

LONG-TAILED SHRIKE *Lanius schach*
Black-headed Shrike, Rufous-backed Shrike

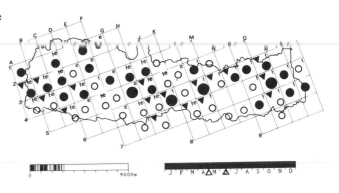

First recorded by B. Hodgson (375,798).
Common. Mainly resident, subject to altitudinal movements. Summers up to
3100m, chiefly between 1500m and
2700m. Some birds remain to winter in
the foothills and tarai, others move south
to India. Two intergrading races occur.
The Black-headed Shrike *L. s. tricolor* (t)
occurs chiefly in central areas (L5,L6),
and eastwards. Proved breeding in the
Gandak-Kosi watershed (L6) (230), in
the Kathmandu Valley and on the surrounding hills (629,659,708), at low alti-

tude at Chitwan (296) and near Dhankuta (Q7) (446). Occasionally reported in winter in the west
(62,153,620,627,647) but these birds may be intermediates
between this race and the Rufous-backed Shrike *L. s.
erythronotus* (e). Introgression is apparent in the Kathmandu Valley (88), but both intermediates (te) and pure
erythronotus are common in the Kali Gandaki valley and
westwards. A birds of each race was observed behaving as a
pair near Jomosom on 12 April 1982 (812). The numbers of
erythronotus are probably increased by winter visitors. The
species inhabits lightly wooded areas and bushes in open
country. **Range** Throughout the subcontinent.

GREY-BACKED SHRIKE *Lanius tephronotus*
Tibetan Shrike

Subspecies *tephronotus*. First recorded by B. Hodgson (375). A fairly common altitudinal migrant. Summers chiefly between 2745m and 4575m; winters mainly from 275m up to at least 2560m, infrequently below 365m. In the Kathmandu Valley chiefly seen from October to March. Frequents open bushy areas and edges of cultivation. **Range** Breeds in the Himalayas from Baltistan east to Arunachal Pradesh. Winters in the foothills and south to the plains of n. and n.e. India.

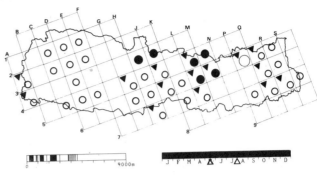

GREAT GREY SHRIKE *Lanius excubitor*
Grey Shrike

Subspecies *lahtora*. First collected by H.S. Nepali near Gauhna village (C5) on 8 February 1969 (591). A locally distributed resident in the tarai near the Indian border. Fairly common in Kapilvastu District especially near Bhairawa (F6,G6) (7,155, 444). Uncommon near Kosi Barrage and Kosi Tappu (P8,Q8,R8), and elsewhere in the far south-east tarai (Q9,R9) (293). Only single records from other areas. Occurs in dry, open scrub country. **Range** Pakistan and n. India east to Bangladesh, and south to Karnataka.

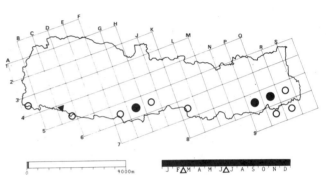

BLACK DRONGO *Dicrurus macrocercus*
(*D. adsimilis*)

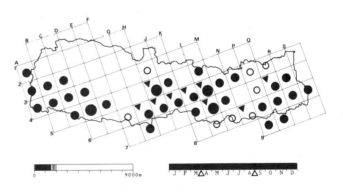

Subspecies *albirictus*. First recorded by B. Hodgson (340). An abundant resident subject to some altitudinal movements. Occurs up to at least 1525m throughout the year, and occasionally up to 2000m in summer. Confirmed breeding at Nepalganj (432), Pokhara (326), in the Kathmandu Valley (629,708), Trisuli valley (L5) (517) and at Hetaura (106). Frequents open wooded country, edges of cultivation and habitation. **Range** Throughout the subcontinent.

ASHY DRONGO   *Dicrurus leucophaeus*
Grey Drongo

Subspecies *longicaudatus*. First recorded
by B. Hodgson (388). Common. Mainly a
resident, subject to altitudinal movements, and with some birds moving south
to winter in India. Summers regularly
between 1220m and 2745m, and winters
between 1065m and 1525m. It is also a
locally common resident in the lowlands
at Bardia and Chitwan. Proved breeding
at Chitwan (296,432), on the hills surrounding the Kathmandu Valley
(629,708,556) and at Bhimpedi (106).
Inhabits broadleaved and coniferous
forests. **Range** Breeds in the Himalayas
from N.W.F.P. east to Arunachal
Pradesh, and in n.e. India and Bangladesh. Winters south to s. India.

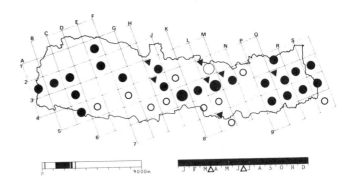

WHITE-BELLIED DRONGO   *Dicrurus caerulescens*

Subspecies *caerulescens*. A Hodgson
specimen was listed for Nepal by Sharpe
(713) but it may have originated in India.
First definitely recorded by J. Scully who
found it commonly at Hetaura in winter in
1876 or 1877 (708). A resident in the
lowlands up to 305m. Common in the
west at Sukla Phanta, Dhangarhi and
Bardia; fairly common in central areas at
Tamaspur, Chitwan, Butwal and
Hetaura; occasionally seen further east.
Confirmed breeding at Mahendranagar
(A4) (811) and Dhangarhi (432). Occurs
in clearings and edges of thin forest.
Range India from Haryana and Kutch
east to Bengal and from Nepal south to
Kerala.

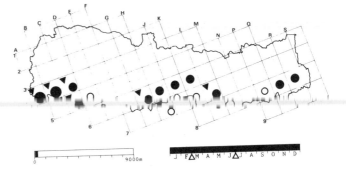

CROW-BILLED DRONGO   *Dicrurus annectans*

The species was described from Nepal by
B. Hodgson (374,798). Its status is uncertain in Nepal and the rest of the subcontinent (45,664) because of confusion with
the Black Drongo. Probably an uncommon summer visitor. Wrongly described
as a common resident at Chitwan (296);

only a few records in spring have been confirmed from
there. The only other acceptable records are from Bardia
(432), Hetaura (106,245), the eastern foothills (P8,Q8)
(293,792), Kosi Barrage (256) and north of Sunischare
(442,794). Frequents humid, broadleaved, evergreen
forests. **Range** Himalayan foothills from Kumaon east to
Arunachal Pradesh; n.e. India and Bangladesh.

CROW-BILLED DRONGO, cont'd ...

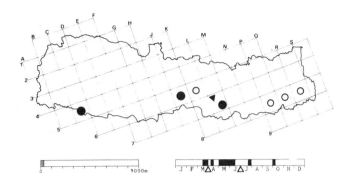

BRONZED DRONGO *Dicrurus aeneus*
Little Bronzed Drongo

Subspecies *aeneus*. First recorded by B. Hodgson (374). A fairly common resident, subject to some altitudinal movements. Usually winters below 1220m; mainly summers up to 1600m, occasionally up to 2000m. Confirmed breeding in the central hills (414), at Dhunche (L5) (771) and at Chitwan (296). In the Kathmandu Valley it is mainly a summer visitor. Frequents clearings and forest paths in broadleaved forests. **Range** Himalayan foothills from Mussoorie east to Arunachal Pradesh; n.e. India and Bangladesh; E. and W. Ghats.

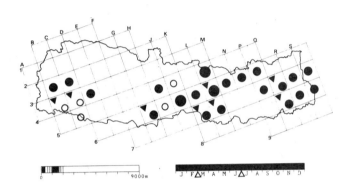

LESSER RACKET-TAILED DRONGO *Dicrurus remifer*
Small Racquet-tailed Drongo

Subspecies *tectirostris*. First recorded by B. Hodgson (374). A locally distributed resident, found mainly between 915m and 1800m. Some birds possibly withdraw from higher elevations in winter. Occasionally seen north-west of Pokhara, at Begnas Tal, and Chitwan north of the Churia range, where it may be only a winter visitor (243,296); uncommon in the Kathmandu Valley and in Ilam District (R8). Mainly single records from elsewhere. Proved breeding at Bhimpedi (106) and in the Kathmandu Valley (243). Inhabits dense, moist broadleaved forests. **Range** Himalayan foothills from Garhwal east to Arunachal Pradesh; n.e. India and Bangladesh.

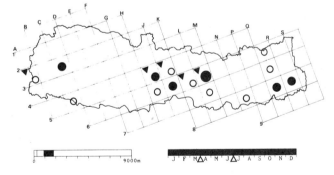

SPANGLED DRONGO *Dicrurus hottentottus*
Hair-crested Drongo

Subspecies *hottentottus*. First recorded by
J. Gould (266). A fairly common resident,
subject to seasonal movements depending on the supply of nectar, its main food.
Occurs chiefly from the tarai up to 1050m,
uncommonly at higher altitudes. A straggler was found at 4115m in June 1971 in
the Dolpo (G3) (224,692). Proved breeding at Hetaura (106). Frequents moist
broadleaved forests; associates with flowering trees, especially silk cotton. **Range**
Himalayan foothills from Kangra east to
Arunachal Pradesh; n.e. India and Bangladesh; E. and W. Ghats.

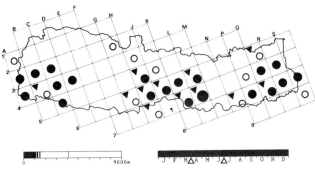

GREATER RACKET-TAILED DRONGO *Dicrurus paradiseus*
Large Racquet-tailed Drongo

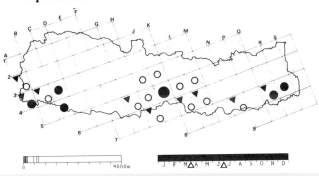

Subspecies *grandis*. First recorded by J.
Gould (266). A locally common resident,
liable to some seasonal wanderings.
Found mainly below 150m, uncommonly
up to 365m, and rarely at higher altitudes.

Regularly seen at Sukla Phanta, Bardia, near Dharan, north
of Sunischare, and also at Chitwan where proved breeding
(296). Occurs in open broadleaved forests. **Range** India east
and south of a line from Gujarat to Kumaon; Bangladesh.

ASHY WOODSWALLOW *Artamus fuscus*
Ashy Swallow-shrike

First recorded by B. Hodgson (388). A
local resident. Found mainly between
75m and 365m, but noted in the upper
Kali Gandaki valley at 2560m on 13 April
1978 (655), and on 1 March 1981 (65).
Common in summer in the eastern tarai
and foothills (Q8) (293), and fairly common at Hetaura, north of Sunischare, and
at Chitwan where proved breeding
(296,432,771). Mainly single records from
elsewhere. Frequents open country and
grassy ridges. **Range** India east and south
of a line from Gujarat to Simla; Bangladesh.

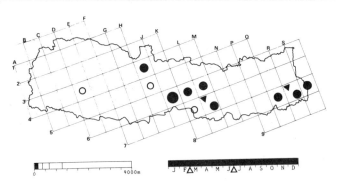

EURASIAN JAY *Garrulus glandarius*
Himalayan Red-crowned Jay, Jay

First recorded by B. Hodgson (388). A
locally distributed resident, found mainly
between 1800m and 2440m throughout
the year, but subject to some altitudinal
movements. Common on the hills surrounding the Kathmandu Valley, fairly
common at Khaptad (C3); occasionally
seen elsewhere. Proved breeding on
Sheopuri (414), and in the Markhu valley
(L6) (106). Two races occur. *G. g. bispecu-*
laris (b) (482,647,659), *G. g. interstinctus*
(i) (736) and intermediates (bi) (106).
Inhabits broadleaved forests, favouring
oak. **Range** Himalayas from Hazara east
to Arunachal Pradesh; n.e. India and
Bangladesh.

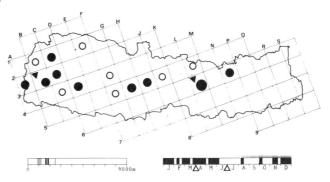

LANCEOLATED JAY *Garrulus lanceolatus*
Black-throated Jay, Black-headed Jay

First recorded by B. Hodgson who found
it breeding on Jahar Powah (L6)
(388,414). Presumably resident. Reported chiefly between 915m and 2500m
and subject to some altitudinal movements. Common in Dandeldhura and
Doti Districts (A3,B3,C2,C3); uncommon further east as far as the hills surrounding the Kathmandu Valley. A pair
was noted at Yarsa (N6) at about 1800m
on 3 April 1981 (159); the eastern limit of
the species's range. Inhabits oak and
mixed broadleaved forests. **Range** Himalayas from N.W.F.P. east to Nepal.

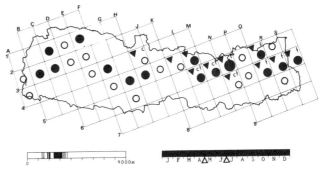

YELLOW-BILLED BLUE MAGPIE *Urocissa flavirostris*
Gold-billed Magpie   (*Cissa flavirostris*)

Obtained by B. Hodgson in his later collection (409) but the specimen may have
originated in India. First definitely recorded by J. Scully from the hills surrounding the Kathmandu Valley and in
Nawakot District in June and July 1877
(708). A common resident subject to
some altitudinal movements. Found
mainly above 2440m throughout the year;
in summer frequently up to 3660m, and in
winter occasionally down to 1850m. In the
far west seen in May as low as 1500m in
Bajhang District (C2) (657) and at 1300m
in Doti District (C3) (438). Proved breeding at Thodung (N6) in May (190). Two
races occur: *U. f. cucullata* (c) (647), *U. f.*

flavirostris (f) (247,482,574,661) and intermediates (cf)
(106). Frequents broadleaved and coniferous forests.
Range Himalayas from Hazara east to Arunachal Pradesh;
n.e. India.

RED-BILLED BLUE MAGPIE   *Urocissa erythrorhyncha*
Blue Magpie   (*Cissa erythrorhyncha*)

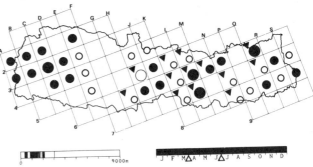

Subspecies *occipitalis*. First recorded by B. Hodgson (388). A common resident subject to some altitudinal movements. Generally occurs at lower elevations than the Yellow-billed Blue Magpie. Reported chiefly between 365m and 1525m, but occasionally up to 2200m in summer, and

noted at 3050m near Rara on 21 June 1979 (626). Found at Hans Pokhari Danda (S8) in March 1988 (485), the easternmost record of the species in the Himalayas. Confirmed breeding in Doti District (C3) (68), at Hetaura (106), in the Kathmandu Valley (629) and upper Arun valley (483). Inhabits broadleaved and mixed forests. **Range** Himalayas from Kangra and Kulu east to Nepal; n.e. India.

GREEN MAGPIE   *Cissa chinensis*

Subspecies *chinensis*. First recorded by B. Hodgson (388). A locally fairly common resident, occurring chiefly below 1200m. Regularly seen north-west of Pokhara, at Degnas Tal, and in the Mai valley (R7,R8). Uncommon at Chitwan (296) and elsewhere. Inhabits dense thickets in moist broadleaved forests. **Range** Himalayas from Garhwal east to Arunachal Pradesh; n.e. India and Bangladesh.

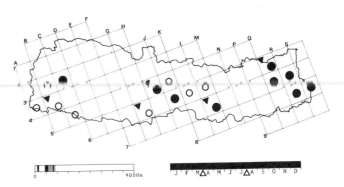

RUFOUS TREEPIE   *Dendrocitta vagabunda*
Indian Treepie

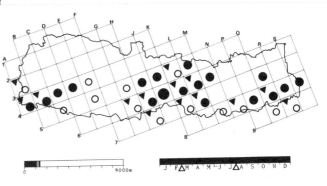

RUFOUS TREEPIE, cont'd ...

Subspecies *vagabunda*. First recorded by B. Hodgson (388). A common resident from the tarai up to 1050m, uncommon up to 1370m. Noted in December 1979 with Grey Treepies, at about 1800m on Phulchowki, and in February 1989 at Kimche (H5) at 1585m (69). Confirmed breeding at Chitwan (296). Frequents open wooded country, groves and trees at edges of cultivation. **Range** Throughout most of the subcontinent.

GREY TREEPIE *Dendrocitta formosae*
Himalayan Treepie

First recorded by B. Hodgson (388). A common resident subject to altitudinal movements. Generally occurs at higher altitudes than Rufous Treepie. Chiefly summers between 1050m and 2150m, and winters between 915m and 1525m. Noted as low as 250m at Chitwan on 25 September 1989 (67). Proved breeding at Phewa Tal (326). Two intergrading races occur: *D. f. occidentalis* (o) and *D. f. himalayensis* (h). Inhabits forests and secondary scrub. **Range** Himalayas from the Jhelum River east to Arunachal Pradesh; n.e. India and Bangladesh; E. Ghats.

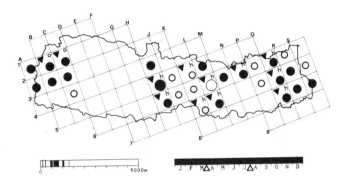

[COLLARED TREEPIE *Dendrocitta frontalis*
Black-browed Treepie

Subspecies *frontalis*. Obtained by B. Hodgson in his later collection (409) but the specimen may have originated in India. No subsequent records. Inhabits dense, mixed, evergreen forest and bamboo jungle (45,664). **Range** Himalayas from Darjeeling east to Arunachal Pradesh; n.e. India.]

HUME'S GROUND JAY *Pseudopodoces humilis*
Hume's Ground Pecker   (*Podoces humilis*)
Hume's Ground Chough, Tibetan Ground-Jay

First definitely recorded on 18 June 1952 at Tuiyegaon (G3) at 5335m by O. Polunin (620). A resident, occasionally found in Trans-Himalayan Nepal between 4000m and 5335m. Shows little seasonal movement. Reported on the Thorong La (H4) (314) and above Manang (J4) (553). Breeding confirmed in Mustang (H3) and in the Dolpo (G3) (243). A juvenile was collected at Bhareal (G3) at 4880m on 28 July 1978 (587). Breeding behaviour has not been described in the Indian subcontinent. Feeds on the ground in the Tibetan steppe facies above the treeline, among scattered bushes, or on stony hillsides. **Range** N. Nepal and n. Sikkim.

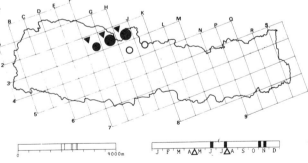

SPOTTED NUTCRACKER *Nucifraga caryocatactes*
Nutcracker, Eurasian Nutcracker

Subspecies *hemispila*. First recorded by B. Hodgson (388). A common resident, subject to some altitudinal movements. Mainly summers between 2745m and 3660m, and winters from at least 2135m up to 3050m, but seen several times at Khaptad (C3) down to 1500m in May (428). A straggler was seen at 305m at Dharan in October (243). Breeding confirmed in the Dhorpatan valley (G5) (499), in the Gandak-Kosi watershed (L5) (633) and in the upper Arun (483) and upper Mai valleys (736). Forages in coniferous forests. **Range** Himalayas from Chitral east to Arunachal Pradesh.

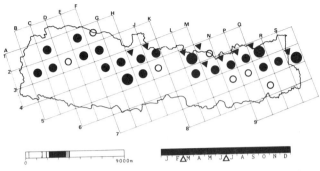

ALPINE CHOUGH *Pyrrhocorax graculus*
Yellow-billed Chough

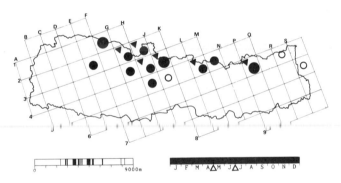

Subspecies *digitatus*. First definitely recorded on the Singalila Range (S7) on 6 March 1912 at 3610m by H. Stevens (736). A common resident, subject to some altitudinal movements. Occurs chiefly above 3500m and up to at least 6250m. Noted as high as 8235m on Sagarmatha (243). Sometimes descends from higher levels in winter, particularly after bad weather. Seen at 2350m near Jumla on 29 March 1977 (464), and below Chame (J4) on 13 November 1978 (553). Breeding confirmed in Khumbu (190) and as low as 3450m below Manang (J4) (757). Inhabits alpine meadows and upland cultivation, often near cliffs. **Range** N. Baluchistan, and the Himalayas from Chitral east to Arunachal Pradesh.

RED-BILLED CHOUGH *Pyrrhocorax pyrrhocorax*
Chough

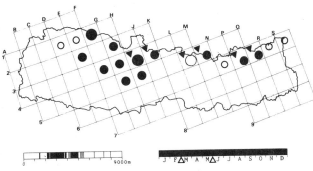

Subspecies *himalayanus*. First recorded by B. Hodgson (277). A common resident, subject to altitudinal movements. Occurs mainly above 2440m, and noted as high as 7340m and 7950m on Sagarmatha in May 1952 (415). May descend from higher elevations in winter, occasionally down to 2135m, and found as low as 1450m at Dana (H4) in February and March 1982 (57,682). Proved breeding in the Langu valley (F2) (330) and at Kagbeni (811). Habitat is similar to that of Alpine Chough, although generally found at lower altitudes. **Range** N. Balu-

chistan, and the Himalayas from Chitral east to Arunachal Pradesh.

HOUSE CROW *Corvus splendens*

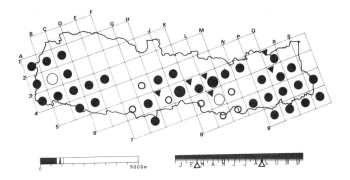

Subspecies *splendens*. First recorded by B. Hodgson (277). An abundant and sedentary resident from the tarai up to 1525m, rare at higher altitudes. The maximum altitude reported is 2100m at

Nagarkot (M6) on 9 February 1983 (593). Confirmed breeding at Chitwan (296), and in the Kathmandu Valley (517,629,708). Entirely associated with man. A scavenger in villages and towns. **Range** Throughout the subcontinent.

JUNGLE CROW *Corvus macrorhynchos*
Large-billed Crow

First recorded by B. Hodgson (388). An abundant resident. Four races occur. *C. m. intermedius* (i) (106) is found mainly between 1200m and 4900m, and shows little evidence of seasonal movements. Seen as high as 5790m below the summit of Paldor East (L5) in October 1982 (583). This race is larger than the other two, has a call similar to that of the Common Raven, and is often confused with that species. Intermediates between

this race and *C. m. tibetosinensis* (it) occur in n.e. Khumbu (45). *C. m. culminatus* (c) (234) and *C. m. levaillantii* (l) (246), have only been collected in the lowlands. Proved breeding at Khaptad (C3) (428), Nepalganj (432) and in the Kathmandu Valley (629,708); also at Chitwan (296), near Dhankuta (Q7) (446), and in the upper Mai valley (736). Frequents forests, cultivation, and open country above the treeline, but usually associated with villages and towns. **Range** N. Baluchistan; Himalayas from N.W.F.P. east to Arunachal Pradesh; n.e. India and Bangladesh; the whole of peninsular India.

JUNGLE CROW, cont'd ...

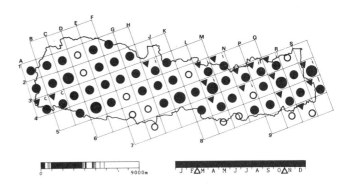

COMMON RAVEN *Corvus corax*
Raven, Northern Raven

Subspecies *tibetanus*. First definitely recorded in July and August 1950 by D.
Lowndes at Manangbhot (J4) between
4265m and 4570m (512). A fairly common
resident subject to some altitudinal movements. Occurs in Trans-Himalayan Nepal
mainly above 3500m, and up to at least
5000m. Seen as high as 8235m on Sagarmatha in 1971 (244). May move south and
to lower altitudes in winter, occasionally
as low as 2500m, particularly after severe
weather. Inhabits dry rocky areas above
the treeline, in the Tibetan facies. Range
Pakistan; Himalayas from Hunza east to
Arunachal Pradesh.

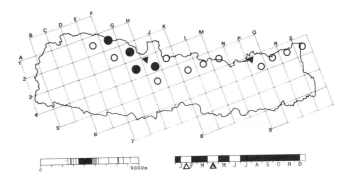

SPOT-WINGED STARLING *Saroglossa spiloptera*
Spot-winged Stare

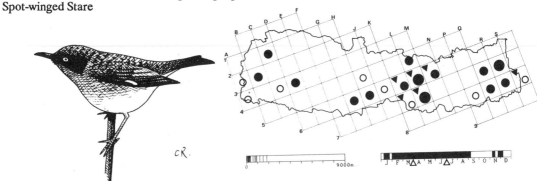

SPOT-WINGED STARLING, cont'd ...

First recorded by B. Hodgson (348). Occasionally seen up to 915m and uncommon up to 1830m. Status is uncertain. A passage migrant to Chitwan from February to April and in July (296). Flocks of up to 50 noted at Dharan in March and June (293), over 100 in Doti District (B3) in May (68) and 125 at Chitwan in February (565) were possibly on migration. Breeding confirmed at Hetaura (105), Betrawati (L6) (299) and Mechi Zone (R7) (658). Frequents open broadleaved forests and feeds on nectar of flowering trees. **Range** Himalayan foothills from Kangra east to Sikkim; n.e. India east to Bangladesh.

CHESTNUT-TAILED STARLING *Sturnus malabaricus*
Grey-headed Myna

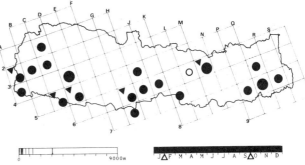

Subspecies *malabaricus*. First recorded by B. Hodgson (348). Fairly common between 75m and 1370m. Although recorded in all months it is not certain that it is resident. A summer visitor to the Kathmandu Valley from mid-March to early November (635). Occurs at Chitwan from February to October, and possibly resident there (296). Described as a winter visitor to Sukla Phanta (700) and as both a resident and local migrant to the eastern tarai and foothills (Q8) (293). Breeding confirmed at Silgadi-Doti (B3) (438), Chitwan (296), in the Kathmandu Valley (629,756) and in the east (Q8) (293). Inhabits lightly wooded country and groves. **Range** The whole of the subcontinent east and south of a line from Rajasthan to Dehra Dun.

BRAHMINY STARLING *Sturnus pagodarum*
Brahminy Mynah

BRAHMINY STARLING, cont'd ...

First recorded by B. Hodgson (348). A resident, reported mainly up to 915m. Seasonal movements are poorly known. Occasionally seen at Nepalganj and westwards; uncommon further east. Noted at the unusually high altitude of 3050m in the Langu valley (F2) in May 1983 (330).

Found breeding at Surkhet (D4) (626), in the eastern foothills (Q8) (293) and by the Indrawati Khola (M6) (243). Only one record from the Kathmandu Valley, possibly referring to escaped birds (3). Inhabits dry open broadleaved forest and scrub. **Range** Throughout the subcontinent, except parts of the north-west and north-east.

COMMON STARLING *Sturnus vulgaris*
Eurasian Starling, Starling

First recorded by B. Hodgson (348). He also provided the only specimen of *S. v. humii* (519), although this may have originated in India. Two other races have been recorded: *S. v. porphyronotus* (p) (62,647) and *S. p. poltaratskyi* (t) (245). The species is an uncommon winter visitor and passsage migrant found chiefly up to 1500m. Several reports from Sukla Phanta, Pokhara, Kathmandu Valley, and Kosi marshes. Mainly single records from elsewhere. The maximum of about 100 was seen on 6 January 1988 by the Bagmati River, Kathmandu Valley (203). Singles noted at Jomosom on 28 March 1983 (56) and Kagbeni on 1 April 1984 (421) were presumably on passage. Found in damp grassland and cultivation. **Range** Winters throughout Pakistan, n. India, and Bangladesh.

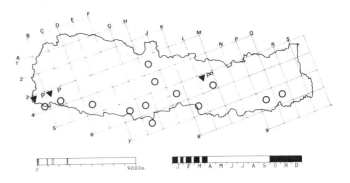

ROSY STARLING *Sturnus roseus*
Rosy Pastor, Rose-coloured Starling

Vagrant. First recorded by B. Hodgson who found it on 10 October in the Kathmandu Valley (336,388). The only other record is of one seen on 14 April 1981 at Kosi Barrage (559). Frequents grassland and cultivation. **Range** Winter visitor to India east to Bengal and south to s. India. Passage migrant in Pakistan.

ASIAN PIED STARLING *Sturnus contra*
Pied Myna

Subspecies *contra*. First recorded by B. Hodgson (388). A fairly common resident throughout the lowlands up to 305m. Possibly subject to local movements. Confirmed breeding at Chitwan (296) and in the eastern tarai (Q8) (293). One located in the Kathmandu Valley (813) was possibly an escaped bird. Forages in cultivation and other open country, usually near habitation and grazing animals. **Range** Haryana east to n.e. India and Bangladesh, and south to Bombay and Andhra Pradesh.

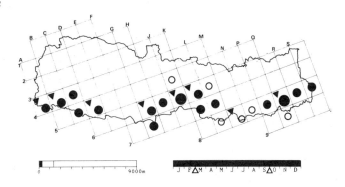

COMMON MYNAH *Acridotheres tristis*
Indian Mynah

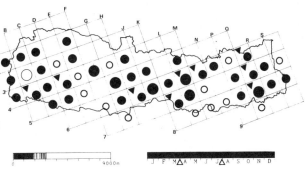

Subspecies *tristis*. First recorded by B. Hodgson (348). An abundant resident, regularly found up to at least 1830m throughout the year. Occasionally summers up to 3050m and winters up to 2135m. Found breeding in the Dhorpatan valley (G5) (499), at Chitwan (296), Hetaura (105), in the Kathmandu Valley (517,629) and eastern lowlands (Q8) (293). Frequents habitation almost everywhere. **Range** Throughout the subcontinent.

BANK MYNAH *Acridotheres ginginianus*

First recorded by B. Hodgson (388). A locally, fairly common resident, occurring mainly in the tarai. Only occasionally seen at higher altitudes. Several reports from the Kathmandu Valley refer possibly to escaped birds. Subject to some local movements but these are poorly understood. Breeding confirmed at Chitwan (296), Mahendranagar (A4) (811), Bardia District (432), and the eastern tarai (P8) (293). Found near villages, often associated with grazing animals. Rarely occurs in urban areas in Nepal. **Range** Pakistan, and n. India east to Assam and Bangladesh, and south to Bombay and n. Orissa.

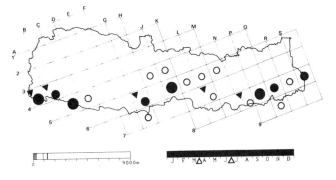

JUNGLE MYNAH *Acridotheres fuscus*

Subspecies *fuscus*. First recorded by B. Hodgson (348). A common resident from the tarai up to 1525m. Noted up to 2200m at Khaptad (C3) in April and May 1988 (428). Subject to local seasonal movements which are poorly understood. Abundant at Chitwan in spring (432) but absent in December (460). Common throughout the year in the Kathmandu Valley but less numerous in winter (629). Breeding confirmed at Chitwan (296), Hetaura (105) and in the Kathmandu Valley (629,708). Inhabits well-wooded areas, cultivation, and edges of towns and villages. **Range** Himalayas from Murree

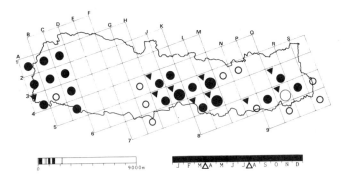

east to Arunachal Pradesh, and south locally throughout the peninsula to s. India.

HILL MYNAH *Gracula religiosa*
Talking Mynah, Grackle

Subspecies *intermedia*. First recorded by B. Hodgson (348). A resident, occasionally found in the central and eastern lowlands, mainly up to 455m. Noted at 1025m in Ilam District (R8) in December (658). Subject to some local and poorly understood seasonal movements. Breeding confirmed at Chitwan (296) and Hetaura (105). One noted in the Kathmandu Valley on 21 December 1980 (576) was probably an escaped bird. Frequents moist broadleaved forests. **Range** Himalayas from Kumaon east to Arunachal Pradesh; n.e. India and Bangladesh; hills of the n.e. peninsula; W. Ghats.

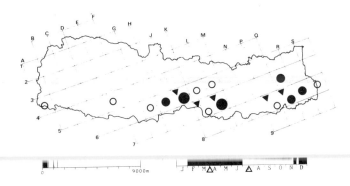

HOUSE SPARROW *Passer domesticus*

First recorded by B. Hodgson (388). An abundant resident from the tarai up to 1600m, occasionally reported up to 2135m. Possibly subject to some local altitudinal movements. Breeding confirmed at Sukla Phanta (432), Surkhet (D4) (626), Nepalganj (626), Chitwan (296), and in the Kathmandu Valley (626,659, 481). *P. d. indicus* (i) has been found up to 1500m (245,482,647). The birds above this altitude are likely to be *P. d. parkini* but specimens are lacking. Birds in the Kathmandu Valley are intermediate between the two races (ip) (105). Frequents villages, towns and nearby cultivation. In

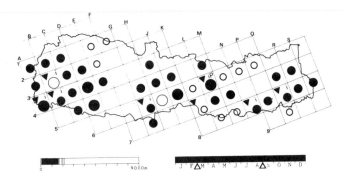

the Kathmandu Valley chiefly occurs in urban areas. **Range** Throughout the subcontinent.

SPANISH SPARROW *Passer hispaniolensis*
Willow Sparrow

Subspecies *transcaspicus*. Vagrant. First
recorded at Kosi Barrage where a flock of
50 was seen on 16 February 1981 by D.
Mills *et al*. (65,559). The only other records are of up to three in mid-March 1982
(682,770), also at Kosi. At least three
males showing intermediate features between Spanish and House Sparrows were
observed in a party of about 20 sparrows
on 17 and 18 February 1981 at Kosi Barrage (180). Frequents cultivation and
semi-desert. **Range** A winter visitor to the
plains of n. Pakistan and n.w. India.

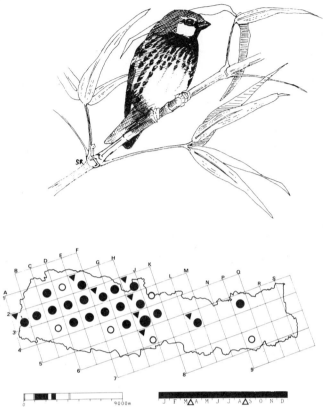

CINNAMON SPARROW *Passer rutilans*
Cinnamon Tree Sparrow, Russet Sparrow

Obtained by B. Hodgson in his later collection (409) but the specimen may have
originated in India. First definitely recorded by F.M. Bailey at Chari Gaon (E2)
on 14 June 1936 (62). A resident subject
to some altitudinal movements. Fairly
common in the Kali Gandaki valley and
westwards; uncommon further east to
Kathmandu. A total of about 50 was seen
at the unusually low altitude of 75m near
Kosi (718). Most frequently reported
between 1000m and 2900m, although it is
also common in Dolpo and Mustang Districts up to 4270m in summer. Also found
breeding at much lower altitudes, at 915m
at Phewa Tal (153) and at 2590m at Sikha

(H5) (153). Frequents open forest and cultivation near hill
villages. **Range** Himalayas from Chitral and Kashmir east to
Arunachal Pradesh; n.e. India.

EURASIAN TREE SPARROW *Passer montanus*
Tree Sparrow

First recorded by B. Hodgson (388). An
abundant resident subject to altitudinal
movements. Occurs chiefly between
610m and 4270m. May withdraw from
higher levels in winter but noted as high
as 3795m in February 1982 (770). Proved
breeding at Tansen (H6) (230), Bhimpedi
(105), Chitwan (67) and in the Kathmandu Valley (629,708). Also breeds at
the unusually low altitude of 75m at Kosi
Tappu where it occurs from January to
May (327). Co-exists with House Sparrow
in Kathmandu and elsewhere. Two races
occur: *P. m. malaccensis* (m) up to 2000m
(62,105,482) and *P. m. tibetanus* (t) at

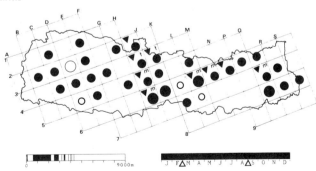

higher altitudes (512,647). Frequents towns, villages and
adjacent cultivation. **Range** N. Baluchistan; Himalayas
from N.W.F.P. east to Arunachal Pradesh; n.e. India.

CHESTNUT-SHOULDERED PETRONIA *Petronia xanthocollis*
Yellow-throated Sparrow

Subspecies*xanthocollis*. First recorded by
B. Hodgson (388). A resident subject to
local movements, found mainly up to
305m. Occasionally seen in the far west
(A4,B4,C4,C5) and at Chitwan; uncommon elsewhere. Proved breeding at Chitwan (296). Inhabits open dry forest,
thorn jungle and trees at the edge of
cultivation. **Range** Pakistan and the
whole of the Indian peninsula east to
Bengal.

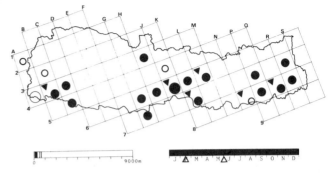

PLAIN-BACKED SNOWFINCH
Montifringilla blanfordi
Blanford's Snowfinch

Subspecies *blanfordi*. Status uncertain,
possibly a scarce resident. The only record received is of one collected at Neachachung, Mustang (H3) at 4815m on 13
June 1977 by H.S. Nepali (587). It was
found within 100m of birds of the two
following species. Inhabits the Tibetan
steppe. **Range** N. Nepal and n. Sikkim.

RUFOUS-NECKED SNOWFINCH
Montifringilla ruficollis
Red-necked Snowfinch

Status uncertain, possibly a scarce resident. The first record
was of one collected one at Neachachung, Mustang (H3) at
4815m on 13 June 1977 by H.S. Nepali (587). Singles seen at
Pipar Hill (H5) at 3290m, and on nearby Kumai Hill at
3340m both in October 1979 (499) were possibly the same
individual. The only other records are of a flock of about 20
seen near Khumjung (P6) at 3700m on 29 October 1987 and
one above Dugla (P6) at 4850m on 5 November 1987 after
a severe blizzard (558). Frequents open stony areas and
short grassland in the Tibetan steppe. **Range** N. Nepal and
n. Sikkim.

WHITE-RUMPED SNOWFINCH *Montifringilla taczanowskii*
Mandelli's Snowfinch

Status uncertain, possibly a scarce resident. The only record received is of one
collected at Neachachung, Mustang (H3)

at 4815m on 13 June 1977 by H.S. Nepali (587). Found in
open stony Tibetan steppe habitat. **Range** N. Nepal and n.
Sikkim.

TIBETAN SNOWFINCH *Montifringilla adamsi*
Adams' Snowfinch, Black-winged Snowfinch

Subspecies *adamsi*. First definitely recorded near Saldang, Dolpo (G3) at
4330m on 16 June 1971 by R.L. Fleming
Jr. (224,246). A common resident in
Dolpo and Mustang Districts. Breeds between 3600m and 4500m (50,664), and is
subject to some poorly understood altitudinal movements. Reported between
November and March from 2530m to
3445m in the upper Kali Gandaki valley
(765,403), on Thorong La (H4) (298),
near Langtang village (M5) (180) and in
Khumbu (546,595,596). Occurs on open
stony hillsides, plateaux and near upland
villages. **Range** N. Himalayas from Ladakh east to Sikkim.

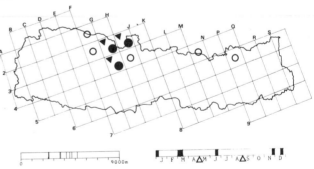

BLACK-BREASTED WEAVER *Ploceus benghalensis*
Black-throated Weaver

First recorded by B. Hodgson (388). A locally distributed resident in the lowlands, occurring up to 245m. Subject to some local movements. Fairly common at Sukla Phanta (700), Chitwan (296) and on Kosi marshes (P8,Q8). Breeding confirmed at Tilaurakot (G6) (157), and Chitwan (296). Frequents tall, damp grassland and reedy marshes. **Range** Mainly in the Gangetic plain east to n.e. India and Bangladesh, but also very locally in Pakistan, Gujarat and near Bombay.

STREAKED WEAVER *Ploceus manyar*

Subspecies *flaviceps*. First recorded at Kosi Barrage by S.C. Madge *et al.* who found a flock of 20 on 8 February 1974 (518). A very local resident and local migrant, in the tarai. In 1976 described as common and breeding at Kosi from June to August (293) but only a few other reports from the area, between February and August. The only other record is from Sukla Phanta where about 17 were seen on 4 May 1982 (432). Inhabits reedy marshes. **Range** Throughout the subcontinent, except some parts of the northwest.

BAYA WEAVER *Ploceus philippinus*

First recorded by B. Hodgson (388,798). A common resident from the tarai up to 1370m, subject to seasonal movements. In the Himalayas mainly a summer visitor. Breeding confirmed near Taulihawa (G6) (157), north-west of Pokhara (499), at Chitwan (296,652), in the Kathmandu Valley (629,708,756,321), Sunischare (321), and elsewhere in the eastern lowlands (P8,Q8) (293,432). Two races occur: *P. p. philippinus* (p) (190,647), *P. p. burmanicus* (b) (247) and also intermediates (pb) (62,105,632). Frequents cultivation and grassland with scattered bushes and trees. **Range** Throughout the subcontinent.

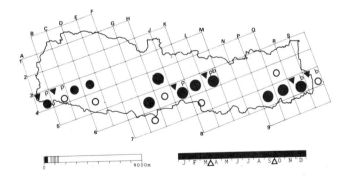

RED AVADAVAT *Amandava amandava*
Red Munia

Subspecies *amandava*. Obtained by B. Hodgson in his later collection (409) but the specimen may have originated in India. First definitely recorded by F.M. Bailey at Bilauri (A4) on 11 February 1937 (62). A locally distributed resident, seen occasionally up to 305m. Noted up to 670m at Bulbuli, near Surkhet (D4) in August 1979 (244). Regularly found at Sukla Phanta, Kosi Barrage, and at Chitwan where proved breeding (296). One seen in Kathmandu was probably an escaped cage-bird (546). Frequents reedy marshes and tall grassland. **Range** Throughout most of the subcontinent.

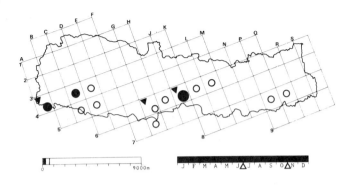

INDIAN SILVERBILL *Euodice malabarica*
White-throated Munia   (*Lonchura malabarica*)

First definitely recorded at Raghunathpur (N8) at 275m in December 1953 by R.L. Fleming Sr (647). An uncommon resident in the tarai and duns up to 305m. Several reports from Kosi and Nepalganj. Mainly single records from elsewhere. Found breeding in old weaver nests at Biratnagar in November (243). Frequents cultivation, grassland and open scrub country. Occurs in drier habitats than other munias. **Range** Throughout the subcontinent.

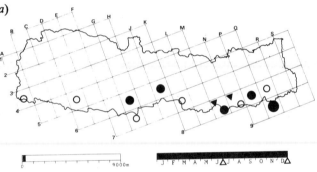

STRIATED MUNIA *Lonchura striata*
Sharp-tailed Munia, White-backed Munia, White-rumped Munia

Subspecies *acuticauda*. First recorded by B. Hodgson (354,798). A local resident, subject to seasonal movements. Seen regularly throughout the year up to about 1220m; but mainly a summer visitor from this altitude up to 2135m. Fairly common near Pokhara and uncommon in the Kathmandu Valley where proved breeding (629). Occasionally reported from elsewhere. Inhabits open wooded areas and scrub near cultivation. **Range** Himalayas from Garhwal east to Arunachal Pradesh; n.e. India and Bangladesh; peninsular India south from s. Gujarat and s. Bihar.

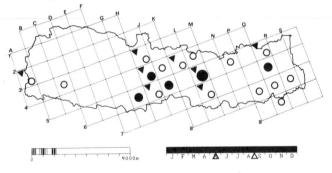

SCALY-BREASTED MUNIA *Lonchura punctulata*
Spotted Munia, Nutmeg Mannikin

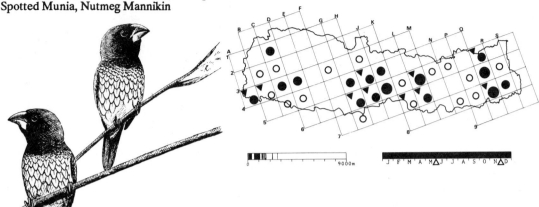

Subspecies *punctulata*. First recorded by B. Hodgson (354). A fairly common resident. Occurs mainly up to 1525m throughout the year, but noted at 2680m in the Dhorpatan valley (F4) in summer 1981 (499). Proved breeding at Chitwan (296); in the Kathmandu Valley (629), in the eastern lowlands (Q8) (293) and as high as 1670m at Uttarpani (Q7) (613). Forages in cultivation, grassland and bushes. **Range** The whole of the subcontinent east and south of a line from Kathiawar to Madhupur.

CHESTNUT MUNIA *Lonchura malacca*
Black-headed Munia

First recorded by B. Hodgson (351). Locally distributed and chiefly found from the tarai up to 1220m. Probably resident. Reported to be fairly common and proved breeding at Chitwan (296). In 1877 described as a common breeding summer visitor to the Kathmandu Valley (708) but there are very few later records. Occasionally seen from April to September in the eastern tarai (P8) (293). Several sightings from the Kosi marshes; mainly single reports from elsewhere. Collected in breeding condition at Hetaura in July (105). Two intergrading races occur: *L. m. rubroniger* (r) (105,247,798) and *L. m. atricapilla* (a) (234,246). The nests and eggs of these races are undescribed. Frequents cultivation and grassland. **Range** Ambala and Lucknow east to n.e. India and Bangladesh, and south to Orissa; Bombay and Raipur south to s. India.

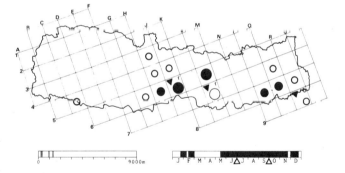

COMMON CHAFFINCH *Fringilla coelebs*

Subspecies *coelebs*. First recorded at Rara at 3050m on 6 February 1971 by R. L. Fleming Jr. (9). An uncommon winter visitor found mainly between 2000m and 2750m, but may descend to lower altitudes in cold winters. Noted as low as 1555m at Lumle (H5) in November 1981 (146). Only three records received from east of the Kali Gandaki valley; in the upper Langtang valley (M5) in January 1981 (180), in the upper Marsyangdi valley (J4) (158) and at Goraibas (S7) in March 1989 (549). Frequents conifer forests and bushy areas. **Range** Winter visitor to Kohat, Gilgit, and Nepal.

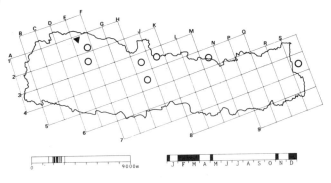

BRAMBLING *Fringilla montifringilla*

First recorded by R.L. Fleming Jr. at Rara and Jumla in winter 1971 (243). An erratic winter visitor, seen mainly in the north and north-west between 2135m and 3050m. Occasionally reported from the upper Kali Gandaki valley in severe winters. The maximum of 30 was noted at Tukche on 18 March 1982 (207,561). In the cold winter of 1978 two were found on Sheopuri summit (243) and one near Godavari at 1525m, both records in January (243,746). Habitat is similar to that of Common Chaffinch. **Range** Winters in n. Baluchistan, and in the Himalayas from N.W.F.P. east to Nepal.

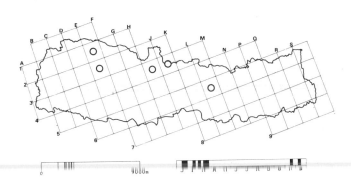

FIRE-FRONTED SERIN *Serinus pusillus*
Red-fronted Serin, Gold-fronted Serin, or Finch

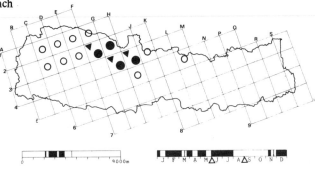

FIRE-FRONTED SERIN, cont'd ...

First recorded by O. Polunin on 12 April 1952 at Jumla at 2345m (620). Fairly common, presumably a resident subject to altitudinal movements. Mainly seen above 2440m but found as high as 4575m in summer; occasionally down to 2100m in winter. Regularly seen in the upper Kali Gandaki valley and westwards; few reports from further east. Found at Manang in November 1981 (553,554) and November 1984 (142), at Hinko (H5) in January 1983 (748), and near Syabru (L5) in March 1987 (484). Frequents Tibetan steppe habitat in summer; bushes and small trees in winter. **Range** N. Baluchistan; Himalayas from Chitral east to Nepal.

TIBETAN SERIN *Serinus thibetanus*
Tibetan Siskin *(Carduelis thibetana)*

First recorded at Godavari at 1525m on 28 January 1952 by D. Proud (634). A local winter visitor, occurring between 1050m and 3355m. Most frequent in the Kathmandu Valley, particularly the Royal Botanic Gardens, Godavari where it occurs from the end of November to end of March (57). The maximum of several hundred birds was reported there in February 1953 (635). Uncommon elsewhere. A flock near Jhingrana (C3) at about 2100m on 18 March 1989 (68) is the most westerly wintering record for the

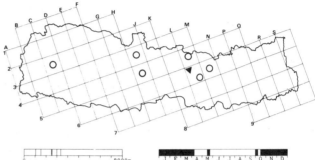

species. Mainly occurs in alders. **Range** Possibly breeds in Arunachal Pradesh. Winters in the Himalayas from Nepal east to Arunachal Pradesh.

SPECTACLED FINCH *Callacanthis burtoni*
Red-browed Finch

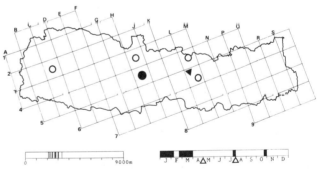

First recorded on Sheopuri at 2500m on 25 March 1961 by D. Proud (639). A local and erratic winter visitor; possibly also breeds but not definitely known to be resident. Regularly occurs near Ghorepani. Found to be fairly common there in February and March 1982 but scarce in some winters. Chiefly single records from elsewhere. Only one summer record: from Ghorepani on 24 July 1978 (688). Frequents forests of fir, oak, hemlock and rhododendron. **Range** Himalayas from Safed Koh and Chitral east to Sikkim.

YELLOW-BREASTED GREENFINCH   *Carduelis spinoides*
Himalayan Goldfinch, Himalayan Greenfinch

Subspecies *spinoides*. First recorded by B. Hodgson (388). A common resident, subject to altitudinal movements. Breeds mainly between 2440m and 3700m, but noted up to 4400m in Khumbu (190). Winters chiefly from 915m to 1850m; rarely in the tarai. A flock of 20 was seen on 4 May 1982 at 160m at Sukla Phanta. Inhabits cultivation, forest edges; also in shrubberies above the treeline in Khumbu (190). **Range** Himalayas from Hazara and Murree east to Arunachal Pradesh.

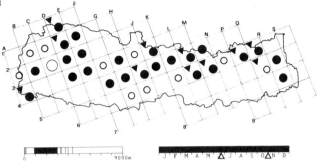

EURASIAN GOLDFINCH   *Carduelis carduelis*
Goldfinch

Subspecies *caniceps*. First recorded by D. Lowndes at Manangbhot (J4) at 3660m on 28 June 1950 (54). An uncommon resident, subject to altitudinal movements which are poorly understood in Nepal. Summers mainly between 2450m and 4200m. Found chiefly between 1920m and 2440m in winter, but collected as low as 75m at Nepalganj in January (243). Found in the Langtang valley near Syabru (100) and Ghorpagaon (207), also in Helambu (243,585); the most easterly localities for the species in the Himalayas. Frequents upland cultivation, shrubberies above the treeline and open coniferous forest. **Range** N. Baluchistan; Himalayas from N.W.F.P. east to Nepal.

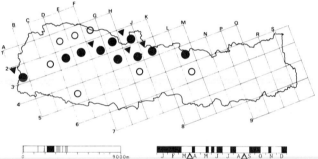

EURASIAN SISKIN   *Carduelis spinus*
Siskin

Vagrant. A male was found at Nagarjung at 1500m on 7 April 1982 by C. Winyard *et al.* (207,561). The second published record from the Indian subcontinent. Inhabits conifers. **Range** Vagrant to Himachal Pradesh and Nepal.

COMMON LINNET *Carduelis cannabina*
Linnet (*Acanthis cannabina*)

Subspecies *bella*. Vagrant. First recorded by R.L. Fleming Sr. in small flocks in Jumla District between 2370m and 2410m in January and February 1971 (9,243).

The only other record is of one seen at Bhoudigaon, south of Jumla on 17 January 1977 (212). Found in meadows, cultivation and bushes. **Range** N. Himalayas from Gilgit east to Nepal.

TWITE *Carduelis flavirostris*
Tibetan Twite (*Acanthis flavirostris*)

First recorded on Gosainkund Pass on 15 and 18 June 1964, between 4200m and 4500m by M. Desfayes (188). Probably resident. Found between 3965m and 4500m. Possibly subject to altitudinal movements, but these are little known. Fairly common in Dolpo (G3) and Mustang (H3), uncommon in the upper Kali Gandaki valley and rare further east. Frequents boulder-strewn alpine meadows and stony hills. **Range** N. Himalayas from Chitral east to n. Sikkim.

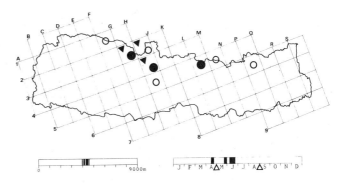

COMMON CROSSBILL *Loxia curvirostra*
Crossbill, Red Crossbill

Subspecies *himalayensis*. First recorded by B. Hodgson (116,388,798). Occasional. Residential status is uncertain and movements are poorly understood. Reported mainly between 2590m and 3660m. Breeding behaviour for this subspecies is little known; presumably breeds in any month depending on the crop of cones like other crossbills. An adult seen feeding young on 8 March 1987 at Kalopani (H4) at about 2530m (480). Found in hemlocks. **Range** Himalayas from Lahul east to Arunachal Pradesh.

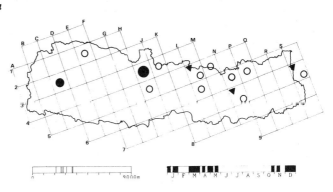

PLAIN MOUNTAIN-FINCH *Leucosticte nemoricola*
Hodgson's Mountain-Finch

Subspecies *nemoricola*. The species was described from Nepal by B. Hodgson (354,798). A common resident, subject to altitudinal movements. Summers chiefly between 4200m and 5200m and winters between 2000m and at least 3650m. Noted at 1650m near Landrung (H5) in March 1989 (166). Breeding confirmed in Khumbu (190). Inhabits alpine meadows and scree slopes high above the treeline in summer; cultivation and open forest in winter. **Range** Himalayas fom Chitral east to Bhutan, and possibly Arunachal Pradesh.

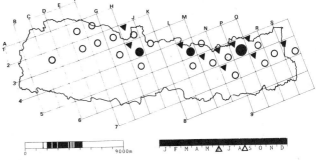

BLACK-HEADED MOUNTAIN-FINCH *Leucosticte brandti*
Brandt's Mountain-Finch

Subspecies *haematopygia*. First recorded at Tingegaon (G3) at 5060m on 18 June 1952 by O. Polunin (620). A fairly common resident, subject to some altitudinal movements. Generally occurs at higher altitudes than Plain Mountain-Finch. Summers chiefly between 4200m and 5250m, but noted at 6000m on 18 June 1952 in the Dolpo (G3) (620). Usually winters above 3500m, but during the particularly cold winter of 1982 found down to 2350m north-west of Pokhara (682,770). A large flock of about 600 was seen at Jomosom on 9 February 1982

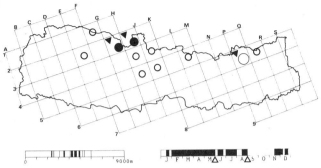

(682). Frequents stony slopes and alpine meadows. **Range** Himalayas from Chitral east to Sikkim.

MONGOLIAN FINCH *Bucanetes mongolicus*
Mongolian Desert Finch, Mongolian Trumpeter Finch
(*Rhodopechys mongolica*)

Vagrant. First recorded by R.L. Fleming Jr. who found a flock of 16 in the Muktinath valley at 3505m on 25 June 1976 (243). The only other reports were during the particularly severe winter of 1982: a party of 34 was noted near Jomosom on 8 February (641), and one on 9 February (606,682). Found in dry rocky areas. Range Himalayas from Ladakh east to Nepal.

BLANFORD'S ROSEFINCH *Carpodacus rubescens*
Crimson Rosefinch

The first record is of a specimen in Mandelli's collection from Dolakha, Bhota Kosi valley (N6) in August 1875 (104). Scarce. It is not clear whether the species is resident, and movements in Nepal are poorly known. Reported between 2745m and 3050m in August and September: collected at Gatlang, Landang Busli and Mangning (L5) in 1935 (62), and at Tarke Gyang (M5) in 1949 (619,621); also south of Bhairakund (M6) in October 1973 (589). Found between 2315m and 3050m in winter. Several reports of up to five birds east of Ghorepani (H5): in December 1985 (546), March 1986 (264,321,260), March 1987 (480) and December 1989 (176,729); also up to five seen at Chitre

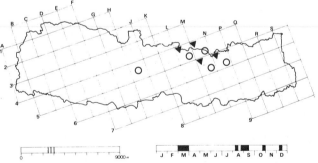

(H5) in March 1987 (594). Breeding behaviour is unknown. Frequents glades in conifer, or mixed conifer and birch forests. **Range** Himalayas from Nepal east to Arunachal Pradesh.

DARK-BREASTED ROSEFINCH   *Carpodacus nipalensis*
Nepal Rosefinch

Subspecies *nipalensis*. The species was described from Nepal by B. Hodgson (354,798). A fairly common altitudinal migrant. Summers chiefly between 3050m and 3900m; winters between 1830m and 2745m, and sometimes down to 1500m. Breeding behaviour is little known. Trapped with a brood patch at Chankeli at 3050m in July 1979 (626), and collected in breeding condition at Khumjung (P6), between 3900m and 4000m on 30 June and 6 July 1962 (190). Inhabits rhododendron and fir forests, and shrubberies above the treeline, in summer; also in cul-

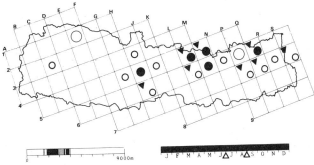

tivation and forest clearings in winter. **Range** Himalayas from Kashmir east to Arunachal Pradesh.

COMMON ROSEFINCH   *Carpodacus erythrinus*
Scarlet Rosefinch

First collected by B. Hodgson (388). Fairly common, *C. e. roseatus* (r) is an altitudinal migrant. Summers mainly between 3350m and 4000m, and winters from 1500m down to the foothills. *C. e. erythrinus* (e) is a winter visitor, reported chiefly between 275m and 2000m. The only record of *C. e. kubanensis* (k) is of one collected at Rekcha (D4) at about 1525m in December 1948 (659). Inhabits shrubberies and open coniferous and birch forests in summmer; cultivation with bushes, and open wooded country in winter. **Range** Breeds in n. Baluchistan, and in the Himalayas from Chitral east to

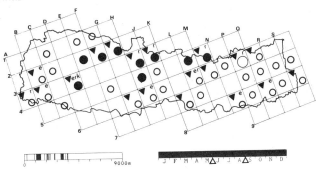

Bhutan and possibly Arunachal Pradesh. Winters throughout the subcontinent.

BEAUTIFUL ROSEFINCH   *Carpodacus pulcherrimus*

Subspecies *pulcherrimus*. The species was described from Nepal by F. Moore, from a specimen in Hodgson's later collection (409,798), but it may have originated in India. First definitely recorded by F.M. Bailey on 18 July 1936 at Bito-kola (D2) (62). A common resident, subject to altitudinal movements. Summers mainly between 3600m and 4650m, and winters between 2100m and at least 3300m. Breeding confirmed in Khumbu (190). Found in bushes on steep slopes, and cultivation in winter; in rhododendron shrubberies, Caragana scrub and on stony slopes in summer. **Range** Himalayas from Garhwal east to Arunachal Pradesh.

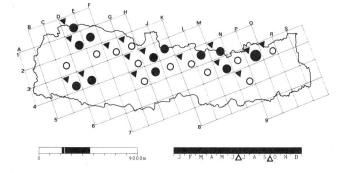

PINK-BROWED ROSEFINCH *Carpodacus rhodochrous*

First recorded by B. Hodgson (388). A
fairly common resident, subject to altitudinal movements. Summers chiefly between 3050m and 3900m. Winters mainly
from 3000m down to 1800m, and occasionally down to 915m. Frequents fir and
birch forests and shrubberies of rhododendron and juniper in summer; oak forests in winter. **Range** Himalayas from
Kashmir east to Sikkim.

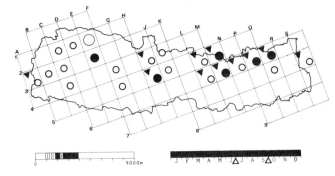

VINACEOUS ROSEFINCH *Carpodacus vinaceus*

Subspecies *vinaceus*. First recorded by
R.L. Fleming Sr. at Belbahadi (B4) at
1065m in December 1952 (647). It was
identified initially as a Dark-rumped
Rosefinch, but has been reidentified by
the Chicago Field Museum (9). Scarce.
Status uncertain, probably a breeding
resident. Reported between 1065m and
3050m in winter; and between 3050m and
3200m in summer. A few records from the
upper Kali Gandaki valley between February and November (527,770) including
a laying female collected near Chadziou
Khola on 3 July 1973 (50). Three reports
from east of Ghorepani: in March
(650,463) and December (176,729).
Single records from near Chandrakot
(H5) in March (147), Sukarmala (C4) in
November (162), Machapuchare and
Milke Danda (Q7) in winter (undated)

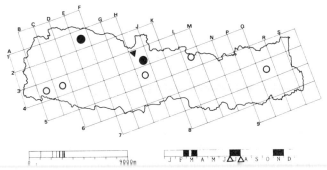

(50), Langtang (L5) in May (421), and trapped at Chankheli
in July 1979 (626). Breeding behaviour is poorly known.
Inhabits bamboo and dense bushes in forest. **Range** Himalayas at Naini Tal and in Nepal.

DARK-RUMPED ROSEFINCH *Carpodacus edwardsii*
Edwards' Rosefinch, Large Rosefinch

Subspecies *rubicunda*. Scarce, status uncertain. A Hodgson specimen was listed
for Nepal by Sharpe (718) but it may have
originated in India. First definitely recorded by H. Stevens from the upper Mai
valley (S7) at 2440m on 28 March 1912
(740). Found nearby, on the Singhalila
ridge (S7) at 3635m in May 1989 (704).
The only other confirmed reports are
from Gosainkund between 3200m and

3505m in May: a maximum of 12 was noted at Gapte, also
seen at Mungun (L5) and Chandabari (L5) in 1980 (440)
and at Gapte in 1986 (321). These are the most westerly
records for the species. A specimen of Vinaceous
Rosefinch, taken in the west in winter was initially misiden-
tified as this species (50,647,664). Breeding behaviour is
little known. Frequents open rhododendron or birch forests; also rhododendron and juniper shrubberies. **Range**
Himalayas from Nepal east to Arunachal Pradesh.

SPOT-WINGED ROSEFINCH *Carpodacus rhodopeplus*

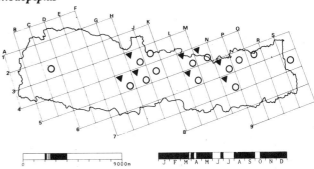

Subspecies *rhodopeplus*. First recorded by B. Hodgson (388). A locally distributed resident, subject to altitudinal movements. Fairly common near Ghorepani in winter, in the upper Kali Gandaki valley, and in Langtang (L5); occasionally seen at Khaptad (C3) and in the Barun valley (Q6), uncommon elsewhere. Summers mainly between 3050m and 4000m, and winters between 2000m and 3050m. Breeding behaviour is poorly known. Inhabits rhododendron shrubberies above the treeline and grassy slopes in summer; dense bushes in forests and damp ravines in winter. **Range** Himalayas in the hills north of Chakrata and Mussoorie, e. Kumaon, Nepal and Sikkim.

WHITE-BROWED ROSEFINCH *Carpodacus thura*

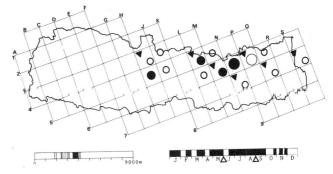

Subspecies *thura*. First recorded by B. Hodgson (336,388). A fairly common resident, subject to altitudinal movements. Summers chiefly between 3800m and 4200m. Winters mainly beteen 2440m and 3660m, but noted as low as 1830m at Ulleri (H5) on 19 December 1981 (309). Proved breeding at Dolaka (N6) (414). Found in dwarf rhododendron and juniper shrubberies and alpine meadows in summer; open bushy hillsides in winter. **Range** Himalayas from N.W.F.P. east to Arunachal Pradesh.

STREAKED ROSEFINCH *Carpodacus rubicilloides*
Eastern Great Rosefinch, Streaked Great Rosefinch, Crimson-eared Rosefinch

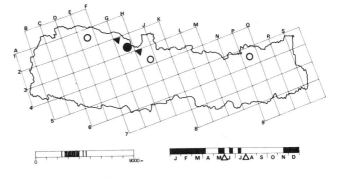

Subspecies *lucifer*. First recorded in December 1949 by R.L. Fleming Sr., in the upper Kali Gandaki valley at Thinigaon at 2805m, and at Jomosom at 2865m (647). Fairly common from mid-November to early April, between 2800m and 3660m, in the upper Kali Gandaki valley north of Jomosom, and near Muktinath. Summers in the Dolpo (G3) up to 4575m (224,587). The only other records are from Rara in February 1977 (464) and Gorak Shep (P6) in May 1987 (769). Occurs on open stony ground in summer and scrub in dry habitats. **Range** N. Himalayas and Tibetan plateau from Ladakh east to Bhutan.

GREAT ROSEFINCH   *Carpodacus rubicilla*
Spot-crowned Rosefinch

Subspecies *severtzovi*. First recorded on 1 August 1962 by R.L. Fleming Sr., at Gokyo Pokhari (P6) at 4575m (247). Occasional, presumably resident. Usually shows little altitudinal movement. Reported chiefly between 3660m and 5000m. Noted as low as 2650m in the upper Kali Gandaki valley in 1982, during a particularly cold winter (57,682) and at 5350m near Everest Base Camp (P6) in March 1986 (546). Breeding behaviour is poorly known. Confirmed breeding in Khumbu, where juveniles were collected at 5000m on 24 August 1962 (190). Frequents the higher part of the alpine zone, on sparsely vegetated and rocky ground. **Range** N. Himalayas from Chitral east to Sikkim.

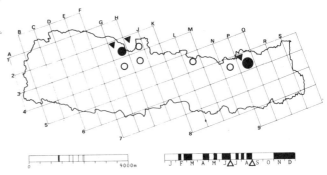

RED-FRONTED ROSEFINCH   *Carpodacus puniceus*
Red-breasted Rosefinch

Subspecies *puniceus*. The species was described from Nepal by E. Blyth, from a Hodgson specimen (116,798). A high altitude resident, subject to some altitudinal movements. Summers between 4265m and 5490m. In winter noted at least as high as 4575m (243), and there have been several reports from about 2745m in the upper Kali Gandaki valley after cold spells. Noted as low as 2980m at Rara in September (68). Breeding behaviour is poorly known. Taken in breeding condition on 29 July and 3 August 1962 at Gokyo at 4850m and 5100m (190). Habitat is similar to that of the Streaked Rosefinch. **Range** N. Himalayas from Ladakh east to Arunachal Pradesh.

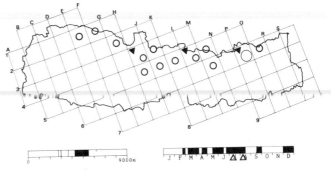

CRIMSON-BROWED FINCH   *Propyrrhula subhimachala*
Juniper Finch, Red-headed Rosefinch   (*Pinicola subhimachala*)

The species was described from Nepal by B. Hodgson (354,798). An uncommon resident, showing some altitudinal movements. Summers chiefly between 3500m and 4000m; winters from 2590m up to at least 3050m. Localities include Phulchowki and east of Ghorepani in winter, and in Langtang (L5,M5). Found twice in the upper Kali Gandaki valley in May 1978 (762,159), the most westerly records of the species. Reported in the Namlang valley (F2) (447), but confirmation of its occurrence so far west is desirable. Breeding behaviour is poorly known. Collected in breeding condition at Trashinga (P6) at 3550m on 9 August 1962 (190). Frequents dense bushes near the treeline in summer; forests with thick undergrowth in winter. Favours junipers. **Range** Himalayas from Nepal east to Arunachal Pradesh; n.e. India.

CRIMSON-BROWED FINCH, cont'd ...

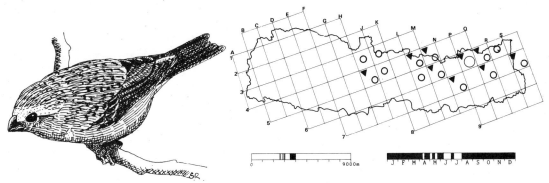

SCARLET FINCH *Haematospiza sipahi*

The species was described from Nepal by
B. Hodgson (354). Uncommon and locally distributed, presumably resident.
Subject to altitudinal movements, but
these are not clearly understood. Reported between 2135m and 3100m in
May, and winters from 1220m up to at
least 2560m. Regularly seen in the lower
Langtang valley in spring, and near
Ghorepani and on Sheopuri in winter.
Breeding behaviour is little known. Inhabits ravines and clearings in dense
broadleaved forests, especially near
streams. **Range** Himalayas from Garhwal
east to Arunachal Pradesh, n.e. India.

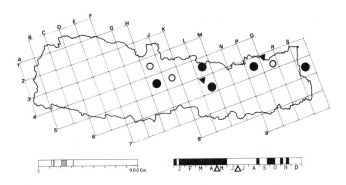

GOLD-NAPED FINCH *Pyrrhoplectes epauletta*
Gold-crowned Black Finch

The species was described from Nepal by
B. Hodgson (354). Probably resident but
has mainly been reported in winter. Subject to altitudinal movements which are
poorly understood in Nepal. Seen at
3260m and 3355m in May, and between
1525m and 3000m in winter. Uncommon
on Phulchowki; several reports from
north-west of Pokhara and in the upper
Mai valley; single records from most
other localities. Breeding behaviour is
unknown. Noted carrying nesting material or food on 10 March 1988 at Hanga
Tham (465). Frequents dense undergrowth in oak and rhododendron forests
in winter, and rhododendron shrubberies
in summer. **Range** Himalayas from Simla
east to Arunachal Pradesh.

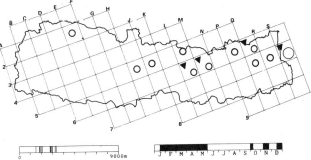

BROWN BULLFINCH   *Pyrrhula nipalensis*

Subspecies *nipalensis*. The species was described from Nepal by B. Hodgson (354,798). Locally distributed, probably resident. Shows little altitudinal movement: recorded between 1600m and 3050m in winter, and up to 3200m in summer. Occasionally seen on Phulchowki throughout the year; also on Sheopuri, at Ghorepani, in Langtang, and in the upper Arun and upper Mai valleys. Mainly single reports from elsewhere. Breeding behaviour is unknown. Noted in June with nesting material at 2380m (243). Found in dense, moist broadleaved forests. **Range** Himalayas from Dharmsala east to Arunachal Pradesh; n.e. India.

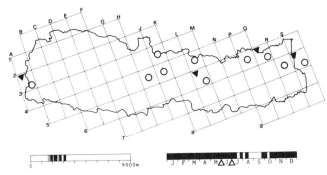

RED-HEADED BULLFINCH   *Pyrrhula erythrocephala*

First recorded by B. Hodgson (388). A fairly common resident, subject to some altitudinal movements. Summers mainly between 3050m and 4000m. May descend in winter to 1830m, but resident at 3865m around Tengboche (P6) (558). Frequents low bushes in broadleaved forests. Favours rhododendrons. **Range** Himalayas from Kashmir east to e. Bhutan.

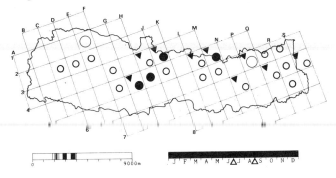

[BLACK-AND-YELLOW GROSBEAK   *Mycerobas icterioides*
(*Coccothraustes icterioides*)

Reported by D. Proud from the Gandak-Kosi watershed in May 1952 (633), but probably in error for Collared Grosbeak.

Range Himalayas from N.W.F.P. east to Garhwal; also a specimen from Darjeeling in Leningrad Museum (592).]

COLLARED GROSBEAK   *Mycerobas affinis*
Allied Grosbeak   (*Coccothraustes affinis*)

First recorded by B. Hodgson (388). A resident, subject to altitudinal movements. Fairly common east to Langtang, uncommon further east. Summers chiefly between 3000m and 3900m, and winters down to 2440m. Noted as low as 1065m at Birethante (H5) in December 1982 (315).

Breeding behaviour is little known. Taken in breeding condition at Bigu (N6) at 3300m on 16 May 1962 (190). Seen carrying nesting material at Kalopani (H4) at 2560m, on 5 May 1981 (811). Frequents coniferous or mixed broadleaved/ coniferous forests. **Range** Himalayas from Hazara east to Arunachal Pradesh.

COLLARED GROSBEAK, cont'd ...

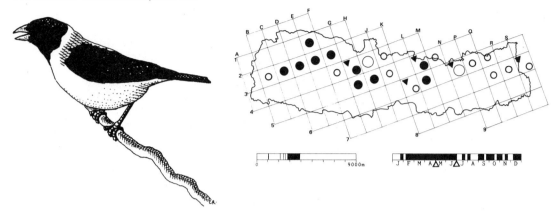

SPOT-WINGED GROSBEAK *Mycerobas melanozanthos*
(*Coccothraustes melanozanthos*)

The species was described from Nepal by B. Hodgson (354,798). Presumably resident. Altitudinal movements are poorly known. Reported between 1400m and 2135m in winter, and up to 3355m in summer. A regular winter visitor to Phulchowki, several records from north-west of Pokhara (H5) in winter, and Langtang in spring. Single reports from elsewhere. Inhabits mixed coniferous/ broadleaved forests. Range Himalayas from the Indus valley east to Arunachal Pradesh; n.e. India.

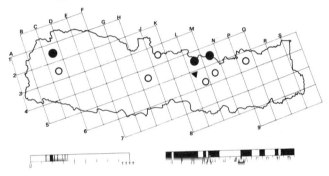

WHITE-WINGED GROSBEAK *Mycerobas carnipes*
(*Coccothraustes carnipes*)

Subspecies *carnipes*. The species was described from Nepal by B. Hodgson (354,798). A fairly common resident, subject to some altitudinal movements. Occurs chiefly between 3050m and 4200m. In winter may descend to 2745m, but sometimes remains at the higher levels. Frequents dwarf juniper and other shrubberies near the treeline in summer; forests in winter. Range Hills of Pakistan; Himalayas from Gilgit and Hazara east to Arunachal Pradesh.

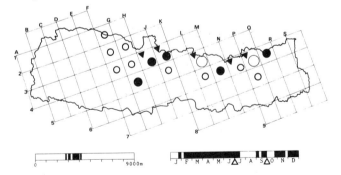

BLACK-FACED BUNTING   *Emberiza spodocephala*

Subspecies *sordida*. First recorded by B. Hodgson (388,798). An uncommon and local winter visitor and passage migrant, occurring from the tarai up to 1280m. Regularly reported from Kosi marshes, the Kathmandu Valley and, since 1984, from Phewa Tal.The only other records are from Chitwan. Inhabits long grass, edges of marshes, and rice paddies; usually found near water. **Range** Winter visitor to Nepal, n.e. India and Bangladesh. Vagrant west to Corbett.

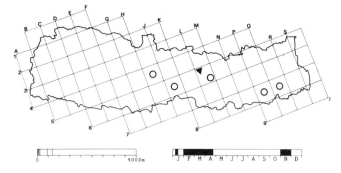

PINE BUNTING   *Emberiza leucocephalos*

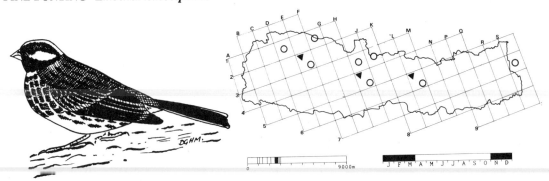

Subspecies *leucocephalos*. First recorded by the Seti River, north of Pokhara (H5) on 22 November 1953 by D. Proud (628,638). A winter visitor, found mainly above 2440m, but occasionally down to 915m. Fairly common in most winters in the upper Kali Gandaki valley, and in the north-west. A rare visitor to the Kathmandu Valley. Noted on the Singhalila ridge (S7) on 22 March 1989 (172), the most easterly record of the species in the Himalayas. Forages in cultivation and grassy areas with bushes. **Range** Winter visitor to Pakistan and the Himalayas from N.W.F.P. east to Nepal.

YELLOWHAMMER   *Emberiza citrinella*

Subspecies *erythrogenys*? First recorded at Kagbeni at 2810m on 25 February 1981 by D. Mills *et al*. (65,559); the first record for the Indian subcontinent. A scarce, irregular and very local winter visitor. Several reports from the Kali Gandaki valley (H4) between January and early April, in most winters between 1981 and 1987: a few birds between Kalopani and Jomosom from 2630m to 2745m, and as low as 1100m at Tatopani (770). The maximum seen, at least six, was at Jomosom in January 1983 (748). The only other confirmed record is of one or two seen at Jumla on 26 January 1983 (627). Found in cultivation; often with flocks of Pine Buntings. **Range** Vagrant to Ladakh and Nepal.

WHITE-CAPPED BUNTING   *Emberiza stewarti*
Chestnut-breasted Bunting

Vagrant. First recorded by F.M. Bailey at Banbassa (A4), at about 75m on 7 January 1937 (62). The only other records are of specimens taken at Tansen (H6) at 1370m in December 1951 (647), and at Barmdeo Mandi (A3) at 290m in January 1953 (647). Frequents fields and dry, grassy scrub jungle. **Range** Summers in n. Baluchistan, and in the Himalayas from Chitral east to Garhwal. Winters in the foothills from N.W.F.P. east to Nepal, and in n.w. India.

ROCK BUNTING   *Emberiza cia*
Eurasian Rock Bunting

First recorded by F.M. Bailey at Puma (E2) on 16 June 1936 (62). A resident, common in the north-west, and east to Manang. Shows little altitudinal movement. Found mainly above 2440m, up to 4600m in summer, and occasionally down to 1800m in winter. Found as low as 1450m in February 1988 at Silgadi Doti (B3) (68). Noted in the Gathlang valley (L5) on 26 October 1980 (516), and in Helambu on 30 January 1981 (300), the most easterly records of the species. The races *E. c. stracheyi* and *E. c. flemingorum* (f) (527) have been collected. Inhabits open grassy and rocky areas. **Range** Breeds in the Himalayas from N.W.F.P. east to Nepal. Winters south to Quetta and Delhi.

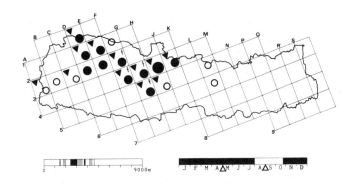

CHESTNUT-EARED BUNTING   *Emberiza fucata*
Grey-headed Bunting

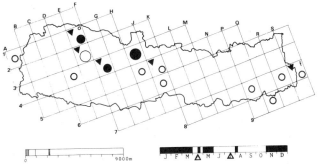

CHESTNUT-EARED BUNTING, cont'd ...

Obtained by B. Hodgson in his later collection (409), but the specimen may have originated in India. First definitely recorded by F.M. Bailey at Nekala (E2) on 9 June 1936 (62). Uncommon, probably resident. Altitudinal movements in Nepal are not clearly understood. Several winter reports from Kosi; uncommon elsewhere between 75m and 915m in winter. A few

reports from Jumla at about 2135m in May and August (587,620,626); adults and young common near the airport (244). Confirmed breeding near Dhaulagiri (H4) in 1973 (243). Two subspecies recorded: *E. f. arcuata* (a) (62), and *E. f. fucata* (f) (234,247). Summers on bushy hillsides, and winters by reedy streams, lakes and wet fields. **Range** Breeds in the Himalayas from Chitral east to Nepal. Winters down to the adjacent foothills and plains east to n.e. India and Bangladesh.

RUSTIC BUNTING *Emberiza rustica*

Subspecies *rustica*? Vagrant. A male was found at Sauraha (J6) at about 245m on 31 January 1981 by A. del-Nevo and P. Ewins (180,181). The only other records

are of another male seen at Kagbeni at about 2810m on 25 February 1981 (65) and two at Pokhara on 25 December 1989 (729). These are the first records for the subcontinent. **Range** Vagrant to Nepal.

LITTLE BUNTING *Emberiza pusilla*

First recorded by B. Hodgson (388). A fairly common winter visitor, occurring mainly between 75m and 2000m; rare up to 3050m. Also noted on spring passage in March and April (50). Feeds in stubble, and ploughed or grass fields. **Range** Winter visitor to Nepal, n.e. India and Bangladesh.

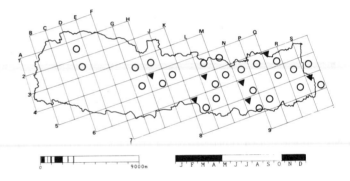

CHESTNUT BUNTING *Emberiza rutila*

Vagrant. The only record is of one collected at Godavari at 1525m in January 1954 by R.L. Fleming Sr. (647). Inhabits rice stubbles, bushes in cultivation, and

forest clearings (664). **Range** Scarce winter visitor to n.e. India; also recorded in the Himalayas in Chitral, Ladakh, Nepal and Sikkim.

YELLOW-BREASTED BUNTING *Emberiza aureola*

Subspecies *aureola*. First recorded by B. Hodgson (388). A common winter visitor and passage migrant, from the tarai up to 1370m. In the Kathmandu Valley it was described in 1955 as a winter visitor in large flocks, from the end of November to May (635). Noted recently mainly as a passage migrant, with some birds overwintering. Flocks of up to 400 are regularly seen in the eastern tarai (P8) from November to April (293). Enormous flocks reported flying to roost in March and April 1982: 3500 were estimated at Chitwan (770) and over 7000 at Kosi

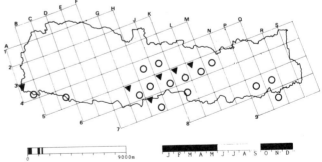

Tappu (199,227). Frequents cultivation and grasslands. **Range** Winter visitor to Nepal, n.e. India and Bangladesh.

REED BUNTING *Emberiza schoeniclus*
Common Reed Bunting

Subspecies unknown. Vagrant. The only
record is of two seen by T.P. Inskipp on 21
December 1970 at Begnas Tal (444).
Found in reedbeds and tall grass. **Range**
Winter visitor to Pakistan, n.w. India and
Nepal.

RED-HEADED BUNTING *Emberiza bruniceps*

Vagrant. A male was seen along the Narayani River, Chi-
twan, at about 130m on 15 April 1975, by R.L. Fleming and
H. Gilston (243,296). Frequents cultivation (664). **Range**
Breeds in n. Baluchistan. Winter visitor to the Indian
peninsula from Haryana east to Bangladesh, and south to s.
India.

BLACK-HEADED BUNTING *Emberiza melanocephala*

First recorded by H.S. Nepali who collected a specimen on 17 November 1969
at Balaju, Kathmandu Valley at 1340m
(591,589). A scarce winter visitor. The
other records are from the eastern tarai:

in December 1975 (293), Kosi Barrage in December 1984
(150), January 1985 (142) and March 1987 (769); also at
Damak (R8), where at least 15 were seen in December 1978
(134). **Range** Winter visitor to w. and central India and
Nepal. Migrates through Pakistan.

CRESTED BUNTING *Melophus lathami*

First recorded by B. Hodgson (354). A
fairly common resident, subject to altitudinal movements. Summers from 2440m
down to 1220m, and possibly even lower;
winters from 1460m down to the tarai.
Breeding confirmed in the Kathmandu
Valley (414), north-west of Pokhara
(811), and near Dhankuta (Q7) (446).
Inhabits cultivation, and hillsides with
rocks and bushes. **Range** Himalayan foothills from Hazara east to Arunachal
Pradesh, and south to Gujarat and
Raipur; n.e. India and Bangladesh.

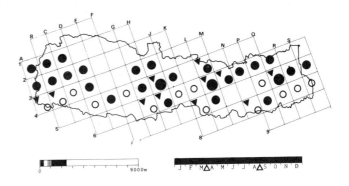

ADDENDUM

The following records of two new species for Nepal were received too late for inclusion in the main text.

SPOTTED CRAKE *Porzana porzana*

One was seen by Rosemary Cooper near
Kusaha, Kosi Tappu Wildlife Reserve at
about 75m on 28 February and 3 March
1990. Frequents marshes. **Range** Winter
visitor to Pakistan and India.

JERDON'S BABBLER *Moupinia altirostris*
(Chrysomma altirostre)

Subspecies *griseigularis*. First recorded by Hem Sagar Baral
who found three birds near Gaida Wildlife Camp, Chitwan
at about 250m on 26 November 1989. On 7 December 1989
he observed a group of six near Dumariya, Chitwan, and
three were seen by him and Jonathon Eames near Lami Tal,
Chitwan on 25 April 1990. Inhabits grassland. **Range** Plains
of the Indus in Pakistan, and in n.e. India and Bangladesh.

BIBLIOGRAPHY

1   Anon (1976) Bird sightings (and other things). *Nepal Nature Conservation Society Newsletter* No.35, November 1976.

2   Anon (1976) Saturday morning bird walk. *Nepal Nature Conservation Society Newsletter* No.32, August 1976.

3   Anon (1977) A new record for the Valley. *Nepal Nature Conservation Society Newsletter* No.40, April 1977.

4   Anon (1977) Observation. *Nepal Nature Conservation Society Newsletter* No.39, March 1977.

5   Anon (1977) Recent observations. *Nepal Nature Conservation Society Newsletter* No. 42, June 1977.

6   Anon (1977) Tawny Pipit in Nepal. *Nepal Nature Conservation Newsletter* No. 41, May 1977.

7   Anon (1979) Some interesting bird sightings. *Nepal Nature Conservation Society Newsletter*, September 1979.

8   Anon (1983) List of specimens collected by C.O. Maser from Nepal in 1967, held in the Chicago Field Museum of Natural History. Unpublished.

9   Anon (1983) List of bird specimens collected by R.L. Fleming Sr. and R.L. Fleming Jr. from Nepal 1965-71, held in the Chicago Field Museum of Natural History. Unpublished.

10 Anon (1983) List of bird specimens collected by E.W. Cronin Jr. from Nepal in 1973, held in the Chicago Field Museum of Natural History. Unpublished.

11 Anon. (1988) A check-list of birds recorded at Machan, Royal Chitwan National Park. Unpublished.

12 Anon. (1988) List of bird specimens collected by E. Cronin Jr. from the Arun River watershed, 1972-1974, stored in the Kathmandu Natural History Museum. Unpublished.

13 Abdulali, H. (1968) A catalogue of the birds in the collection of Bombay Natural History Society - 1 Gaviiformes to Ciconiiformes. *J. Bombay nat. Hist. Soc.* 65(1): 182-199.

14 Abdulali, H. (1968) A catalogue of the birds in the collection of Bombay Natural History Society - 2 Anseriformes. *J. Bombay nat. Hist. Soc.* 65(2): 418-430.

15 Abdulali, H. (1968) A catalogue of the birds in the collection of Bombay Natural History Society - 3 Falconiformes. *J. Bombay nat. Hist. Soc.* 65(3): 696-723.

16 Abdulali, H. (1969) A catalogue of the birds in the collection of Bombay Natural History Society - 4 Megapodidae, Phasianidae, Turnicidae. *J. Bombay nat. Hist. Soc.* 66: 251-285.

17 Abdulali, H. (1969) A catalogue of the birds in the collection of Bombay Natural History Society - 5 Gruidae to Charadriidae (Charadriinae). *J. Bombay nat. Hist. Soc.* 66: 542-559.

18 Abdulali, H. (1970) A catalogue of the birds in the collection of Bombay Natural History Society - 6 Scolopacinae (part). *J. Bombay nat. Hist. Soc.* 67(1): 51-56.

19 Abdulali, H. (1970) A catalogue of the birds in the collection of Bombay Natural History Society - 7 Scolopacinae (part) to Laridae. *J. Bombay nat. Hist. Soc.* 67(2): 279-298.

20 Abdulali, H. (1971) A catalogue of the birds in the collection of Bombay Natural History Society - 8 Pteroclididae and Columbidae. *J. Bombay nat. Hist. Soc.* 68(1): 127-152.

21 Abdulali, H. (1971) A catalogue of the birds in the collection of Bombay Natural History Society - 9 Psittacidae. *J. Bombay nat. Hist. Soc.* 68(2): 328-338.

22 Abdulali, H. (1971) A catalogue of the birds in the collection of Bombay Natural History Society - 10 Cuculidae. *J. Bombay nat. Hist. Soc.* 68(3): 756-772.

23 Abdulali, H. (1972) A catalogue of the birds in the collection of Bombay Natural History Society - 11 Strigidae and Caprimulgidae. *J. Bombay nat. Hist. Soc.* 69(1): 102-129.

24 Abdulali, H. (1972) A catalogue of the birds in the collection of Bombay Natural History Society - 12 Apodidae and Trogonidae. *J. Bombay nat. Hist. Soc.* 69(2): 378-389.

25 Abdulali, H. (1972) A catalogue of the birds in the collection of Bombay Natural History Society - 13 Alcedinidae. *J. Bombay nat. Hist. Soc.* 69(3): 538-546.

26 Abdulali, H. (1973) A catalogue of the birds in the collection of Bombay Natural History Society - 14 Meropidae and Coraciidae. *J. Bombay nat. Hist. Soc.* 70(1): 147-155.

27 Abdulali, H. (1973) A catalogue of the birds in the collection of Bombay Natural History Society - 15 Upupidae and Bucerotidae. *J. Bombay nat. Hist. Soc.* 70(2): 339-345.

28 Abdulali, H. (1974) A catalogue of the birds in the collection of Bombay Natural History Society - 16 Capitonidae, Indicatoridae and Picidae (part). *J. Bombay nat. Hist. Soc.* 71(2): 244-265.

29 Abdulali, H. (1975) A catalogue of the birds in the collection of Bombay Natural History Society - 17 Picidae (concluded). *J. Bombay nat. Hist. Soc.* 72(1): 113-131.

30 Abdulali, H. (1975) A catalogue of the birds in the collection of Bombay Natural History Society - 18 Eurylaimidae, Pittidae, Alaudidae. *J. Bombay nat. Hist. Soc.* 72(2): 477-505.

31 Abdulali, H. (1976) A catalogue of the birds in the collection of Bombay Natural History Society - 19 Hirundinidae. *J. Bombay nat. Hist. Soc.* 73(2): 348-355.

32 Abdulali, H. (1976) A catalogue of the birds in the collection of Bombay Natural History Society - 20 Laniidae, Oriolidae, Dicruridae, Artamidae. *J. Bombay nat. Hist. Soc.* 73(3): 491-515.

33 Abdulali, H. (1978) A catalogue of the birds in the collection of Bombay Natural History Society - 21 Sturnidae. *J. Bombay nat. Hist. Soc.* 75(2): 373-384.

34 Abdulali, H. (1980) Catalogue of the birds in the collection of Bombay Natural History Society - 22 Corvidae, Bombycillidae. *J. Bombay nat. Hist. Soc.* 77(1): 81-89.

35 Abdulali, H. (1981) A catalogue of the birds in the collection of Bombay Natural History Society - 23 Campephagidae and Irenidae. *J. Bombay nat. Hist. Soc.* 78(2): 261-286.

36 Abdulali, H. (1982) A catalogue of the birds in the collection of Bombay Natural History Society - 24 Pycnonotidae. *J. Bombay nat. Hist. Soc.* 79(1): 135-145.

37 Abdulali, H. (1982) A catalogue of the birds in the collection of Bombay Natural History Society - 25 Muscicapidae (Timaliinae) (part). *J. Bombay nat. Hist. Soc.* 79(2): 336-360.

38 Abdulali, H. (1982) A catalogue of the birds in the collection of Bombay Natural History Society - 26 Muscicapidae (Timaliinae) (contd.). *J. Bombay nat. Hist. Soc.* 79(3): 607-619.

39 Abdulali, H. (1983) A catalogue of the birds in the collection of Bombay Natural History Society - 27 Muscicapidae (Timaliinae) (contd.). *J. Bombay nat. Hist. Soc.* 80: 149-165.

40 Abdulali, H. (1983) A catalogue of the birds in the collection of Bombay Natural History Society - 28 Muscicapidae (Timaliinae) (contd.). *J. Bombay nat. Hist. Soc.* 80: 349-369.

41 Abdulali, H. (1985) A catalogue of the birds in the collection of Bombay Natural History Society - 29 Muscicapidae (Muscicapinae, Pachycephalinae). *J. Bombay nat. Hist. Soc.* 82: 87-113.

42 Abdulali, H. (1986) A catalogue of the birds in the collection of Bombay Natural History Society - 30 Muscicapidae (Sylviinae). *J. Bombay nat. Hist. Soc.* 83: 130-163.

43 Abdulali, H. (1986) A catalogue of the birds in the collection of Bombay Natural History Society - 31 Muscicapidae (Sylviinae) (contd). *J. Bombay nat. Hist. Soc.* 83: 339-359.

44 Abdulali, H. (1987) A catalogue of the birds in the collection of Bombay Natural History Society - 32 Muscicapidae (Turdinae). *J. Bombay nat. Hist. Soc.* 84: 105-125.

45 Ali, S. and Ripley, S.D. (1972) *Handbook of the birds of India and Pakistan*, 5. Bombay and London: Oxford University Press.

46 Ali, S. and Ripley, S.D. (1971) *Handbook of the birds of India and Pakistan*, 6. Bombay and London: Oxford University Press.

47 Ali, S. and Ripley, S.D. (1972) *Handbook of the birds of India and Pakistan*, 7. Bombay and London: Oxford University Press.

48 Ali, S. and Ripley, S.D. (1973) *Handbook of the birds of India and Pakistan*, 8. Bombay and London: Oxford University Press.

49 Ali, S. and Ripley, S.D. (1973) *Handbook of the birds of India and Pakistan*, 9. Bombay and london: Oxford University Press.

50 Ali, S. and Ripley, S.D. (1974) *Handbook of the birds of India and Pakistan*, 10. Bombay and London: Oxford University Press.

51 Ali, S. and Ripley, S.D. (1978) *Handbook of the birds of India and Pakistan*, 1 (Second edition). Bombay and London: Oxford University Press.

52 Ali, S. and Ripley, S.D. (1980) *Handbook of the birds of India and Pakistan*, 2 (Second edition). Bombay and London: Oxford University Press.

53 Ali, S. and Ripley, S.D. (1981) *Handbook of the birds of India and Pakistan*, 3 (Second edition). Bombay and London: Oxford University Press.

54 Ali, S. and Ripley, S.D. (1983) *Handbook of the birds of India and Pakistan*, 4 (Second edition). Bombay and London: Oxford University Press.

55 Alind, P. (1986) Notes on birds recorded in Nepal, February - March 1986. Unpublished.

56 Alstrom, P. and Olsson, U. (1983) Notes on birds recorded in Nepal, 1983. Unpublished.

57 Andell, P. et. al. (1982) Nepal Norra Indien, 1982. Unpublished.

58 Andersen, U., Madsen, P.-E. and Molgaard, E. (1986) *Fugleiagttagelser fra Nepal - Indien Vinteren 1984-85*. Copenhagen: Dansk Ornitologisk Forenings.

59 Andrews, T. (1986) Notes on birds recorded in northern India and Nepal, winter 1984-1985. Unpublished.

60 Arjal, N. (1976) Sighting of Red-footed Falcons and Lesser Kestrels in Pokhara. *Nepal Nature Conservation Newsletter* No.31, July 1976.

61 Arjal, N. (1976) Birds in the Lukla-Syangboche area. *Nepal Nature Conservation Society Newsletter No.36, December* 1976.

62 Bailey, F.M. (1938) Register of bird specimens collected in Nepal 1935-38, and presented to the British Museum (Natural History). Unpublished.

63 Baker, E.C.S. (1922-1930) *Fauna of British India: Birds*. 2nd edition, 8 vols. Taylor and Francis, London.

64 Baker, E.C.S. (1923) *A hand-list of genera and species of birds of the Indian Empire*.

65 Baker, T. (1981) Notes on birds recorded in Nepal, 1981. Unpublished.

66 Baker, T. (1983) Notes on birds recorded in Nepal, February - March 1983. Unpublished.

67 Baral, H.S. (1989) Notes on birds recorded at Gaida Widlife Camp, Royal Chitwan National Park, 1988-1989. Unpublished.

68 Barber, I. (1989) Notes on birds recorded in Nepal 1988 - 1989. Unpublished.

69 Barnes, L.J. (1989) Bird list for Nepal, India and Malaysia, 27 October 1988 to 9 April 1989. Unpublished.

70 Barrett, D., Prescott, T. and Barker, I. (1989) Notes on birds recorded in Langtang National Park, February 1989. Unpublished.

71 Barus, V. and Daniel, M. (1976) Capillariids (Nematoda: Capillariidae) from Passeriform birds of Nepal. *Folia Parasitologica* (Praha) 23: 105-110.

72 Barus, V. Rysavy, B. and Daniel, M. (1975) Some cestodes and nematodes parasitizing gallinaceous and columbiform birds in Nepal. *Folia Parasitologica* (Praha) 22(4): 327-335.

73 Bauer, C.-A. (1982) Indien och Nepal, 22.1 - 7/8.2 1982. Unpublished.

74 Bauer, C.-A. (1984) Indien och Nepal, January 1984. Unpublished.

75 Bauer, C.-A. (1986) Birds and mammals seen on 'Skof' tour to India and Nepal, April - May 1986. Unpublished.

76 Beaman, M.A.S. (1973) Report of the ornithological Cambridge expedition to the Himalayas, 1973. Unpublished.

77 Beaman, M.A.S. (1982) Notes on birds recorded in Nepal, 1973-1982. Unpublished.

78 Beaman, M.A.S. and Sharrock, J.T.R. (1980) Sunbird Holidays tour report, February 1980. Unpublished.

79 Beavan, R.C. (1867) Notes on various Indian birds. *Ibis* (2)3: 430-455.

80 Bensch, S. (1982) Two weeks bird-watching in Nepal, late January - early February 1982. Unpublished.

81 Benson, C.W. In prep. Type specimens of birds (skins) in the University of Zoology, Cambridge.

82 van den Berg, A.B. and Bosman, C.A.W. (1976) List of birds observed in Nepal, April 1976. Unpublished.

83 Bergstrom, T. (1975) Notes on birds recorded in Nepal, October - November 1975. Unpublished.

84 Bezuijen, M. (1988) Notes on birds recorded when trekking in the Jugal Himal region of Nepal, 24 March - 6 April 1988. Unpublished.

85 Bhandary, H.R., Schemnitz, S.D. and Picozzi, N. (1986) Autumn foods of forest pheasants of Pipar, central Nepal. *J. World Pheasant Assoc.* 11: 29-33.

86 Bijlsma, R. (1989) Nest-building in Bonelli's Eagle *Hieraaetus fasciatus* in October in Nepal. Unpublished.

87 Binford, L.C. (1977) Birds and mammals observed in India and Nepal on California Academy of Sciences tour, 26 February - 27 March 1977. Unpublished.

88 Biswas, B. (1950) On the shrike *Lanius tephronotus* (Vigors), with remarks on the *erythronotus* and *tricolor* groups of *Lanius schach* Linn., and their hybrids. *J. Bombay nat. Hist. Soc.* 49: 444-455.

89 Biswas, B. (1950) On the taxonomy of some Asiatic pygmy woodpeckers. *Proc. zool. Soc. Bengal* 3: 1-37.

90 Biswas, B. (1950) The Himalayan races of the Nutcracker (*Nucifraga caryocatactes*) (Linn.) [Aves]. *J. zool. Soc. India* 2: 26.

91 Biswas, B. (1951) On some larger spine-tailed swifts, with the description of a new subspecies from Nepal. *Ardea* 39: 318-321.

92 Biswas, B. (1955) Zoological results of the 'Daily Mail' Himalayan Expedition 1954. Two new birds from Khumbu, eastern Nepal. *Bull. Brit. Orn.Club* 75: 87-88.

93 Biswas, B. (1959) On the validity of *Harpactes erythrocephalus hodgsoni* (Gould) [Aves: Trogonidae]. *J. Bombay nat. Hist. Soc.* 56: 335-338.

94 Biswas, B. (1959) Taxonomic status of the blood pheasants of Nepal and Sikkim. *J. zool. Soc. India* 10(1): 100-101.

95 Biswas, B. (1960) The birds of Nepal. *J.Bombay nat. Hist. Soc.* 57(2): 278-308.

96 Biswas, B. (1960) The birds of Nepal, Part 2. *J. Bombay nat. Hist. Soc.* 57(3): 516-546.

97 Biswas, B. (1960) Zoological results of the 'Daily Mail' Himalayan Expedition 1954. Notes on some birds from Khumbu, Eastern Nepal. Unpublished. See Biswas, 1974.

98 Biswas, B. (1961) The birds of Nepal, Part 3. *J. Bombay nat. Hist. Soc.* 58(1): 100-134.

99 Biswas, B. (1961) The birds of Nepal, Part 4. *J. Bombay nat. Hist. Soc.* 58(2): 444-474.

100 Biswas, B. (1961) The birds of Nepal, Part 5. *J. Bombay nat. Hist. Soc.* 58(3): 653-677.

101 Biswas, B. (1962) The birds of Nepal, Part 6. *J. Bombay nat. Hist. Soc.* 59(1): 200-227.

102 Biswas, B. (1962) The birds of Nepal, Part 7. *J. Bombay nat. Hist. Soc.* 59(2): 405-429.

103 Biswas, B. (1962) The birds of Nepal, Part 8. *J. Bombay nat. Hist. Soc.* 59(3): 807-821.

104 Biswas, B. (1963) The birds of Nepal, Part 9. *J. Bombay nat. Hist. Soc.* 60(1): 173-200.

105 Biswas, B. (1963) The birds of Nepal, Part 10. *J. Bombay nat. Hist. Soc.* 60(2): 388-399.

106 Biswas, B. (1963) The birds of Nepal, Part 11. *J. Bombay nat. Hist. Soc.* 60(3): 638-654.

107 Biswas, B. (1966) The birds of Nepal, Part 12. *J. Bombay nat. Hist. Soc.* 63(2): 365-377.

108 Biswas, B. (1968) Some new bird records for Nepal. *J. Bombay nat. Hist. Soc.* 65: 782-784.

109 Biswas, B. (1974) Zoological results of the Daily Mail Himalayan Expedition 1954: notes on some birds of eastern Nepal. *J. Bombay nat. Hist. Soc.* 71: 456-495.

110 Biswas, B. (1983) Additional notes on birds recorded on 1954 'Daily Mail' Himalayan Expedition. Unpublished.

111 Blanchon, J.-J. and Dubois, P.J. (1987) Voyage au Nepal Mars 1987. Unpublished.

112 Bland, J.D. (1987) Notes on the distribution and ecology of some Himalayan pheasants. *J. World Pheasant Assoc.* 12: 22-29.

113 Blyth, E. (1842) Notes on various Indian and Malayan birds, with descriptions of some presumed new species. *J. Asiat. Soc. Bengal* 11: 160-195.

114 Blyth, E. (1843) Monthly report for December meeting, 1842. *J. Asiat. Soc. Bengal* 12: 931-1011.

115 Blyth, E. (1844) Appendix to report for December meeting, 1842. *J. Asiat. Soc. Bengal* 13: 361-395.

116 Blyth, E. (1844) "On the Leiotrichane Birds of the Subhemalayas," by B.H.Hodgson, Esq.: with some additions and annotations, - a synopsis of the Indian Pari, - and of the Indian Fringillidae. *J. Asiat. Soc. Bengal* 13: 933-963.

117 Blyth, E. (1844) List of birds obtained in the vicinity of Calcutta, from September 1841 to March 1843 inclusive. *Ann. Mag. nat. Hist.* 12: 90-101.

118 Blyth, E. (1845) Notices and descriptions of various new or little known species of birds. *J. Asiat. Soc. Bengal* 14: 173-212; 546-602.

119 Blyth, E. (1845) Drafts for a Fauna Indica. No. 1. The Columbidae, or pigeons and doves. *J. Asiat. Soc. Bengal* 14: 845-878.

120 Blyth, E. (1846) Notices and descriptions of various new or little known species of birds. *J. Asiat. Soc. Bengal* 15: 1-51; 280-313.

121 Blyth, E. (1847) Notices and descriptions of various new or little known species of birds. *J. Asiat. Soc. Bengal* 16: 117-157; 428-476.

122 Blyth, E. (1849) *Catalogue of the birds in the museum Asiatic Society, Calcutta.* Calcutta: Asiatic Society of Bengal.

123 Blyth, E. (1865) A few identifications and rectifications of synonymy. *Ibis* (2)1: 27-50.

124 Blyth, E. (1866) The ornithology of India - a commentary on Dr. Jerdon's 'Birds of India'. *Ibis* (2)2: 225-258; 336-376.

125 Blyth, E. (1867) The ornithology of India - a commentary on Dr. Jerdon's 'Birds of India'. *Ibis* (2)3: 1-48; 147-185.

126 Bolding, J. and Jorgensen, T. (1987) List of birds recorded in Nepal and India, October 1986 - January 1987. Unpublished.

127 Bolton, M. (1976) *Lake Rara National Park Management Plan 1976-81.* FO NEP/72/002 Project Working Document No. 3. Kathmandu: UNDP/FAO.

128 Bolton, M. (1976) *Royal Karnali Wildlife Reserve Management Plan 1976-81.* FO NEP/72/002 Project Working Document No. 4. Kathmandu: UNDP/FAO.

129 Bonaparte, C.L. (1850) *Conspectus Generum Avium*, 1. Lugduni Batavarum, apud E.J.Brill, Academiae Typographum.

130 Bonaparte, C.L. (1856) Especes nouvelles d'oiseaux d'Asie et d'Amerique. *Compt. Rend. Acad. Sci. Paris* 42: 764-776.

131 Bonaparte, C.L. (1856) Suite et fin des additions et corrections au coup d'oeil sur l'Ordre des pigeons, et a la partie correspondant du Conspectus Avium. *Compt. Rend. Acad. Sci. Paris* 43: 942-949.

132 Bonaparte, C.L. (1857) *Conspectus Generum Avium*, 2. Lugduni Batavarum, apud E.J.Brill, Academiae Typographum.

133 Boot, K.J. (1982) List of bird specimens from Nepal in Royal Albert Memorial Museum, Exeter. Unpublished.

134 Bowden, C. (1979) Bird records from Nepal; in report of University of East Anglia Expedition 1978/79. Unpublished.

135 Bradbear, P. (1986) Notes on birds recorded in Nepal, September - October 1986. Unpublished.

136 Brearey, D. (1985) Record of Amur Falcon *Falco amurensis* in Nepal, April 1983. Unpublished.

137 Brearey, D.M. and Pritchard, D.E. (1985) Birds and other wildlife of Lake Rara National Park, northwest Nepal. Saipal 82-83. Report No. 3. Unpublished.

138 Buckton, S. (1990) Notes on birds recorded in Nepal, December 1989 - February 1990. Unpublished.

139 Burton, E. (1836) Characters of several birds from the Himalayan Mountains. *Proc. zool. Soc. London* 3: 152-154.

140 Byers, C. and Adams, A. (1983) Notes on birds recorded in Nepal, 1983. Unpublished.

141 Byrne, R.W. and Harris, S.M. (1975) Skeletal report of birds and mammals seen during September - November 1975 in Nepal. Unpublished.

142 Calladine, J. (1985) Nepal and India. Notes on birds and mammals recorded, 18 October - 16 February 1985. Unpublished.

143 Carty, P., Jackson, S., McCarthy, B., and Woolly, B. (1984) Notes on birds recorded in Nepal, winter 1983/84. Unpublished.

144 Chapple, J.L. (1976) A visit to Kosi Barrage. *Army Birdwatching Soc. Bull.* No.4/76.

145 Christensen, S., Bijlsma, R., De Roder, F. and Henriksen, M. (1984) Notes on birds recorded in Nepal, 1984. Unpublished.

146 Clements, A. and Bradbear, N. (1981) Systematic list of species seen in Nepal and India, November - December 1981. Unpublished.

147 Clugston, D.L. (1985) A checklist of the birds and mammals seen in Nepal from 8 - 30 March 1985. Unpublished.

148 Cocker, P.M. and Adams, A. (1983) Notes on birds recorded in Nepal, 1983. Unpublished.

149 Cocker, P.M. and Inskipp, C. (1988) *A Himalayan ornithologist: the life and work of Brian Houghton Hodgson.* Oxford: Oxford University Press.

150 Collins, A.R. (1986) Notes on birds recorded in Nepal, November 1984 - February 1985. Unpublished.

151 Conder, P.J. (1978) Notes on birds recorded in Nepal, February - March 1978. Unpublished.

152 Cooper, D. and Cooper, J.F. (1989) Notes on birds recorded in Nepal, 1 - 28 January 1989. Unpublished.

153 Corbett, G.B. (1974) Birds recorded on the RAF Dhaulagiri Expedition, March - May 1974. Unpublished.

154 Couronne, B. and Kovacs, J.-C. (1986) Observations ornithologiques au Nepal, Fevrier - Mars 1986. Unpublished.

155 Cox, J. Jr. (1978) Avian jottings for Nepal, 1978. Unpublished.

156 Cox, J. Jr. (1979) New and interesting birds observed on a month's journey in east Nepal. *Nepal Nature Conservation Society Newsletter* July 1979.

157 Cox, J. Jr. (1982) Avian checklist of species observed during 1978 in the district of Kapilvastu, central tarai. Unpublished.

158 Cox, J. Jr. (1984) Notes on birds recorded in Nepal, 1984. Unpublished.

159 Cox, J. Jr. (1984) Further notes on birds recorded in Nepal, 1976-1984. Unpublished.

160 Cox, J. Jr. (1985) Birds of the Rara-Jumla area, west Nepal. 1976-1984. Unpublished.

161 Cox, J. Jr. (1985) Partial checklist of birds recorded within Rara Lake National Park, Nepal, May 1985. Unpublished.

162 Cox, J. Jr. (1985) Selected notes from a brief avian survey of Royal Bardia Wildlife Reserve and periphery, west Nepal during November 1985. Unpublished.

163 Cox, J. Jr. (1988) A note on treecreeper Certhiidae nesting in west Nepal. Unpublished.

164 Cox, J. Jr. (1989) Birds observed in the south-east terai, Nepal, 12 - 26 February 1989. Unpublished.

165 Cox, J., Lindvall, M. and Underwood, L. (1982) Notes on birds recorded in Nepal, per P. Hall. Unpublished.

166 Cox, S., Cox, P., Loud, P. and Brown, G. (1989) Notes on birds recorded in Nepal, 12 - 31 March 1989. Unpublished.

167 Cronin, E.W. Jr. (1979) *The Arun, a natural history of the world's deepest valley.* Boston: Houghton Mifflin Co.

168 Cronin, E.W. Jr. (1979) The legacy of Chang Hua. *Animal Kingdom* 82(4): 31-35.

169 Cronin, E.W. Jr. and Sherman, P.W. (1976) A resource-based mating system: the Orange-rumped Honeyguide. *Living Bird* 15: 5-32.

170 Curry-Lindahl, K. (1979) Notes on birds recorded in Nepal, 1979. Unpublished.

171 Curry-Lindahl, K. (1980) The Forest Wagtail *Motacilla indica* recorded in Nepal. *Bull. Brit. Orn. Club* 100: 201-202.

172 Curson, J. and Bose, A. (1989) Notes on birds recorded in Nepal, February - April 1989. Unpublished.

173 Cuvier, C. (1829) *Le regne animal distribue d'apres son organisation, pour servir de base a l'histoire naturelle des animaux et d'introduction a l'anatomie comparee.* Second edition. Paris.

174 Dahmer, T.A. (1976) Birds of Kosi Tappu Reserve. Unpublished.

175 Dahmer, T.A. (1976) Occurrence of the Dusky Horned Owl in Kosi Tappu. *Nepal Nature Conservation Society Newsletter* No.35, November 1976.

176 Davison, A. (1990) Note on birds recorded in Nepal, December 1989 - February 1990. Unpublished.

177 Dawson, I. (1983) Notes on birds recorded in Nepal, December 1982 - January 1983. Unpublished.

178 De Witt, R. (1982) Notes on birds recorded in Nepal. Unpublished.

179 Deignan, H. (1954) On the nomenclature of the Himalayan Goldcrests. *Bull. Brit. Orn. Club* 74: 103-104.

180 del-Nevo, A. and Ewins, P. (1981) Bird watching in Nepal, 7th December 1980 - 19th February 1981. Unpublished.

181 del-Nevo, A. and Ewins, P. (1983) Rustic Bunting (*Emberiza rustica*) - a new species for Nepal. *J. Bombay nat. Hist. Soc.* 80: 417-418.

182 del-Nevo, A. and Ewins, P.J. (1984) Birds feeding on fire-driven insects. *J. Bombay Nat. Hist. Soc.* 80: 413-414.

183 DeLuce, P. and Goodyer, N. (1990) An investigation of the status and conservation of forest birds in the Mai valley of far east Nepal. Survey report. Unpublished.

184 Derry, J.F. and Hornby, G.M. (1981) Nepal bird list, Stowe Himalayan Expedition Journal, 1981. Unpublished.

185 Desfayes, M. (1965) Field notes on *Grandala coelicolor. Ibis* 107: 400-401.

186 Desfayes, M. (1969) The Smoky Leaf Warbler, *Phylloscopus fuligiventer* (Hodgson) in Nepal. *J. Bombay nat. Hist. Soc.* 66: 623-624.

187 Desfayes, M. (1970) The Blackbird, *Turdus merula maximus* in Nepal. *J. Bombay nat. Hist. Soc.* 67: 571-572.

188 Desfayes, M. (1971) Tibetan Twite, *Acanthis flavirostris* in Nepal. *J. Bombay nat. Hist. Soc.* 68: 832.

189 Diesselhorst, G. (1965) Winter habitat of *Acrocephalus dumetorum* Blyth. *Bull. Brit. Orn. Club* 85: 111.

190 Diesselhorst, G. (1968) Beitrage zur Okologie der Vogel Zentral- und Ost-Nepals. *Khumbu Himal* 2: 1-417.

191 Diesselhorst, G. and Martens, J. (1972) Hybriden von *Parus melanolophus* und *Parus ater* im Nepal-Himalaya. *J. Orn.* 113(4): 374-390.

192 Dinerstein, E. (1979) An ecological survey of the Royal Karnali-Bardia Wildlife Reserve, Nepal. University of Washington. Unpublished thesis.

193 Dodman, T. and Guinan, Y. (1989) Notes on birds recorded in Nepal, March - April 1989. Unpublished.

194 Dunkley, A. (1989) Notes on birds recorded in Nepal 1988-1989. Unpublished.

195 Durham University Himalayan Expedition. (1977) *Langtang National Park Management Plan 1977-82.* FO NEP/72/002 Field Document No. 7. DUHE/HMG/UNDP/FAO, Kathmandu.

196 Durrai, D. (1984) Dusky Eagle Owl at Chitwan, February 1984. Unpublished.

197 Dymond, J.N. (1986) Selected bird list, Nepal, February - March 1986. Unpublished.

198 Dymond, J.N. and Thorpe, R.I. (1980) Notes on birds recorded in Nepal, February 1980. Unpublished.

199 Eames, J. (1982) Notes on birds recorded in Nepal, 1982. Unpublished.

200 Eames, J. and Grimmett, R.F. (1982) Birds recorded at Kosi Tappu Wildlife Reserve, April 1982. Unpublished.

201 Ebels, E.B. (1986) Ornithological records during a trip to Russia, Japan, Thailand, Nepal and India, August - December 1985. Unpublished.

202 Egger, J., Lemke, G.W. and Timm,H. (1990) Nepal, 3 - 24 Februar 1990. Unpublished.

203 Ellen, R.E.T. (1988) Notes on birds recorded in Nepal, January 1988. Unpublished.

204 Elwes, H.J. (1873) Geographical distribution of Asiatic birds. *Proc. zool. Soc. London* 42: 645-682.

205 Eve, V. and Hibberd, G. (1987) Notes on birds recorded in Nepal. Unpublished.

206 Fairbank, R.J. (1980) Notes on birds recorded in Nepal, November 1979 - January 1980. Unpublished.

207 Fairbank, R.J. (1982) Notes on birds recorded in Nepal, 1982. Unpublished.

208 Farrow, D. (1982) Notes on birds recorded in Nepal, March - April 1982. Unpublished.

209 Fleming, R.L. Jr. (1968) Winter observations on the ecology and distribution of birds on the Kosi-Gandak watershed ridge, central Nepal. *Pavo* 6: 1-11.

210 Fleming, R.L. Jr. (1968) *Buceros bicornis*, Linnaeus, in Nepal. *Pavo* 6: 59-61.

211 Fleming, R.L. Jr. (1968) The Waxwing, *Bombycilla garrulus* (Linnaeus) in Nepal. *J. Bombay nat. Hist. Soc.* 65: 488.

212 Fleming, R.L. Jr. (1969) Birds of Thakkhola, north Nepal. *J. Bombay nat. Hist. Soc.* 66: 132-139.

213 Fleming, R.L. Jr. (1971) Avian zoogeography of Nepal. *The Himalayan Review* 4: 28-33.

214 Fleming, R.L. Jr. (1972) The Kathmandu Christmas Bird Count. *Nepal Nature Conservation Society Newsletter* No.7, January 1972.

215 Fleming, R.L. Jr. (1973) Notes on the nest and behaviour of the Yellow-browed Titmouse, *Parus modestus* (Burton). *J. Bombay nat. Hist. Soc.* 70: 326-329.

216 Fleming, R.L. Jr. (1974) Rediscovery of the Yellow-vented Flowerpecker in Nepal. *Nepal Nature Conservation Society Newsletter* No.22, January 1974.

217 Fleming, R.L. Jr. (1975) Christmas bird counts. *Nepal Nature Conservation Society Newsletter* No. 28, February 1975.

218 Fleming, R.L. Jr. (1975) The discovery of the Black-capped Kingfisher. *Nepal Nature Conservation Society Newsletter* No. 28, February 1975.

219 Fleming, R.L. Jr. (1975) A pink seagull in Nepal. *Nepal Nature Conservation Society Newsletter* No.29, July 1975.

220 Fleming, R.L. Jr. (1978) An invasion of European Blackbirds. *Nepal Nature Conservation Society Newsletter* No. 52, May 1978.

221 Fleming, R.L. Jr. (1979) Notes on birds seen in the Everest National Park, Nepal, May 1979. Unpublished.

222 Fleming, R.L. Jr. (1979) The Kathmandu Christmas Bird Count, 1977. *Nepal Nature Conservation Society Annual* Volume II 1978-79: 21-27.

223 Fleming, R.L. Jr. (1981) Distribution information on various bird species in Nepal. Pers. comm. March 1981.

224 Fleming, R.L. Jr. (1982) List of birds recorded in Dolpo district in 1971. Unpublished.

225 Fleming, R.L. Jr. (1983) An east-west Aquila eagle migration in the Himalayas. *J. Bombay nat. Hist. Soc.* 80: 58-62.

226 Fleming, R.L. Jr. *in litt.* 5 September 1989.

227 Fleming, R.L. Jr. *in litt.* 19 January 1990.

228 Fleming, R.L. Sr. (1952) Notes on the Nepal Koklas Pheasant (*Pucrasia macrolopha nipalensis*) and the Spiny Babbler (*Acanthoptila nipalensis*). *J. Bombay nat. Hist. Soc.* 50: 658-661.

229 Fleming, R.L. Sr. (1953) Birds of Nepal. *J. Bombay nat. Hist. Soc.* 51: 939-943.

230 Fleming, R.L. Sr. (1959) An ornithologist revisits west Nepal (March 21-25, 1959). *J. Bombay nat. Hist. Soc.* 56: 570-80.

231 Fleming, R.L. Sr. (1959) Spiny Babblers in Kathmandu Valley. *J. Bombay nat. Hist. Soc.* 56: 628-630.

232 Fleming, R.L. Sr. (1963) Occurrence of the Orange-rumped Honey Guide (*Indicator x. xanthonotus*) in Nepal. *Pavo* 1: 66-67.

233 Fleming, R.L. Sr. (1963) Two new records for Nepal. *Pavo* 1: 126-127.

234 Fleming, R.L. Sr. (1968) Nepal birds: supplement to Biswas' list. *J. Bombay nat. Hist. Soc.* 65: 326-334.

235 Fleming, R.L. Sr. (1974) Two new bird records for Nepal. *Nepal Nature Conservation Society Newsletter* No. 23, April 1974.

236 Fleming, R.L. Sr. (1976) May trek to the Annapurna Range. *Nepal Nature Conservation Society Newsletter* No. 32, August 1976.

237 Fleming, R.L. Sr. (1977) Bird movements in Nepal. *Nepal Nature Conservation Society Annual* Vol.1 1977: 40-43.

238 Fleming, R.L. Sr. (1977) Sukla Phanta Wildlife Reserve. *Nepal Nature Conservation Society Newsletter* No. 39, March 1977.

239 Fleming, R.L. Sr. (1977) Birds in the Kosi area, 5 November 1977. *Nepal Nature Conservation Society Newsletter* No. 46, October 1977.

240 Fleming, R.L. Sr. and Fleming, R.L. Jr. (1970) *Birds of Kathmandu Valley and surrounding hills: a check list.* Kathmandu.

241 Fleming, R.L. Sr. and Fleming R.L. Jr. (1970) Avian sapdrinkers of the Himalayas. *J. Bengal nat. Hist. Soc.* 36: 54-57.

242 Fleming, R.L. Sr. and Fleming R.L. Jr. (1980) A checklist of the birds of Kathmandu Valley. Unpublished.

243 Fleming, R.L. Sr., Fleming R.L. Jr. and Bangdel, L.S. (1979) *Birds of Nepal.* Second edition. Kathmandu: Avalok.

244 Fleming, R.L. Sr., Fleming, R.L. Jr. and Bangdel, L.S. (1984) *Birds of Nepal.* Third edition. Kathmandu: Avalok.

245 Fleming, R.L. Sr. and Traylor, M.A. (1961) Notes on Nepal birds. *Fieldiana: zool.* 35(9): 447-487.

246 Fleming, R.L. Sr. and Traylor, M.A. (1964) Further notes on Nepal birds. *Fieldiana: zool.* 35(9): 495-558.

247 Fleming, R.L. Sr. and Traylor, M.A. (1968) Distributional notes on Nepal birds. *Fieldiana: zool.* 53(3): 147-203.

248 Forbes, H.C. and Robinson, H.C. (1898-1900) Catalogue of the Psittaci, Coraciae, Charadriiformes, Pici and Cuculii in the Derby Museum. *Bull. Liverpool Museum* Vols. I,II.

249 Forester, J.A. and Lelliott, A.D. (1983) Pipar Wildlife Reserve management proposals. *World Pheasant Association News* 3: 4-6.

250 Forster, E. (1982) *Himalayan solo.* Shrewsbury: Anthony Nelson.

251 Fox, J.L. (1974) An ecological survey of the proposed Langtang National Park. Report to National Parks and Wildlife Conservation Office. Kathmandu: mimeo.

252 Fraser, L. (1848-1850) Catalogue of the birds of Knowsley Museum. Six volumes. Unpublished.

253 Gadow, H. (1883) *Catalogue of the Birds in the collection of the British Museum,* 8 - Paridae, Laniidae, Certhiomorphae. London: British Museum.

254 Gadow, H. (1883) *Catalogue of the birds in the collection of the British Museum,* 9 - Nectariniidae, Meliphagidae. London: British Museum.

255 Gantlett, S.J.M. (1981) Notes on birds recorded in Nepal, November 1981. Unpublished.

256 Gardiner, S. (1990) Notes on birds recorded in Nepal, 1989-1990. Unpublished.

257 Gardiner, S. (in prep.) Sighting of a Mandarin Duck in east Nepal.

258 Garnatt, K.J. (1981) Sagarmartha National Park Management Plan. Department of National Parks and Wildlife Conservation, Kathmandu. Unpublished.

259 Gaston, A.J. (1974) List of species seen between Pokhara and Annapurna Sanctuary, May 1974. Unpublished.

260 Gawn, S. (1987) Birding in India and Nepal, 5 February - 10 April 1986: a trip report. Unpublished.

261 Gibbs, H. (1961) *The hills of India.* London: Jarrolds.

262 Good, J.B. and Ryan, J. (1988) Notes on birds recorded in Nepal. 10 February - 5 March 1988. Unpublished.

263 Gooders, J. (1978) A new bird for Nepal and notes on some other scarce species. *J. Bombay nat. Hist. Soc.* 75(3): 925-926.

264 Goodwin, A. (1986) Notes on birds recorded in Nepal, 1986. Unpublished.

265 Gould, J. (1835) Characters of several new species of insessorial birds, including a new genus (*Stenorhynchus*). *Proc. zool. Soc. London* 3: 185-187.

266 Gould, J. (1836) Characters of some new species of birds in the Society's collection. *Proc. zool. Soc. London* 4: 5.

267 Gould, J. (1836) Characters of some new birds in the Society's collection, including two new genera, *Paradoxornis* and *Actinodura*. *Proc. zool. Soc. London* 4: 17-19.

268 Gould, J. (1837-1838) *Icones Avium, or figures and descriptions of new and interesting species of birds from various parts of the globe.* London.

269 Gould, J. (1838) *A monograph of the Trogonidae, or family of trogons.* London.

270 Gould, J. (1854) Descriptions of two new species of *Pucrasia. Proc. zool. Soc. London* 22: 99-100.

271 Gould, J. (1861) *The birds of Asia,* 3 (13). London.

272 Gould, J. (1868) On four new species of birds. *Proc. zool. Soc. London* 1868: 218-220.

273 Grahame, I. (1971) *Blood Pheasant - a Himalayan adventure.* London: Mitre Press.

274 Gray, G.R. (1844) *The genera of birds.* London: Longman, Brown, Green and Longmans.

275 Gray, J.E. (1829) [Descriptions of *Phasianus Hamiltonii* and *Phasianus nepaulensis.*] In *Griffith's Animal Kingdom.* 8 (Aves, 3): 27.

276 Gray, J.E. (1863) *Catalogue of the specimens and drawings of mammals, birds, reptiles and fishes of Nepal and Tibet, presented by B.H.Hodgson, Esq. to the British Museum.* Second edition. London.

277 Gray, J.E. and Gray, G.R. (1846) *Catalogue of the specimens and drawings of Mammalia and birds of Nepal and Thibet, presented by B.H.Hodgson, Esq. to the British Museum.* London.

278 Green, M.J.B. (1980) A report on conservation and management issues within the Langtang National Park. Unpublished.

279 Greensmith, A. (1971) Notes on birds recorded in Nepal, October 1970-March 1971. Unpublished.

280 Gregory-Smith, R.C. (1974) Birds seen at Dharan. *Army Birdwatching Soc. Bull.* No. 4/74.

281 Gregory-Smith, R.C. (1975) Notes on birds seen in Nepal. *Army Birdwatching Soc. Bull.* No. 2/75.

282 Gregory-Smith, R.C. (1976) Notes on birds seen in Nepal. *Army Birdwatching Soc. Bull.* No. 4/75.

283 Gregory-Smith, R.C. (1976) Notes on birds seen at Dharan. *Army Birdwatching Soc. Bull.* No. 1/76.

284 Gregory-Smith, R.C. (1976) Birds of Sangure Ridge. *Army Birdwatching Soc. Bull.* No. 2/76.

285 Gregory-Smith, R.C. (1976) Ringing in Nepal, April-May 1976. *Army Birdwatching Soc. Bull.* No. 2/76.

286 Gregory-Smith, R.C. (1976) The Kosi Barrage as a nature reserve. *Army Birdwatching Soc. Bull.* No. 3/76.

287 Gregory-Smith, R.C. (1976) Ringing statistics, Nepal 1976. *Army Birdwatching Soc. Bull.* No. 3/76.

288 Gregory-Smith, R.C. (1976) Notes on birds seen in Nepal. *Army Birdwatching Soc. Bull.* No. 4/76.

289 Gregory-Smith, R.C. (1976) The Kosi Barrage area as a nature reserve. *Nepal Nature Conservation Society Newsletter* No. 35, November 1976.

290 Gregory-Smith R.C. (1976) Visit to the Kosi Barrage, 5 March 1976. *Nepal Nature Conservation Society Newsletter* No. 32, August 1976.

291 Gregory-Smith, R.C. (1976) Birds in silk cotton trees. *Nepal Nature Conservation Society Newsletter* No. 31, July 1976.

292 Gregory-Smith, R.C. (1980) The birds of south-east Nepal. *Adjutant* 8: 31-35.

293 Gregory-Smith, R.C. and Batson F. (1976) Birds of south-east Nepal. Unpublished.

294 Grimmett, R.F. (1982) Notes on birds recorded in Nepal, 1982. Unpublished.

295 Groh, G. (1981) Notes on birds recorded in Nepal, 1981. Unpublished.

296 Gurung, K.K. (1983) *Heart of the jungle*. London: Andre Deutsch.

297 Hagen, P. (1979) Notes on birds seen at Surkhet, Nepal, March - April 1979. Unpublished.

298 Halberg, K. (1987) Notes on birds recorded in Nepal, November 1985 and April - June 1987. Unpublished.

299 Halberg, K. and Petersen, I. (1973) Himalaya 1978-1983. Observations of birds, mammals and some reptiles. Unpublished.

300 Hall, J. (1981) Notes on birds recorded in Nepal, November 1980 - March 1981. Unpublished.

301 Hall, P. (1978) Notes on birds recorded in Nepal, September 1976 - December 1978. Unpublished.

302 Hall, P. (1980) Revised altitudinal ranges of some Nepalese birds. Unpublished.

303 Haller, H. (1983) Die Thermikabhangigkeit des Bartgeiers *Gypaetus barbatus* als mogliche Mitursache fur sein Aussterben in den Alpen. *Orn. Beob.* 80, 263-272.

304 Halliday, J. (1982) A study of the ecological distribution of resident and migratory birds along the Rapti and Narayani rivers in the Royal Chitwan National Park, November - December 1982. Unpublished.

305 Halliday, J. (1983) Birds recorded in Nepal (excluding Chitwan National Park), 12 October 1982 - 8 January 1983. Unpublished.

306 Halliday, J. (1986) Notes on birds recorded in Nepal, October - December 1986. Unpublished.

307 Halliday, J. (1989) Notes on birds recorded in Nepal, 12 November 1988 - 2 February 1989. Unpublished.

308 Halliday, J. and McKnight, G. (1990) An investigation of the status and conservation of forest birds in the Mai and Tamur valleys in eastern Nepal. Unpublished.

309 Hamon, P. (1981) Bird observations in Nepal, December 1980 - January 1981. Unpublished.

310 Hansen, P.S. (1989) Notes on birds recorded in Nepal, 6 February - 6 March 1988. Unpublished.

311 Hardwicke, T. (1821) On the wild dog of Sumatra, a new species of Viverra, and a new species of pheasant. *Trans. Linn. Soc. London* 13(1): 237.

312 Hargitt, E. (1890) *Catalogue of the birds in the collection of the British Museum, 18* - Picidae. London: British Museum.

313 Harrap, S. (1985) Birding in Nepal in 1985. Unpublished.

314 Harris, E. (1978) Birds identified from Lamosangu to Everest Base Camp, October - November 1978. Unpublished.

315 Harrison, K., Colston, P. and Cook, S. (1983) Notes on birds recorded in Nepal, December 1982 - January 1983. Unpublished.

316 Harrop, A.H.J. (1986) Notes on birds recorded in Nepal, March - April 1986. Unpublished.

317 Hartert, E. (1891) *Katalog der Vogelsammlung im Museum der Senckenbergischen naturforschenden Gesellschaft Frankfurt.*

318 Hartert, E. and Salvin, O. (1892) *Catalogue of the birds in the collection of the British Museum, 16* - Coraciae, Upupae, Trochili. London: British Museum.

319 Hartley, M.M. (1981) List of bird specimens from Nepal in the Cliffe Castle Art Gallery and Museum. Unpublished.

320 Harvey, W.G. (1988) An annotated list of the birds seen in and around the Kathmandu Valley in Nepal, 10 - 14 January 1988. Unpublished.

321 Heath, P.J. (1986) Notes on birds recorded in Nepal, 25 January - 4 April 1986. Unpublished.

322 Heath, P.J. (1988) Rusty-bellied Shortwing. *Bull. Oriental Bird Club* 8: 16-19.

323 Heath, P.J. (1989) A Short-billed Minivet *Pericrocotus brevirostris* nest in Nepal. *Forktail* 4: 117-118.

324 Heath, P.J. and Thorns, D.M. (1989) Bristled Grass Warbler *Chaetornis striatus* new to and breeding in Nepal, and its separation from Large Grass Warbler *Graminicola bengalensis*. *Forktail* 4: 118-121.

325 Heathcote, P. and Heathcote, P. (1987) Notes on birds recorded in Nepal, December 1986 - January 1987. Unpublished.

326 Heathcote, P. and Heathcote, P. (1988) Notes on birds recorded in Nepal, 1 April - 15 May 1988. Unpublished.

327 Heinen, J. ([1986] 1988) Rare and new bird records for Kosi Barrage and Kosi Tappu Wildlife Reserve, Nepal during winter and spring, 1987. *J. Nat. Hist. Mus.* (Tribhuvan Univ., Kathmandu) 10: 23-30.

328 Heinen, J. (1988) Notes on birds recorded at Kosi Barrage and Kosi Tappu from January 1987 to March 1988. Unpublished.

329 Hendricks, P. (1982) Some post-monsoon birds observed in central Nepal. *J. Bombay nat. Hist. Soc.* 79: 247-253.

330 Hillard, D. (1989) Notes on birds recorded in Nepal, 1982-1985. Unpublished.

331 Hillard, D. (1989) *Vanishing tracks. Four years among the Snow Leopards of Nepal.* New York: Arbor House/ William Morrow.

332 Hines, P. (1987) Notes on birds recorded in Nepal in spring 1986. Unpublished.

333 Hjarsen, T. (1988) List of species seen in Pakistan, India and Nepal, 1987 - 1988. Unpublished.

334 Hoare, E. (1977) Notes on birds recorded at Tiger Tops, May - June 1977. Unpublished.

335 Hodgson, B.H. (1827) [Description of *Phasianus nipalensis*]. *Quart. Oriental Mag. Rev. and Regist.* 8 (Sci.): 44.

336 Hodgson, B.H. (1829) Notes and original watercolour paintings of the birds of Nepal, Tibet and India, held in the Zoological Society of London Library. Unpublished.

337 Hodgson, B.H. (1829) On a new species of *Buceros. Gleanings in Science* 1: 249-252; (1832) *Proc. zool. Soc. London* 2: 10-16; (1833) *Asiat. Res.* 18(2): 178-186.

338 Hodgson, B.H. (1831) On some of the Scolopacidae of Nepal. *Gleanings in Science* 3: 233-243.

339 Hodgson, B.H. (1833) Characters of a new species of *Perdix. Proc. zool. Soc. London* 1: 107.

340 Hodgson, B.H. (1833) On a species of *Aquila, Circaeetus* and *Dicrurus. Asiat. Res.* 18(2): 13-26.

341 Hodgson, B.H. (1833) On the migration of the Natatores and Grallatores, as observed at Kathmandu. *Asiat. Res.* 18(2): 122-128.

342 Hodgson, B.H. (1833) Description of the *Buceros Homrai* of the Himalaya. *Asiat. Res.* 18(2): 169-188.

343 Hodgson, B.H. (1835) Description of the Bearded Vulture of the Himalaya. *J. Asiat. Soc. Bengal* 4: 454-458; (1837) *Bibl. Univ.* 8: 212.

344 Hodgson, B.H. (1835) Red-billed Erolia. *J. Asiat. Soc. Bengal* 4: 458-461.

345 Hodgson, B.H. (1835) Note on the Red-billed Erolia. *J. Asiat. Soc. Bengal* 4: 701-702.

346 Hodgson, B.H. (1836) Description of a new species of *Columba. J. Asiat. Soc. Bengal* 5: 122-124.

347 Hodgson, B.H. (1836) Description of two new species belonging to a new form of the Meruline group of birds, with indication of their generic character. *J. Asiat. Soc. Bengal* 5: 358-360.

348 Hodgson, B.H. (1836) Additions to the ornithology of Nepal. 1. Indication of a new genus of Insessorial birds. *J. Asiat. Soc. Bengal* 5: 770-775; (1837) 6: 110-112.

349 Hodgson, B.H. (1836) Additions to the ornithology of Nepal. 2. Indication of a new genus of waders, belonging to the Charadriatic family. *J. Asiat. Soc. Bengal* 5: 775-777.

350 Hodgson, B.H. (1836) Additions to the ornithology of Nepal. 3. Indication of a new genus of the Falconidae. *J. Asiat. Soc. Bengal* 5: 777-778.

351 Hodgson, B.H. (1836) Additions to the ornithology of Nepal. 4. Indication of a new genus of the Picidae, with description of the type. A new species, also, of two new species of the genus *Sitta. J. Asiat. Soc. Bengal* 5: 778-779.

352 Hodgson, B.H. (1836) Additions to the ornithology of Nepal. 5. New species of Hirundinidae. *J. Asiat. Soc. Bengal* 5: 779-781.

353 Hodgson, B.H. (1836) Notices of the ornithology of Nepal. 1. Eight new species of *Cinclosoma. Asiat. Res.* 19: 143-150.

354 Hodgson, B.H. (1836) Notices of the ornithology of Nepal. 2. New species of the thick billed finches. *Asiat. Res.* 19: 150-159.

355 Hodgson, B.H. (1836) Notices of the ornithology of Nepal. 3. New genera of the Columbidae. *Asiat. Res.* 19: 159-164.

356 Hodgson, B.H. (1836) Notices of the ornithology of Nepal. 4. New genus and 3 new species of the Silviadae. *Asiat. Res.* 19: 165-167; (1837) *J. Asiat. Soc. Bengal* 6: 230-232.

357 Hodgson, B.H. (1836) Notices of the ornithology of Nepal. 5. New species of the Strigine family. *Asiat. Res.* 19: 168-177.

358 Hodgson, B.H. (1836) Notices of the ornithology of Nepal. 7. Two new species of the parrot tribe. *Asiat. Res.* 19: 177-178.

359 Hodgson, B.H. (1836) Notices of the ornithology of Nepal. 8. New species of *Pomatorhinus*, and its allies. *Asiat. Res.* 19: 179-186.

360 Hodgson, B.H. (1836) Notices of the ornithology of Nepal. 9. New species of Motacillinae. *Asiat. Res.* 19: 186-190.

361 Hodgson, B.H. (1836) Summary description of some new species of Falconidae. *J. Asiat. Soc. Bengal* 5: 227-231.

362 Hodgson, B.H. (1836) On a new genus of the Meropidae. *J. Asiat. Soc. Bengal* 5: 360-362.

363 Hodgson, B.H. (1836) On a new piscatory genus of the Strigine family. *J. Asiat. Soc. Bengal* 5: 363-365.

364 Hodgson, B.H. (1836) On some of the Scolopacidae of Nipal. *Proc. zool. Soc. London* 4: 7-8; (1837) *Madras J. Lit. Sci.* 5: 410-412; (1838) *Ind. Rev.* 2: 117.

365 Hodgson, B.H. (1836) Summary description of some new species of birds of prey. *Bengal Sporting Mag.* 8: 177-183.

366 Hodgson, B.H. (1837) Description of sundry new species of *Cinnyris* inhabiting Nepal. *India Review* 1: 272-274.

367 Hodgson, B.H. (1837) Description of three new species of woodpecker. *J. Asiat. Soc. Bengal* 6: 104-109.

368 Hodgson, B.H. (1837) Indian quails. *Bengal Sporting Mag.* 9: 343-346.

369 Hodgson, B.H. (1837) Indication of a new genus of Insessores, tending to connect the Sylviadae and Muscicapidae. *India Review* 1: 650-652.

370 Hodgson, B.H. (1837) Indication of a new genus belonging to the Strigine family, with description of the new species and type. *Madras J. Lit. Sci.* 5: 23-25.

371 Hodgson, B.H. (1837) On three new genera or sub-genera of long-legged thrushes, with descriptions of their species. *J. Asiat. Soc. Bengal* 6: 101-104.

372 Hodgson, B.H. (1837) On some new genera of Raptores, with remarks on the old genera. *J. Asiat. Soc. Bengal* 6: 361-373.

373 Hodgson, B.H. (1837) New species of Scolopacidae, Indian snipes. *J. Asiat. Soc. Bengal* 6: 489-492.

374 Hodgson, B.H. (1837) On some new species of the Edolian and Ceblepyrine subfamilies of the Laniidae of Nepal. *India Review* 1: 325-328.

375 Hodgson, B.H. (1837) On some new species of the more typical Laniidae of Nepal. *India Review* 1: 445-447.

376 Hodgson, B.H. (1837) On the structure and habits of the *Elanus melanopterus. Madras J. Lit. Sci.* 6: 75-78.

377 Hodgson, B.H. (1837) On two new genera of Rasorial birds. *Madras J. Lit. Sci.* 5: 300-305.

378 Hodgson, B.H. (1838) Indication of some new forms belonging to the Parianae. *India Review* 2: 30-34, 87-90.

379 Hodgson, B.H. (1838) Remarks on D. McClelland's paper on the *Bathyrynchus brevirostris* and *Ciconia nudifrons. India Review* 2: 563.

380 Hodgson, B.H. (1839) On a new Genus of the Fissirostral tribe. *J. Asiat. Soc. Bengal* 8: 35-36.

381 Hodgson, B.H. (1839) Description of two new species of a new form of Meruline birds. *J. Asiat. Soc. Bengal* 8: 37-38.

382 Hodgson, B.H. (1839) On *Cuculus. J. Asiat. Soc. Bengal* 8: 136-137.

383 Hodgson, B.H. (1841) Notice of a new form of the Glaucopinae, or Rasorial crows, inhabiting the northern region of Nepal - *Conostoma Aemodius* (Nobis type). *J. Asiat. Soc. Bengal* 10: 856-857; (1843) *Ann. Mag. nat. Hist.* 10: 77-79.

384 Hodgson, B.H. (1843) Description of a new genus of Falconidae. *J. Asiat. Soc. Bengal* 12: 127-128.

385 Hodgson, B.H. (1843) Catalogue of Nepalese birds presented to the Asiatic Society. *J. Asiat. Soc. Bengal* 12: 301-313.

386 Hodgson, B.H. (1843) Additions to the catalogue of Nepal birds. *J. Asiat. Soc. Bengal* 12: 447-450.

387 Hodgson, B.H. (1844) "On the Leiotrichane birds of the Sub-hemalayas". *J. Asiat. Soc. Bengal* 13: 933-941.

388 Hodgson, B.H. (1844) Catalogue of Nipalese birds, collected between 1824 and 1844. In Gray, J.E., *Zoological Miscellany*, June 1844.

389 Hodgson, B.H. (1844) *Falco-Rufipedoides*, Dhuti-Dhuter of India. *Calcutta J. nat. Hist.* 4: 283-284.

390 Hodgson, B.H. (1845) Characters of six new species of Nepalese birds. *Ann. Mag. nat. Hist.* 15: 326-327.

391 Hodgson, B.H. (1845) On Nipalese birds. *Proc. zool. Soc. London* 13: 22-37.

392 Hodgson, B.H. (1845) [Description of *Yuhina nigrimenta*]. In Blyth, E., *J. Asiat. Soc. Bengal* 14: 562.

393 Hodgson, B.H. (1845) [Description of *Neornis flavolivacea*]. In Blyth, E., *J. Asiat. Soc. Bengal* 14: 590.

394 Hodgson, B.H. (1845) [Description of *Abrornis castaniceps*]. In Blyth, E., *J. Asiat. Soc. Bengal* 14: 593.

395 Hodgson, B.H. (1847) [Description of *Pteruthius melanotis*]. In Blyth, E., *J. Asiat. Soc. Bengal* 16: 448.

396 Hodgson, B.H. (1847) On the Charj or *Otis Bengalensis. J. Asiat. Soc. Bengal* 16: 883-889.

397 Hodgson, B.H. (1848) On a new genus of Insessorial birds. *Calcutta J. nat. Hist.* 8: 45-48.

398 Hodgson, B.H. (1848) On the buzzards of the Himalaya and of Tibet. *Calcutta J. nat. Hist.* 8: 94-97.

399 Hodgson, B.H. (1855) Catalogue of Nipalese birds, collected between 1824 and 1844. *J. Asiat. Soc. Bengal* 24: 572-582.

400 Hodgson, B.H. (1855) On the geographical distribution of the Mammalia and birds of the Himalaya. *Proc. zool. Soc. London* 23: 124-128.

401 Holmstrom, G. (1982) Notes on birds recorded in Nepal, 1982. Unpublished.

402 Holmstrom, G. (1983) Notes on birds recorded in Nepal during 1981 and 1983. Unpublished.

403 Holt, P., Crossley, R. and Moores, C. (1986) Notes on birds recorded in Nepal, January - April 1986. Unpublished.

404 Hooker, J.D. (1854) *Himalayan journals. Notes of a naturalist in Bengal, the Sikkim and Nepal Himalayas, the Khasia Mountains, etc.* 2 volumes. London: J. Murray.

405 Hopkins, J. (1971) Notes on birds recorded in Nepal, December 1971. Unpublished.

406 Hopwood, S.F. (1940) Birds eating butterflies. *J. Bombay Nat. Hist. Soc.* 42: 199.

407 Hornbuckle, J. (1980) Notes on birds recorded in Nepal, 1980. Unpublished.

408 Hornskov, J. (1984) *Indien & Nepal, Vinteren '83-'84.* Copenhagen: Dansk Ornitologisk Forening.

409 Horsfield, T. and Moore, F. (1854) *A catalogue of birds in the Museum of the Hon. East-India Company.* London: W.H. Allen.

410 Hounsome, M. (1981) List of bird specimens from Nepal in the Manchester Museum. Unpublished.

411 Housden, S. (1982) Notes on birds recorded in Nepal, December 1981 - January 1982. Unpublished.

412 Howman, K. (1979) Notes and News from the World Pheasant Association. *Cage and Aviary Birds* 15 February 1979.

413 Hume, A.O. (1877) *Pratincola insignis. Stray Feathers* 5: 132-133.

414 Hume, A.O. and Oates, E.W. (1890) *The nests and eggs of Indian birds.* 3 volumes. Second edition. London: Porter.

415 Hunt, J. (1953) *The ascent of Everest.* London: Hodder and Stoughton.

416 Hunter, M.L. Jr. (1989) Himalayan birds face uphill while singing. *Auk* 106: 728-729.

417 Hurrell, A.G. (1985) List of birds seen in the British Embassy compound, Kathmandu, November 1983 - June 1985. Unpublished.

418 Hurrell, A.G. (1988) Notes on birds recorded in Nepal, 1984-1988. Unpublished.

419 Hyatt, K.H. (1954) Some notes on birds in central Nepal during 1954. Unpublished.

420 Hyatt, K.H. (1966) Notes on birds seen in Nepal, 1966. Unpublished.

421 Innes, R. and Lewis, P. (1984) Notes on birds recorded in Nepal, March to May 1984. Unpublished.

422 Inskipp, C. (1981) List of bird specimens from Nepal in the collection of the University Museum of Zoology, Cambridge, collected by R.C.Lawrence in 1870. Unpublished.

423 Inskipp, C. (1981) List of bird specimens from Nepal in the collection of the Bombay Natural History Society. Unpublished.

424 Inskipp, C. (1982) A classification of the Hodgson original watercolour paintings of the birds of India, Nepal and Tibet in the Zoology Library of the British Museum (Natural History), London. Unpublished.

425 Inskipp, C. (1982) A classification of the Hodgson original watercolour paintings of the birds of India, Nepal and Tibet in the library of the Zoological Society of London. Unpublished.

426 Inskipp, C. (1982) List of bird specimens from Nepal in Merseyside Museum. Unpublished.

427 Inskipp, C. (1982) List of bird specimens from Nepal in Oxford University Museum. Unpublished.

428 Inskipp, C. (1988) Khaptad National Park. An account of current knowledge and conservation value. A report to the Department of National Parks and Wildlife Conservation, Nepal. Unpublished.

429 Inskipp, C. (1989) *Nepal's forest birds: their status and conservation.* Monograph No. 4. Cambridge, U.K.: International Council for Bird Preservation.

430 Inskipp, C. (1989) The ornithological importance of Khaptad National Park, Nepal. *Forktail* 5: 49-60.

431 Inskipp, C. and Collar, N.J. (1984) The Bengal Florican: its conservation in Nepal. *Oryx* 18(1): 30-35.

432 Inskipp, C. and Inskipp, T.P. (1982) Notes on birds recorded in Nepal, April-June 1982. Unpublished.

433 Inskipp, C. and Inskipp, T.P. (1983) *Report on a survey of Bengal Floricans* Houbaropsis bengalensis *in Nepal and India, 1982.* Study Report No. 2. Cambridge, U.K.: International Council for Bird Preservation.

434 Inskipp, C. and Inskipp, T.P. (1984) Additions to the bird species recorded from Nepal. *J. Bombay nat. Hist. Soc.* 81: 702-706.

435 Inskipp, C. and Inskipp, T.P. (1985) *A guide to the birds of Nepal.* Beckenham: Croom Helm.

436 Inskipp, C. and Inskipp, T.P. (1986) Notes on birds recorded in Nepal, October - November 1986. Unpublished.

437 Inskipp, C. and Inskipp, T.P. (1986) Some important birds and forests in Nepal. *Forktail* 1: 53-64.

438 Inskipp, C. and Inskipp, T.P. (1988) Notes on birds recorded in Nepal, 10 April - 7 June 1988. Unpublished.

439 Inskipp, T.P. and Inskipp, C. (1977) Notes on birds recorded in Nepal, December 1977. Unpublished.

440 Inskipp, T.P. and Inskipp, C. (1980) Notes on birds recorded in Nepal, April - May 1980. Unpublished.

441 Inskipp, T.P. and Inskipp, C. (1981) List of some birds specimens from Nepal in the collection of R.L. Fleming, 1957-73. Unpublished.

442 Inskipp, T.P. and Inskipp, C. (1981) Notes on birds recorded in Nepal, February - March 1981. Unpublished.

443 Inskipp, T.P. and Round, P.D. (1989) A review of the Black-tailed Crake *Porzana bicolor. Forktail* 5: 3-15.

444 Inskipp, T.P. et. al. (1971) Notes on birds recorded in Nepal, September 1970 - March 1971. Unpublished.

445 Isherwood, R.J. (1975) Birds in the Himalayas. *Hong Kong Bird Report* 1974: 37-40.

446 Isherwood, R.J. (1978) *Birds of the Pakhribas Area.* Technical Paper No.27. Dhankuta: Pakhribas Agriculture Centre, British Gurkha Ex-Servicemen Reintegration Training Scheme.

447 Jackson, R. (1978) A report on wildlife and hunting in the Namlang (Langu) Valley of west Nepal. Report to National Parks and Wildlife Conservation Dept. Kathmandu. Unpublished.

448 Jardine, W. (1886) A catalogue of the birds contained in the collection of Sir William Jardine.

449 Jardine, W. and Selby, P.J. (1830) [Description of *Chloropsis Hardwickii*] in *Illustrations of Ornithology* 2: 1.

450 Jarman, R. (1971) Notes on birds recorded in Nepal, 1970-1971. Unpublished.

451 Jepson, P. (1985) Systematic list of birds seen in Nepal March - May 1985 and March 1987. Unpublished.

452 Jepson, P. (1988) List of wildlife seen at Chitwan National Park, 26-29 November 1988. Unpublished.

453 Jepson, P. (1988) *Naturetrek* list of birds and mammals seen in Mount Everest area and Gokyo lakes, 5 - 27 November 1988. Unpublished.

454 Jepson, P. (1989) *Naturetrek* list of birds and mammals seen in the Langtang National Park, 29 April - 21 May 1989. Unpublished.

455 Jepson, P. (1989) *Naturetrek* list of birds and mammals seen at Royal Chitwan National Park, 25 - 30 May 1989. Unpublished.

456 Jepson, P. (in prep.) Occurrence of Kessler's Thrush in Nepal.

457 Jerdon, T.C. (1862-1864) *The birds of India.* 3 volumes. Calcutta:

458 Jerdon, T.C. (1871) Supplementary notes to 'The birds of India'. *Ibis* (3)1: 234-247; 335-356.

459 Jerdon, T.C. (1872) Supplementary notes to 'The birds of India'. *Ibis* (3)2: 1-22; 114-139; 297-310.

460 Johns, R.J. (1982) Notes on birds recorded in Nepal, December 1981 - January 1982. Unpublished.

461 Jongeling, B. (1983) Notes on birds recorded in Nepal, 1983. Unpublished.

462 Joshi, A.R. (1986) Shivapuri Watershed and Wildlife Reserve. Unpublished.

463 Juliusberger, R. (1987) A birdwatching tour to India and Nepal, 31 November 1986 - 16 April 1987. Unpublished.

464 Justice, S. (1978) Notes on birds recorded in Nepal, 1976-78. Unpublished.

465 Kall, M. and Wallander, J. (1988) Notes on birds recorded in Nepal, 14 February - 28 March 1988. Unpublished.

466 Kattel, B. (1981) A cursory ecological survey of Khaptad area. *J. Nat. Hist. Mus.* (Tribhubvan Univ., Kathmandu) 5(2): 67-73.

467 Kennerley, P. (1982) Notes on recorded in Nepal, 1982. Unpublished.

468 Kennerley, P. and Turnbull, M. (1989) Report on a birding trip to Nepal, 4 - 20 February 1989. Unpublished.

469 Khadka, R.B., Mishra, P.N. and Bhatta, B. (1980) Studies on the feeding ecology of Cattle Egret *Bubulcus ibis coromandus* (Bonaparte) in Kirtipur meadows. *J. Nat. Hist. Mus.* (Tribhuvan Univ., Kathmandu) 4(1): 1-14.

470 Khanal, B. ([1986] 1988) Birds of Kanchanpur District. *J. Nat. Hist. Mus.* (Tribhuvan Univ., Kathmandu) 10: 145-150.

471 Khanal, B. and Bhandary, H.R. (1988) A study on natural environment of Dang valley. Report to the Royal Nepal Academy, Kathmandu. Unpublished.

472 Khatri, H.S. (1974) Birds from Baitadi. *Nepal Nature Conservation Society Newsletter* No.23, April 1974.

473 Kihara, H. (1955) Fauna and flora of Nepal Himalaya. Scientific results of the Japanese Himalayan Expedition to Nepal Himalaya. *Kyoto Univ. Fauna and Flora Res. Soc.* 1-390.

474 King, B. (1980) Notes on birds recorded in Nepal, 1972-79. Unpublished.

475 King, B. (1982) Pipar bird list, May 1982. Unpublished.

476 Kjellen, N., Jirle, E. and Walinder, G. (1981) Asien-81. Unpublished.

477 Klapste, J. (1986) List of birds seen on Langtang trek, north-central Nepal, March - April 1986. Unpublished.

478 Klapste, J. (1986) Trekking in Nepal Himalaya in search of Ibisbills. *Bird Observer* 655: 73-74.

479 Koelz, W. (1954) 'Ornithological Studies'; I. New Birds from Iran, Afghanistan, and India. *Contrib. Inst. Regional Exploration*, No.1, Ann Arbor, Michigan.

480 Kovacs, J.-C. (1987) Compte rendu d'un voyage naturaliste au Nepal, Fevrier - Mars 1987. Unpublished.

481 Kovacs, J.-C. (1988) Voyage Indie - Nepal (Fevrier - Mars 1988). Compte rendu des observations ornithologiques & mammalogiques. Unpublished.

482 Krabbe, E. (1983) List of bird specimens in the Zoological Museum of Copenhagen, collected by G.B. Gurung, S. Rana and P.W. Soman from Nepal, 1959. Unpublished.

483 Krabbe, N. (1981) India and Nepal, 1981, ornithological report. Unpublished.

484 Kratter, A. (1987) Notes on birds recorded in Nepal, 1987. Unpublished.

485 Lalchan, L. and Battachan, S. (1989) Notes on birds recorded in Nepal, 1988-1990. Unpublished.

486 Lambert, F. (1979) Notes on birds recorded in Nepal, 1978-79. Unpublished.

487 Lancaster, R. (1981) *Plant hunting in Nepal.* London: Croom Helm.

488 Lancaster, R. (1983) Additional notes on birds recorded in Nepal, September - December 1971. Unpublished.

489 Langlands, A.M. (1970) Tales from Nepal. *Adjutant* 7: 28-34.

490 LaPersonne, V.S. (1933) The Common Central Asian Kingfisher (*Alcedo atthis pallasii* Reichenb.) in Nepal. *J. Bombay nat. Hist. Soc.* 36: 508.

491 Larsen, J.T. (1988) Notes on birds recorded in Nepal, May - June 1988. Unpublished.

492 Larsson, C. (1988) Notes on birds recorded in Nepal, May 1988. Unpublished.

493 Latham, J. (1790) *Index ornithologicus, sive Systema ornithologiae* 2: 633.

494 LeClerq, S. *in litt.*, 22 February 1990.

495 Leece, J. (1977) Notes on birds recorded in Nepal, October - December 1977. Unpublished.

496 Lelliott, A.D. (1979) Notes on birds recorded in Nepal, April - October 1979. World Pheasant Association project. Unpublished.

497 Lelliott, A.D. (1980) Preliminary report of an ecological study of highland pheasants in Nepal, March - May 1980. Unpublished.

498 Lelliott, A.D. (1981) Cheer Pheasants in West-Central Nepal. *J. World Pheasant Association* 6: 89-95.

499 Lelliott, A.D. (1981) Notes on the birds recorded in Nepal, 1978-81. Unpublished.

500 Lelliott, A.D. (1981) Report on 1981 field season in Nepal. Unpublished.

501 Lelliott, A.D. (1981) Studies of Himalayan pheasants in Nepal, with reference to their conservation. M. Sc. thesis, Univ. of Durham. Unpublished.

502 Lelliott, A.D. (1982) Blood Pheasants in the Himalayas. *Cage and Aviary Birds* October 16 1982.

503 Lelliott, A.D. (1982) Censusing the Cheer Pheasant. *Cage and Aviary Birds*, September 4 1982.

504 Lelliott, A.D. and Yonzon, P.B. (1980) Pheasant studies in Annapurna Himal (1) Field studies. Pp. 53-55 in C. Savage, ed., *Pheasants in Asia* 1979. Exning, U.K.: World Pheasant Association.

505 Lelliott, A.D. and Yonzon, P.B. (1980) Studies of Himalayan pheasants in Nepal. *J. World Pheasant Association* 5: 11-30.

506 Linderstrom, S.A. (1989) Notes on birds recorded in India and Nepal, 28 January - 27 February 1989. Unpublished.

507 Lindvall, M.L. and Dhital, P. (1978) Occurrence and habitat preference of birds in a Duns area, Part 1. *Forestry* 7.

508 Lindvall, M.L. and Dhital, P. (1978) Occurrence and habitat preference of birds in a Duns area, Part 2. *Forestry* 7.

509 Lister, V. (1979) Notes on birds recorded in Nepal, April - June 1979. Unpublished.

510 Lohrl, H. 1981. Zur kenntnis der Laubmeise *Sylviparus modestus. J. Orn.* 122: 89-92.

511 Low, G.C., Dewar, D., Newman, T.H. and Levett-Yeats, G.A. (1930) A classification of the original watercolour paintings of birds of India by B.H. Hodgson, S.R. Tickell and C.F. Sharpe in the library of the Zoological Society of London. *Proc. zool. Soc. London* 1930: 549-625.

512 Lowndes, D. (1955) Some birds from north-western Nepal. *J. Bombay nat. Hist. Soc.* 53: 29-37.

513 Madge, S.C. (1983) Notes on birds recorded during the Birdquest Nepal tour, March 1983. Unpublished.

514 Madge, S.C. (1986) Selected notes on *Birdquest* Nepal tour, February - March 1986. Unpublished.

515 Madge, S.C. (1989) Swinhoe's Snipe *Gallinago megala*: a new species for Nepal. *Forktail* 4: 121-123.

516 Madge, S.C. and Appleby, R.H. (1980) *Sunbird Holidays* tour report, October - November 1980. Unpublished.

517 Madge, S.C. and Madge, P. (1982) Notes on birds recorded in Nepal, April - May 1982. Unpublished.

518 Madge, S.C. et. al. (1974) Notes on birds recorded in Nepal, December 1973 - February 1974. Unpublished.

519 Madsen, J. and Poulsen, M.K. (1980) Artsliste for Nepal, 7 April - 14 Maj 1980. Unpublished.

520 Madsen, S.T. (1990) Notes on birds recorded at Royal Bardia National Park, October - November 1989. Unpublished.

521 Malherbe, A. (1849) Description de quelques nouvelles especes de Picinees (*Picus*, Linn). *Rev. et Mag. de Zoologie* (2)1: 530.

522 Malling Olsen, K. (1979) Notes on birds recorded in Nepal, December 1978 - January 1979. Unpublished.

523 Malling, S. (1981) Notes on birds recorded in Nepal. Unpublished.

524 Marshall, T. (1982) Notes on birds recorded in Nepal, 1982. Unpublished.

525 Martens, J. (1971) Artstatus von *Parus rufonuchalis* Blyth. *J. Orn.* 112: 451-458.

526 Martens, J. (1971) Zur Kenntnis des Vogelzuges im nepalischen Himalaya. *Vogelwarte* 26: 113-128.

527 Martens, J. (1972) Brutverbreitung palaarktischer Vogel im Nepal-Himalaya. *Bonn. zool. Beitr.* 23: 95-121.

528 Martens, J. (1975) Akustische Differenzierung verwandtschaftlicher Beziehungen in der *Parus* Gruppe nach Untersuchungen im Nepal-Himalaya. *J. Orn.* 116: 369-433.

529 Martens, J. (1975) Verbreitung, Biotop und Gesang des Bambusseidensangers (*Cettia acanthizoides*) im Nepal. *Bonn. zool. Beitr.* 26: 164-174.

530 Martens, J. (1979) Die Fauna des Nepal-Himalaya - Entstehung und Erforschung. *Natur und Museum* 109: 221-243.

531 Martens, J. (1980) *Lautausserungen, verwandtschaftliche Beziehungen und Verbreitungsgeschichte asiatischer Laubsanger* (Phylloscopus). (Fortschritte der Verhaltensforschung, H 22). Berlin and Hamburg: Parey.

532 Martens, J. (1980) Ornithogeography of the Himalayas. *Senckenbergiana biol.* 60: 241 - 247.

533 Martens, J. (1981) Lautausserungen der baumlaufer des Himalaya und zur akustichen evolution in der gattung *Certhia. Behaviour* 77(4): 287-318.

534 Martens, J. (1984) Vertical distribution of Palaearctic and Oriental faunal components in the Nepal Himalayas. *Senckenbergiana biol.* 65: 321-336.

535 Martens, J. (1985) Speciation and the development of Himalayan avifaunas. Pp. 358-372 in V.D. Ilyichev and V.M. Gavrilov, eds., *Acta XVIII Congressus Internationalis Ornithologici*, 1. Moscow: Nauka.

536 Martens, J. (1987) Remarks on my Himalayan expeditions. *Courier Forsch.-Inst. Senckenberg* 93: 7-31.

537 Martens, J. (1988) Selected bird observations, Nepal 1988. Unpublished.

538 Martens, J. and Geduldig, G. (1988) Akustische Barrieren beim Waldbaumlaufer (*Certhia familiaris*). *J. Orn.* 129: 417-432.

539 Martens, J. and Geduldig, G. (1989) Acoustic adaptations of birds living close to Himalayan torrents. *Proc. Int. 100 DO-G Meeting, Current Topics Avian Biol.*, Bonn 1988, pp. 123-131.

540 Martins, R.P. (1982) Birds seen in Khumbu National Park from Lukla northwards, May 1982, and other notes on birds seen in Nepal, 1982. Unpublished.

541 Martins, R.P., Parr, M.J., Robson, C.R., Speight, G.J., and Turton, J.M. (1983) Hodgson's Stonechats in Nepal in March and April 1982. *Dutch Birding* 5(4): 99-101.

542 Masatomi, H. (1971) [Aves]. In [*Animals and plants of Nepal Himalaya*]. (In Japanese.)

543 Masatomi, H. (1975) Some observations on birds at high altitude lake sides in Gosainkund, central Nepal. *J. Bombay nat. Hist. Soc.* 72: 46-55.

544 Matsuda, Y. (1979) [The Siberian Cranes surmount giant peaks of Himal.] (In Japanese.)

545 Matthiessen, P. (1979) *The Snow Leopard*. London: Chatto and Windus.

546 Mayer, S. (1986) Notes on birds recorded in Nepal, October 1985 - April 1986. Unpublished.

547 McCarty, C. (1983) Notes on birds recorded in Nepal, winter 1982/83. Unpublished.

548 McDougal, C. and Gurung, K.K. (1979) Checklist of birds of the Chitwan National Park. Unpublished.

549 McKnight, G., Curson, J., Bose, A., Lalchan, L. and Battachan, S. (1989) Systematic list of birds, Mai valley, March 1989. Unpublished.

550 Mees, G.F. (1981) List of bird specimens from Nepal in the Rijksmuseum van Natuurlijke Historie Leiden. Unpublished.

551 Meilstrup, H. (1971) Notes on birds recorded in Nepal, November 1970 - May 1971. Unpublished.

552 Meilstrup, H. and Olsen, I. (1987) *Stortur til Indien og Nepal, 20/2 - 14/3 1987.* Copenhagen: Dansk Ornitologisk Forening.

553 Melville, D.S. and Hamilton, V.J. (1981) Notes on birds recorded in Nepal, November - December 1981. Unpublished.

554 Melville, D.S. and Melville, V.J. (1983) Sight record of *Serinus pusillus* near Manang, central Nepal. *J. Bombay nat. Hist. Soc.* 80: 222-223.

555 Mertens, P. von (1977) Rafting the Trisuli River. *Nepal Nature Conservation Society Newsletter* No. 41, May 1977.

556 Millin, D.J. and Woolner, J.D. (1988) Annotated list of birds seen in and around Kathmandu Valley, Nepal, 14 -18 May 1988. Unpublished.

557 Mills, D.G.H. (1985) Notes on birds recorded in Nepal. Unpublished.

558 Mills, D.G.H. (1988) Notes on birds recorded in Sagarmatha National Park. Unpublished.

559 Mills, D.G.H. and Preston, N.A. (1981) Notes on birds recorded in Nepal, 1981. Unpublished.

560 Mills, D.G.H. and Preston, N.A. (1982) Identification of Blyth's Pipit. *Brit. Birds* 12: 381.

561 Mills, D.G.H., Preston, N.A. and Winyard, C. (1982) Notes on birds recorded in Nepal. Unpublished.

562 Mills, D.J. (1988) Systematic list of birds recorded during a holiday to Langtang and Royal Chitwan National Parks, May 1988. Unpublished.

563 Mischler, T. (1977) Notes on birds recorded in Nepal, February - April 1977. Unpublished.

564 Mitchell, R. and Dick, J.A. (1977) Ectoparasites from Nepal birds. *J. Bombay nat. Hist. Soc.* 74: 264-274.

565 Molgaard, E. (1983) The Far East 1981-82. Unpublished.

566 Moore, F. (1854) A monograph of the genus *Ruticilla*, with description of some new species. *Proc. zool. Soc. London* 22: 25-30.

567 Moore, F. (1854) Descriptions of some new and little known species of birds from Northern India, contained in the Museum of the Hon. East India Company. *Proc. zool. Soc. London* 22: 74-78.

568 Moore, F. (1854) Notice of a new Indian swallow. *Proc. zool. Soc. London* 22: 104.

569 Moore, F. (1854) Notice of some new species of birds contained in the Museum of the Hon. East India Company. *Proc. zool. Soc. London* 22: 104-107.

570 Moore, F. (1854) Notice of all the known species of the genus *Accentor*, with the description of an uncharacterized species from Nepal. *Proc. zool. Soc. London* 22: 116-120.

571 Moore, F. (1854) Notice of some imperfectly-known species of birds contained in the Museum of the Hon. East India Company. *Proc. zool Soc. London* 22: 141-142.

572 Moore. F. (1855) Notice of some new species of birds. *Proc. zool. Soc. London* 23: 213-217.

573 Morioka, H. (1985) Notes on birds of Dhorpatan, central Nepal. *Tori* 33: 113-122.

574 Morioka, H. and Sakane, T. (1981) Notes on the birds of Khumba-karna Himal, eastern Nepal. *Tori* 29:129-146.

575 Morita, M. (1989) Notes on birds recorded in Nepal, 1988-1989. Unpublished.

576 Munthe, K. (1981) Notes on birds recorded in Nepal, December 1980 - January 1981. Unpublished.

577 Murdoch, D. (1988) Notes on birds recorded in Nepal, May 1988. Unpublished.

578 Murphy, C. (1986) Notes on birds recorded on Sheopuri in May 1986. Unpublished.

579 Murray, J. (1890) *The avifauna of British India and its dependencies*. London: Trubner.

580 Muston, A.J. (1975) Ornithological report of the Joint British Army Mountaineering Association, and Royal Nepal Army Nuptse Expedition, 1975. Unpublished.

581 Muston, A.J. (1976) Ornithological report on the recent army expedition to Everest. *Army Birdwatching Soc. Bull.* No. 2/76.

582 Muston, A.J. (1977) Ornithological report. Pp. 236-239 in J. Fleming and R. Faux *Soldiers on Everest*. The joint Army Mountaineering Association, Royal Nepalese Army Mount Everest Expedition 1976. London: Her Majesty's Stationery Office.

583 Muston, A.J. (1982) Ornithological report of the British Army West Nepal Expedition 1982. Unpublished.

584 Nazarenko, A. (1985) Some historic-biogeographic problems connected with the Himalayas (with special reference to the dendrophilous avifauna). *Zhurnal obshch. Biol.* 46: 41-54.

585 Nepali, H.S. (1972) The Goldfinch in Nepal. *Nepal Nature Conservation Society Newsletter* No.12, July 1972.

586 Nepali, H.S. (1974) Rediscovery of the Dunlin in Nepal. *Nepal Nature Conservation Society Newsletter* No. 23, April 1974.

587 Nepali, H.S. (1982) List of Nepalese bird specimens, and notes on birds seen in Nepal. Unpublished.

588 Nepali, H.S. (1984) Bird report from the Barun Valley Report. Unpublished.

589 Nepali, H.S. (1986) List of bird specimens collected in Nepal. Unpublished.

590 Nepali, H.S. (1986) Notes on birds recorded in the Arun and Barun valleys, Nepal in 1986. Unpublished.

591 Nepali, H.S. and Fleming, R.L. Jr. (1971) Some birds from Nepal. *J. Bombay nat. Hist. Soc.* 68: 833-835.

592 Neufeldt, I.A. and Vietinghoff-Scheel, E. v. (1984) *Mycerobas icterioides* (Vigors). In *Atlas der Verbreitung Palaearktischer Vogel*, 12. Berlin: Akademie Verlag.

593 Nickel, H. and Trost, R. (1983) Vogelkundliche beobachtungen einer reise nach Indien und Nepal, January - April 1983. Unpublished.

594 Nicolle, S. (1987) Notes on birds recorded in Nepal, 1987. Unpublished.

595 Nielsen, J.T. (1986) Some bird observations in Nepal, 3 October - 10 December 1986. Unpublished.

596 Nielsen, J.T. (1988) Notes on birds recorded in Nepal 18 November 1988 - 6 January 1989. Unpublished.

597 Nielsen, J.T. and Jakobsen, O.F. (1989) Notes on birds recorded in Nepal, 25 October - 23 November 1989. Unpublished.

598 Nilsson, T. (1982) Notes on birds recorded in Nepal, 1982. Unpublished.

599 Nordin, T. and Wallander, J. (1982) Notes on birds recorded in Nepal. Unpublished.

600 Numme, G. (1985) Notes on birds recorded in Nepal, November 1983. Unpublished.

601 O'Donnell, J. (1977) A brief survey of the birds of the North Churia Hills. Unpublished.

602 Ogilvie-Grant, W.R. (1893) *Catalogue of the birds in the collection of the British Museum*, 22 - gamebirds. London: British Museum.

603 Ogilvie-Grant, W.R. and Sharpe, R.B. (1892) *Catalogue of the birds in the collection of the British Museum*, 17 - Coraciae (contd.), Halcyones, Bucerotes, Trogones. London: British Museum.

604 Oliver, W.L.R. (1984) Notes on birds recorded at Bardia, 24 to 29 February 1984. Unpublished.

605 Owens, G.F. (1975) Notes on birds seen on the Everest trek and in the Kathmandu Valley. Unpublished.

606 Parr, M. (1982) Notes on birds recorded in Nepal, 1982. Unpublished.

607 Paynter, R.A. (1961) Notes on some Corvidae from Nepal, Pakistan and India. *J. Bombay nat. Hist. Soc.* 58: 379-386.

608 Paynter, R.A. (1962) Taxonomic notes on some Himalayan Paridae. *J. Bombay nat. Hist. Soc.* 59: 951-956.

609 Penard, A.P. (1919) *Muscicapa sibirica cacabata*. New name for *Hemichelidon fuliginosa* Hodgson, 1844, preoccupied in *Muscicapa* by *M. fuliginosa* Sparrman, 1787, and *M. fuliginosa* Gmelin, 1789. *Proc. New Eng. zool. Club* 7: 22.

610 Percival, D. pers. comm. to R.L. Fleming Jr. (1981).

611 Persson, M. (1989) Notes on birds recorded in Nepal, 1986-1989. Unpublished.

612 Petersen, I. (1983) Notes on birds recorded in Nepal, 1980. Unpublished.

613 Pickering, R. (1990) Notes on birds recorded in eastern Nepal 1988-90. Unpublished.

614 Picozzi, N. (1984) The Pipar Project. Progress report. *World Pheasant Association News* 4: 7-9.

615 Picozzi, N. (1984) Pipar Project - Nepal. An ecological survey of a proposed reserve for Himalayan pheasants at Pipar, Nepal. Abstract. *World Pheasant Association News* 5: 9-11.

616 Picozzi, N. (1985) WPA trek and survey to Pipar, Nepal, May 1985. *World Pheasant Association News* 10: 21-23.

617 Picozzi, N. (1986) Human impact on pheasant habitat and numbers of pheasants on Pipar, central Nepal. In M. Ridley, ed., *Pheasants in Asia* 1986. Basildon: World Pheasant Association.

618 Pierce, R. (1989) Mountain birds amidst stones. *Birds International* 1(4): 22-28.

619 Polunin, O. (1950) List of bird specimens from Nepal in the British Museum (Natural History). Zoological Accessions, Aves 26. Unpublished.

620 Polunin, O. (1952) Notes on birds recorded in Nepal, 1952. Unpublished.

621 Polunin, O. (1955) Some birds collected in Langtang Khola, Rasua Garhi district, central Nepal. *J. Bombay nat. Hist. Soc.* 52: 856-896.

622 Porter, R.F., Oddie, W.E. and Marr, B.A.E. (1981) Notes on birds recorded in Nepal, February 1981. Unpublished.

623 Post, P.W. (1985) Notes on birds recorded in Nepal, April - May 1984. Unpublished.

624 Powell, N. and Pierce, R. (1984) Notes on birds recorded in Nepal, 14 March to 30 April 1984. Unpublished.

625 Prater, S.H. (1928) Fauna of Nepal. Appendix XIII pp. 279-334 in P. Landon *Nepal*. London: Constable.

626 Pritchard, D.E. (1980) The birds of western Nepal: the report of the ornithologists. In Saipal 79. Univ. of Durham Expedition to Western Nepal 1979. Unpublished.

627 Pritchard, D.E. and Brearey, D. (1983) Notes on birds recorded during the Saipal 1982/83 expedition to Nepal. Unpublished.

628 Proud, D. (1949-1954) List of bird specimens from Nepal in the British Museum (Natural History). Zoological Accessions, Aves 27. Unpublished.

629 Proud, D. (1949) Some notes on the birds of the Nepal Valley. *J. Bombay nat. Hist. Soc.* 48: 695-719.

630 Proud, D. (1951) More bird notes from Nepal Valley. *J. Bombay nat. Hist. Soc.* 49: 784-785.

631 Proud, D. (1952) Some birds seen on the Gandak-Kosi watershed in March 1951. *J. Bombay nat. Hist. Soc.* 50: 355-365.

632 Proud, D. (1952) Further notes on the birds from Nepal Valley. *J. Bombay nat. Hist. Soc.* 50: 667-670.

633 Proud, D. (1953) More notes on the birds of the Gandak-Kosi watershed, Nepal. *J. Bombay nat. Hist. Soc.* 51: 653-670.

634 Proud, D. (1953) The Tibetan Siskin [*Spinus thibetanus* (Hume)] in Nepal. *J. Bombay nat. Hist. Soc.* 51: 737.

635 Proud, D. (1955) More notes on the birds of the Nepal Valley. *J. Bombay nat. Hist. Soc.* 53: 57-78.

636 Proud, D. (1957) Bird notes from Nepal. *J. Bombay nat. Hist. Soc.* 55: 345-350.

637 Proud, D. (1959) Notes on the Spiny Babbler, *Acanthoptila nipalensis* (Hodgson), in the Nepal Valley. *J. Bombay nat. Hist. Soc.* 56: 330-332.

638 Proud, D. (1961) Notes on some Nepalese birds. *J. Bombay nat. Hist. Soc.* 58: 277-279.

639 Proud, D. (1961) Notes on the birds of Nepal. *J. Bombay nat. Hist. Soc.* 58: 798-805.

640 Proud, D. (1961) Corrections to 'Some notes on the birds of the Nepal valley'. *J. Bombay nat. Hist. Soc.* 58: 806-807.

641 Pyle, P. (1982) Notes on birds recorded in Nepal, 1982. Unpublished.

642 Rahmani, A.R. (1989) Status of the Black-necked Stork in the Indian subcontinent. *Forktail* 5: 99-110.

643 Rand, A.L. (1953) Geographical variation in the laughing thrush, *Garrulax affinis*. *Nat. Hist. Miscellanea* 116: 1-6.

644 Rand, A.L. (1967) The flower-adapted tongue of a Timaliinae bird and its implications. *Fieldiana (zool.)* 51(3): 53-61.

645 Rand, A.L. and Fleming, R.L. (1953) A new fruit pigeon from Nepal. *Fieldiana: zool.* 34: 201-202.

646 Rand, A.L. and Fleming, R.L. (1956) Two new birds from Nepal. *Fieldiana: zool.* 39: 1-3.

647 Rand, A.L. and Fleming, R.L. (1957) Birds of Nepal. *Fieldiana: zool.* 41: 1-218.

648 Rassel, P. (1988) Notes on birds recorded in Nepal, March - November 1976. Unpublished.

649 Ratna, A. (1977) Birds in the Chobar area. *Nepal Nature Conservation Society Newsletter* No.43, July 1977.

650 Redman, N.J. (1984) Notes on birds recorded in Nepal, February - March 1984. Unpublished.

651 Redman, N.J., Lambert, F. and Grimmett, R.F. (1984) Some observations of scarce birds in Nepal. *J. Bombay nat. Hist. Soc.* 81: 49-53.

652 Redman, N.J. and Murphy, C. (1979) Notes on birds recorded in Nepal, December 1978 - June 1979. Unpublished.

653 Reichenow, A. (1886) Monographie der Gattung *Ploceus* Cuv. *Zool. Jahrb.* 1: 113-164.

654 Reid, T. (1984) Notes on birds recorded in Nepal, winter 1983/84. Unpublished.

655 Rice, C. (1978) Notes on birds seen on a trek to Muktinath, April 1978. Unpublished.

656 Richards, G. and Richards, L. (1981) Notes on birds recorded in Nepal, February-April 1981. Unpublished.

657 van Riessen, A. (1986) Notes on birds recorded in far western Nepal, 1983-1985. Unpublished.

658 van Riessen, A. (1989) Birds recorded in far eastern Nepal 1986 - 1989. Unpublished.

659 Ripley, S.D. (1950) Birds from Nepal 1947-49. *J. Bombay nat. Hist. Soc.* 49: 355-417.

660 Ripley, S.D. (1950) New birds from Nepal and the Indian region. *Proc. Biol. Soc. Wash.* 63: 101-106.

661 Ripley, S.D. (1953) *Search for the Spiny Babbler.* London: Victor Gollancz.

662 Ripley, S.D. (1961) *A synopsis of the birds of India and Pakistan.* First edition. Bombay: Bombay Natural History Society.

663 Ripley, S.D. (1962) The Lesser Whitethroat [*Sylvia curruca blythi* Ticehurst & Whistler] in Nepal. A new record. *J. Bombay nat. Hist. Soc.* 59:290.

664 Ripley, S.D. (1982) *A synopsis of the birds of India and Pakistan.* Second edition. Bombay: Bombay Natural History Society.

665 Roberts, J.O.M. (1950) List of bird specimens from Nepal in the British Museum (Natural History) Zoological Accessions, Aves 26: 321-323. Unpublished.

666 Roberts, J.O.M. (1977) Pheasant conservation in Nepal. *Nepal Nature Conservation Society Annual* I: 44-48.

667 Roberts, J.O.M. (1978) Breeding of the Mallard (*Anser (sic) platyrhynchos*) in Nepal. *J. Bombay nat. Hist. Soc.* 75: 485-486.

668 Roberts, J.O.M. (1979) Late sighting of Bar-headed Geese. *Nepal Nature Conservation Society Newsletter,* August 1979.

669 Roberts, J.O.M. (1980) Nepal (2) status of the pheasants of Nepal. Pp. 22-26 in C. Savage, ed., *Pheasants in Asia 1979.* Exning, U.K.: World Pheasant Association.

670 Roberts, J.O.M. (1980) The captive breeding of Himalayan pheasants and some experience in release. Pp. 63-65 in C. Savage, ed., *Pheasants in Asia 1979.* Exning, U.K.: World Pheasant Association.

671 Roberts, J.O.M. (1987) Notes on birds recorded in Nepal. Unpublished.

672 Roberts, J.O.M. (1987) Record of Bar-headed Geese sightings - Karnali Tented Camp 1987. Unpublished.

673 Roberts, J.O.M. (1988) Report on Bar-headed Goose sightings, 1988. Unpublished.

674 Roberts, J.O.M. (1990) Notes on birds recorded in Nepal, 1987-1990. Unpublished.

675 Roberts, M. (1989) Notes on birds recorded in Nepal, 1989. Unpublished.

676 Roberts, P. (1978) Notes on birds recorded in Nepal, February 1978. Unpublished.

677 Roberts, R. (1985) Notes on birds recorded in Nepal, 1985. Unpublished.

678 Roberts, T.J. and King, B. (1986) Vocalizations in owls of the genus *Otus* in Pakistan. *Ornis Scand.* 17: 299-305.

679 Robinson, P. (1977) Notes on birds recorded in Nepal, May 1977. Unpublished.

680 Robinson, T. (1988) Kessler's Thrush (*Turdus kessleri*) from Nepal *J. Bombay nat. Hist. Soc.* 85: 618-619.

681 Robson, C. (1979) Notes on birds recorded in Nepal, November - December 1979. Unpublished.

682 Robson, C. (1982) A report of birds seen in Nepal, 1982. Unpublished.

683 de Roder, F. (1989) The migration of raptors south of Annapurna, Nepal, autumn 1985. *Forktail* 4: 9-17.

684 de Roder, F. (1985) Notes on birds recorded in Nepal, autumn 1985. Unpublished.

685 Rogers, M.J. (1987) Record of Red Kite *Milvus milvus* from Nepal, March 1987. Unpublished.

686 Rooke, S. (1982) Notes on birds recorded in Nepal, December 1982. Unpublished.

687 Ross, J. (1983) Notes on birds recorded in Nepal, January - April 1983. Unpublished.

688 Rossetti, J.B.O. (1978) Notes on birds recorded in Nepal, August 1978. Unpublished.

689 Rossetti, J.B.O. (1979) Black-necked Crane *Grus nigricollis* seen at Begnas Tal near Pokhara, Nepal. *J. Bombay nat. Hist. Soc.* 76: 513.

690 Round, P.D. (1986) List of bird specimens collected in Nepal by E. Cronin and stored in the Thai National Reference Collection, Thailand Institute of Scientific and Technological Research, Bangkok. Unpublished.

691 Russell, V. (1981) Notes on birds recorded in Nepal, 1981. Unpublished.

692 Sakya, K. (1978) *Dolpo, the world behind the Himalayas.* Kathmandu: Sharda Prakashan Griha.

693 Sakya, K. (1980) Reports on the status of pheasants: Nepal (1) introductory paper. Pp. 21-22 in C. Savage, ed., *Pheasants in Asia 1979.* Exning: World Pheasant Association.

694 Sakya, S. (1989) Notes on birds recorded in Nepal, January 1989. Unpublished.

695 Salvadori, T. (1891) *Catalogue of the birds in the collection of the British Museum,* 20 - Psittaci. London: British Museum.

696 Salvadori, T. (1893) *Catalogue of the birds in the collection of the British Museum,* 21 - Columbae. London: British Museum.

697 Salvadori, T. (1895) *Catalogue of the birds in the collection of the British Museum,* 27 - Chenomorphae, Crypturi, Ratitae. London: British Museum.

698 Saunders, H. (1896) *Catalogue of the birds in the collection of the British Museum,* 25 - Gaviae. London: British Museum.

699 Sayers, D. (1975) Birds identified on Nepal spring trek, 1975. Unpublished.

700 Schaaf, D., Rice, C.G., Fleming, R.L. Sr.and Fleming R.L. Jr. (1980) A partial checklist of the birds of Sukla Phanta Wildlife Reserve, Nepal, with remarks on the relevance of species inventories. Unpublished.

701 Schaller, G.B. (1980) *Stones of silence.* London: Andre Deutsch.

702 Scharringa, J. (1987) Ornithological observations Nepal, December 1986 - January 1987. Unpublished.

703 Schofield, R. (1982) Notes on birds recorded in Nepal, 1982. Unpublished.

704 Schrijver, L. and Scharringa, J. (1989) Ornithological records from Darjeeling District, West Bengal, India, 17 - 23 May 1989. Unpublished.

705 Sclater, P.L. (1888) *Catalogue of the birds in the collection of the British Museum,* 14 - Oligomyidae.

706 Scott, D.A., ed. (1989) *A directory of Asian wetlands.* Gland, Switzerland and Cambridge, U.K.: International Union for Conservation of Nature and Natural Resources.

707 Scott, D.A. and Rose, P.M. (1989) *Asian waterfowl census 1989: midwinter waterfowl counts in southern and eastern Asia, January 1989.* Slimbridge: International Waterfowl and Wetlands Research Bureau.

708 Scully, J. (1879) A contribution to the ornithology of Nepal.

708 Scully, J. (1879) A contribution to the ornithology of Nepal. _Stray Feathers_ 8: 204-368.

709 Searle, M. (1980) Notes on birds recorded in Nepal, 1980. Unpublished.

710 Seebohm, H. (1881) _Catalogue of the birds in the collection of the British Museum_, 5 - Turdidae. London: British Museum.

711 Sharpe, R.B. (1874) _Catalogue of the birds in the collection of the British Museum_, 1 - Accipitres. London: British Museum.

712 Sharpe, R.B. (1875) _Catalogue of the birds in the collection of the British Museum_, 2 - Striges. London: British Museum.

713 Sharpe, R.B. (1877) _Catalogue of the birds in the collection of the British Museum_, 3 - Coliomorphae. London: British Museum.

714 Sharpe, R.B. (1879) _Catalogue of the birds in the collection of the British Museum_, 4 - Campephagidae, Muscicapidae. London: British Museum.

715 Sharpe, R.B. (1881) _Catalogue of the birds in the collection of the British Museum_, 6 - Timaliidae (part). London: British Museum.

716 Sharpe, R.B. (1883) _Catalogue of the birds in the collection of the British Museum_, 7 - Timaliidae (part). London: British Museum.

717 Sharpe, R.B. (1885) _Catalogue of the birds in the collection of the British Museum_, 10 - Fringilliformes, Part 1. London: British Museum.

718 Sharpe, R.B. (1888) _Catalogue of the birds in the collection of the British Museum_, 12 - Fringillidae. London: British Museum.

719 Sharpe, R.B. (1890) _Catalogue of the birds in the collection of the British Museum_, 13 - Sturniformes. London: British Museum.

720 Sharpe, R.B. (1890) Notes on specimens in the Hume Collection of birds - No.6. On the Coraciidae of the Indian Region with descriptions of some new Species. _Proc. zool. Soc. London_ 1890: 546-552.

721 Sharpe, R.B. (1894) _Catalogue of the birds in the collection of the British Museum_, 23 - Fulicariae, Alectorides. London: British Museum.

722 Sharpe, R.B. (1896) _Catalogue of the birds in the collection of the British Museum_, 24 - Limicolae. London: British Museum.

723 Sharpe, R.B. (1898) _Catalogue of the birds in the collection of the British Museum_, 26 - Plataleae, Herodiones, Steganopodes. London: British Museum.

724 Shelley, G.E. (1891) _Catalogue of the birds in the collection of the British Museum_, 19 - Indicatoridae, Capitonidae, Cuculidae, Musophagidae. London: British Museum.

725 Shrestha, T.R. ([1986] 1988) Habitat ordination of birds in a managed grassland of Kathmandu Valley. _J. Nat. Hist. Mus._ (Tribhuvan Univ., Kathmandu) 10: 31-51.

726 Sieurin, P. (1987) Record of Bean Goose _Anser fabalis_ in Nepal, December 1985. Unpublished.

727 Simpson, N. (1985) Notes on birds recorded in Nepal, 1985. Unpublished.

728 Singh, G. (1961) The eastern Steppe Eagle [_Aquila nipalensis nipalensis_ (Hodgson)] on the south col of Everest. _J. Bombay nat. Hist. Soc._ 58: 270.

729 Slack, R.S. (1990) Notes on birds recorded in Nepal, December 1989 - February 1990. Unpublished.

730 Slack, R.S., Green, J., Leonard, P. and Richardson, D. (1988) Trip to Nepal, 31 March - 21 April 1988. Unpublished.

731 Smith, S. (1988) Notes on birds recorded in Nepal, February 1988. Unpublished.

732 Smythies, B.E. (1947) Some birds of the Gandak-Kosi watershed including the pilgrim trail to the sacred lake of Gosainkund. _J. Bombay nat. Hist. Soc._ 47: 432-443.

733 Smythies, B.E. (1950) More notes on the birds of the Nepal Valley. _J. Bombay nat. Hist. Soc._ 49: 513-518.

734 Sorensen, U.G. (1988) Observations from Kathmandu Valley and Royal Chitwan National Parks, 9-21 February 1988. Unpublished.

735 Stevens, H. (1912) Notes on birds recorded in Nepal, 1912. Hancock Museum, Newcastle-upon-Tyne. Unpublished.

736 Stevens, H. (1923) Notes on the birds of the Sikkim Himalayas, Part 1. _J. Bombay nat. Hist. Soc._ 29: 503-518.

737 Stevens, H. (1923) Notes on the birds of the Sikkim Himalayas, Part 2. _J. Bombay nat. Hist. Soc._ 29: 723-740.

738 Stevens, H. (1924) Notes on the birds of the Sikkim Himalayas, Part 3. _J. Bombay nat. Hist. Soc._ 29: 1007-1030.

739 Stevens, H. (1924) Notes on the birds of the Sikkim Himalayas, Part 4. _J. Bombay nat. Hist. Soc._ 30: 54-71.

740 Stevens, H. (1925) Notes on the birds of the Sikkim Himalayas, Part 5. _J. Bombay nat. Hist. Soc._ 30: 352-379.

741 Stevens, H. (1925) Notes on the birds of the Sikkim Himalayas, Part 6. _J. Bombay nat. Hist. Soc._ 30: 664-685.

742 Stevens, H. (1925) Notes on the birds of the Sikkim Himalayas, Part 7. _J. Bombay nat. Hist. Soc._ 30: 872-893.

743 Stirrup, S. (1986) Systematic list of species recorded in Nepal (Kathmandu and Chitwan), August - September 1986. Unpublished.

744 Stones, A.J. (1987) Bird species recorded in Nepal, 8 March - 5 April 1987. Unpublished.

745 Stresemann, E. (1920) [_Picus myrmecophoneus_: a new name for _P. striolatus_ Blyth, preoccupied]. _Verh. Orn. Ges. Bayern_ 14: 289.

746 Sudbury, A. (1978) Notes on birds recorded in Nepal, December 1977 - January 1978. Unpublished.

747 Sutcliffe, R. (1981) List of bird specimens from Nepal in the Glasgow Museum. Unpublished.

748 Suter, W. (1983) Ornithological and mammalogical observations in Nepal and NW India, including a few observations in Bangladesh and Pakistan, December 1982 - February 1983. Unpublished.

749 Suwal, R.N., Nepali, H.S. and Harris, J. (1989) Notes on birds recorded around the Lumbini Development Area on 21-22 February 1989. Unpublished.

750 Suwal, R.N. and Shrestha, M.K. (1988) Birds recorded in a wetland survey of western Nepal, June 1988. Unpublished.

751 Suwal, R.N. and Shrestha, M.K. (1988) Sarus Crane survey project, Nepal 1988. Unpublished.

752 Sykes, W.R. (1954) Notes on birds recorded in Nepal, 1954. Unpublished.

753 Taylor, I.R. and Aldous, D.G. (1988) Enumeration list of bird species in the Annapurna Conservation Area, 3 - 12 January 1988. Unpublished.

754 Thapa, B.B. (1988) Notes on birds recorded at Khaptad National Park. Unpublished.

755 Thiede, W. and Thiede, U. (1973) Zur Biologie des Turmfalken (_Falco tinnunculus_) im Nepal. _Bonn. zool.Beitr._ 24: 285-290.

756 Thiede, W. and Thiede, U. (1974) Feldbeobachtungen an Vogeln Nepals. _Vogelwelt_ 95(3): 88-95.

757 Thiollay, J.M. (1977) Notes on birds recorded in Nepal. Unpublished.

758 Thiollay, J.M. (1978) Distributions des Falconiformes nicheurs autour du massif de l'Annapurna (Himalaya Central). _Oiseau et R.F.O._ 48: 291-310.

759 Thiollay, J.M. (1978) Ornithological survey of Royal Chitwan National Park, October - November 1978. Unpublished.

760 Thiollay, J.M. (1978) Structures ecologiques comparees de peuplement aviens de forets mixtes temperees. _Gerfaut_ 68: 347-372.

761 Thiollay, J.M. (1979) La migration des grues a travers l'Himalaya et la predation par les aigles royaux. _Alauda_ 47: 83-92.

762 Thiollay, J.M. (1980) L'evolution des peuplements d'oiseaux le long d'un gradient altitudinal dans l'Himalaya Central. _Rev. Ecol. (Terre et Vie)_ 34: 199-269.

763 Thorns, D. (1987) Notes on birds recorded in Nepal, 1986. Unpublished.

764 Tolk, R. (1988) Notes on birds recorded in Nepal, 1984. Unpublished.

765 Toohig, T. (1986) Notes on birds recorded in Nepal, December 1985 - January 1986. Unpublished.

766 Tristram, H.B. (1889) *A catalogue of a collection of birds belonging to H.B. Tristram.* Durham.

767 Tuladhar, A. (1977) Ranipokhari birds. *Nepal Nature Conservation Society Newsletter* No.45, September 1977.

768 Tuladhar, A. (1979) The avifaunal ecology of Sunderghat (June 19 - October 12, 1977). *Nepal Nature Conservation Society Annual* II 1978-79: 28-35.

769 Turin, R., Heegaard, M. and Prieme, A. (1987) Northern part of the Indian subcontinent 87. Unpublished.

770 Turton, J.M. and Speight, G.J. (1982) A report on birds seen in Nepal, 1982. Unpublished.

771 Tyler, C. (1988) Notes on birds recorded in Nepal, May 1988. Unpublished.

772 Underwood, L. (1978) Birds identified in Royal Chitwan National Park, specifically Sauraha, during the monsoon, August 1978. Unpublished.

773 Underwood, L. (1979) Notes on birds seen at Sheopuri, Kathmandu Valley, Nepal, March 13 1979. Unpublished.

774 Underwood, L. (1979) Nagarjung is alive and wild. *Nepal Nature Conservation Society Newsletter*, September 1979.

775 Underwood, L. (1979) North of Pokhara during the monsoon, Part I. *Nepal Nature Conservation Society Newsletter*, September 1979.

776 Underwood, L. (1979) Natural history north of Pokhara during the monsoon, Part II. *Nepal Nature Conservation Society Newsletter*, October 1979.

777 Underwood, L. (1980) Random bird news in Nepal. *Nepal Nature Conservation Society Newsletter*, February 1980.

778 Underwood, L. (1980) Report on the Kathmandu Annual Christmas Bird Count 1979. *Nepal Nature Conservation Society Newsletter*, February 1980.

779 Underwood, L. (1980) Spring's nature calling. *Nepal Nature Conservation Society Newsletter*, March-April 1980.

780 Uprety, D.R. (1968) Information on some 'birds from Nepal'. In *The faunal studies of Nepal.* Nepal National Commission for UNESCO. Regional Seminar on the Ecology of Tropical Highlands.

781 Vaurie, C. (1953) Geographical variation in *Garrulax erythrocephalus* in central and western Himalayas with description of a new race from Nepal. *Bull. Brit. Orn. Club* 73, 77-79.

782 Vaurie, C. (1955) Remarks on the nomenclature of the Himalayan races of *Regulus regulus*. *Bull. Brit. Orn. Club* 75: 99-101.

783 Vaurie, C. (1955) Systematic notes on Palearctic birds. No. 13, *Zoothera mollissima* and *Z. dixoni. Amer. Mus. Novitates* 1706: 1-8.

784 Vaurie, C. (1959) *The birds of the Palearctic fauna, Passeriformes.* London: Witherby.

785 van der Ven, J. (1987) *Asian waterfowl 1987: midwinter bird observations in some Asian countries.* Slimbridge: International Waterfowl Research Bureau.

786 van der Ven, J. (1988) *Asian waterfowl 1988: midwinter bird observations in most Asian countries.* Slimbridge: International Waterfowl Research Bureau.

787 Vernon, J.D.R. and Griffin, D. (1984) Notes on birds recorded in Nepal, March 1984. Unpublished.

788 Vigors, N.A. (1831) Observations on a collection of birds from the Himalayan Mountains, with characters of new genera and species. *Proc. zool. Soc. London* 1: 7-9, 22-23, 35, 41-44, 54-56, 170-176.

789 Vigors, N.A. (1832) [Description of *Columba Hodgsonii*]. *Proc. zool. Soc. London* 2: 16.

790 Voous, K.H. (1988) *Owls of the northern Hemisphere.* London: Collins.

791 Voous, K.H. and Bijleveld, M.F.I. (1964) A note on Himalayan Buzzards *Buteo buteo* (Aves). *Beaufortia* 11: 37-43.

792 Vyas, S. (1988) Notes on birds recorded in Nepal, 1986-1988. Unpublished.

793 Wahlstrom, C. (1979) Notes on birds recorded in Nepal, 16 November - 13 December 1979. Unpublished.

794 Walinder, G. and Sandgren, B. (1983) Artlista over faglar observerade i Nepal, 10.3 - 12.4 1982. Unpublished.

795 Walters, M. (1984) Notes on eggs, in the collection of the British Museum (Natural History), ascribed to *Carpodacus nipalensis, Propyrrhula subhimachala*, and *Pyrrhoplectes epauletta.* Unpublished.

796 Wangdi, G. (1988) Notes on some bird species recorded at Royal Bardia National Park by naturalist guides at Karnali Tented Camp. Unpublished.

797 Warren, R.L.M. (1966) *Type-specimens of birds in the British Museum (Natural History)*, 1, Non-Passerines. London: British Museum (Natural History).

798 Warren, R.L.M. and Harrison, C.J.O. (1971) *Type-specimens of birds in the British Museum (Natural History)*, 2, Passerines. London: British Museum (Natural History).

799 Warwick, J. (1986) A pheasant census trek in central Nepal. *Cage and Aviary Birds* 11 January 1986.

800 Warwick, J. (1986) Selected bird records for Nepal, April - May 1985. Unpublished.

801 Waugh, D. (1982) Notes on birds recorded in Nepal, winter 1982. Unpublished.

802 Wegge, P. (1976) *Himalayan Shikar Reserves, surveys and management proposals.* FO NEP/72/002 Field Document No. 5. Kathmandu: UNDP/FAO.

803 Weir, T. (1955) *East of Kathmandu.* Edinburgh: Oliver and Boyd.

804 Whitehouse, S. (1982) Notes on birds recorded in Nepal, 1982. Unpublished.

805 Whiteley, D. (1981) List of bird specimens from Nepal in the Sheffield Museum. Unpublished.

806 Willan, R.G.M. (1967) Great Crested Grebe (*Podiceps cristatus* Linn.) in Nepal. *J. Bombay nat. Hist. Soc.* 64: 108-109.

807 Willard, D. (Chicago Field Museum), *in litt.*, 29 January 1988.

808 Wilson, P. (1981) Ecology and habitat utilisation of Blue Sheep *Pseudois nayaur* in Nepal. *Biol. Conserv.* 21: 55-74.

809 Winkel, W. (1987) Naturkundliche Studienreise 'Nepal und Nordindien' vom 8.11 - 29.11.87. Unpublished.

810 Wittenberg, J. (1989) Indien - Nepal, 17 February - 11 March 1989. Unpublished.

811 Wolstencroft, J.A. (1981) Notes on birds recorded in Nepal, March - May 1981. Unpublished.

812 Wolstencroft, J.A. (1982) Notes on birds recorded in Nepal, 1982. Unpublished.

813 Woodcock, M.W. (1979) India & Nepal 27 October - 17 November 1979. Sunbird Holidays tour report.

814 Woodcock, M.W. and Woodcock, B.J. (1976) Some birds observed in the monsoon in central Nepal. *J. Bombay nat. Hist. Soc.* 73: 296-303.

815 Wotham, M. and Bond, G. (1984) Notes on birds recorded in Nepal, 1984. Unpublished.

816 Yonzon, P. and Lelliott, A.D. (1981) Food habits and feeding of Himalayan pheasants. *J. Nat. Hist. Mus.* (Tribhuvan Univ., Kathmandu) 5(4): 93-98.

817 Zimmer, J.T.T. and Vaurie, C. (1954) The type species of the genera *Tesia, Pnoepyga and Oligura. Bull. Brit. Orn. Club* 74: 40-41.

818 Kirkpatrick, Colonel (1811) *Account of the Kingdom of Nepaul, being the substance of observations made during a mission to that country in the year 1793.* London: W. Miller.

819 Inskipp, C. (1988) *A Birdwatcher's Guide to Nepal.* Sandy: Prion.

INDEX TO ENGLISH NAMES

Plate numbers are in bold.

INDEX TO SCIENTIFIC NAMES

Plate numbers are in bold.

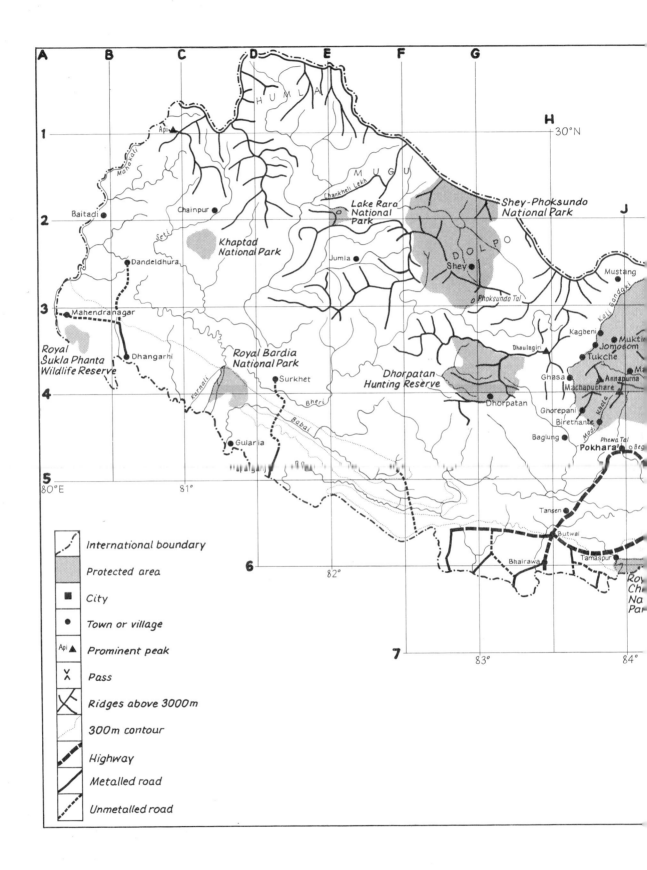

Legend:

- International boundary
- Protected area
- ■ City
- ● Town or village
- Api ▲ Prominent peak
- ⋎ Pass
- ✕ Ridges above 3000m
- 300m contour
- Highway
- Metalled road
- Unmetalled road

Map labels:

HUMLA
MUGU
DOLPO

Api
Baitadi
Chainpur
Mahakali
Seti
Khaptad National Park
Chankheli Lekh
Lake Rara National Park
Jumla
Shey-Phoksundo National Park
Dandeldhura
Shey
Phoksundo Tal
Mustang
Mahendranagar
Kali Gandaki
Royal Sukla Phanta Wildlife Reserve
Dhangarhi
Kagbeni
Karnali
Royal Bardia National Park
Dhaulagiri
Muktin
Jomosom
Tukche
Dhorpatan Hunting Reserve
Ghasa
Annapurna
Ma
Surkhet
Machapuchare
Bheri
Dhorpatan
Ghorepani
Babai
Birethante
Modi
Gularia
Baglung
Phewa Tal
Pokhara
Beg
Nepalganj
Tansen
Butwal
Bhairawa
Tamaspur
Roy Ch Na Par

Coordinates: 80°E, 81°, 82°, 83°, 84°, 30°N

Grid: A B C D E F G H J, 1 2 3 4 5 6 7